A2-Level Physics for AQA A

The Complete Course for AQA A

Contents

Introduction

How Science Works

Unit 4

Section 1: Further Mechanics

Section 2: Gravitation and Electric Fields

Section 3: Capacitance

Section 4: Magnetic Fields

Unit 5

Section 1: Radioactivity and Nuclear Energy

Section 2: Thermal Physics

Option A: Astrophysics

Option B: Medical Physics

Option D: Turning Points in Physics

Investigative and Practical Skills

HOW SCIENCE WORKS

Exam Help

EXAM HELP

Reference

How to use this book

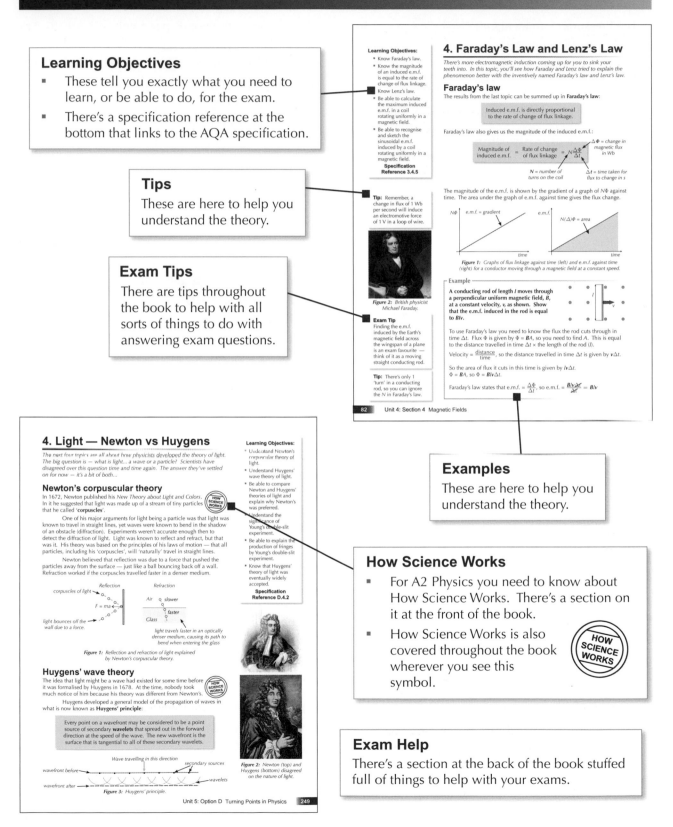

Learning Objectives

- These tell you exactly what you need to learn, or be able to do, for the exam.
- There's a specification reference at the bottom that links to the AQA specification.

Tips

These are here to help you understand the theory.

Exam Tips

There are tips throughout the book to help with all sorts of things to do with answering exam questions.

Learning Objectives:

- Know Faraday's law.
- Know the magnitude of an induced e.m.f. is equal to the rate of change of flux linkage.
- Know Lenz's law.
- Be able to calculate the maximum induced e.m.f. in a coil rotating uniformly in a magnetic field.
- Be able to recognise and sketch the sinusoidal e.m.f. induced by a coil rotating uniformly in a magnetic field.

Specification Reference 3.4.5

4. Faraday's Law and Lenz's Law

There's more electromagnetic induction coming up for you to sink your teeth into. In this topic, you'll see how Faraday and Lenz tried to explain the phenomenon better with the inventively named Faraday's law and Lenz's law.

Faraday's law

The results from the last topic can be summed up in **Faraday's law**:

Induced e.m.f. is directly proportional to the rate of change of flux linkage.

Faraday's law also gives us the magnitude of the induced e.m.f.:

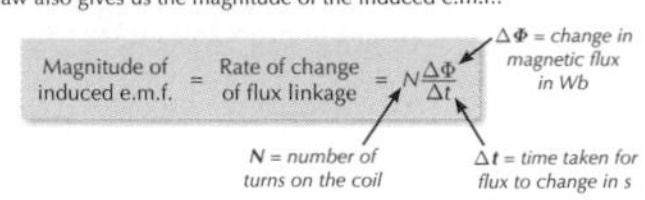

Tip: Remember, a change in flux of 1 Wb per second will induce an electromotive force of 1 V in a loop of wire.

The magnitude of the e.m.f. is shown by the gradient of a graph of $N\Phi$ against time. The area under the graph of e.m.f. against time gives the flux change.

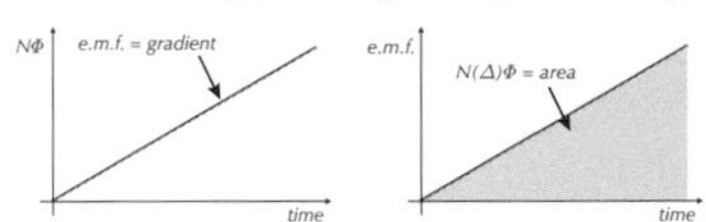

Figure 1: Graphs of flux linkage against time (left) and e.m.f. against time (right) for a conductor moving through a magnetic field at a constant speed.

Figure 2: British physicist Michael Faraday.

Example

A conducting rod of length l moves through a perpendicular uniform magnetic field, B, at a constant velocity, v, as shown. Show that the e.m.f. induced in the rod is equal to Blv.

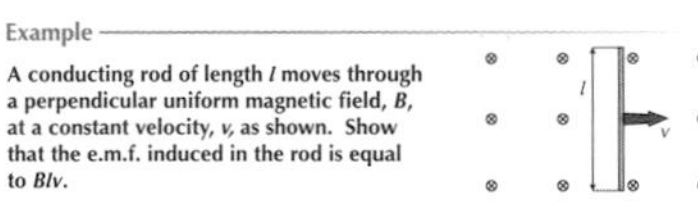

To use Faraday's law you need to know the flux the rod cuts through in time Δt. Flux Φ is given by $\Phi = BA$, so you need to find A. This is equal to the distance travelled in time Δt × the length of the rod (l).

Velocity = $\frac{\text{distance}}{\text{time}}$, so the distance travelled in time Δt is given by $v\Delta t$.

So the area of flux it cuts in this time is given by $lv\Delta t$.
$\Phi = BA$, so $\Phi = Blv\Delta t$.

Faraday's law states that e.m.f. = $\frac{\Delta\Phi}{\Delta t}$, so e.m.f. = $\frac{Blv\Delta t}{\Delta t} = Blv$

Exam Tip
Finding the e.m.f. induced by the Earth's magnetic field across the wingspan of a plane is an exam favourite — think of it as a moving straight conducting rod.

Tip: There's only 1 'turn' in a conducting rod, so you can ignore the N in Faraday's law.

Examples

These are here to help you understand the theory.

4. Light — Newton vs Huygens

The next four topics are all about how physicists developed the theory of light. The big question is — what is light... a wave or a particle? Scientists have disagreed over this question time and time again. The answer they've settled on for now — it's a bit of both...

Newton's corpuscular theory

In 1672, Newton published his *New Theory about Light and Colors*. In it he suggested that light was made up of a stream of tiny particles that he called '**corpuscles**'.

One of his major arguments for light being a particle was that light was known to travel in straight lines, yet waves were known to bend in the shadow of an obstacle (diffraction). Experiments weren't accurate enough then to detect the diffraction of light. Light was known to reflect and refract, but that was it. His theory was based on the principles of his laws of motion — that all particles, including his 'corpuscles', will 'naturally' travel in straight lines.

Newton believed that reflection was due to a force that pushed the particles away from the surface — just like a ball bouncing back off a wall. Refraction worked if the corpuscles travelled faster in a denser medium.

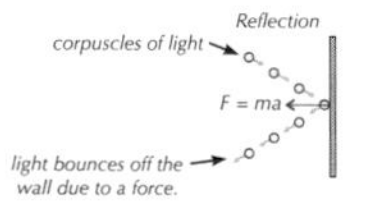

Figure 1: Reflection and refraction of light explained by Newton's corpuscular theory.

Huygens' wave theory

The idea that light might be a wave had existed for some time before it was formalised by Huygens in 1678. At the time, nobody took much notice of him because his theory was different from Newton's.

Huygens developed a general model of the propagation of waves in what is now known as **Huygens' principle**:

Every point on a wavefront may be considered to be a point source of secondary **wavelets** that spread out in the forward direction at the speed of the wave. The new wavefront is the surface that is tangential to all of these secondary wavelets.

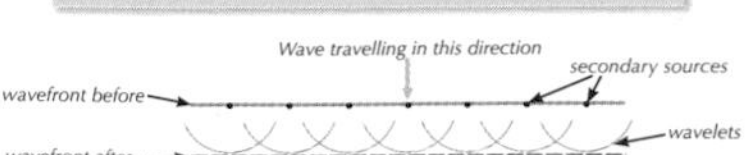
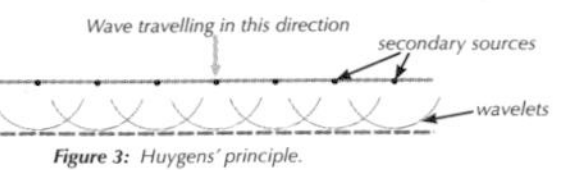

Figure 3: Huygens' principle.

Learning Objectives:

- Understand Newton's corpuscular theory of light.
- Understand Huygens' wave theory of light.
- Be able to compare Newton and Huygens' theories of light and explain why Newton's was preferred.
- Understand the significance of Young's double-slit experiment.
- Be able to explain the production of fringes by Young's double-slit experiment.
- Know that Huygens' theory of light was eventually widely accepted.

Specification Reference D.4.2

Figure 2: Newton (top) and Huygens (bottom) disagreed on the nature of light.

How Science Works

- For A2 Physics you need to know about How Science Works. There's a section on it at the front of the book.
- How Science Works is also covered throughout the book wherever you see this symbol.

HOW SCIENCE WORKS

Exam Help

There's a section at the back of the book stuffed full of things to help with your exams.

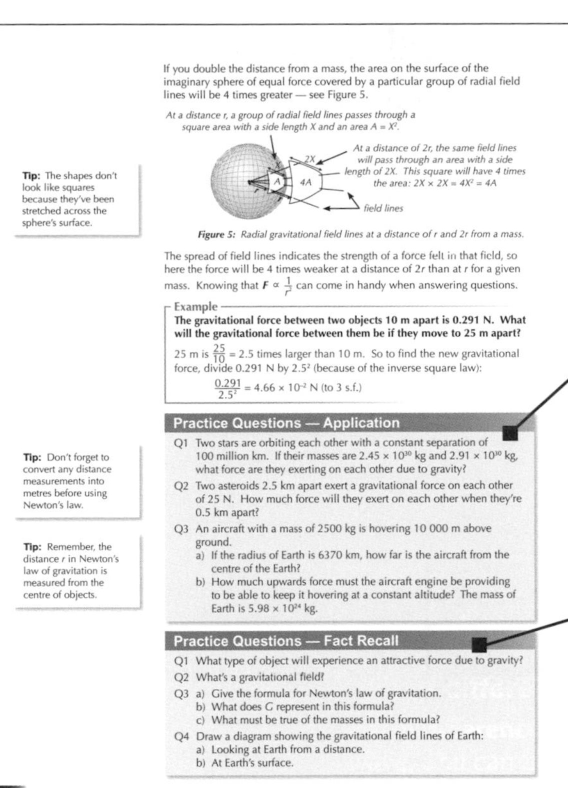

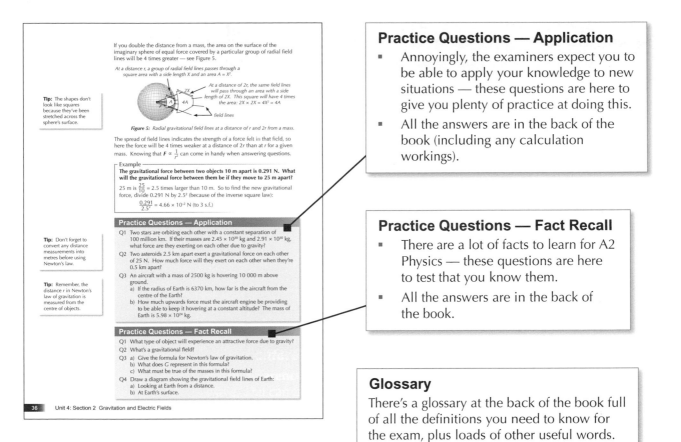

If you double the distance from a mass, the area on the surface of the imaginary sphere of equal force covered by a particular group of radial field lines will be 4 times greater — see Figure 5.

At a distance r, a group of radial field lines passes through a square area with a side length X and an area $A = X^2$.

At a distance of 2r, the same field lines will pass through an area with a side length of 2X. This square will have 4 times the area: $2X \times 2X = 4X^2 = 4A$

field lines

Figure 5: *Radial gravitational field lines at a distance of r and 2r from a mass.*

Tip: The shapes don't look like squares because they've been stretched across the sphere's surface.

The spread of field lines indicates the strength of a force felt in that field, so here the force will be 4 times weaker at a distance of $2r$ than at r for a given mass. Knowing that $F \propto \frac{1}{r^2}$ can come in handy when answering questions.

Example

The gravitational force between two objects 10 m apart is 0.291 N. What will the gravitational force between them be if they move to 25 m apart?

25 m is $\frac{25}{10} = 2.5$ times larger than 10 m. So to find the new gravitational force, divide 0.291 N by 2.5^2 (because of the inverse square law):

$$\frac{0.291}{2.5^2} = 4.66 \times 10^{-2} \text{ N (to 3 s.f.)}$$

Practice Questions — Application

Q1 Two stars are orbiting each other with a constant separation of 100 million km. If their masses are 2.45×10^{30} kg and 2.91×10^{30} kg, what force are they exerting on each other due to gravity?

Q2 Two asteroids 2.5 km apart exert a gravitational force on each other of 25 N. How much force will they exert on each other when they're 0.5 km apart?

Q3 An aircraft with a mass of 2500 kg is hovering 10 000 m above ground.
a) If the radius of Earth is 6370 km, how far is the aircraft from the centre of the Earth?
b) How much upwards force must the aircraft engine be providing to be able to keep it hovering at a constant altitude? The mass of Earth is 5.98×10^{24} kg.

Tip: Don't forget to convert any distance measurements into metres before using Newton's law.

Tip: Remember, the distance r in Newton's law of gravitation is measured from the centre of objects.

Practice Questions — Fact Recall

Q1 What type of object will experience an attractive force due to gravity?

Q2 What's a gravitational field?

Q3 a) Give the formula for Newton's law of gravitation.
b) What does G represent in this formula?
c) What must be true of the masses in this formula?

Q4 Draw a diagram showing the gravitational field lines of Earth:
a) Looking at Earth from a distance.
b) At Earth's surface.

36 Unit 4: Section 2 Gravitation and Electric Fields

Practice Questions — Application

- Annoyingly, the examiners expect you to be able to apply your knowledge to new situations — these questions are here to give you plenty of practice at doing this.
- All the answers are in the back of the book (including any calculation workings).

Practice Questions — Fact Recall

- There are a lot of facts to learn for A2 Physics — these questions are here to test that you know them.
- All the answers are in the back of the book.

Glossary

There's a glossary at the back of the book full of all the definitions you need to know for the exam, plus loads of other useful words.

Exam-style Questions

- Practising exam-style questions is really important — you'll find some at the end of each section.
- They're the same style as the ones you'll get in the real exams — some will test your knowledge and understanding and some will test that you can apply your knowledge.
- All the answers are in the back of the book, along with a mark scheme to show you how you get the marks.

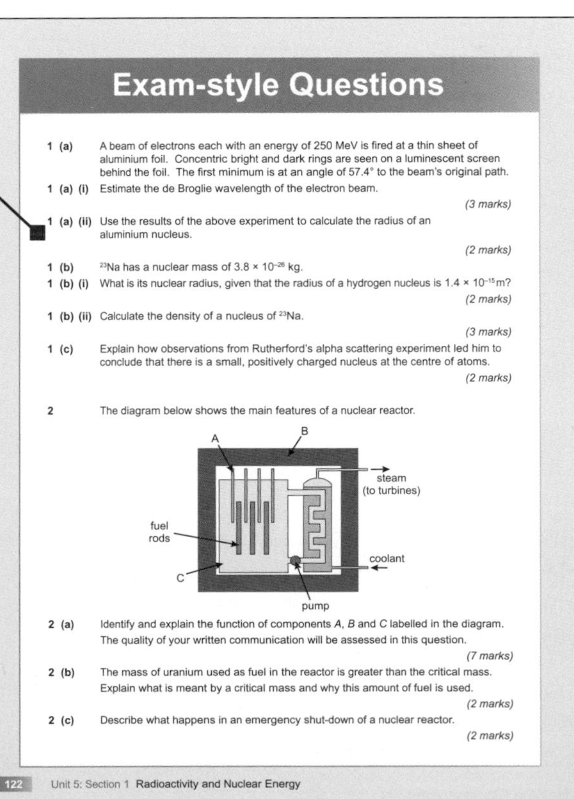

Exam-style Questions

1 (a) A beam of electrons each with an energy of 250 MeV is fired at a thin sheet of aluminium foil. Concentric bright and dark rings are seen on a luminescent screen behind the foil. The first minimum is at an angle of 57.4° to the beam's original path.

1 (a) (i) Estimate the de Broglie wavelength of the electron beam. *(3 marks)*

1 (a) (ii) Use the results of the above experiment to calculate the radius of an aluminium nucleus. *(2 marks)*

1 (b) ^{23}Na has a nuclear mass of 3.8×10^{-26} kg.

1 (b) (i) What is its nuclear radius, given that the radius of a hydrogen nucleus is 1.4×10^{-15} m? *(2 marks)*

1 (b) (ii) Calculate the density of a nucleus of ^{23}Na. *(3 marks)*

1 (c) Explain how observations from Rutherford's alpha scattering experiment led him to conclude that there is a small, positively charged nucleus at the centre of atoms. *(2 marks)*

2 The diagram below shows the main features of a nuclear reactor.

2 (a) Identify and explain the function of components *A*, *B* and *C* labelled in the diagram. The quality of your written communication will be assessed in this question. *(7 marks)*

2 (b) The mass of uranium used as fuel in the reactor is greater than the critical mass. Explain what is meant by a critical mass and why this amount of fuel is used. *(2 marks)*

2 (c) Describe what happens in an emergency shut-down of a nuclear reactor. *(2 marks)*

122 Unit 5: Section 1 Radioactivity and Nuclear Energy

Investigative and Practical Skills

- For A2 Physics you'll have to complete Unit 6 — Investigative and Practical Skills.
- There's a section at the back of the book with loads of stuff to help you plan, analyse and evaluate experiments.

Published by CGP

Editors:
Helena Hayes, Matteo Orsini Jones, Karen Wells, Charlotte Whiteley, Sarah Williams

Contributors:
Mark A Edwards, Duncan Kamya, Barbara Mascetti, John Myers, Zoe Nye, Moira Steven, Andy Williams, Tony Winzor

ISBN: 978 1 84762 905 0

With thanks to Mark Edwards, Ian Francis and Glenn Rogers for the proofreading.
With thanks to Anna Lupton for the copyright research.

Groovy website: www.cgpbooks.co.uk

Printed by Elanders Ltd, Newcastle upon Tyne.
Jolly bits of clipart from CorelDRAW®

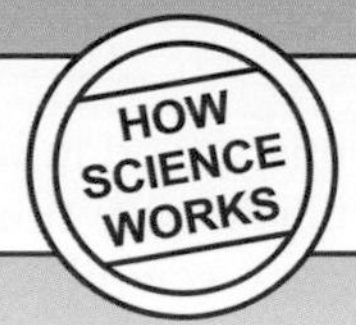

How Science Works

The Scientific Process

Science tries to explain how and why things happen. It's all about seeking and gaining knowledge about the world around us. Scientists do this by asking questions and suggesting answers and then testing them, to see if they're correct — this is the scientific process.

Developing and testing theories

A **theory** is a possible explanation for something. Theories usually come about when scientists observe something and wonder why or how it happens. (Scientists also sometimes form a **model** too — a simplified picture or representation of a real physical situation.) Scientific theories and models are developed and tested in the following way:

- Ask a question — make an observation and ask why or how whatever you've observed happens.
- Suggest an answer, or part of an answer, by forming a theory or a model (a possible explanation of the observations or a description of what you think is happening).
- Make a prediction or **hypothesis** — a specific testable statement, based on the theory, about what will happen in a test situation.
- Carry out tests — to provide evidence that will support the prediction or refute it.

Tip: A theory is only scientific if it can be tested.

Examples

Question: What is the nature of light?

Theory: Light is a wave.

Hypothesis: If light is a wave, then it should diffract through narrow gaps and interfere.

Test: Shine a laser light through a narrow slit and observe what happens to the light by placing a screen behind the slit. If the light has spread out (it's no longer a narrow beam), and if there are light and dark fringes of light on the screen (a diffraction pattern caused by the interference of light), the evidence supports the hypothesis.

Question: Why does pushing against a sharp object hurt even though you're the one doing the pushing?

Theory: If an object A exerts a force on object B, then object B exerts an opposite force on object A.

Hypothesis: Applying a force to an object will cause it to apply the same force back in the opposite direction. Increasing the applied force will increase the force applied back, and vice versa.

Test: Take two newton meters and hook them together, then attach the top end of one of them to the floor (or wall, etc.). Pull against the other meter and record the force shown on each, then repeat by pulling with differing strength. If the force shown on one meter always matches the force shown on the other meter, the evidence supports the hypothesis.

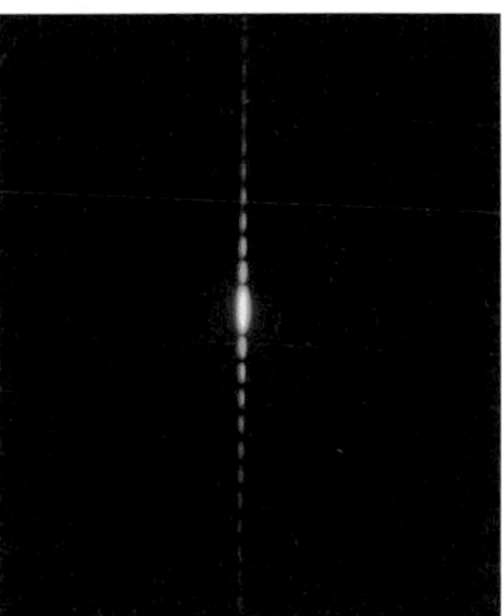

Figure 1: *The diffraction pattern created by green light from a laser shone through a single slit.*

Tip: The results of one test can't prove that a theory is true — they can only suggest that it's true. They can however disprove a theory — show that it's wrong.

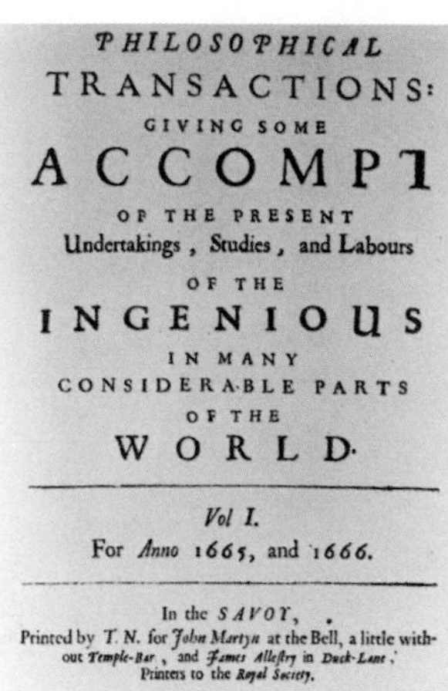

PHILOSOPHICAL
TRANSACTIONS:
GIVING SOME
ACCOMPT
OF THE PRESENT
Undertakings, Studies, and Labours
OF THE
INGENIOUS
IN MANY
CONSIDERABLE PARTS
OF THE
WORLD.

Vol I.
For Anno 1665, and 1666.

In the SAVOY,
Printed by T. N. for John Martyn at the Bell, a little without Temple-Bar, and James Allestry in Duck-Lane, Printers to the Royal Society.

Figure 2: *The first scientific journal, 'Philosophical Transactions of the Royal Society', published in the 17th century.*

Tip: Scientific research is often funded by companies who have a vested interest in its outcomes. Scientists are ethically obliged to make sure that this does not bias their results.

Communicating results

The results of testing a scientific theory are published — scientists need to let others know about their work. Scientists publish their results in scientific journals. These are just like normal magazines, only they contain scientific reports (called papers) instead of the latest celebrity gossip.

Scientists use standard terminology when writing their reports. This way they know that other scientists will understand them. For instance, there are internationally agreed units for measuring certain **variables**, so that scientists across the world will know exactly what the results of an experiment show.

Scientific reports are similar to the lab write-ups you do in school. And just as a lab write-up is reviewed (marked) by your teacher, reports in scientific journals undergo **peer review** before they're published. The report is sent out to peers — other scientists who are experts in the same area. They go through it bit by bit, examining the methods and data, and checking it's all clear and logical, and the conclusion is reasonable. Thorough evaluation allows decisions to be made about what makes a good methodology or experimental technique. Individual scientists may have their own ethical codes (based on their humanistic, moral and religious beliefs), but having their work scrutinised by other scientists helps to reduce the effect of personal bias on the conclusions drawn from the results.

When the report is approved, it's published. This makes sure that work published in scientific journals is of a good standard. But peer review can't guarantee the science is correct — other scientists still need to reproduce it. Sometimes mistakes are made and bad work is published. Peer review isn't perfect but it's probably the best way for scientists to self-regulate their work and to publish quality reports.

Validating theories

Tip: Once an experimental method is found to give good evidence it becomes a protocol — an accepted method to test that particular thing that all scientists can use.

Other scientists read the published theories and results, and try to test the theory themselves. This involves repeating the exact same experiments, as well as using the theory to make new predictions, and then testing them with new experiments. This is known as **validation**. If all the experiments in the world provide evidence to back it up, the theory is thought of as scientific 'fact' (for now). If new evidence comes to light that conflicts with the current evidence the theory is questioned all over again. More rounds of testing will be carried out to try to find out where the theory falls down. This is how the scientific process works — evidence supports a theory, loads of other scientists read it and test it for themselves, eventually all the scientists in the world agree with it and then bingo, you get to learn it.

Example

The structure of the atom

It took years and years for the current model of the atom to be developed and accepted — this is often the case with the scientific process.

Dalton's theory in the early 1800s, that atoms were solid spheres, was disputed by the results of Thomson's experiments at the end of that century. As a result, Thomson developed the 'plum pudding' model of the atom, which was proven wrong by Rutherford's alpha scattering experiments in 1909. Rutherford's 'nuclear model' has since been developed and modified further to create the currently accepted model of the atom we use today — but scientists are still searching for more accurate models.

How do theories evolve?

Our currently accepted theories have survived this 'trial by evidence'. They've been tested over and over again and each time the results have backed them up. But they never become totally indisputable fact. Scientific breakthroughs or advances could provide new ways to question and test the theory, which could lead to changes and challenges to it. Then the testing starts all over again. This is the tentative nature of scientific knowledge — it's always changing and evolving.

Tip: Sometimes data from one experiment can be the starting point for developing a new theory.

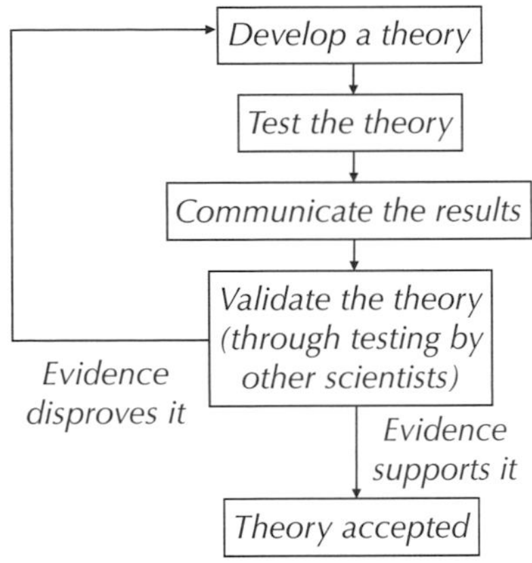

Figure 3: *Flow diagram summarising the scientific process.*

Example

Gravity and the speed of falling objects

For over a thousand years, the generally accepted theory was that heavier objects accelerated to the ground quicker than lighter objects — and why not? There was no evidence to say otherwise, and it seems like a fairly logical thing to think.

Then Galileo came on the scene and set up systematic and rigorous experiments to test this theory. He showed that, actually, all objects accelerate towards Earth at the same rate, regardless of their mass. Physicists around the world were able to reproduce his results and verify his conclusions, and Galileo's theory is still accepted today, over 400 years on.

Figure 4: *Italian physicist and astronomer Galileo Galilei.*

Collecting evidence

1. Evidence from lab experiments

Results from controlled experiments in laboratories are great. A lab is the easiest place to control variables so that they're all kept constant (except for the one you're investigating). This means you can draw meaningful conclusions. You always need to make your experiments as controlled as possible so you can be confident that any effects you see are linked to the variable you're changing. If you find a relationship, you need to be careful what you conclude. You need to decide whether the effect you're seeing is caused by changing a variable, or whether the two are just correlated.

Tip: There's more on controlling variables (p.278) and drawing conclusions from lab experiments (p.289) in the Practical and Investigative Skills section.

Example

Resistance of a piece of material

If you're investigating the resistance of a piece of material by altering a voltage across it and measuring the current flowing through it, you need to keep everything else constant. For example, you should make sure the dimensions of the piece of material are the same throughout.

Figure 5: Some people think using mobile phones increases our risk of developing certain cancers.

2. Investigations outside the lab

There are things you can't study in a lab. And outside the lab controlling the variables is tricky, if not impossible.

Example

Do the microwaves emitted by mobile phones increase the risk of developing certain types of cancer?

There are always differences between groups of people. The best you can do is to have a well-designed study using matched groups — choose two groups of people (those who use mobile phones and those who don't) which are as similar as possible (same mix of ages, same mix of diets etc.). But you still can't rule out every possibility. Taking newborn identical twins and treating them identically, except for making one use mobile phones regularly and not allowing the other near a mobile phone, might be a fairer test, but it would present huge ethical problems. It's also unlikely to be very practical, considering you'd need many sets of twins for any hope of a statistically significant result.

Science and decision-making

Tip: Don't get mixed up — it's not the scientists who make the decisions, it's society. Scientists just produce evidence to help society make the decisions.

Lots of scientific work eventually leads to important discoveries that could benefit humankind and improve everyone's quality of life. But there are often risks attached (and almost always financial costs). Society (that's you, me and everyone else) must weigh up the information in order to make decisions — about the way we live, what we eat, what we drive, and so on. Information can also be used by politicians to devise policies and laws. However, there is not always enough information available for society and politicians to be certain about the decisions made. The scientific evidence we do have can also be overshadowed by other influences such as personal bias and beliefs, public opinion, and the media. Decisions are also affected by social, ethical and economic factors.

Examples

Diagnosing illnesses

Sources of ionising radiation are used in hospitals to diagnose certain illnesses. Studies have provided fairly conclusive evidence that ionising radiation increases the risks of developing cancer. However, ionising radiation is often the best way to diagnose a patient. Without it, an illness could be diagnosed and treated wrongly, or take longer to diagnose correctly. So the benefits usually outweigh the risks.

Wind farms

Many scientists suggest that building wind farms would be a cheap and environmentally friendly way to generate electricity in the future. But some people think that because wind turbines can harm wildlife such as birds and bats, other methods of generating electricity should be used.

Investigating the atom

Large-scale experiments in particle physics, such as those at the Large Hadron Collider, cost billions of pounds. However, with the cooperation of scientists from countries all over the world, they could answer questions in science that we've been trying to solve for years.

Figure 6: Part of the 27 km loop of the Large Hadron Collider in its tunnel at CERN, Switzerland.

Unit 4 Section 1: Further Mechanics

1. Conservation of Momentum

Momentum is how much 'oomph' an object has, and the direction in which the 'oomph' acts. When objects collide, their overall momentum is conserved.

What is momentum?

The linear **momentum** of an object depends on two things — its mass and velocity. The product of these two values is the momentum of the object.

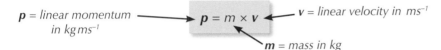

$$\mathbf{p} = m \times \mathbf{v}$$

p *= linear momentum in* $kg\,ms^{-1}$

v *= linear velocity in* ms^{-1}

m *= mass in kg*

Vectors are quantities that have both size and direction — you may see them written in **bold** or <u>underlined</u>. Momentum and velocity are vectors, so you need to remember to think about direction when doing calculations.

Example

A water balloon of volume 4.2×10^{-3} m³ is thrown at a speed of 8.5 ms^{-1}. If water has density 1000 $kg\,m^{-3}$ and the rubber balloon itself has mass 12 g, calculate the balloon's total momentum.

Momentum = mass × velocity
= (mass of water + mass of balloon) × velocity
= ((density of water × volume of water) + mass of balloon) × velocity
= $((1000 \times 4.2 \times 10^{-3}) + 0.012) \times 8.5 = 36\ kg\,ms^{-1}$ (to 2 s.f.)

The principle of linear momentum

Assuming no external forces act, linear momentum is always conserved. This means the total linear momentum of two objects before they collide equals the total linear momentum after the collision. This can be used to work out the velocity of objects after a collision.

Example

A skater of mass 75 kg and velocity 4.0 ms^{-1} collides with a stationary skater of mass 50 kg. The two skaters join together and move off in the same direction. Calculate their velocity *v* after impact.

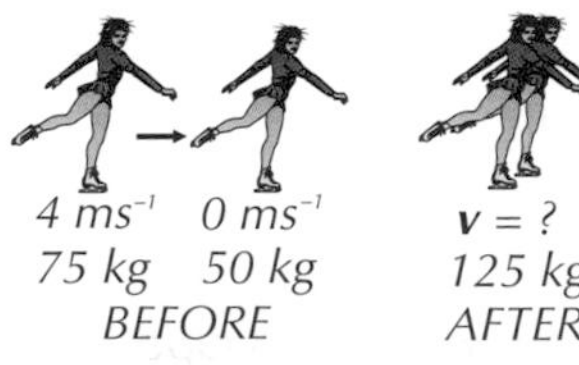

Figure 1: *The skaters, before and after the collision.*

Momentum before = Momentum after
$(75 \times 4.0) + (50 \times 0) = 125\mathbf{v}$
$300 = 125\mathbf{v}$
So $\mathbf{v} = 2.4\ ms^{-1}$ (to 2 s.f.)

Learning Objectives:

- Know that linear momentum is the product of mass and linear velocity.
- Understand that linear momentum is always conserved in a collision when no external forces act.
- Be able to use the principle of linear momentum to solve collision problems in one dimension.
- Know that kinetic energy is conserved in elastic collisions, but not in inelastic collisions.

Specification Reference 3.4.1

Tip: Remember, density = $\frac{\text{mass}}{\text{volume}}$.

Tip: Here the positive direction was taken to be the direction in which the balloon was thrown. If you took the opposite direction as the positive, the balloon would have a negative momentum.

Exam Tip
Before you start a momentum calculation, always draw a quick sketch of the relevant objects, before and after the collision — then it's much easier to figure out what's going on.

The same principle can be applied in situations that don't involve a collision, like explosions. For example, if you fire an air rifle, the forward momentum gained by the pellet is equal in magnitude to the backward momentum of the rifle, and you feel the rifle recoiling into your shoulder.

Tip: There was no momentum before the explosion, so after the explosion both the rifle and the bullet must have the same magnitude of momentum, but in opposite directions. The rifle has a much smaller final velocity than the bullet because it's got a much greater mass.

Example

A bullet of mass 0.0050 kg is shot from a rifle at a speed of 220 ms^{-1}. The rifle has a mass of 4.0 kg. Calculate the velocity at which the rifle recoils.

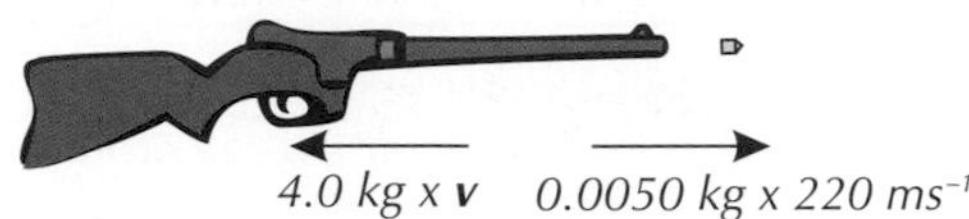

Figure 2: *The rifle and bullet after the explosion.*

Momentum before explosion = Momentum after explosion

$$0 = (0.0050 \times 220) + (4.0 \times \boldsymbol{v})$$

$$0 = 1.1 + 4\boldsymbol{v}$$

$$\boldsymbol{v} = -0.28 \text{ ms}^{-1} \text{ (to 2 s.f.)}$$

Elastic and inelastic collisions

An **elastic collision** is one where momentum is conserved and **kinetic energy** is conserved — i.e. no energy is dissipated as heat, sound, etc. Kinetic energy is the energy that an object has due to its motion. The equation for kinetic energy is:

Tip: Collisions between gas particles are elastic, otherwise air would get colder and colder until there was no motion left.

$$E_K = \frac{1}{2}m\boldsymbol{v}^2$$

$\boldsymbol{E_K}$ = kinetic energy in J

$\boldsymbol{v}$ = velocity in ms^{-1}

$\boldsymbol{m}$ = mass in kg

Example

A bowling ball of mass 5.00 kg is travelling at a velocity of 5.00 ms^{-1} when it collides with a stationary bowling ball of mass 3.00 kg. The velocity of the lighter ball after the collision is 6.25 ms^{-1} in the same direction as the heavier ball before the collision. Show that the collision is elastic.

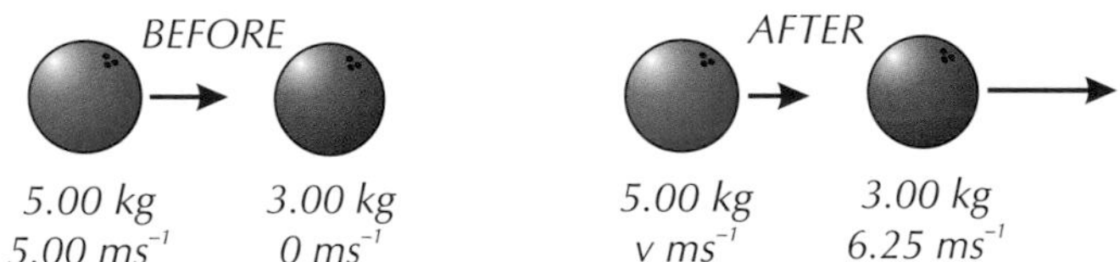

Figure 3: *The balls, before and after the collision.*

Momentum is conserved, so momentum before = momentum after.

$$(5.00 \times 5.00) + (3.00 \times 0) = (5.00 \times v) + (3.00 \times 6.25)$$

$$25 = 5v + 18.75$$

$$v = 1.25 \text{ ms}^{-1}$$

Check to see if kinetic energy is conserved:

Kinetic energy before = $(\frac{1}{2} \times 5.00 \times 5.00^2) + (\frac{1}{2} \times 3.00 \times 0^2) = 62.5$ J

Kinetic energy after = $(\frac{1}{2} \times 5.00 \times 1.25^2) + (\frac{1}{2} \times 3.0 \times 6.25^2) = 62.5$ J

So total kinetic energy is conserved in the collision — therefore this is an elastic collision.

If a collision is **inelastic**, it means that some of the kinetic energy is converted into other forms during the collision. Linear momentum is always conserved in inelastic collisions though.

Example

A toy lorry (mass 2 kg) travelling at 3 ms^{-1} crashes into a toy car (mass 800 g), travelling in the same direction at 2 ms^{-1}. The velocity of the lorry after the collision is 2.6 ms^{-1} in the same direction. Calculate the new velocity of the car and the total kinetic energy before and after the collision.

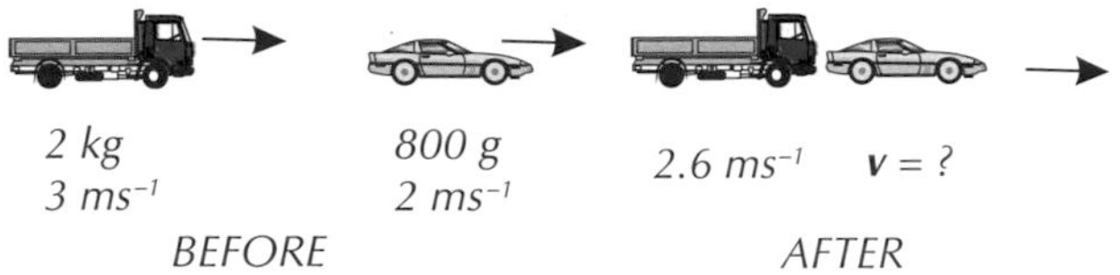

Figure 5: *The toy lorry and car, before and after the collision.*

Momentum is conserved, so:
Momentum before collision = Momentum after collision

$$(2 \times 3) + (0.8 \times 2) = (2 \times 2.6) + (0.8 \times \boldsymbol{v})$$
$$7.6 = 5.2 + 0.8\boldsymbol{v}$$
$$2.4 = 0.8\boldsymbol{v}$$
$$\boldsymbol{v} = 3 \text{ ms}^{-1}$$

Kinetic energy before = KE of lorry + KE of car

$$= \tfrac{1}{2}m\boldsymbol{v}^2 \text{ (lorry)} + \tfrac{1}{2}m\boldsymbol{v}^2 \text{ (car)}$$
$$= \tfrac{1}{2}(2 \times 3^2) + \tfrac{1}{2}(0.8 \times 2^2)$$
$$= 10.6 \text{ J}$$

Kinetic energy after $= \tfrac{1}{2}(2 \times 2.6^2) + \tfrac{1}{2}(0.8 \times 3^2)$

$$= 10.36 \text{ J}$$

The difference in the two values is the amount of kinetic energy dissipated as heat, sound, or in damaging the vehicles — so this is an inelastic collision.

Figure 4: *In the real world, most collisions are at least slightly inelastic. These billiard balls will lose energy as sound when they collide.*

Practice Questions — Application

Q1 A man sitting in a stationary boat throws a 1.0 kg rock horizontally out of the boat at 10 ms^{-1}. If the total mass of the man and boat is 125 kg, how fast will the boat move in the opposite direction to the rock?

Q2 An ice hockey puck of mass 165 g has a velocity 2.25 ms^{-1} (in the positive direction) when it collides with an identical puck moving at 4.75 ms^{-1} in the opposite (negative) direction. If the first puck has a final velocity of –4.25 ms^{-1}, calculate the final velocity of the second puck. Is this an elastic or inelastic collision?

Q3 The nozzle of a fire hose has a cross-sectional area of 5.6×10^{-4} m^2 and shoots water at a rate of 8.4×10^{-3} m^3s^{-1}. Find the momentum of the water leaving the fire hose, if water has a density of 1000 kgm^{-3}.

Tip: If you're struggling with Q3, first find the mass of water that leaves the hose every second, then find how fast the water leaves the nozzle.

Practice Questions — Fact Recall

Q1 What is the equation for linear momentum?

Q2 What is the principle of linear momentum?

Q3 What is the difference between an elastic and an inelastic collision?

2. Force, Momentum and Impulse

Force and momentum are quite closely linked — here you'll see how they can form a different version of Newton's 2nd law to the one you met at AS.

Learning Objectives:

- Know that force is equal to the rate of change of momentum: $F = \frac{\Delta(mv)}{\Delta t}$
- Know that impulse is equal to the change in momentum, and is given by $F\Delta t = \Delta(mv)$.
- Know that the area under a force-time graph is equal to impulse.

Specification Reference 3.4.1

Newton's second law of motion

You met **Newton's second law** for a constant mass at AS. There it was written as:

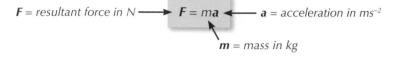

$$F = ma$$

F = resultant force in N, *a = acceleration in ms⁻²*, *m = mass in kg*

It says that the more force you have acting on a certain mass, the more acceleration you get — and for a given force, the more mass you have, the less acceleration you get.

Remember:

- The resultant force, F, is the vector sum of all the forces.
- The force is always measured in newtons.
- The mass is always measured in kilograms.
- a is the acceleration of the object as a result of F. It's always measured in metres per second per second (ms^{-2}). The acceleration is always in the same direction as the resultant force.

Tip: The vector sum is the resultant of adding the size and direction of all the individual forces.

Tip: F and a are both vectors, so you need to consider their directions when doing calculations with them.

Example

A boat of mass 450 kg is accelerating at 1.2 ms⁻² west. If it experiences a drag of 130 N due to water resistance, what force is its engine providing?

Figure 1: *The forces experienced by the boat.*

$F_{resultant} = m \times a = 450 \times 1.2 = 540$ N

The resultant force is the sum of the engine force and the drag, so:

$F_{resultant} = F_{engine} - F_{drag} \Rightarrow F_{engine} = F_{resultant} + F_{drag} = 540 + 130 = 670$ N (to 2 s.f.)

Tip: Drag always acts in the opposite direction to an object's motion, so it's given a negative value here.

Newton's second law can also be written in terms of momentum. To show this, remember that acceleration is just the rate of change of velocity:

$$F = ma = m \times \frac{\Delta v}{\Delta t}$$

A change in momentum could also happen due to a change in mass, so you can replace $m\Delta v$ with $\Delta(mv)$, giving:

$$F = \frac{\Delta(mv)}{\Delta t}$$

The product of mass and velocity is just momentum, so this means that resultant force equals the rate of change of momentum:

$$F = \frac{\Delta(mv)}{\Delta t}$$

F = resultant force in N, $\frac{\Delta(mv)}{\Delta t}$ *= rate of change of momentum in kgms⁻²*

Tip: Resultant force can also be in units of $kg\,ms^{-2}$, although it's normally just in N.

Tip: The units of the rate of change of momentum ($kgms^{-2}$) are the same as those for $m \times a$.

$\Delta(mv)$ is the change in momentum:

$$\Delta(m\mathbf{v}) = m\mathbf{v} - m\mathbf{u}$$

Δ(mv) = *change in momentum in kgms⁻¹*

m = *mass in kg*

u = *initial velocity in ms⁻¹*

v = *final velocity in ms⁻¹*

Example

A train of mass 7500 kg is moving with momentum 150 000 kgms⁻¹. The driver applies the brakes for 15 s and the train's momentum decreases to 37 500 kgms⁻¹. Calculate the force applied by the brakes.

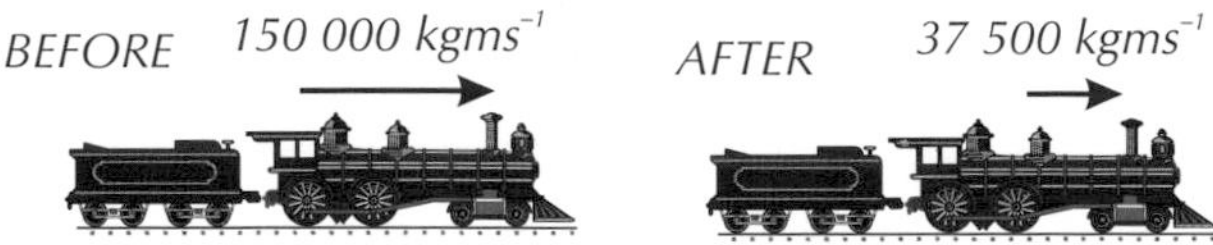

Figure 2: *The momentum of the train, before and after braking.*

$$\mathbf{F} = \frac{\Delta(m\mathbf{v})}{\Delta t} = \frac{m\mathbf{v} - m\mathbf{u}}{\Delta t}$$

$$= \frac{37\,500 - 150\,000}{15} = -7500\text{ N}$$

Tip: The force is negative because it's in the opposite direction to the train's motion.

Example

A car of mass 850 kg accelerates from rest. If its engine provides a constant force of 3500 N, how long does it take the car to accelerate to 24 ms⁻¹?

BEFORE *0 ms⁻¹*

AFTER *24 ms⁻¹*

Figure 3: *The velocity of the car, before and after accelerating.*

$$\mathbf{F} = \frac{\Delta(m\mathbf{v})}{\Delta t} \Rightarrow \Delta t = \frac{\Delta(m\mathbf{v})}{\mathbf{F}}$$

$$= \frac{m\mathbf{v} - m\mathbf{u}}{\mathbf{F}}$$

$$= \frac{(850 \times 24) - (850 \times 0)}{3500} = 5.8\text{ s (to 2 s.f.)}$$

Impulse

Newton's second law says force = rate of change of momentum (page 8), or:

$$\mathbf{F} = \frac{\Delta(m\mathbf{v})}{\Delta t}$$

Newton's 2nd law can be rearranged to give:

$$\mathbf{F}\Delta t = \Delta(m\mathbf{v})$$

Impulse is defined as the product of force and time. So, the impulse on an object is equal to the change in momentum of that object and is measured in Ns.

$$\mathbf{F}\Delta t = \Delta(m\mathbf{v})$$

FΔt = *impulse in Ns*

Δ(mv) = *change in momentum in kgms⁻¹*

Impulse is the area under a force-time graph — this is really handy for solving problems where the force changes.

Exam Tip
Remember to convert velocities to ms⁻¹ (if they're given in other units) before doing any calculations.

Exam Tip
For more complicated force-time graphs, you might need to estimate the area under the graph by counting squares or approximating curves as straight lines.

Example

The graph shows the resultant force acting on a toy car of mass 1.5 kg. If the car is initially at rest, what are its momentum and velocity after 3 s?

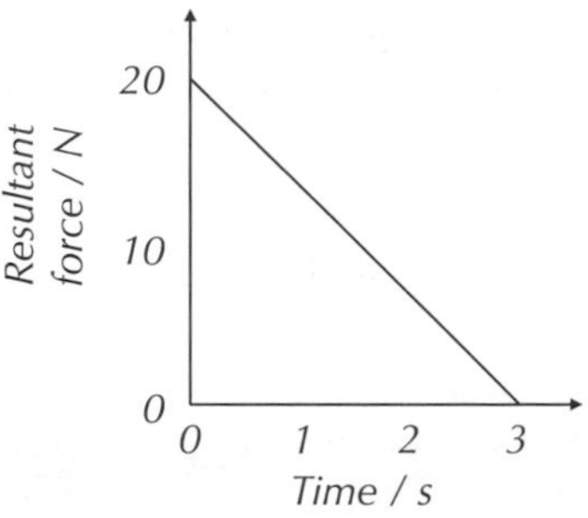

Figure 4: *Graph of resultant force against time.*

Impulse = change of momentum = $m\mathbf{v} - m\mathbf{u}$.
The initial momentum, $m\mathbf{u}$, is zero because the toy car is stationary to begin with. So, impulse = $m\mathbf{v}$.

Impulse is the area under the graph, so to find the momentum of the car after 3 s, you need to find the area under the graph between 0 and 3 s.

Area under graph = $\frac{1}{2} \times 3 \times 20 = 30$ Ns

$$\mathbf{p} = m\mathbf{v}, \text{ so } \mathbf{v} = \frac{\mathbf{p}}{m} = \frac{30}{1.5} = 20 \text{ ms}^{-1}$$

Tip: The mass before and after is the same, so the velocity is the only thing that changes.

Tip: Area = $\frac{1}{2}bh$. This is just the area of a triangle.

Since impulse is the product of force and time, the force of an impact can be reduced by increasing the time of the impact.

Practice Questions — Application

Q1 A landing aeroplane of mass 18 000 kg touches down on a runway at a velocity of 125 km h^{-1}. The brakes are applied and a resultant horizontal force of 62 000 N acts on the aeroplane. Find the time it takes for the aeroplane to come to a stop.

Q2 A car of mass 1200 kg is moving at 25 ms^{-1} and a resultant force of 2500 N is acting on the car in the direction of its motion. The resultant force acting on the car drops steadily to 0 N over 15 s.

a) Sketch a force-time graph for the car during these 15 seconds.

b) Find the car's velocity after 15 seconds.

Q3 A tennis ball with a mass of 57 g moving at 5.1 ms^{-1} hits a tennis racket, which provides an impulse of 0.57 Ns in the opposite direction to the tennis ball's motion.

a) Find the speed of the tennis ball after the collision.

b) How would the ball's speed be different after the collision if it had a larger initial velocity, but received the same impulse? (Assume the ball still travels in the opposite direction after the collision).

Tip: Make sure you convert the velocity of the plane to ms^{-1} in Q1.

Figure 5: *Cars have specially designed 'crumple zones' that extend the time of a collision. This reduces the force experienced by the car and occupants.*

Practice Questions — Fact Recall

Q1 What is Newton's second law in terms of momentum?

Q2 What are the units of impulse?

Q3 A cricket ball moving horizontally hits a cricket bat. How would you calculate the impulse acting on the ball?

Q4 What does the area under a force-time graph show?

3. Circular Motion

You might have met radians before, but only as an alternative option to using degrees. In circular motion, you'll see that all angle measurements use radians, so make sure you're comfortable with them before tackling this topic.

Learning Objectives:

- Know that angular speed, ω, is the angle an object rotates through in one second.
- Be able to calculate angular speed using $\omega = \frac{v}{r}$.
- Know the definitions of frequency and period, and how to calculate ω from each.

Specification Reference 3.4.1

Radians

Objects in circular motion travel through angles — these angles are usually measured in radians.

The angle in **radians**, θ, is equal to the arc-length divided by the radius of the circle (see Figure 1).

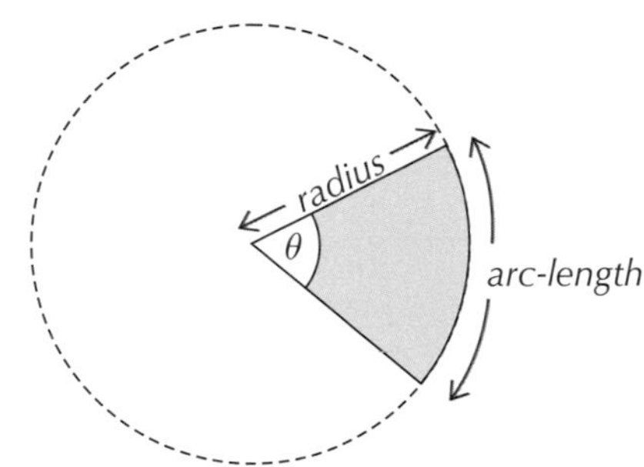

Figure 1: *The radius of a circle, and the angle and arc-length of a sector.*

Exam Tip
You're given formulas for the arc length and other properties of a circle in the Data and Formulae booklet.

For a complete circle (360°), the arc-length is just the circumference of the circle ($2\pi r$). Dividing this by the radius (r) gives 2π. So there are 2π radians in a complete circle.

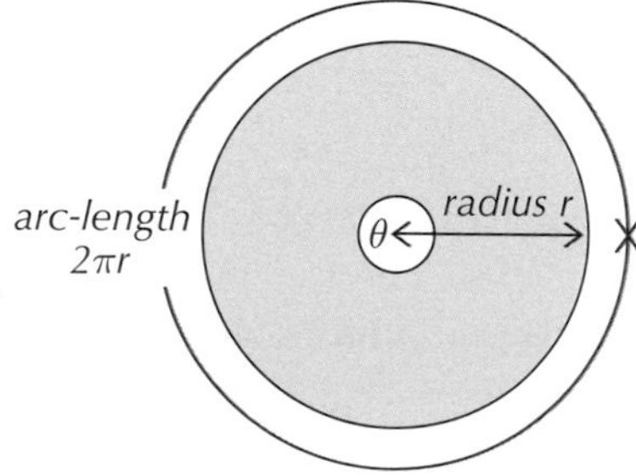

Figure 2: *For a complete circle, the angle* $\theta = 2\pi$.

Tip: Radians are used in preference to degrees in lots of branches of physics. Because of their mathematical 'naturalness', they make many equations easier to work with.

To convert from degrees to radians, you multiply the angle by $\frac{2\pi}{360}$:

$$\text{angle in radians} = \text{angle in degrees} \times \frac{2\pi}{360}$$

Tip: 1 radian is equal to about 57°.

Figure 3 shows some common angles, given in both degrees and radians.

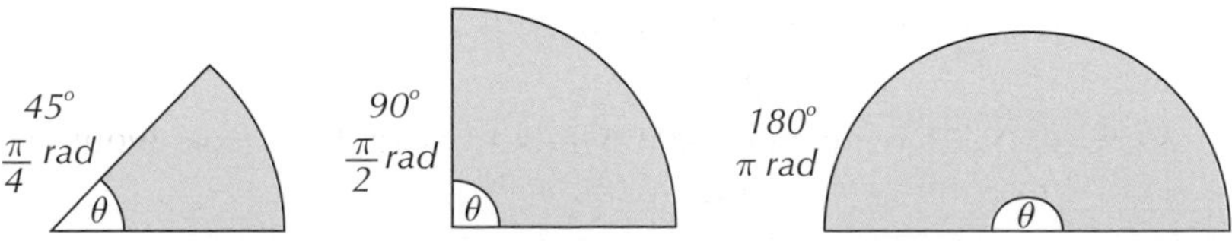

Figure 3: *Angles of sectors in degrees and radians.*

Exam Tip
You should remember the equation to convert between radians and degrees, but it's a good idea to memorise these common angles too, it'll save you time in the exam.

Tip: The symbol for angular speed is the little Greek 'omega', not a w.

Tip: The linear speed v is how fast an object would be travelling in a straight line if it broke off from circular motion.

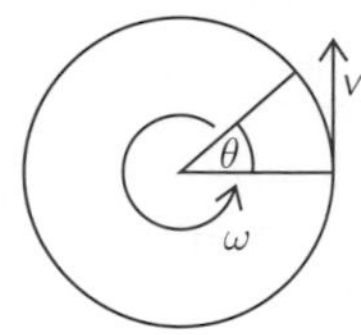

Tip: Angular speed is the same at any point on a solid rotating object.

Figure 5: *One of the first cyclotrons, built by Ernest Lawrence at the University of California.*

Tip: The cyclist's speed is the same as the linear speed of the tyre, as long as there's enough friction between the tyre and ground so that the wheel doesn't slip.

Angular speed

The **angular speed** is the angle an object moves through per second. Just as linear speed, v, is defined as distance ÷ time, the angular speed, ω, is defined as angle ÷ time. The unit is rad s^{-1} (radians per second).

$$\omega = \frac{\theta}{t}$$

ω = angular speed in rad s^{-1}
θ = angle that the object turns through in rad
t = time in s

The linear speed (sometimes called the tangential speed), v, and angular speed, ω, of a rotating object are linked by the equation:

$$\omega = \frac{v}{r}$$

ω = angular speed in rad s^{-1}
v = linear speed in ms^{-1}
r = radius of circle of rotation in m

Example

A cyclotron is a type of particle accelerator. Particles start off in the centre of the accelerator, and electric and magnetic fields cause them to move in circles of increasing size.

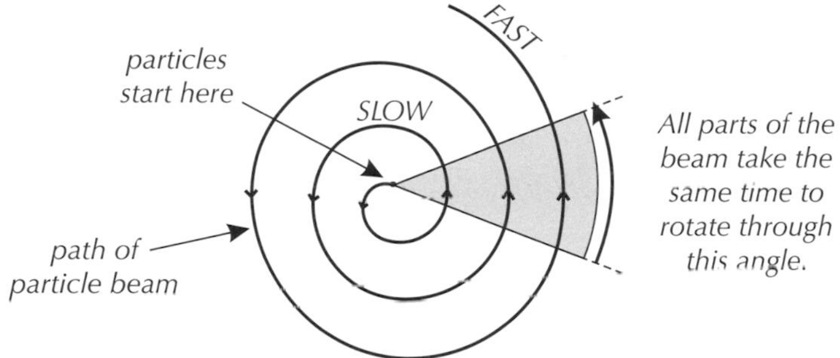

Figure 4: *The path of a particle in a cyclotron.*

Different parts of the particle beam are rotating at different linear speeds, v. But all the parts rotate through the same angle in the same time — so they have the same angular speed, ω.

Example

A cyclist is travelling at a speed of 28.8 kmh^{-1} along a road. The diameter of his front wheel is 68 cm. What is the angular speed of the wheel? How long does it take for the wheel to turn one complete revolution?

Linear speed in ms^{-1} = 28.8 × 1000 ÷ 3600 = 8 ms^{-1}

Angular speed = $\omega = \frac{v}{r}$, where $r = \frac{1}{2}$ × diameter = $\frac{1}{2}$ × 0.68 = 0.34 m

So angular speed:

$$\omega = \frac{8}{0.34} = 23.5294... = 24 \text{ rad s}^{-1} \text{ (to 2 s.f.)}$$

Time to complete one revolution:

$$t = \frac{\theta}{\omega} = \frac{2\pi}{23.5...}$$
$$= 0.27 \text{ s (to 2 s.f.)}$$

Frequency and period

Circular motion has a frequency and period. The **frequency**, *f*, is the number of complete revolutions per second (rev s^{-1} or hertz, Hz). The **period**, *T*, is the time taken for a complete revolution (in seconds). Frequency and period are linked by the equation:

$$f = \frac{1}{T}$$

f = *frequency in rev* s^{-1} ; ***T*** = *period in s*

For a complete circle, an object turns through 2π radians in a time *T*. So the equation for angular speed becomes:

$$\omega = \frac{2\pi}{T}$$

ω = *angular speed in rad* s^{-1} ; ***T*** = *period in s*

By replacing $\frac{1}{T}$ with frequency, *f*, you get an equation that relates ω and *f*:

$$\omega = 2\pi f$$

ω = *angular speed in rad* s^{-1} ; ***f*** = *frequency in rev* s^{-1}

Exam Tip
Working with angular speed can be confusing when you're used to linear speed, but don't worry — these formulas are in the exam Data and Formulae booklet.

Example

A wheel is turning at a frequency of 20 rev s^{-1}. Calculate the period and angular speed of its rotation.

$f = \frac{1}{T}$, so $T = \frac{1}{f} = \frac{1}{20} = 0.05$ s

Angular speed = $2\pi f = 2 \times \pi \times 20 = 40\pi$ rad s^{-1}

Exam Tip
When you calculate something with units rad or rad s^{-1}, try and leave π in your answer — then it's less likely to become a horrible fraction or decimal.

Practice Questions — Application

Q1 The Moon orbits the Earth at a distance of roughly 384 000 km. If it takes the Moon 28 days to complete a full orbit, what are its angular and linear speeds?

Q2 An observation wheel of diameter 125 m turns four times every hour. What angle does it rotate through each minute? What is the tangential speed of one of the passenger cars?

Q3 A CD is spinning at a frequency of 460 rpm. What are the angular and linear speeds at points 2.0 and 4.0 cm from the centre of the CD?

Q4 A ball with mass *m* is spun in a circle on the end of a string of length *l* with time period *T*. Find the kinetic energy of the ball in terms of *m*, *l* and *T*.

Tip: The radii of the Earth and Moon are much smaller than the distance between them, so you can just treat them as two points.

Tip: 'rpm' is 'revolutions per minute'.

Practice Questions — Fact Recall

Q1 How would you convert an angle from degrees to radians?

Q2 What is the definition of angular speed?

Q3 Write down the formula that links angular speed and linear speed.

Q4 What is meant by the period and frequency of rotation?

Q5 How would you calculate the angular speed of an object in circular motion using its frequency?

Learning Objectives:

- Understand that an object travelling in a circle is accelerating towards the centre of the circle.
- Understand that centripetal acceleration is due to a centripetal force.
- Know how to use the equations for centripetal acceleration and force.

Specification Reference 3.4.1

4. Centripetal Force and Acceleration

Objects moving in a circle are accelerating even if their speed isn't changing. This might sound strange, but it's because acceleration is a vector quantity and the direction of the object's velocity is constantly changing.

Centripetal acceleration

Objects travelling in circles are accelerating since their velocity is changing. Even if the car shown in Figure 1 below is going at a constant speed, its velocity is changing since its direction is changing. Since acceleration is defined as the rate of change of velocity, the car is accelerating even though it isn't going any faster. This acceleration is called the **centripetal acceleration** and is always directed towards the centre of the circle.

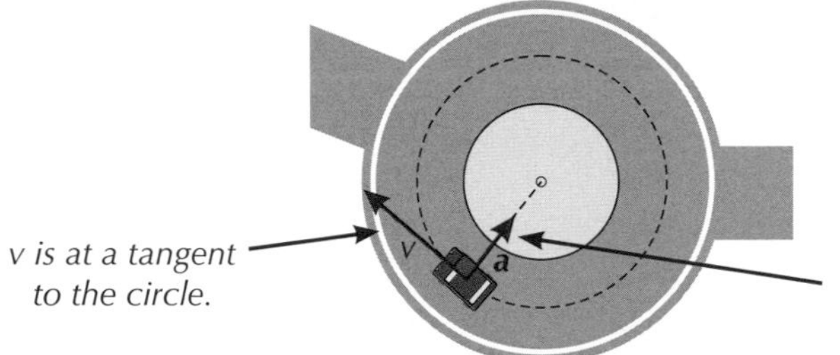
v is at a tangent to the circle.
v
a
The acceleration of the car is directed towards the centre of the circle.

Figure 1: *A car moving in a circle.*

Derivation of formula for centripetal acceleration

Tip: You don't need to know this derivation for the exam, it's just here so you can see where the equation for centripetal acceleration comes from. You do need to know the two formulas for centripetal acceleration though (see next page).

A ball is moving at linear speed v in a circle with radius r (see Figure 2). The centre of the circle is the point O. During time Δt, the ball moves from a point on the circle, A, to another point, B. The ball turns through the angle θ (the angle between the lines OA and OB).

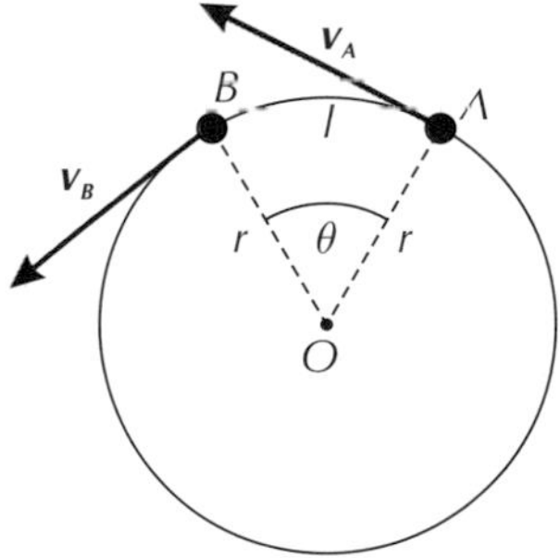
v_A
B
A
l
v_B
r
θ
r
O

Figure 2: *A ball travelling in a circular path travels through angle θ when it moves from point A to point B.*

Tip: Linear velocity has the same magnitude as linear speed, but is a vector that is a tangent to the circle. $\boldsymbol{v}_A$ and $\boldsymbol{v}_B$ have the same magnitude but different directions.

The distance, l, that the ball travels along the circle from A to B is equal to the ball's linear speed multiplied by the time it takes to move that distance:

$$l = v\Delta t$$

At point A the ball has linear velocity $\boldsymbol{v}_A$ and at point B it has linear velocity $\boldsymbol{v}_B$. The change in linear velocity, $\boldsymbol{\Delta v}$, is:

$$\boldsymbol{\Delta v} = \boldsymbol{v}_B - \boldsymbol{v}_A$$

Tip: Isosceles triangles have two sides the same length.

You can draw a triangle made up of the velocity vectors $\boldsymbol{v}_A$, $\boldsymbol{v}_B$ and $\boldsymbol{\Delta v}$ (see Figure 3). The angle between $\boldsymbol{v}_A$ and $\boldsymbol{v}_B$ is also θ. This triangle is the same shape as the triangle ABO, since both are isosceles triangles with the same angle θ between the two sides of identical length.

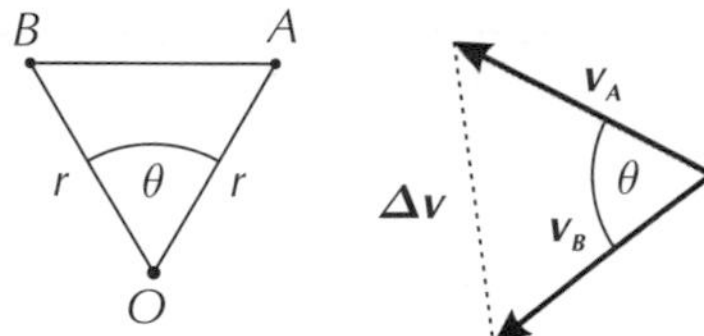

Figure 3: *The velocity vectors $\mathbf{v}_A$, $\mathbf{v}_B$ and $\Delta\mathbf{v}$ form an isosceles triangle.*

Tip: These two triangles are similar — they're the same shape, just different sizes.

If θ is small, then the length of the straight line AB is approximately equal to the length of the arc l. Because the two triangles in Figure 3 have the same shape, the ratio of l and r is the same as the ratio of $\Delta\mathbf{v}$ and $\mathbf{v}_A$.

$$\frac{l}{r} = \frac{\Delta\mathbf{v}}{\mathbf{v}_A} = \frac{\Delta\mathbf{v}}{v}$$

Tip: If θ is small, $l \approx$ AB.

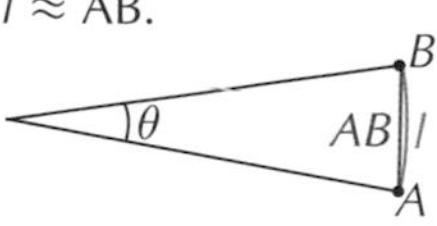

The previous equation, $l = v\Delta t$, can be substituted in:

$$\frac{v\Delta t}{r} = \frac{\Delta\mathbf{v}}{v} \Rightarrow \frac{\Delta\mathbf{v}}{\Delta t} = \frac{v \times v}{r} = \frac{v^2}{r}$$

Tip: The length of each of the vectors $\mathbf{v}_A$ and $\mathbf{v}_B$ is just v.

Since acceleration, **a**, is equal to the change in velocity over time, this gives:

$$\mathbf{a} = \frac{\Delta\mathbf{v}}{\Delta t} = \frac{v^2}{r}$$

The formula for centripetal acceleration can then be written in terms of either linear or angular speed:

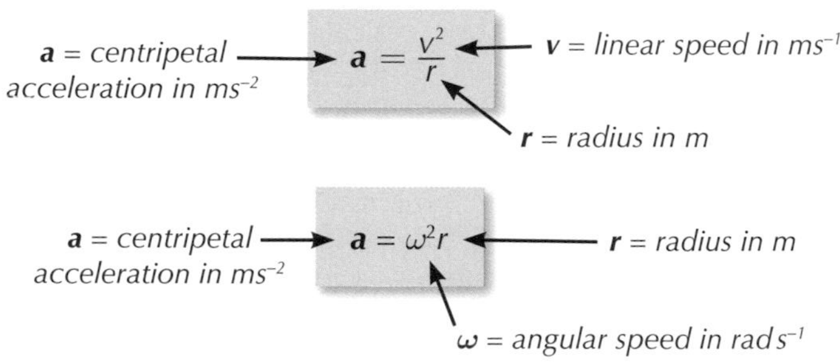

a = centripetal acceleration in ms^{-2}
$\mathbf{a} = \frac{v^2}{r}$
v = linear speed in ms^{-1}
r = radius in m
a = centripetal acceleration in ms^{-2}
$\mathbf{a} = \omega^2 r$
r = radius in m
ω = angular speed in rad s^{-1}

Exam Tip
You'll be given both of these formulas in the exam Data and Formulae booklet.

Tip: $\omega = \frac{v}{r}$, so $v^2 = \omega^2 r^2$. This gives $\frac{v^2}{r} = \frac{\omega^2 r^2}{r} = \omega^2 r$.

Centripetal force

Newton's first law of motion says that an object's velocity will stay the same unless there's a force acting on it. Since an object travelling in a circle has a centripetal acceleration, there must be a force causing this acceleration. This force is called the **centripetal force** and acts towards the centre of the circle.

Newton's second law says $\mathbf{F} = m\mathbf{a}$, so substituting this into the equations above for the centripetal acceleration gives you equations for the centripetal force:

$$\mathbf{F} = \frac{mv^2}{r}$$

$\mathbf{F}$ = centripetal force in N; *$\mathbf{m}$ = mass in kg*; *v = linear speed in ms^{-1}*; *$\mathbf{r}$ = radius in m*

$$\mathbf{F} = m\omega^2 r$$

$\mathbf{F}$ = centripetal force in N; *$\mathbf{m}$ = mass in kg*; *$\boldsymbol{\omega}$ = angular speed in rad s^{-1}*; *$\mathbf{r}$ = radius in m*

Tip: You met Newton's laws of motion at AS.

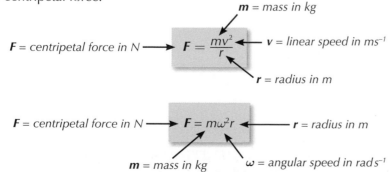

Tip: Don't confuse the centripetal force with the centrifugal force. The centrifugal force is the outwards reaction force you experience when you're spinning

Figure 4: When a hammer thrower is spinning, the centripetal force acting along the chain keeps the hammer moving in a circle. When the thrower lets go of the chain, this force vanishes and the hammer flies off with an initial velocity equal to its linear velocity.

The centripetal force is what keeps the object moving in a circle — remove the force and the object would fly off at a tangent with velocity $\boldsymbol{v}$.

Example

A car of mass 890 kg is moving at 15 ms⁻¹. It travels around a circular bend of radius 18 m. Calculate the centripetal acceleration and centripetal force experienced by the car.

Acceleration = $\boldsymbol{a} = \frac{v^2}{r}$

$= \frac{15^2}{18} = 12.5 = 13 \text{ ms}^{-2}$ (to 2 s.f.)

Force = $\boldsymbol{F} = \frac{mv^2}{r} = m\boldsymbol{a}$

$= 890 \times 12.5 = 11\,000$ N (to 2 s.f.)

Example

A satellite orbits the Earth twice every 24 hours. The acceleration due to the Earth's gravity is 0.57 ms⁻² at the satellite's orbiting altitude. How far above the Earth's surface is it orbiting? The radius of the Earth is 6400 km.

1 orbit takes 12 hours, so period in seconds = $T = 12 \times 3600 = 43\,200$ s

Angular speed = $\omega = \frac{2\pi}{T}$

$= \frac{2\pi}{43\,200} = 1.4544... \times 10^{-4}$ rad s⁻¹

Acceleration $\boldsymbol{a} = \omega^2 r$ so radius $r = \frac{\boldsymbol{a}}{\omega^2}$

$= \frac{0.57}{(1.4544... \times 10^{-4})^2} = 26\,945.2...$ km

Altitude = radius of orbit – radius of Earth

$= 26\,945.2... - 6400 = 20\,545.2... = 21\,000$ km (to 2 s.f.)

Tip: The acceleration due to the Earth's gravity decreases as you move further away from the centre of the planet — only at the surface is it 9.81 ms⁻². See page 37 for more.

Practice Questions — Application

Q1 On a ride at a theme park, riders are strapped into seats attached to the edge of a spinning horizontal wheel of diameter 8.5 m. The wheel rotates 15 times a minute. Calculate the force felt by a rider of mass 60 kg.

Q2 A planet follows a circular orbit of radius r around a star. The planet experiences a constant centripetal acceleration a. How long does it take for the planet to orbit the star 3 times?

a) $3\pi\sqrt{\frac{a}{r}}$ b) $6\pi\sqrt{\frac{a}{r}}$ c) $6\pi\sqrt{\frac{r}{a}}$ d) $\frac{2}{3}\pi\sqrt{ar}$

Q3 A biker rides in a vertical circle around the inside of a cylinder of radius 5 m (so he's upside down at the top of the cylinder). For the biker to not fall off at the top of the loop, he must be going fast enough that his centripetal acceleration does not drop below the acceleration due to gravity, 9.81 ms⁻¹. What's the minimum speed he must be travelling at the top of the loop?

Tip: For Q2, start by finding expressions for ω in terms of $\boldsymbol{a}$ and r and in terms of T. You can then rearrange and combine them to find the answer.

Practice Questions — Fact Recall

Q1 What is meant by centripetal acceleration and centripetal force?

Q2 Give the equation for centripetal acceleration in terms of angular speed. Define all the symbols you use.

Q3 Give the equation for centripetal force in terms of linear speed. Define all the symbols you use.

5. Simple Harmonic Motion

A swinging pendulum moves with simple harmonic motion — this topic is all about what simple harmonic motion is and where you might see it occurring.

What is simple harmonic motion?

An object moving with **simple harmonic motion** (SHM) oscillates to and fro, either side of an equilibrium position (see Figure 1). This equilibrium position is the midpoint of the object's motion. The distance of the object from the equilibrium is called its displacement.

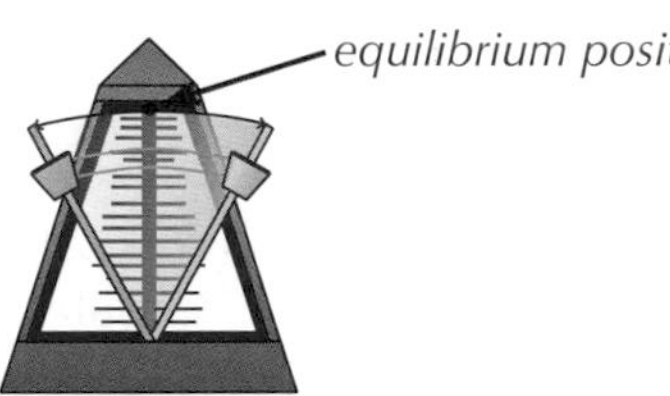

Figure 1: *A metronome moves with simple harmonic motion about an equilibrium position.*

There is always a restoring force pulling or pushing the object back towards the equilibrium position. The size of the restoring force depends on the displacement (see Figure 2). The restoring force makes the object accelerate towards the equilibrium.

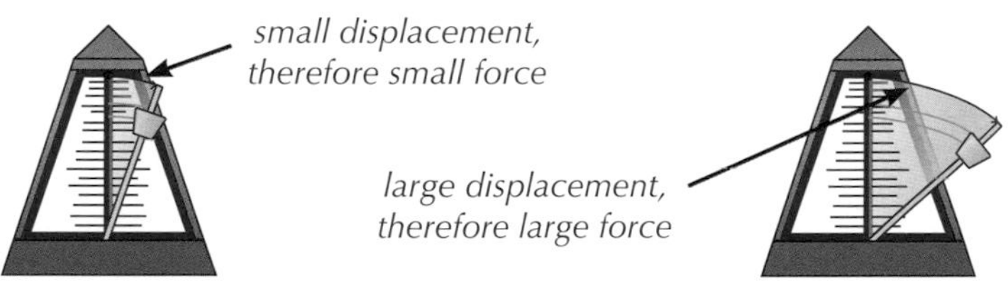

Figure 2: *The size of the restoring force for an object moving with simple harmonic motion depends on its displacement from its equilibrium position.*

SHM can be defined as:

> An oscillation in which the acceleration of an object is directly proportional to its displacement from its equilibrium position, and is directed towards the equilibrium.

Graphs of simple harmonic motion

You can draw graphs to show how the displacement, velocity and acceleration of an oscillating object change with time (see Figure 3).

Displacement

Displacement, $\boldsymbol{x}$, varies as a cosine or sine wave with a maximum value, A (the amplitude).

Velocity

Velocity, $\boldsymbol{v}$, is the gradient of the displacement-time graph. It has a maximum value of $(2\pi f)A$ (where f is the frequency of the oscillation).

Acceleration

Acceleration, $\boldsymbol{a}$, is the gradient of the velocity-time graph. It has a maximum value of $(2\pi f)^2A$.

Learning Objectives:

- Understand that simple harmonic motion (SHM) is an oscillation with acceleration proportional to the displacement from the equilibrium.
- Be able to sketch the graphs of displacement, velocity and acceleration for an object moving with SHM as a function of time, and understand the phase difference between them.
- Know that velocity is given by the gradient of the displacement-time graph, and that acceleration is the gradient of the velocity-time graph.
- Be able to describe how kinetic and potential energy change with time and displacement for an object moving with SHM.

Specification Reference 3.4.1

Tip: As acceleration is proportional to displacement, the force is also proportional to displacement.

Tip: Sine and cosine waves are graphs plotted of the functions sin and cos of some changing value (like time).

Tip: Velocity is the gradient of the displacement-time graph because $\boldsymbol{v} = \frac{\Delta \boldsymbol{x}}{\Delta t}$.

Tip: See the next topic for where these maximum values of velocity and acceleration come from.

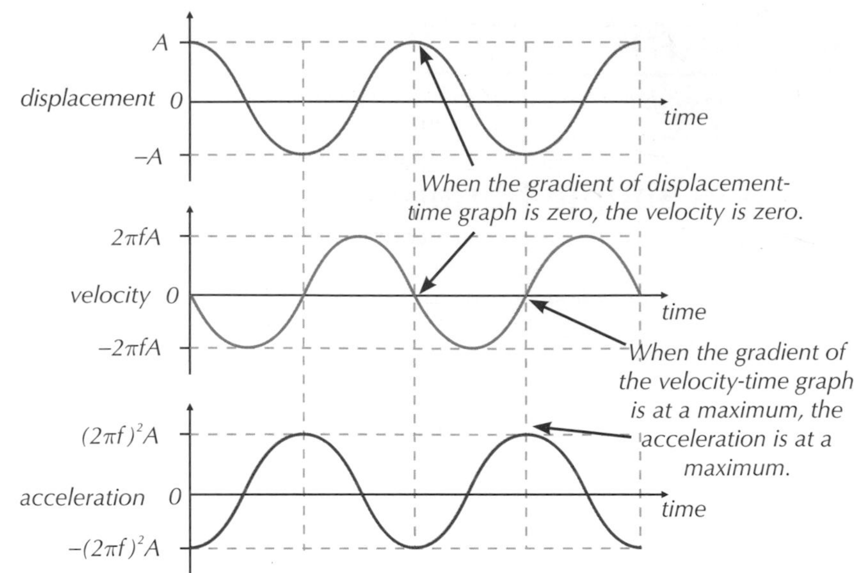

A
displacement 0
−A
time
When the gradient of displacement-time graph is zero, the velocity is zero.
2πfA
velocity 0
−2πfA
time
When the gradient of the velocity-time graph is at a maximum, the acceleration is at a maximum.
(2πf)²A
acceleration 0
−(2πf)²A
time

Figure 3: *Graphs showing how displacement, velocity and acceleration of an object experiencing SHM change with time.*

Tip: Kinetic energy (E_K) will vary in a similar way to $\boldsymbol{v}$, since $E_K = \frac{1}{2}mv^2$ — except the graph for E_K will also be positive (as v^2 is always positive).

Tip: Remember there are 2π radians in a full cycle, so $\frac{\pi}{2}$ radians is a quarter cycle.

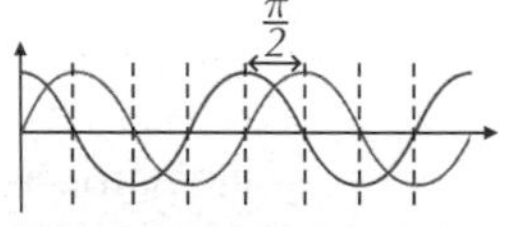

π/2

Phase difference

Phase difference is a measure of how much one wave lags behind another wave, and can be measured in radians, degrees, or fractions of a cycle. Two waves that are in phase with each other have a phase difference of zero (or 2π radians) — i.e. the maxima and minima in each wave occur at the same time. If two waves are out of phase ('in antiphase'), they have a phase difference of π radians or 180° — one wave's maximum occurs at the same time as the other's minimum.

The velocity is a quarter of a cycle in front of the displacement in the velocity-time and displacement-time graphs for an object in SHM (see Figure 3) — it's $\frac{\pi}{2}$ radians out of phase. The acceleration is another $\frac{\pi}{2}$ radians ahead of the velocity, and so is in antiphase with the displacement.

Frequency and period

From maximum positive displacement (e.g. maximum displacement to the right) to maximum negative displacement (e.g. maximum displacement to the left) and back again is called a cycle of oscillation. The frequency, f, of the SHM is the number of cycles per second (measured in Hertz, Hz). The period, T, is the time taken for a complete cycle (in seconds).

The amplitude of an oscillation is the maximum value of the displacement. In SHM, the frequency and period are independent of the amplitude (i.e. they're constant for a given oscillation). So a pendulum clock will keep ticking in regular time intervals even if its swing becomes very small (see page 25).

Figure 4: *Some clocks use pendulums, as the amplitude of the pendulum's swing does not affect its frequency.*

Tip: Gravitational potential energy is gained by moving away from a mass (page 41), and elastic potential energy is stored by elastic objects when they're taut.

Potential and kinetic energy

An object in SHM exchanges potential energy and kinetic energy as it oscillates. The type of **potential energy** (E_P) depends on what it is that's providing the restoring force. This will be gravitational E_P for pendulums and elastic E_P (elastic potential energy) for masses on springs.

- As the object moves towards the equilibrium position, the restoring force does work on the object and so transfers some E_P to E_K.

- When the object is moving away from the equilibrium, all that E_K is transferred back to E_P again.
- At the equilibrium, the object's E_P is zero and its E_K is maximum — therefore its velocity is maximum.
- At the maximum displacement (the amplitude) on both sides of the equilibrium, the object's E_P is maximum, and its E_K is zero — so its velocity is zero.

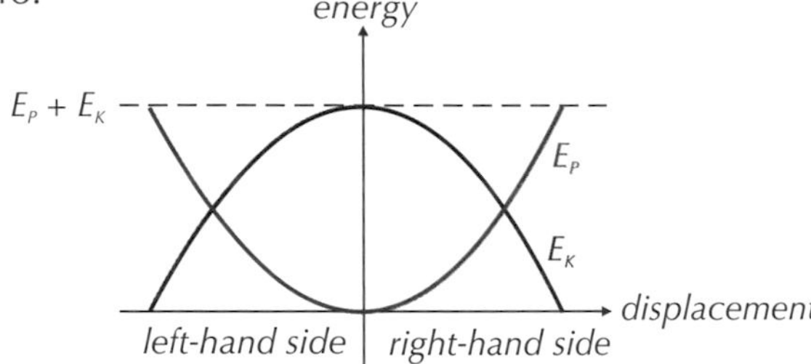

***Figure 5:** Graph to show how the kinetic and potential energy of an object in SHM change with displacement.*

Tip: Gravitational potential energy is equal to *mgh*, where *h* is the height from rest position, and kinetic energy is equal to $\frac{1}{2}mv^2$. For a simple pendulum, the sum of these two is a constant, i.e. $mgh + \frac{1}{2}mv^2 = \text{constant}$.

The sum of the potential and kinetic energy is called the **mechanical energy** and stays constant (as long as the motion isn't damped — see page 28). The energy transfer for one complete cycle of oscillation (see Figure 6) is: E_P to E_K to E_P to E_K to E_P ... and then the process repeats...

Exam Tip
Make sure you know both of these graphs well — you could be asked to recognise, sketch and apply them to other things.

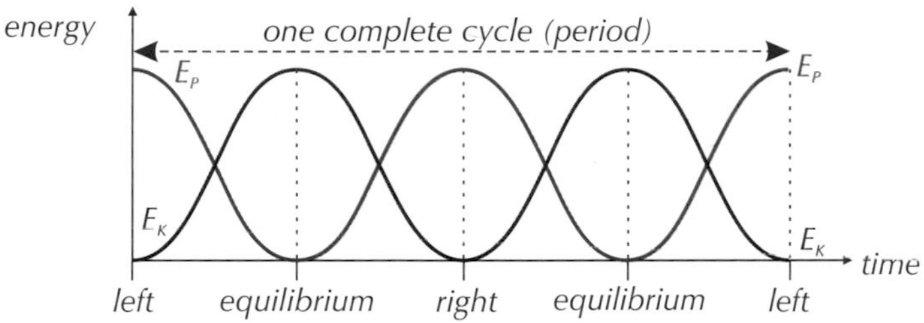

***Figure 6:** Graph to show how the kinetic and potential energy of an object in SHM change with time.*

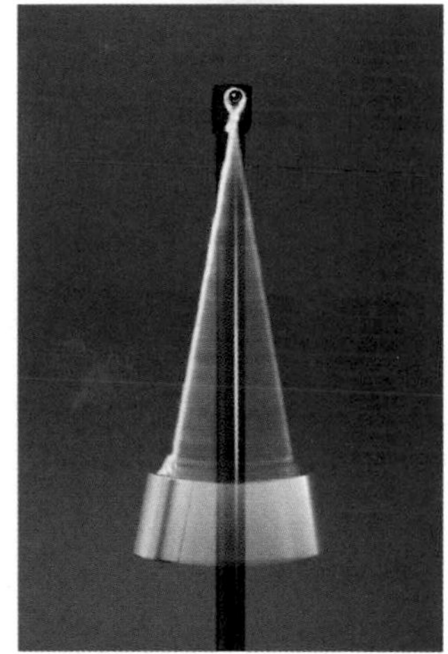

***Figure 7:** An oscillating pendulum moves fastest when it passes through its equilibrium position — when all its energy is kinetic.*

Practice Question — Application

Q1 A girl with a mass of 35 kg is sitting on a swing, which is undergoing simple harmonic motion. To start the motion, she raised the swing 0.4 m above its lowest position, then lifted her feet off the ground.

a) Find the maximum speed the girl reaches on the swing.

b) Sketch a graph of the girl's kinetic energy against time for one complete oscillation of the swing.

Practice Questions — Fact Recall

Q1 What is the definition of simple harmonic motion?

Q2 What is meant by frequency and period of oscillation?

Q3 What is the phase difference between the displacement and the velocity of an object moving with SHM?

Q4 Sketch the graphs of displacement, velocity and acceleration against time for an object moving with SHM. Mark on your graphs the maximum values that each can take.

Q5 Describe how the kinetic and potential energy of an object moving with SHM change with time.

6. Calculations with SHM

Now you've met SHM, this topic's all about the maths you can use to describe what's going on.

Learning Objectives:

- Know that the defining equation of SHM is: $a = -(2\pi f)^2 x$
- Know that the maximum acceleration is: $a_{max} = (2\pi f)^2 A$
- Know that the displacement is given by: $x = A\cos(2\pi ft)$.
- Know that the velocity is given by: $v = \pm 2\pi f\sqrt{A^2 - x^2}$
- Know that the maximum velocity is given by: $v_{max} = 2\pi fA$

Specification Reference 3.4.1

Equations for simple harmonic motion

To understand the maths behind SHM, it's useful to think about it as the 'projection' of circular motion onto a horizontal plane (see Figure 1). Imagine a ball spinning in a circle along the same plane. From above it will look like it's following a circular path. From the side (i.e. in the plane of rotation) it will look like it's oscillating from side to side, and moving with SHM. Its speed, v, will appear fastest when $\boldsymbol{x} = 0$ and appear slowest when $\boldsymbol{x} = \pm A$.

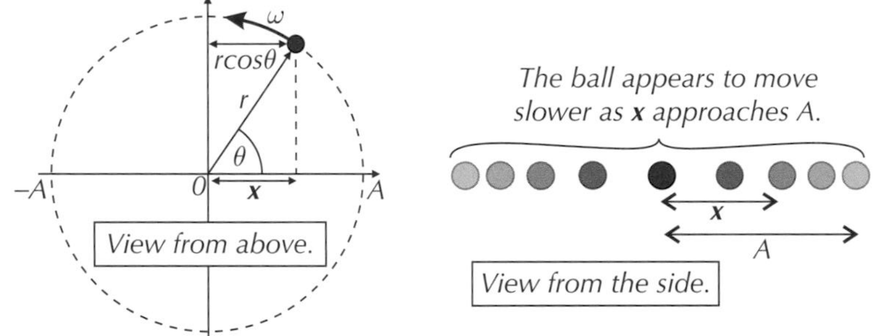

Figure 1: *A ball following a circular path, pictured from above (left) and from the side (right).*

Displacement

- Figure 1 shows that the displacement, $\boldsymbol{x}$, of the ball is just equal to the horizontal component of the ball's position, i.e. $\boldsymbol{x} = r\cos\theta$.
- The radius of the circle, r, is the same as the amplitude of the ball's simple harmonic motion (as viewed from the side), A. This is the maximum displacement, $\boldsymbol{x}$, of the ball.
- The angular speed, ω, is defined as $\omega = \frac{\theta}{t}$, so $\theta = \omega t$.
- The angular speed is also given by $\omega = 2\pi f$.
- Combining these equations gives you an expression for the displacement, $\boldsymbol{x}$, of any object undergoing SHM:

$$\boldsymbol{x} = r\cos\theta = A\cos(\omega t) = A\cos(2\pi ft)$$

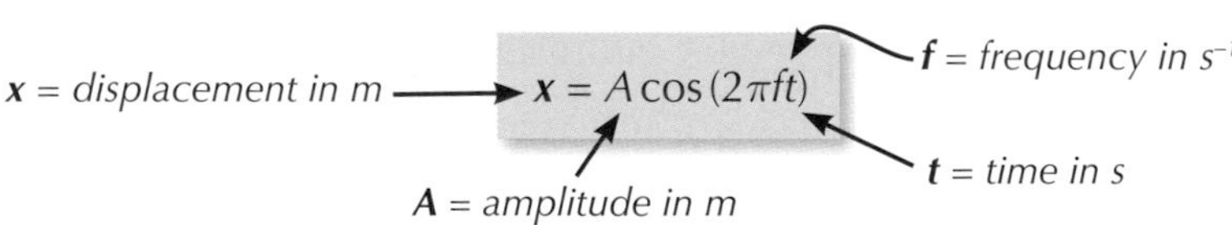

To use this equation you need to start timing when the pendulum is at its maximum displacement — i.e. when $t = 0$, $\boldsymbol{x} = \pm A$.

Acceleration

The acceleration of an object moving with SHM is also related to the acceleration of an object in circular motion.

- For circular motion, $\boldsymbol{a} = \omega^2 r$.
- The angular speed of the ball, ω, is given by $\omega = 2\pi f$. Putting these two equations together gives the acceleration of the ball as $\boldsymbol{a} = (2\pi f)^2 r$.
- The acceleration of an object in SHM is then the horizontal component of this (in the same plane as the displacement x, as shown above):

$$\boldsymbol{a} = -(2\pi f)^2 r\cos\theta$$

Tip: Go back and have a flick through AS mechanics if you'd like a reminder on resolving vectors into components.

Tip: See pages 12-13 for more about circular motion and where these equations come from.

Exam Tip
Remember to set your calculator to radians when using this equation.

Tip: Don't forget, A is the maximum displacement — it's not acceleration.

Tip: You don't need to know the derivations of all these equations — they're just here to help you understand SHM a little more.

There's a minus sign because the acceleration is always acting towards the centre of the circle. $r\cos\theta$ is equal to the horizontal component of the ball's position, $\boldsymbol{x}$, so the acceleration of the object is:

$$\boldsymbol{a} = -(2\pi f)^2\boldsymbol{x}$$

$\boldsymbol{a}$ = acceleration in ms^{-2}

$\boldsymbol{x}$ = displacement in m

$\boldsymbol{f}$ = frequency in s^{-1}

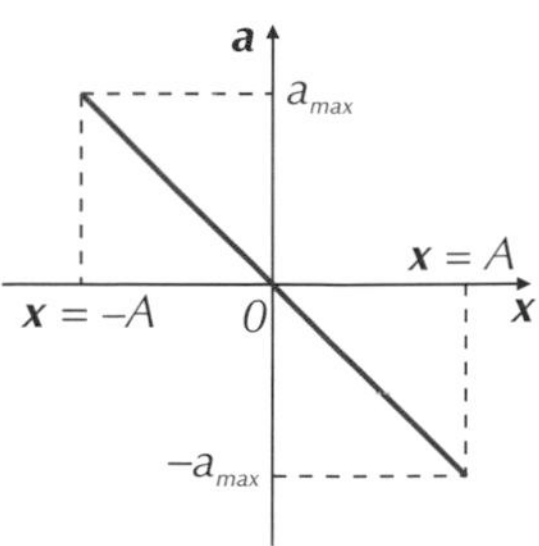

Figure 2: Graph showing how acceleration varies with displacement for an object moving with SHM.

The object's maximum acceleration occurs when it's at its maximum displacement — i.e. when $\boldsymbol{x} = \pm A$:

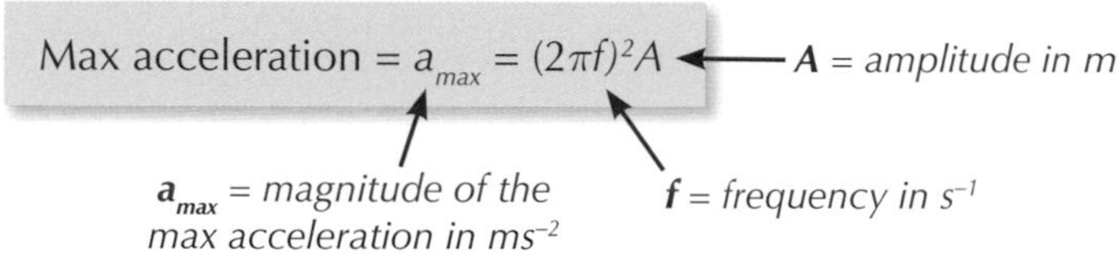

Max acceleration = $a_{max} = (2\pi f)^2 A$
$\boldsymbol{A}$ = amplitude in m
$\boldsymbol{a_{max}}$ = magnitude of the max acceleration in ms^{-2}
$\boldsymbol{f}$ = frequency in s^{-1}

Velocity

You also need to know the equation for the velocity of an object moving with SHM. This is given by:

$$\boldsymbol{v} = \pm 2\pi f\sqrt{A^2 - \boldsymbol{x}^2}$$

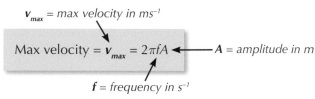

$\boldsymbol{v}$ = velocity in ms^{-1}

$\boldsymbol{x}$ = displacement in m

$\boldsymbol{f}$ = frequency in s^{-1}

$\boldsymbol{A}$ = amplitude in m

The velocity is positive if the object is moving in the positive direction (e.g. to the right), and negative if it's moving in the negative direction (e.g. to the left) — that's why there is a ± sign in there. The maximum velocity is when the object is passing through the equilibrium, where $\boldsymbol{x} = 0$:

$$\text{Max velocity} = \boldsymbol{v}_{max} = 2\pi f A$$

$\boldsymbol{v}_{max}$ = max velocity in ms^{-1}

$\boldsymbol{A}$ = amplitude in m

$\boldsymbol{f}$ = frequency in s^{-1}

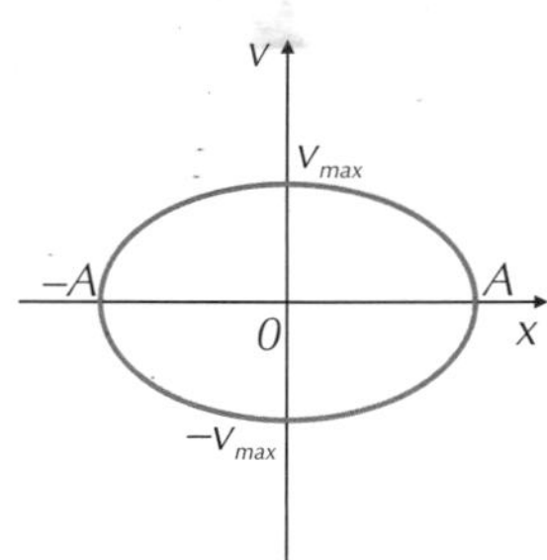

Figure 3: Graph showing how velocity varies with displacement for an object moving with SHM.

Example

A mass is attached to a horizontal spring. It is pulled 7.5 cm from its equilibrium position and released. It begins oscillating with SHM, and takes 1.2 s to complete a full cycle.

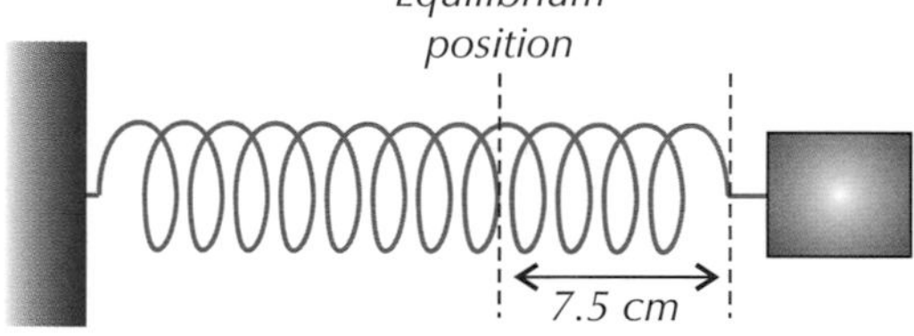

a) What is the frequency of oscillation of the mass?
b) What is its maximum acceleration?
c) What is its speed when it is 2.0 cm from its equilibrium position?

a) Frequency $= \frac{1}{T} = \frac{1}{1.2} = 0.8333... = 0.83\ s^{-1}$ (to 2 s.f.)

b) Amplitude in m = 7.5 ÷ 100 = 0.075 m

$\boldsymbol{a}_{max} = (2\pi f)^2 A$
$= (2 \times \pi \times 0.8333...)^2 \times 0.075 = 2.1\ ms^{-2}$ (to 2 s.f.)

c) Speed at $\boldsymbol{x} = 0.02$ m
$\boldsymbol{v} = 2\pi f\sqrt{A^2 - x^2}$
$= 2 \times \pi \times 0.8333... \times \sqrt{0.075^2 - 0.02^2} = 0.38\ ms^{-1}$ (to 2 s.f.)

Exam Tip
I know it looks like there are loads of complicated equations to learn here, but don't panic — it's not that bad really. You'll be given these formulas on the Data and Formulae booklet, so just make sure you know what they mean and how to use them.

Tip: Remember the time period is just the inverse of the frequency.

Tip: The velocity is at its maximum value when the mass passes through its equilibrium position.

Tip: See page 25 for more on pendulums.

Practice Questions — Application

Q1 A pendulum oscillating with SHM has a frequency of 0.25 Hz and an amplitude of 1.6 m.

a) How long does it take to complete 15 oscillations?

b) Calculate its acceleration when it has a displacement of 1.6 m.

Q2 A mass attached to a spring oscillates with SHM. It has a period of 0.75 s, and moves with velocity 0.85 ms^{-1} when passing through its equilibrium position.

a) What is the amplitude of its oscillation?

b) What will its velocity be when it is 10 cm to the right of its equilibrium position?

Q3 A pendulum is pulled a distance 0.45 m from its equilibrium position and is released at time $t = 0$. If it takes 4.5 s to complete 5 oscillations, how far will it be from its equilibrium position after 10 s?

Q4 A mechanical metronome produces a ticking sound every time a pendulum arm moving with SHM passes through its equilibrium position. Its maximum displacement from its equilibrium position is 6.2 cm. If it is set to produce 120 ticks per minute, what is the magnitude of the arm's maximum acceleration?

Practice Questions — Fact Recall

Q1 Give the equations for the acceleration and velocity of an object moving with SHM as a function of displacement.

Q2 What is the equation for the displacement of an object moving with SHM as a function of time?

Q3 What is the maximum velocity of an object moving with SHM?

Q4 What is the maximum acceleration of an object moving with SHM?

a) $(2\pi fA)^2$ b) $(2\pi f)^2A$ c) $2\pi fA$ d) $2\pi f^2A$

Q5 Sketch the graph of velocity as a function of displacement for an object moving with SHM.

Q6 Sketch the graph of acceleration as a function of displacement for an object moving with SHM.

7. Simple Harmonic Oscillators

Simple harmonic oscillators are systems that oscillate with SHM. There are two types you need to know about — masses on springs, and pendulums.

Learning Objectives:

- Know that a mass on a spring and a simple pendulum are both simple harmonic oscillators.
- Know the formulae for the period of a mass-spring system and the period of a simple pendulum.
- Know how to verify these formulae using experiments.

Specification Reference 3.4.1

A mass on a spring

A mass on a spring is a **simple harmonic oscillator** (SHO). When the mass is pushed or pulled either side of the equilibrium position, there's a restoring force exerted on it (see Figure 1).

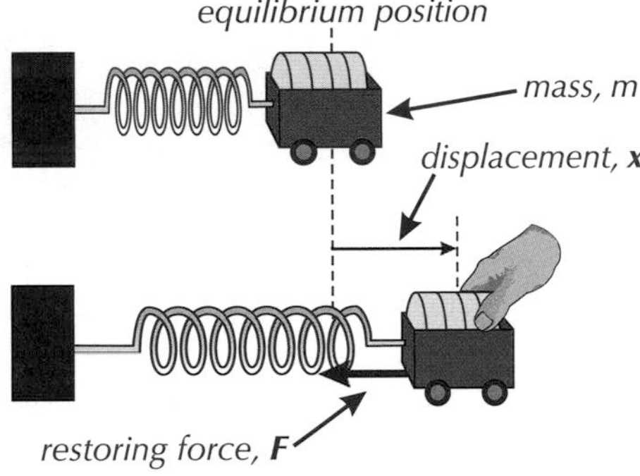

Figure 1: *A mass on a spring is pulled from its equilibrium position and displaced by amount x.*

The size and direction of this restoring force is given by Hooke's Law:

$$F = -kx$$

F = restoring force in N; *k = spring constant in Nm^{-1}*; *x = displacement in m*

Exam Tip
You met Hooke's law at AS, and you'll still find the formula for it in the exam Data and Formulae booklet for A2.

Newton's second law states that the resultant force on an object equals the mass of the object times its acceleration, $F = ma$. Inserting this into the equation above, and replacing a with the acceleration for an object oscillating with SHM, $a = -(2\pi f)^2 x$, gives:

$$-(2\pi f)^2 m x = -kx$$

Exam Tip
You don't need to know this derivation — just make sure you know how to use the equation at the end for the period, *T*.

The *x*'s cancel, and rearranging this equation gives the frequency of a mass oscillating on a spring:

$$f = \frac{1}{2\pi}\sqrt{\frac{k}{m}}$$

Using $f = \frac{1}{T}$ (see page 13) gives the period of a mass oscillating on a spring:

$$T = 2\pi\sqrt{\frac{m}{k}}$$

T = period of oscillation in s; *m = mass in kg*; *k = spring constant in Nm^{-1}*

Tip: Remember, the period is the time it takes for one complete oscillation (maximum left position, to maximum right position, back to maximum left position).

Example

A trolley of mass 2.5 kg is attached to a horizontal spring. The trolley is pulled past its equilibrium position and begins oscillating with SHM. The period of the oscillation is measured as 1.2 s. What is the spring constant?

Period = $T = 2\pi\sqrt{\frac{m}{k}}$ so rearranging for *k* gives:

$$k = \frac{4\pi^2 m}{T^2} = \frac{4\pi^2 \times 2.5}{1.2^2} = 69\ \text{Nm}^{-1}\ \text{(to 2 s.f.)}$$

Investigating the mass-spring system

This experiment backs up the relationships shown by the formulas from the previous page. It's not too tricky — you just have to change one variable at a time and see what happens. Attach a trolley between two springs, pull it to one side by a certain amount and then let go. The trolley will oscillate back and forth as the springs pull it in each direction. You can measure the period, T, by getting a computer to plot a displacement-time graph from a data logger (see Figure 2).

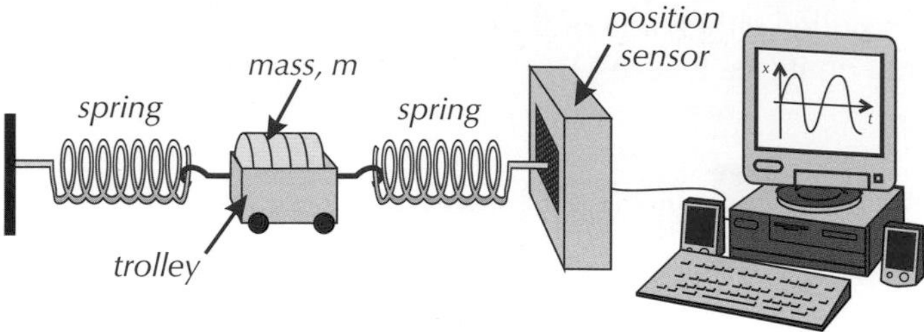

Figure 2: *An experiment to investigate how the period of an oscillating mass on a spring varies with mass, amplitude and spring constant.*

Variable: mass

Tip: The symbol $\propto$ in an equation means "is proportional to."

Change the mass, m, by loading the trolley with masses — don't forget to include the mass of the trolley in your calculations. Since $T \propto \sqrt{m}$, the square of the period, T^2, should be proportional to the mass (see Figure 3).

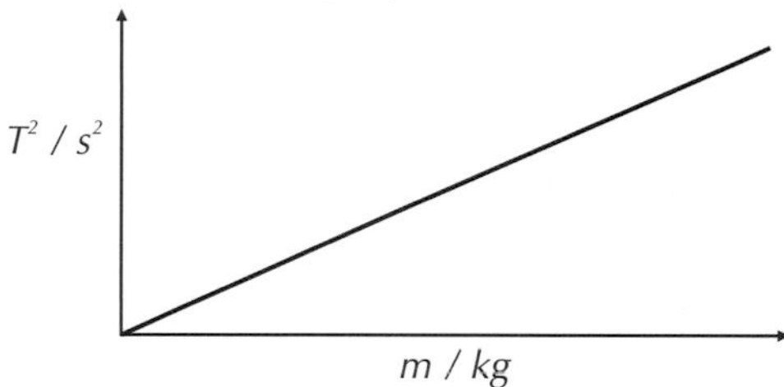

Figure 3: *A graph showing how the square of the period varies with increasing mass.*

Variable: spring stiffness

Tip: When you place springs in parallel (side by side), spring constants add normally: ($k_{total} = k_1 + k_2 + ...$). When they're in series (end to end), the inverses of the spring constants are added: $\left(\frac{1}{k_{total}} = \frac{1}{k_1} + \frac{1}{k_2} + ...\right)$

Change the spring stiffness, k, e.g. by using different combinations of springs (see Figure 4).

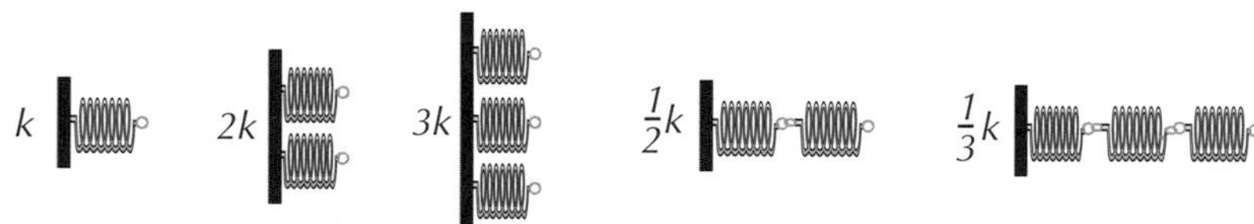

Figure 4: *Using different combinations of springs to change the spring constant.*

Since $T \propto \sqrt{\frac{1}{k}}$, the square of the period, T^2, should be proportional to the inverse of the spring constant (see Figure 5).

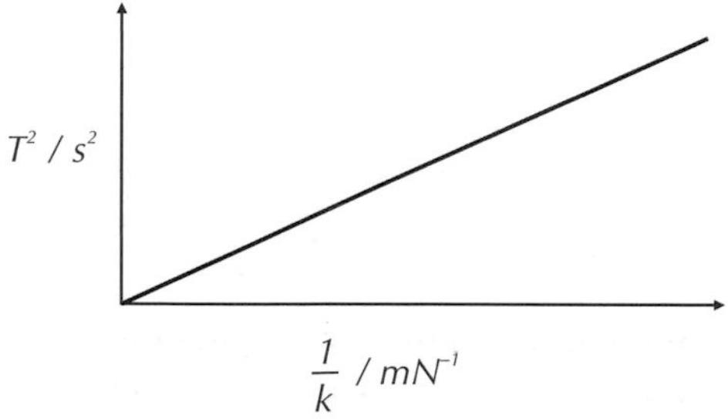

Figure 5: *A graph showing how the square of the period varies with the inverse of the spring constant.*

Change the amplitude, A, by pulling the trolley across by different amounts. Since T doesn't depend on amplitude, A, there should be no change in the period (see Figure 6).

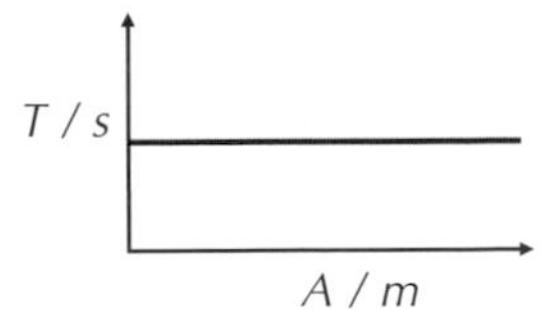

Figure 6: *A graph showing how the period is independent of amplitude.*

The simple pendulum

The simple pendulum is the classic example of an SHO. The formula for the period of an oscillating pendulum is similar to the one for a spring.

$$T = 2\pi\sqrt{\frac{l}{g}}$$

T = period, s

l = length of pendulum, m

g = gravitational field strength, 9.81 Nkg^{-1}

Tip: You don't need to remember this derivation — it's just here so you understand where the equation for the period of a pendulum comes from.

To derive this formula, you need to think about the forces acting on the bob (the weight at the end of the pendulum (see Figure 7)).

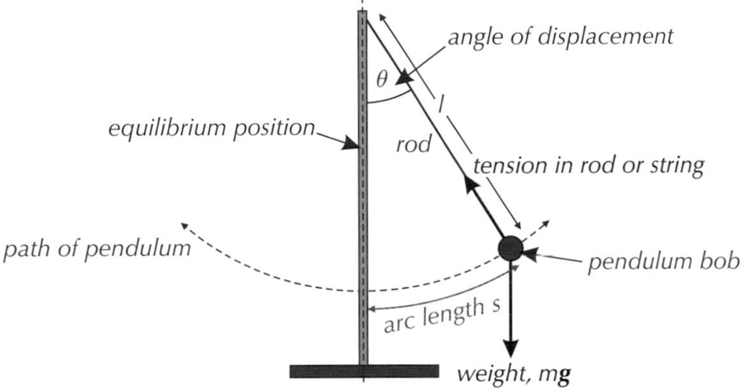

Figure 7: *The forces acting on a pendulum bob at angle θ to its equilibrium position.*

Tip: Have a look back at AS mechanics if you're struggling to follow the bits about vector components.

Tension acts up along the rod or string, while the bob's weight, $m\mathbf{g}$, acts vertically downwards. The component of the weight in the direction of the bob's motion (and perpendicular to the rod or string) is the restoring force, $\mathbf{F} = m\mathbf{g}\sin\theta$ (see Figure 8), which acts towards the equilibrium position. This is the only force that acts in the direction of motion, so you can use Newton's second law, $\mathbf{F} = m\mathbf{a}$, to write:

$$\mathbf{F} = m\mathbf{a} = -m\mathbf{g}\sin\theta$$

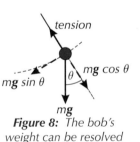

Figure 8: *The bob's weight can be resolved into components.*

Tip: In case you were wondering, the other component of the weight (parallel to the rod), balances out the tension force.

The masses cancel on either side of the equation, so the acceleration is $\mathbf{a} = -\mathbf{g}\sin\theta$. When the angle of displacement, θ, is only small, $\sin\theta$ is approximately θ. The formulas derived here depend on this approximation.

The ratio of the angle θ to the total angle in a circle, 2π, is equal to the ratio of the length of the arc, s, to the circumference of the circle, $2\pi r$. This lets you derive a formula for the acceleration in terms of s and l (here $l = r$):

$$\frac{\theta}{2\pi} = \frac{s}{2\pi r} \Rightarrow \theta = \frac{s}{r} \quad \text{and} \quad \mathbf{a} = -\mathbf{g}\sin\theta = -\mathbf{g}\theta \Rightarrow \mathbf{a} = -\mathbf{g}\frac{s}{l}$$

The formula for acceleration in SHM is $\mathbf{a} = -(2\pi f)^2\mathbf{x}$, so $\frac{\mathbf{a}}{\mathbf{x}} = -(2\pi f)^2$.

For small angles the arc length, s, is the same as the displacement, $\mathbf{x}$. So:

$$-\frac{\mathbf{a}}{\mathbf{x}} = -\frac{\mathbf{a}}{s} = (2\pi f)^2 = \frac{\mathbf{g}}{l}$$

Tip: Because we took the approximation that $\sin\theta \approx \theta$, this formula only works for small angles, about 10° or less.

Rearranging this for frequency, and then taking the inverse gives the period of an oscillating pendulum — the formula given at the top of the page:

$$T = 2\pi\sqrt{\frac{l}{\mathbf{g}}}$$

Example

A clockmaker wants to build a grandfather clock with a pendulum that swings with frequency 1.0 Hz. How long must the pendulum be?

Period = 1 ÷ frequency, so the period = 1 s.

$T = 2\pi\sqrt{\frac{l}{g}}$, so rearranging for length:

$l = \frac{gT^2}{4\pi^2} = \frac{9.81 \times 1^2}{4 \times \pi^2} = 0.25$ m (to 2 s.f.)

Checking this formula experimentally

You can use a simple pendulum attached to an angle sensor and computer (see Figure 9) to test this formula.

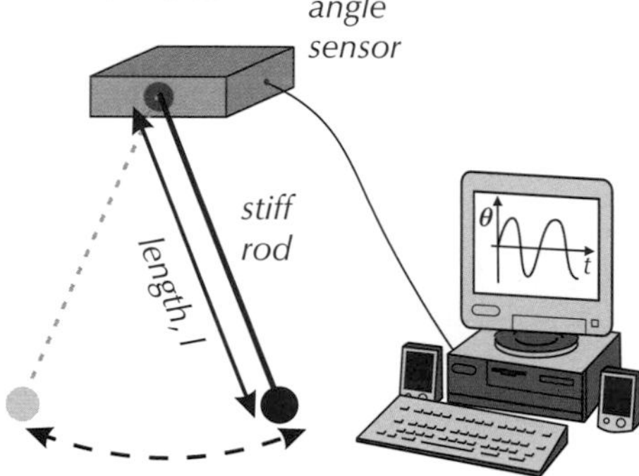

Figure 9: Apparatus to test the formula for the period of an oscillating pendulum.

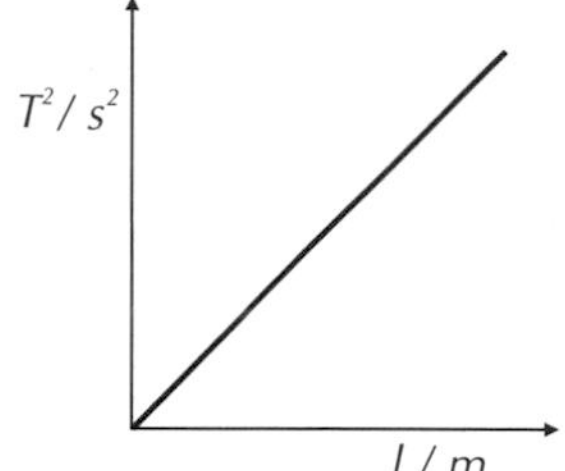

Figure 10: *Graph showing how period squared varies with pendulum length.*

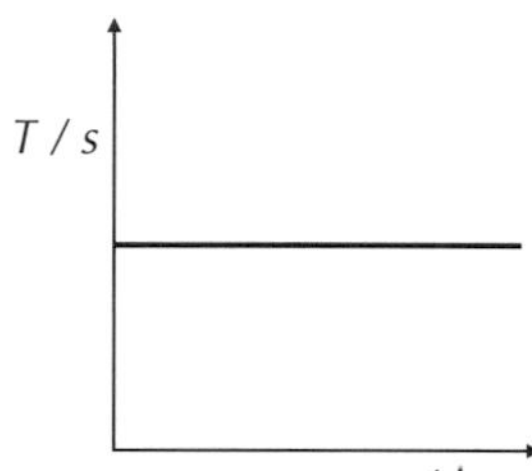

Figure 11: *Graph showing how period is independent of mass.*

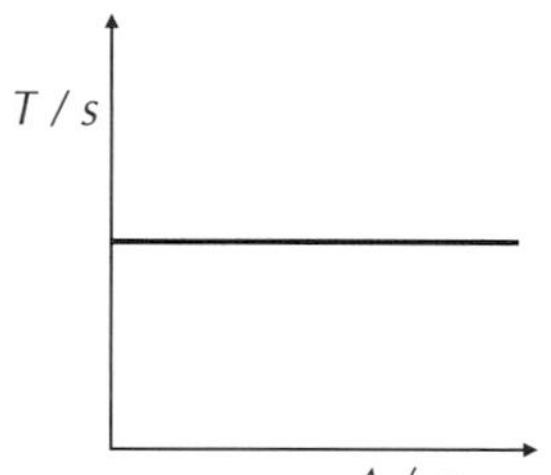

Figure 12: *Graph showing how period is independent of amplitude.*

As for a spring (page 24), you can change one variable at a time and measure what happens. Since the period, T, is proportional to the square root of the length of the pendulum, $\sqrt{l}$, varying l should show that $T^2 \propto l$ (see Figure 10). T is independent of the mass of the bob, m, and the amplitude of the oscillation, A, so varying these should not change T (see Figures 11 and 12).

Practice Questions — Application

Assume the motion in all of these questions is SHM.

Q1 Find the time period of a pendulum of length 2.50 m (g = 9.81 Nkg^{-1}).

Q2 A trolley is connected to two horizontal springs (like in Figure 2), one with spring constant 25 Nm^{-1} and the other with spring constant 45 Nm^{-1}. What will the size of the resultant force on the trolley be if it is pulled 2.5 cm from its equilibrium position?

Q3 A 1.0 kg mass hung on a spring is pulled 45 mm from its equilibrium position. Doing this requires a force of 18 N. If the mass is then released, what will the period of its oscillation be?

Practice Questions — Fact Recall

Q1 a) What's the formula for the period of oscillation of a mass on a spring?

b) Describe an experiment you could do to verify the formula for the period of oscillation of a pendulum.

Q2 What's the formula for the period of oscillation for an oscillating pendulum?

Q3 Sketch graphs to show how you would expect T^2 (the period squared) for a pendulum to vary with pendulum length, mass and amplitude.

8. Free and Forced Vibrations

An object can be forced to oscillate by providing a driving frequency. If this is near the object's natural frequency, the object will start to resonate — which can be good or bad news, depending on what the object is needed for.

Free vibrations

Free vibrations involve no transfer of energy to or from the surroundings. If you stretch and release a mass on a spring, it oscillates at its **natural frequency**. The same happens if you strike a metal object — the sound you hear is caused by vibrations at the object's natural frequency. If no energy's transferred to or from the surroundings, it will keep oscillating with the same amplitude forever. In practice this never happens, but a spring vibrating in air is called a free vibration anyway.

Forced vibrations

Forced vibrations happen when there's an external driving force. A system can be forced to vibrate by a periodic external force. The frequency of this force is called the **driving frequency**. If the driving frequency is much less than the natural frequency then the two are in phase (see page 18). But if the driving frequency is much greater than the natural frequency, the oscillator won't be able to keep up — you end up with the driver completely out of phase with the oscillator (in antiphase).

Resonance

When the driving frequency approaches the natural frequency, the system gains more and more energy from the driving force and so vibrates with a rapidly increasing amplitude. When this happens the system is **resonating**. At resonance the phase difference between the driver and oscillator is 90°. Figures 1 and 2 show how the relationship between amplitude and driving frequency can be investigated by experiment.

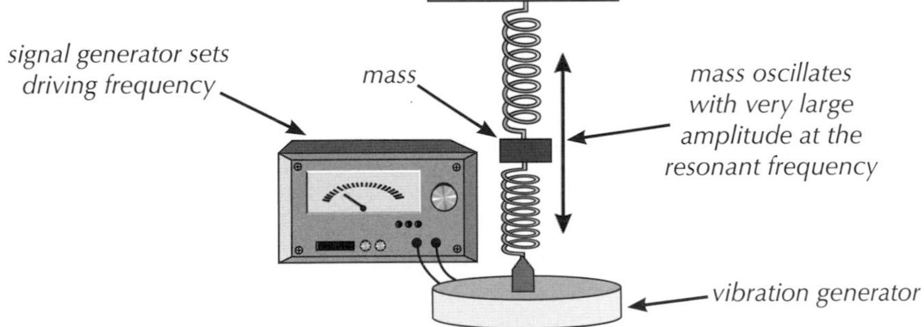

Figure 1: *Using a vibration generator to oscillate a mass-spring system. The system resonates when the driving frequency equals the natural frequency.*

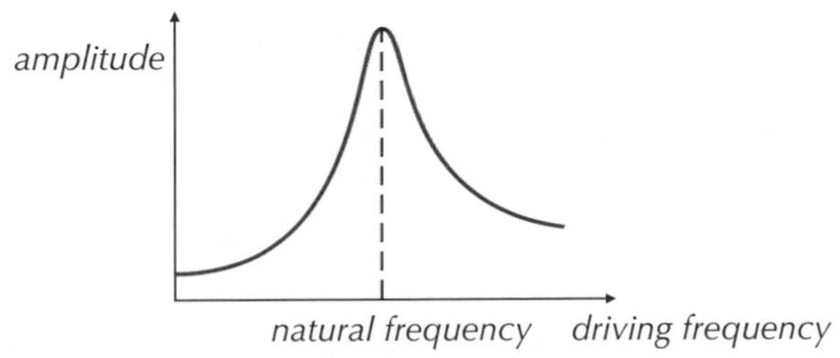

Figure 2: *Graph showing how the amplitude of oscillation of a system changes with driving frequency.*

Learning Objectives:

- Understand what is meant by free and forced vibrations.
- Know how the phase difference between the driving and driven oscillations changes with increasing driving frequency.
- Know what resonance is, and that it occurs when the driving frequency approaches the natural frequency.
- Know that damping reduces the amplitude of oscillations, and how different amounts of damping have different effects.

Specification Reference 3.4.1

Tip: Remember phase differences from page 18? They're a measure of how far ahead one wave is ahead of another — given in radians, degrees or a fraction of a total wave cycle.

Tip: At resonance, the driver displacement is 90° out of phase to the displacement of the oscillator — i.e. the displacement of the driver is at its maximum when the oscillator is passing through its equilibrium point.

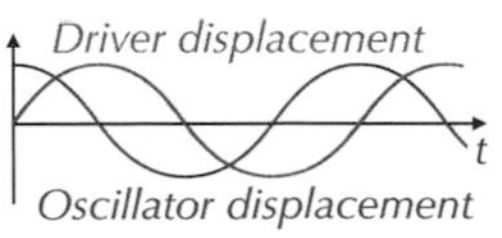

> **Tip:** Make sure you know some examples of resonance.

Examples

Here are some examples of resonance:

A radio is tuned so the electric circuit resonates at the same frequency as the radio station you want to listen to.

A glass resonates when driven by a sound wave at the right frequency.

The column of air resonates in an organ pipe, driven by the motion of air at the base.

A swing resonates if it's driven by someone pushing it at its natural frequency.

Damping

> **Tip:** Another name for damping forces is 'dissipative forces', since they dissipate the energy of the oscillator to its surroundings.

In practice, any oscillating system loses energy to its surroundings. This is usually down to frictional forces like air resistance. These are called **damping** forces. Systems are often deliberately damped to stop them oscillating or to minimise the effect of resonance.

Example

Shock absorbers in a car's suspension provide a damping force by squashing oil through a hole when compressed.

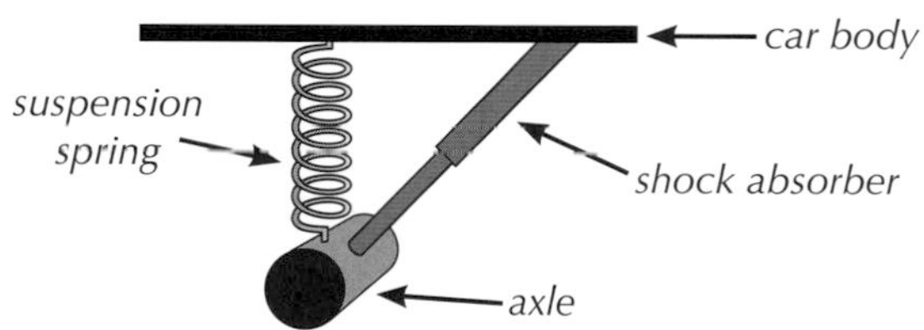

Figure 3: *Damping in a car suspension system.*

The degree of damping can vary from light damping (where the damping force is small) to overdamping. Damping reduces the amplitude of the oscillation over time. Generally, the heavier the damping, the quicker the amplitude is reduced to zero (although overdamping is an exception). Figure 6 shows how different degrees of damping reduce the amplitude to zero at different speeds.

Light and heavy damping

> **Exam Tip**
> Make sure you're able to describe the four different types of damping (the next two are on the next page), and sketch these graphs showing how the amplitude of oscillation changes with time.

Lightly damped systems take a long time to stop oscillating, and their amplitude only reduces a small amount each period. Heavily damped systems take less time to stop oscillating, and their amplitude gets much smaller each period.

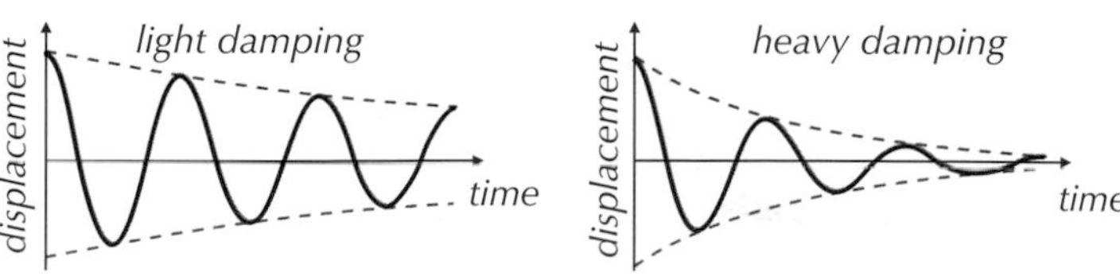

Figure 4: *Graphs showing the effect of light and heavy damping.*

Example
A pendulum formed of a small bob on a rod is an example of a lightly damped system — air resistance will cause the pendulum to slow down only very slightly each period. If the pendulum bob was removed and replaced with this book, the larger surface area of the book would increase air resistance, and the damping forces would be larger, slowing the oscillation more quickly.

Tip: Remember the period of a pendulum doesn't depend on its mass, so the mass of the book wouldn't affect the SHM in any way.

Critical damping

Critical damping reduces the amplitude (i.e. stops the system oscillating) in the shortest possible time (see Figure 6).

Example
Car suspension systems are critically damped so that they don't oscillate but return to equilibrium as quickly as possible.

Figure 5: Safety doors are critically damped to stop them swinging open.

Overdamping

Systems with even heavier damping are **overdamped**. They take longer to return to equilibrium than a critically damped system (see Figure 6).

Example
Some heavy doors are overdamped, so that they don't slam shut too quickly, but instead close slowly, giving people time to walk through them.

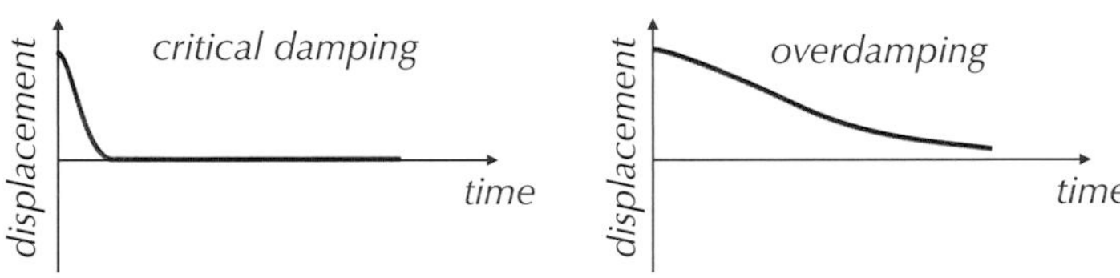

***Figure 6:** Graphs showing the effects of different amounts of damping.*

Plastic deformation of ductile materials reduces the amplitude of oscillations in the same way as damping. As the material changes shape, it absorbs energy, so the oscillation will be smaller.

Tip: You met plastic deformation at AS — it's when a material is permanently stretched, beyond its elastic limit.

Damping and resonance peaks

Lightly damped systems have a very sharp resonance peak. Their amplitude only increases dramatically when the driving frequency is very close to the natural frequency. Heavily damped systems have a flatter response. Their amplitude doesn't increase very much near the natural frequency and they aren't as sensitive to the driving frequency. Figure 6 shows the effect of increasing levels of damping on oscillations near the natural frequency.

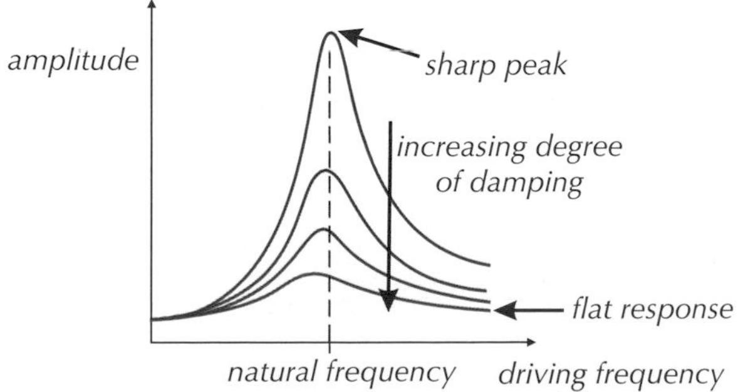

***Figure 7:** Graph showing how damping affects resonance.*

Tip: For heavier damping, resonance occurs at a slightly lower driving frequency than the natural frequency.

Figure 8: *The Taipei 101 building in Taiwan, standing at 508 m tall. A 660-tonne pendulum suspended down the centre of the building acts as a tuned mass damper, reducing the amplitude of the building's oscillations in earthquakes.*

Example

Some structures are damped to avoid being damaged by resonance. Some buildings in regions prone to earthquakes have a large mass called a tuned mass damper. When an earthquake causes the building to shake, the mass moves in the opposite direction to the building, damping its oscillation (see Figure 8). This is an example of critical damping.

Example

Loudspeakers are made to have as flat a response as possible so that they don't 'colour' the sound by oscillating with greater amplitude near their natural frequency. They are damped to play all frequencies at the same volume, so that they can accurately reproduce sounds.

Figure 9 shows apparatus that can be used to demonstrate the effect of damping on the resonance of a spring-mass system. A flat disc is attached to the set-up you saw in Figure 1. As the mass oscillates, air resistance on the disc acts as a damping force, reducing the amplitude of the oscillation. The larger the disc, the larger the damping force and the smaller the amplitude of oscillation of the system at resonance.

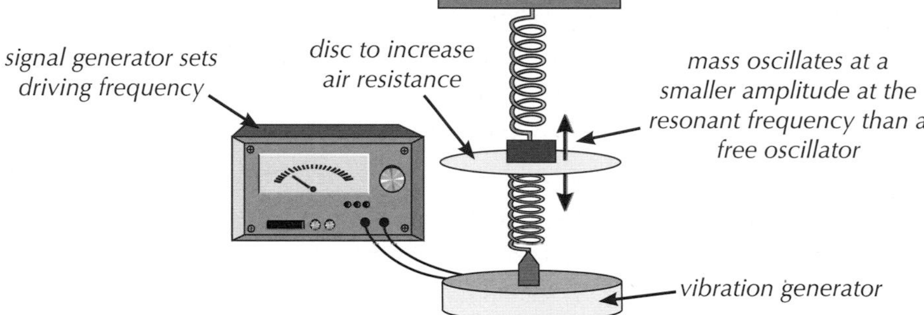

Figure 9: *Experiment to show how damping affects resonance.*

Practice Questions — Fact Recall

Q1 What is the difference between a free vibration and a forced vibration?

Q2 What is resonance, and when does it occur?

Q3 Give three examples of situations where resonance can occur.

Q4 Describe the phase difference between a driving oscillation and an oscillating object in each of the following cases:

a) The driving frequency is much lower than the natural frequency.

b) The driving frequency is equal to the natural frequency.

c) The driving frequency is much higher than the natural frequency.

Q5 What is meant by a damping force?

Q6 Name and briefly describe the four types of damping.

Q7 Sketch a graph of amplitude against driving frequency for a system to show how the level of damping affects the sharpness of the resonance peak at the natural frequency.

Section Summary

Make sure you know...

- That linear momentum is the product of mass and linear velocity.
- That if there are no external forces, linear momentum is always conserved in a collision or explosion.
- How to apply the conservation of linear momentum to one-dimensional collisions or explosions.
- That kinetic energy is conserved in an elastic collision, but not in an inelastic collision.
- That Newton's second law ($\boldsymbol{F} = m\boldsymbol{a}$) can also be written as $\boldsymbol{F} = \frac{\Delta(m\boldsymbol{v})}{\Delta t}$.
- That impulse is the product of force and time, and that it is equal to the change in momentum.
- That impulse is equal to the area under a force-time graph.
- That angular speed is the angle an object moving with circular motion rotates through per second.
- How to calculate the angular speed of an object moving with circular motion given its linear speed.
- That the frequency of rotation is the number of complete revolutions per second.
- That the period of rotation is the time taken for one complete revolution in seconds.
- The relationship between frequency and period.
- How to calculate angular speed from the frequency or period.
- That objects moving with circular motion experience a centripetal acceleration.
- How to calculate centripetal acceleration and force from angular and linear speeds.
- That simple harmonic motion is the oscillation of an object with an acceleration that is proportional to its displacement from its equilibrium position, and that is always directed towards the equilibrium.
- How to sketch the graphs of displacement, velocity and acceleration against time for SHM.
- That the velocity is given by the gradient of the displacement-time graph.
- The phase differences between displacement, velocity and acceleration for SHM.
- That frequency and period are independent of amplitude for an object moving with SHM.
- How the kinetic and potential energy of an object moving with SHM vary with time and displacement.
- That mechanical energy is the sum of the kinetic and potential energy of an object and that it stays constant for undamped oscillations.
- How to use the formula for the displacement of an object in SHM as a function of time, and the formulas for the acceleration and velocity of an object in SHM as functions of displacement.
- How to sketch the graphs of acceleration and velocity of an object in SHM as functions of displacement.
- That a mass on a spring and a simple pendulum are examples of simple harmonic oscillators.
- How to use the formulae for the period of oscillation of a mass on a spring, and of a pendulum, and how to experimentally verify these formulas.
- That free vibrations involve no transfer of energy between an object and its surroundings, and that an object oscillating freely does so at its natural frequency.
- That a forced vibration is driven by a periodic, external driving force at a driving frequency.
- That resonance is a rapid increase in the amplitude of oscillation of an object, and that it usually occurs at the object's natural frequency.
- How the phase difference between the driver and driven displacements changes with driving frequency.
- That a damping force causes an oscillator to lose energy to its surroundings, and reduces the amplitude of its oscillations.
- How different amounts of damping affect an oscillator's amplitude over time.
- How damping affects the sharpness of resonance peaks, and examples of where damping is used.

Exam-style Questions

Questions 1 to 3 are worth 1 mark each.

1 A ball of mass 0.25 kg is travelling with a velocity of 1.2 ms^{-1} when it collides with an identical, stationary ball. After the collision, the two balls move together with the same velocity. How fast are they moving?

A 1.2 ms^{-1}

B 0.6 ms^{-1}

C 0.12 ms^{-1}

D 0.18 ms^{-1}

2 A trolley of mass 1.0 kg is attached to a horizontal spring, and is moving with simple harmonic motion with period *T*. The amplitude of its oscillation is 5 cm. What is the trolley's maximum kinetic energy?

A $\frac{\pi}{200T}$

B $\frac{\pi^2}{200T^2}$

C $\frac{\pi^2 T^2}{200}$

D $\frac{\pi T}{200}$

3 A pendulum is oscillating with simple harmonic motion. At time $t = 0$, the pendulum passes through its equilibrium position, and passes through it again 1.5 s later. Which of the following graphs shows how the pendulum's potential energy, E_P, varies with time?

A

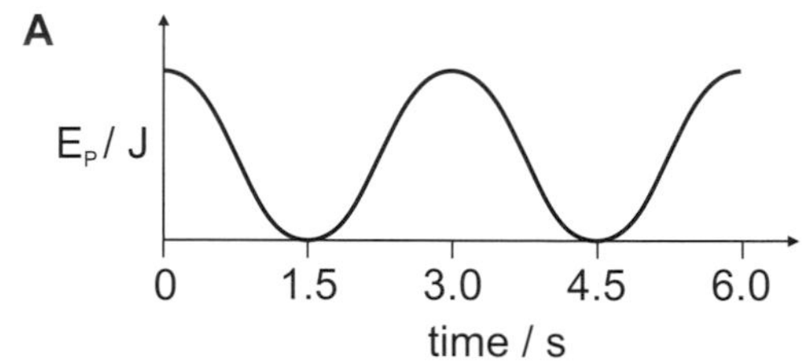

B

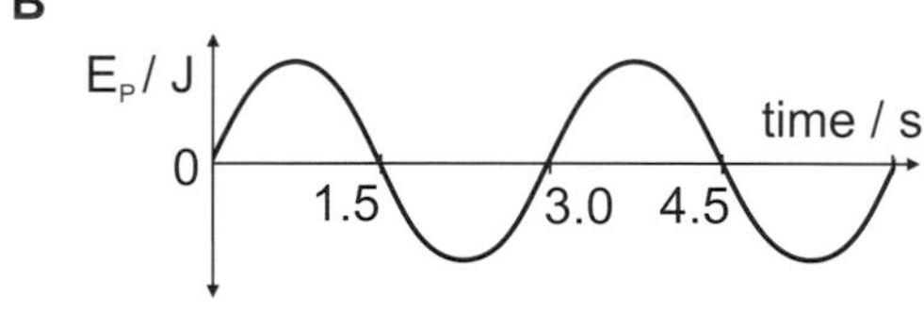

C

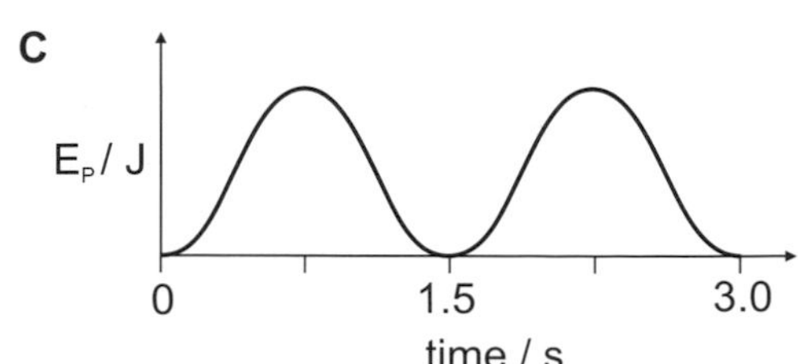

D

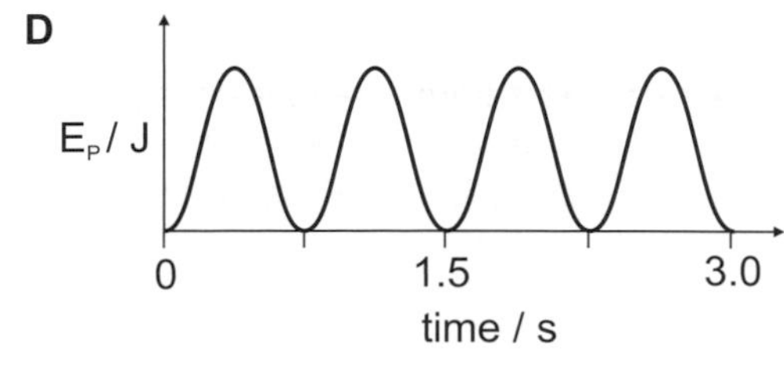

4 At a fairground, a dodgem car of mass 125 kg travelling at 2.40 ms^{-1} collides loudly with the wall of the dodgem arena, and comes to a complete stop. The wall is fixed and does not move.

4 (a) Is this an elastic or inelastic collision? Explain your answer.

(2 marks)

4 (b) (i) Calculate the magnitude of the impulse that acts on the dodgem.

(2 marks)

4 (b) (ii) What would the impulse be if the dodgem had been travelling at 4.80 ms^{-1}.

(1 mark)

4 (b) (iii) State Newton's second law in terms of momentum in words.

(1 mark)

5 (a) A mass of 1.8 kg attached to a horizontal spring oscillates with simple harmonic motion. The period of oscillation is 3.2 s, and the oscilllation has amplitude 0.22 m.

5 (a) (i) Calculate the spring constant of the spring.

(2 marks)

5 (a) (ii) Calculate the magnitude of the maximum force experienced by the mass.

(2 marks)

5 (a) (iii) Calculate the kinetic energy of the mass when it is 0.12 m from its equilibrium position.

(4 marks)

5 (a) (iv) Sketch a graph of the mass's acceleration against its displacement on the axes below. Mark on your graph the maximum values of the acceleration, and the values of displacement these occur at.

(3 marks)

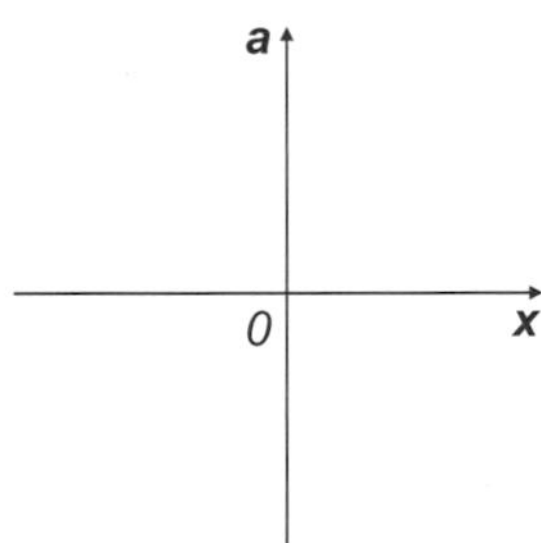

5 (b) A simple pendulum is made to oscillate in a vacuum by a periodic driving force, at a frequency below its natural frequency.

5 (b) (i) Describe what happens as the driving frequency is increased to the pendulum's natural frequency. Give the name of this phenomenon.

(2 marks)

5 (b) (ii) The same pendulum is placed in a tank of water, and made to oscillate again. Describe and explain what happens this time as the driving frequency is increased up to the pendulum's natural frequency.

(3 marks)

1. Gravitational Fields

So far you've probably only seen forces acting at a specific point, with a specific cause (e.g. pushing a swing). Fields, on the other hand, are regions in which a charge or mass will experience a force.

Learning Objectives:
- Understand that gravity is an attractive force that acts between all matter.
- Understand what a gravitational field is.
- Know how to calculate the force due to gravity between two point masses using Newton's law of gravitation.
- Know the significance of *G*.
- Be able to represent gravitational fields graphically.

Specification Reference 3.4.2

What is a gravitational field?

Any object with mass will experience an attractive force if you put it in the gravitational field of another object. A gravitational field is a **force field**.

A force field is a region in which a body experiences a force.

Only objects with a large mass, such as stars and planets, have gravitational fields that produce a significant effect. E.g. the gravitational fields of the Moon and the Sun are noticeable here on Earth — they're the main causes of our tides. Smaller objects do still have gravitational fields that attract other masses, but the effect is too weak to detect without specialised equipment.

Representation of gravitational fields

You can draw lines of force to show the field around an object. Gravitational lines of force, or "field lines", are arrows showing the direction of the force that masses would feel in a gravitational field.

If you put a small mass, m, anywhere in the Earth's gravitational field, it will always be attracted towards the Earth. The Earth's gravitational field is radial — the lines of force meet at the centre of the Earth (see Figure 1).

Tip: The smaller mass, m, has a gravitational field of its own. This doesn't have a noticeable effect on Earth though, because the Earth is so much more massive.

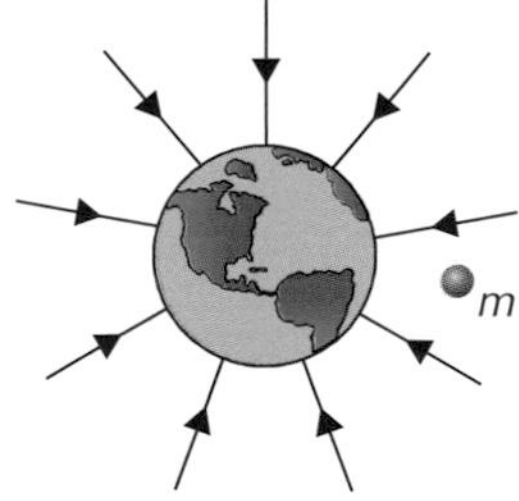

Figure 1: *A small mass in Earth's gravitational field.*

If you move mass m further away from the Earth — where the lines of force are further apart — the force it experiences decreases. The lines can be used to show the strength of the field at each point, where a higher line density shows a stronger gravitational field. Close to Earth's surface, the field is (almost) uniform — the field lines are (almost) parallel.

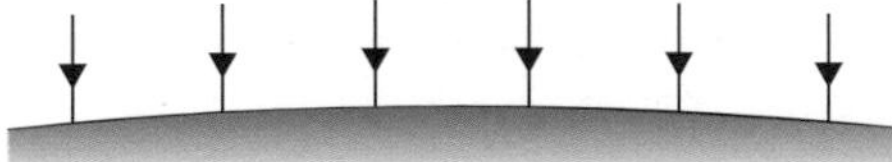

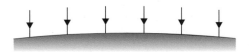

Figure 2: *The gravitational field at Earth's surface is roughly uniform.*

Newton's law of gravitation

The force experienced by an object in a gravitational field is always attractive. It's a vector which depends on the masses involved and the distances between them. It's easy to work this out for **point masses** — or objects which behave as if all their mass is concentrated at the centre, e.g. uniform spheres. You just put the numbers into this equation, known as Newton's law of gravitation:

Figure 3: Tides are caused by gravitational forces

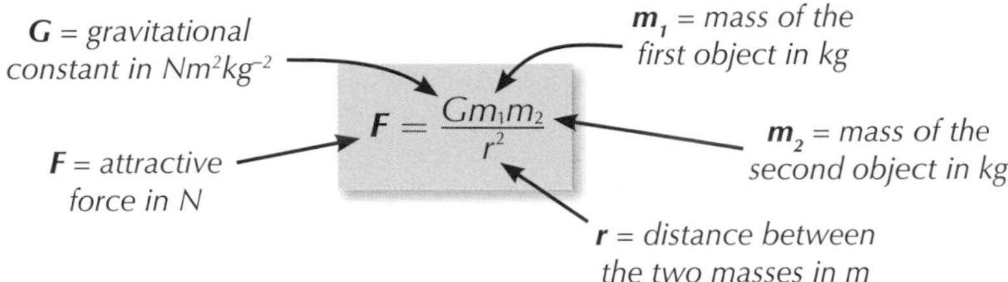

Tip: m_1 is usually the larger mass, but it doesn't really matter which way you label them.

G is the gravitational constant — 6.67×10^{-11} Nm²kg⁻². Don't get this confused with g, the gravitational field strength (see page 37). The force on m_1 due to m_2 is equal and opposite to the force on m_2 due to m_1.

We sometimes only consider the force acting on the smaller object because that's the one that experiences a greater acceleration — $a = \frac{F}{m}$, so as m becomes bigger, a becomes smaller. In this case, r might be measured from the larger mass to the smaller mass (i.e. from Earth to a ball), and F is given a minus sign (i.e. from the ball to Earth). Also note that r is the distance between the centre of each object, not the edges.

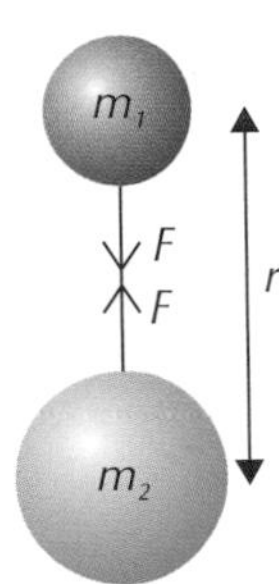

Figure 4: The forces acting on the two masses are equal but opposite.

Tip: This is why we don't notice Earth's acceleration towards us when we're falling to the ground.

Example

Two planets have masses of 7.55×10^{24} kg and 9.04×10^{24} kg respectively. If the force due to gravity between the two planets is 6.69×10^{17} N, how far apart are the planets?

You want to find r, so start by rearranging Newton's law of gravitation:

$$F = \frac{Gm_1m_2}{r^2} \Rightarrow r^2 = \frac{Gm_1m_2}{F} \Rightarrow r = \sqrt{\frac{Gm_1m_2}{F}}$$

Then just put the numbers in:

$$r = \sqrt{\frac{Gm_1m_2}{F}} = \sqrt{\frac{(6.67 \times 10^{-11}) \times (7.55 \times 10^{24}) \times (9.04 \times 10^{24})}{6.69 \times 10^{17}}}$$

$$= 8.2491... \times 10^{10}\text{m}$$

$$= 82.5 \text{ million km (to 3 s.f.)}$$

Exam Tip
An exam question might ask you to work out the mass of one of the objects first. E.g. you might need to use density = $\frac{\text{mass}}{\text{volume}}$.

Inverse square laws

The law of gravitation is an **inverse square law**: $F \propto \frac{1}{r^2}$

This means if the distance r between the masses increases, then the force F will decrease. Because it's r^2 and not just r, if the distance doubles then the force will be one quarter the strength of the original force.

The law of gravitation is an inverse square law because it is radial. The force on any point a distance r from the mass will be the same — if you draw an imaginary sphere with radius r (see Figure 5) then the force will be the same at any point on its surface.

Tip: The ∝ symbol means "is proportional to".

If you double the distance from a mass, the area on the surface of the imaginary sphere of equal force covered by a particular group of radial field lines will be 4 times greater — see Figure 5.

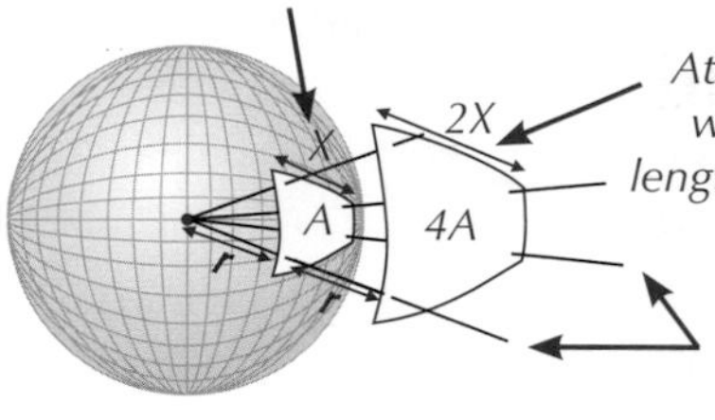

At a distance r, a group of radial field lines passes through a square area with a side length X and an area $A = X^2$.

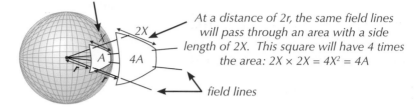

At a distance of 2r, the same field lines will pass through an area with a side length of 2X. This square will have 4 times the area: $2X \times 2X = 4X^2 = 4A$

field lines

Figure 5: *Radial gravitational field lines at a distance of r and 2r from a mass.*

Tip: The shapes don't look like squares because they've been stretched across the sphere's surface.

The spread of field lines indicates the strength of a force felt in that field, so here the force will be 4 times weaker at a distance of 2*r* than at *r* for a given mass. Knowing that $F \propto \frac{1}{r^2}$ can come in handy when answering questions.

Example

The gravitational force between two objects 10 m apart is 0.291 N. What will the gravitational force between them be if they move to 25 m apart?

25 m is $\frac{25}{10} = 2.5$ times larger than 10 m. So to find the new gravitational force, divide 0.291 N by 2.5^2 (because of the inverse square law):

$$\frac{0.291}{2.5^2} = 4.66 \times 10^{-2} \text{ N (to 3 s.f.)}$$

Practice Questions — Application

Q1 Two stars are orbiting each other with a constant separation of 100 million km. If their masses are 2.45×10^{30} kg and 2.91×10^{30} kg, what force are they exerting on each other due to gravity?

Q2 Two asteroids 2.5 km apart exert a gravitational force on each other of 25 N. How much force will they exert on each other when they're 0.5 km apart?

Q3 An aircraft with a mass of 2500 kg is hovering 10 000 m above ground.
a) If the radius of Earth is 6370 km, how far is the aircraft from the centre of the Earth?
b) How much upwards force must the aircraft engine be providing to be able to keep it hovering at a constant altitude? The mass of Earth is 5.98×10^{24} kg.

Tip: Don't forget to convert any distance measurements into metres before using Newton's law.

Tip: Remember, the distance *r* in Newton's law of gravitation is measured from the centre of objects.

Practice Questions — Fact Recall

Q1 What type of object will experience an attractive force due to gravity?

Q2 What's a gravitational field?

Q3 a) Give the formula for Newton's law of gravitation.
b) What does *G* represent in this formula?
c) What must be true of the masses in this formula?

Q4 Draw a diagram showing the gravitational field lines of Earth:
a) Looking at Earth from a distance.
b) At Earth's surface.

2. Gravitational Field Strength

*It's no use being able to draw gravitational field lines if you can't use them to work anything out. The gravitational field strength, **g**, tells you how strong the force due to gravity is at any point in a gravitational field.*

Learning Objectives:

- Know what is meant by gravitational field strength and be able to calculate it.
- Be able to calculate the gravitational field strength in a radial field.
- Be able to calculate the gravitational field strength due to more than one object.

Specification Reference 3.4.2

The gravitational field strength, g

Gravitational field strength, g, is the force per unit mass. Its value depends on where you are in the field. There's a really simple equation for working it out:

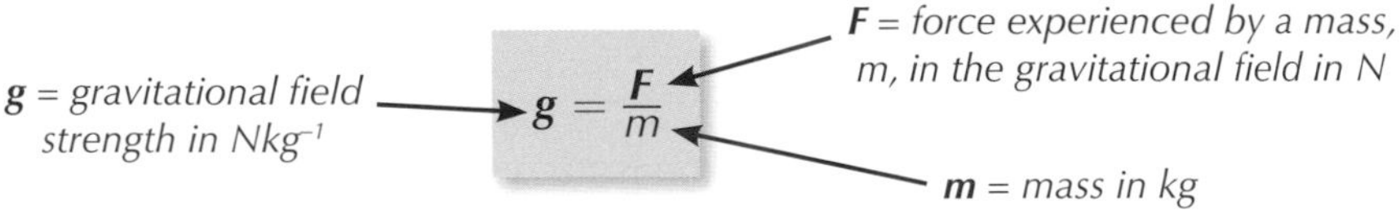

g is a vector quantity — it has a magnitude and a direction. It's always pointing towards the centre of mass of the object whose field you're describing. Since the gravitational field is almost uniform at the Earth's surface, you can assume **g** is a constant.

The value of **g** at the Earth's surface is approximately 9.81 Nkg^{-1}

g can also be seen as the acceleration of a mass in a gravitational field. It's often called the acceleration due to gravity. On Earth, this is approximately 9.81 ms^{-2}.

Tip: From $\boldsymbol{F} = m\boldsymbol{a}$ you can get $\boldsymbol{a} = \boldsymbol{F}/m$, which has the units Nkg^{-1} — just another way of measuring acceleration.

Example

An 80 kg astronaut feels a force of 130 N due to gravity on the Moon. What's the value of g on the moon?

Just put the numbers into the formula:

$$\boldsymbol{g} = \frac{\boldsymbol{F}}{m} = \frac{130}{80} = 1.63\,\text{Nkg}^{-1} \text{ (to 3 s.f.)}$$

Radial fields

Point masses have radial gravitational fields (see page 34). The magnitude of **g** depends on the distance *r* from the point mass *M*.

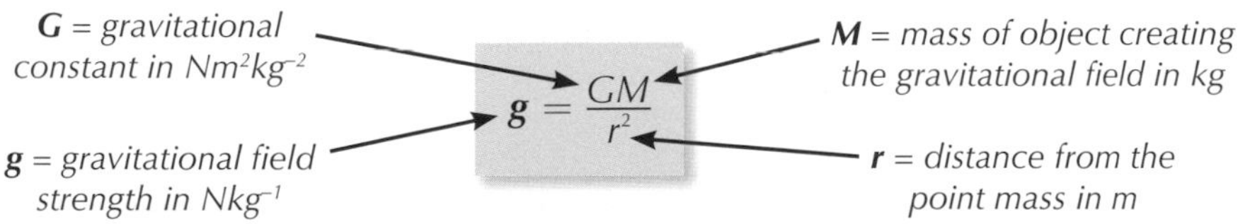

Tip: Magnitude means size without the direction (so **g** is always positive in this equation).

You can derive this formula by looking at Newton's law of gravitation (p. 35):

Start with $\boldsymbol{F} = \frac{Gm_1m_2}{r^2}$. Replace m_1 with M and m_2 with m:

$$\boldsymbol{F} = \frac{GMm}{r^2}$$

Then substitute this into $\boldsymbol{g} = \frac{\boldsymbol{F}}{m}$, cancelling down where possible:

$$\boldsymbol{g} = \frac{\boldsymbol{F}}{m} = \frac{\left(\frac{GM\cancel{m}}{r^2}\right)}{\cancel{m}} = \frac{GM}{r^2}$$

Tip: If you're not dealing with a point mass, *r* is the distance from the centre of the object with mass *M*.

Example

The mass of the Earth is 5.98 × 10^{24} kg and its radius is 6.37 × 10^{6} m. Find the value of *g* at the Earth's surface.

Just put the numbers into the equation:

$$\mathbf{g} = \frac{GM}{r^2} = \frac{(6.67 \times 10^{-11}) \times (5.98 \times 10^{24})}{(6.37 \times 10^{6})^2} = 9.83\,\text{Nkg}^{-1} \text{ (to 3 s.f.)}$$

Tip: As you probably know by now, we usually use 9.81 Nkg^{-1} as the value of **g** — the difference here is just because of the number of significant figures given in the question.

This is another case of the inverse square law (page 35) — as r doubles, **g** decreases to a quarter of its original value.

*Figure 1: The value of **g** on top of a mountain is slightly lower than at sea level.*

Example

If you plot a graph of **g** against r for the Earth, you get a curve like this:

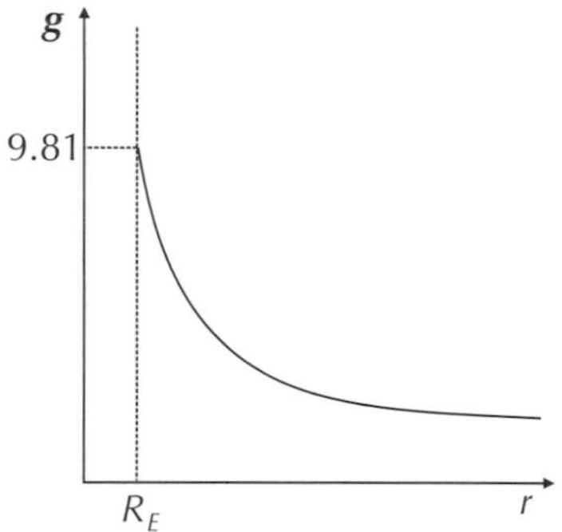

It shows that **g** is greatest at the surface of the Earth (R_E), but decreases rapidly as r increases and you move further away from the centre of the Earth. The area under this curve can be used to find the gravitational potential, V (p. 40).

Combining gravitational field strengths

Gravitational fields are vector fields, which means you can add them up to find the combined effect of more than one object. And remember, vector fields means the direction matters.

Example

What's the value of the gravitational field strength at the point *P* below?

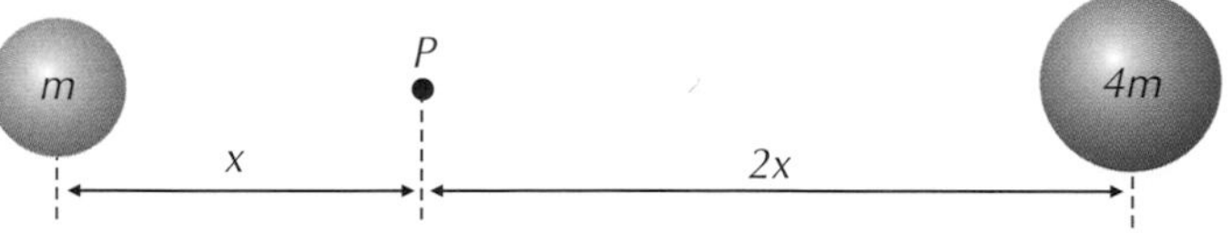

Tip: Remember, an object's gravitational field points towards the object — gravity's an attractive force.

Take the right direction to be positive and the left direction to be negative, then add up the effect of each sphere:

$$\mathbf{g} = \sum\frac{GM}{r^2} = \frac{G(4m)}{(2x)^2} - \frac{Gm}{x^2}$$
$$= \frac{4}{4}\frac{Gm}{x^2} - \frac{Gm}{x^2}$$
$$= 0\,\text{Nkg}^{-1}$$

Practice Questions — Application

Q1 A 105 kg object experiences an attractive force due to gravity of 581 N. What's the gravitational field strength?

Q2 Why would an astronaut find it easier to pick up a rock with a mass of 20 kg on the Moon than a rock with a mass of 20 kg on Earth?

Q3 Find the gravitational field strength at point P in the diagram below.

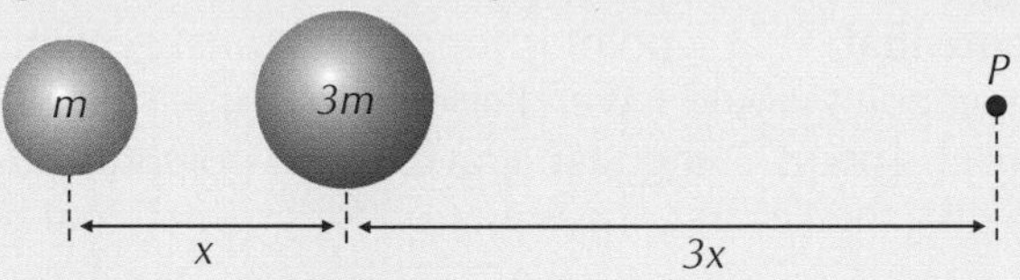

Tip: The mass of an object is always the same wherever it is.

Exam Tip
In some questions you'll need to give the final answer in terms of variables (e.g. m), so don't panic if you can't work out how to get rid of all the letters in your answer.

Practice Questions — Fact Recall

Q1 Other than the acceleration due to gravity, how is $\mathbf{g}$ defined and what are its units?

Q2 What does M represent in the formula for gravitational field strength in a radial field?

Q3 Which of the following shows how gravitational field strength changes with distance r?

a) 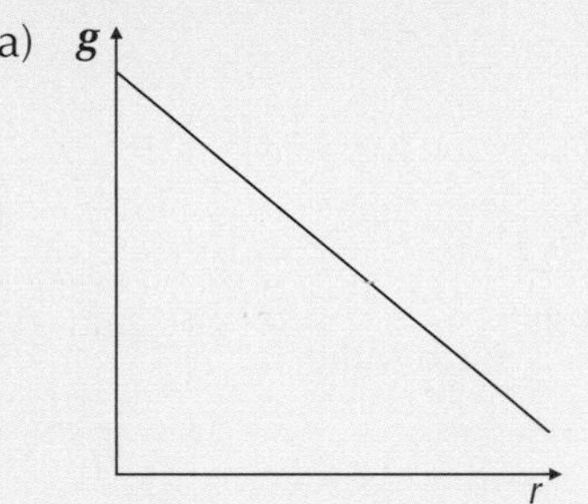

b) 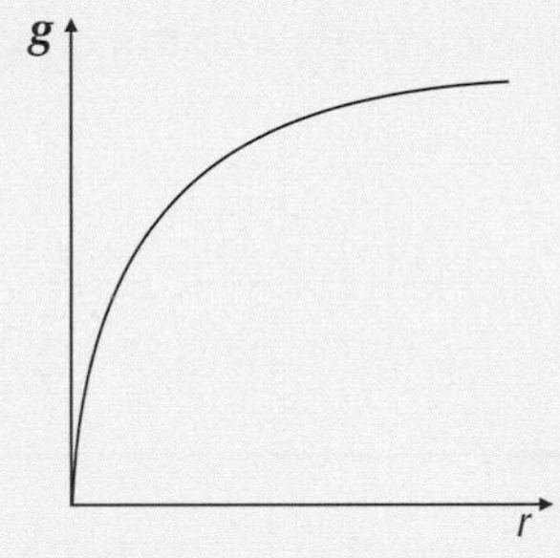

c) 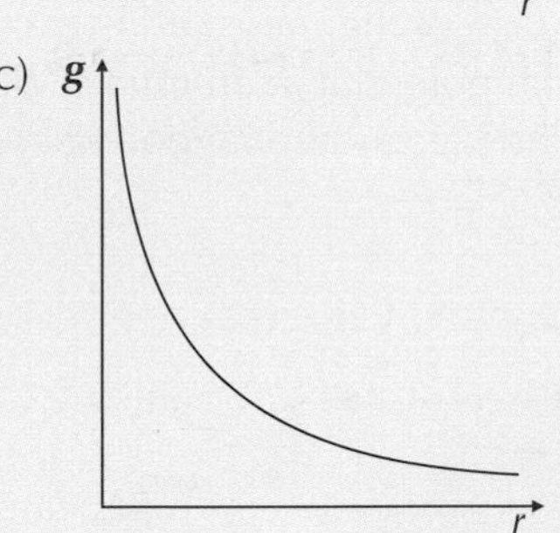

d) 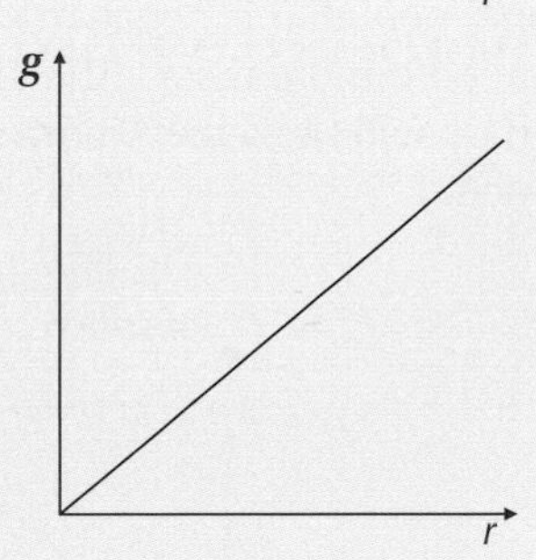

3. Gravitational Potential

All objects in a gravitational field have a gravitational potential that increases the further they are from the centre of the field. It can be hard to get your head round at first, but try not to get it confused with gravitational potential energy.

Learning Objectives:

- Know what's meant by gravitational potential.
- Be able to calculate the gravitational potential, V, of an object in a radial gravitational field.
- Be able to draw and interpret graphical representations of the relationship between V and r in a radial gravitational field.
- Be able to calculate the value of g at a given point using the gradient of a graph of V against r.
- Be able to find the work done and the change in gravitational potential energy caused by changing an object's gravitational potential.

Specification Reference 3.4.2

What is gravitational potential?

Gravitational potential, V, at a point is the gravitational potential energy that a unit mass at that point would have. For example, if a 1 kg mass has 10 J of potential energy at a point Z, then the gravitational potential at Z is 10 Jkg^{-1}. In a radial field (like the Earth's), the equation for gravitational potential is:

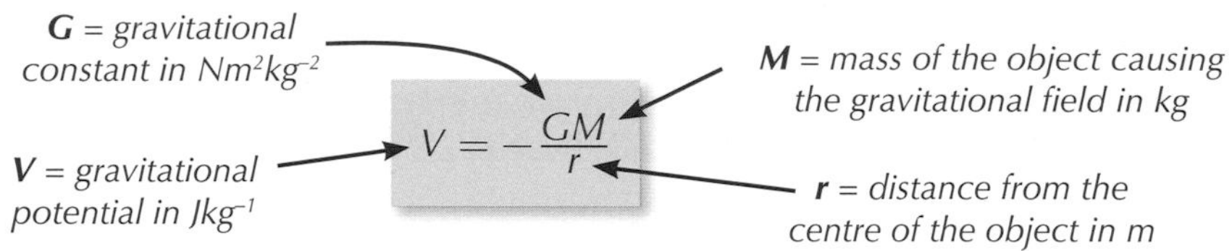

Example

Find the gravitational potential V at the surface of the Earth. The Earth's mass is 5.98×10^{24} kg and its radius is 6.37×10^{6} m.

Just put the numbers into the equation:

$$V = -\frac{GM}{r}$$
$$= -\frac{(6.67 \times 10^{-11}) \times (5.98 \times 10^{24})}{6.37 \times 10^{6}}$$
$$= -6.26 \times 10^{7}\ \text{Jkg}^{-1}\ \text{(to 3 s.f.)}\ (= -62.6\ \text{MJkg}^{-1})$$

Tip: This means a 1 kg mass needs 62.6 MJ of energy to be able to fully escape the Earth's gravitational pull.

Gravitational potential is negative on the surface of the mass and increases with distance from the mass. The gravitational potential at an infinite distance from the mass will be zero. Figure 1 shows how gravitational potential varies with distance.

Tip: Note that V is proportional to $1/r$, not $1/r^2$ like the gravitational field strength.

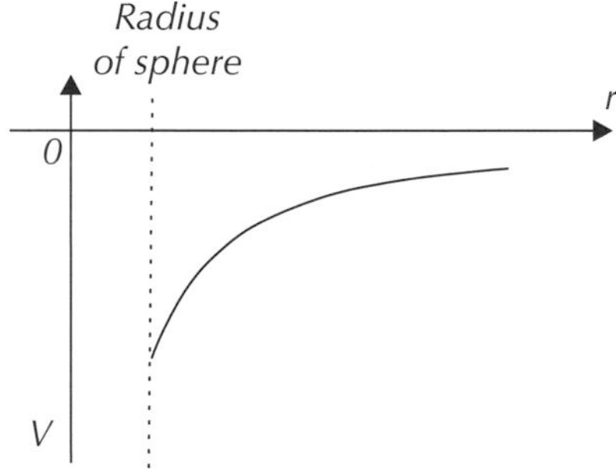

Figure 1: *A graph of gravitational potential against distance for a sphere.*

If you find the gradient of this graph at a particular point, you get the value of $-g$ at that point. In other words:

$$g = -\frac{\Delta V}{\Delta r}$$

- g = gravitational field strength in Nkg^{-1}
- ΔV = change in gravitational potential in Jkg^{-1}
- Δr = change in distance from the centre of the object in m

Tip: Remember g is negative — you need to add a minus sign as the gradient of the graph is always positive.

Example

The graph below shows the gravitational potential *V* against the distance *r* from the centre of a planet. Find the gravitational field strength *g* at $r = 15 \times 10^6$ m.

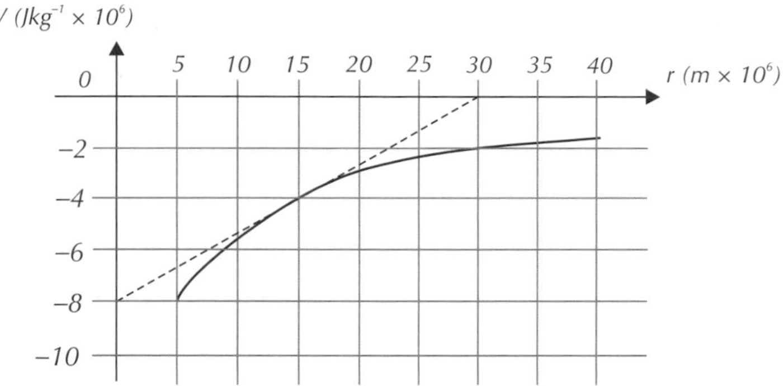

The gravitational field strength is given by the gradient:

$$g = -\frac{\Delta V}{\Delta r} = -\frac{0 - (-8 \times 10^6)}{(30 \times 10^6) - 0} = -0.27\ \text{Nkg}^{-1}\ \text{(to 2 s.f.)}$$

Tip: g is negative because it points 'downwards' towards the centre of the planet.

Gravitational potential difference

Gravitational potential difference is the energy needed to move a unit mass. Two points at different distances from a mass will have different gravitational potentials (because gravitational potential increases with distance) — this means that there is a gravitational potential difference between these two points.

When you move an object you do work against the force of gravity — the amount of energy you need depends on the mass of the object and the gravitational potential difference you move it through:

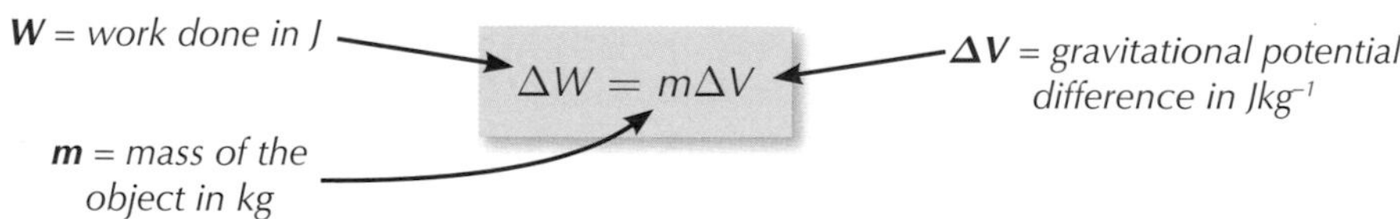

Tip: In physics, doing work means using a force to transfer energy from one type to another. In this case, gravitational potential energy is converted to kinetic energy (or kinetic energy to gravitational potential energy).

You can also use this relationship to describe an object's (change in) gravitational potential energy (E_p) at a given gravitational potential:

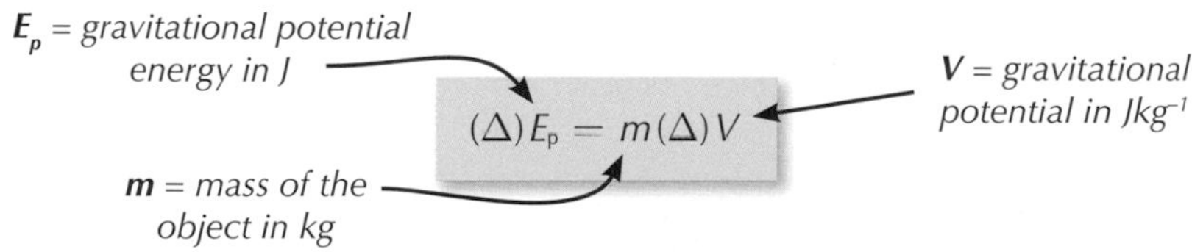

Substituting in the formula for V from the previous page, the gravitational potential energy of an object of mass m is:

$$E_p = m\left(-\frac{GM}{r}\right) = -\frac{GMm}{r}$$

Figure 2: Rollercoasters convert gravitational potential energy to kinetic energy and back.

Tip: This is really useful when you're doing calculations with satellites — see p. 44.

Example

How much energy is needed to move a mass *m* through a gravitational potential difference of ΔV?

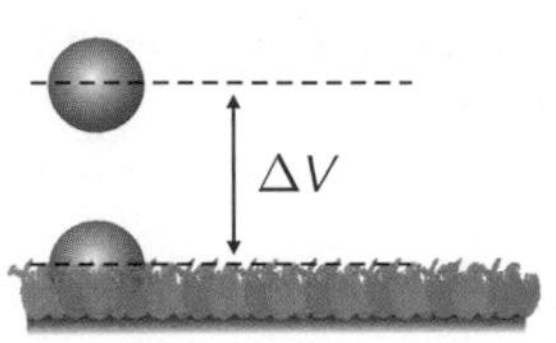

The gravitational field strength is given by:

$$g = -\frac{\Delta V}{\Delta r} = \frac{F}{m}$$

g in a uniform field — *g defined as force per unit mass (page 37).*

Which rearranges to give:

$$m\Delta V = -F\Delta r$$

Tip: ***F*** is negative because you're working against gravity.

To throw a ball *m* from *A* to *B*:

work done = force × distance moved = $m\Delta V$

So the energy needed to move a mass *m* against a gravitational potential difference is given by $m\Delta V$.

Example

A forklift truck does 2120 J of work to increase a pig's gravitational potential by 26.5 Jkg^{-1}. What's the mass of the pig?

You're given the work done and the change in gravitational potential and you need to find the mass, so rearrange the formula on page 41 to make mass the subject:

$$\Delta W = m\Delta V \Rightarrow m = \frac{\Delta W}{\Delta V} = \frac{2120}{26.5} = 80\,\text{kg}$$

Figure 3: *Forklift trucks do work against gravity to convert mechanical (or kinetic) energy to gravitational potential energy.*

Practice Questions — Application

Q1 A satellite is orbiting Earth. What's the effect (if any) on the following values of halving the satellite's orbital radius? Explain your answers.

a) *G*

b) *V*

c) *g*

d) *m*

Q2 A 1.72 kg brick is dropped off the side of a cliff. If its gravitational potential changes by 531 Jkg^{-1}, how much work is done by gravity on the brick?

Practice Questions — Fact Recall

Q1 What is gravitational potential, *V*? What are its units?

Q2 Sketch a graph of the gravitational potential (*V*) against distance (*r*) for an object in Earth's gravitational field.

Q3 What does the gradient of a graph of *V* against *r* tell you?

Q4 What does ΔW represent in the equation $\Delta W = m\Delta V$?

Tip: Make sure your graph for Q2 starts at the radius of Earth and not at its centre.

4. Orbits

You saw circular motion in the mechanics section, and here it's covered again for objects in gravitational fields. Gravity acts as the centripetal force that keeps objects in orbit around a much larger body.

Learning Objectives:

- Understand how the speed and orbital period of a satellite are affected by the radius of its orbit.
- Understand the relationship between the kinetic energy and gravitational potential energy of a satellite.
- Know what a geosynchronous satellite is and understand why they're useful.

Specification Reference 3.4.2

Satellites

Planets and **satellites** are kept in orbit by gravitational forces. A satellite is just any smaller mass which orbits a much larger mass — the Moon is a satellite of the Earth, planets are satellites of the Sun, etc.

Satellites are kept in orbit by the gravitational 'pull' of the mass they're orbiting. In our Solar System, the planets have nearly circular orbits, so you can use the equations of circular motion (pages 11-16) to investigate their speed and **orbital period** (see below).

Orbital period and speed

Any object undergoing circular motion (e.g. a satellite) is kept in its path by a centripetal force. What causes this force depends on the object — in the case of satellites it's the gravitational attraction of the mass they're orbiting. This means that, in this case the centripetal force is the gravitational force.

You saw on page 15 that the force acting on an object in circular motion is given by:

$$F = \frac{mv^2}{r}$$

And on page 37, you saw that the force of attraction due to gravity between two objects is given by:

$$F = \frac{GMm}{r^2}$$

Figure 1: The planets in our Solar System are satellites of the Sun.

Which means you can set the two expressions to be equal to each other and rearrange to find the speed, v, of a satellite in a gravitational field:

$$\frac{mv^2}{r} = \frac{GMm}{r^2} \Rightarrow v^2 = \frac{GM\cancel{m}\cancel{r}}{r^{\cancel{2}}\cancel{m}} \Rightarrow v = \sqrt{\frac{GM}{r}}$$

So the speed of a satellite is inversely proportional to the square root of its orbital radius, or $v \propto \frac{1}{\sqrt{r}}$.

The time taken for a satellite to make one orbit is called the orbital period, T. Remember, speed = $\frac{\text{distance}}{\text{time}}$, and the distance for a circular orbit is $2\pi r$, so $v = \frac{2\pi r}{T}$:

$$v = \frac{2\pi r}{T} \Rightarrow T = \frac{2\pi r}{v}$$

Tip: Need a reminder on circular motion? Flick back to pages 11-16.

Then substitute the expression for v found above and rearrange:

$$T = \frac{2\pi r}{v} = \frac{2\pi r}{\left(\sqrt{\frac{GM}{r}}\right)} = \frac{2\pi r\sqrt{r}}{\sqrt{GM}} = \sqrt{\frac{4\pi^2 r^3}{GM}}$$

Tip: Here the square root was taken of everything to make the expression neater. That's why anything that wasn't already rooted got squared (e.g. 2 → 4).

The period of an orbit is proportional to the square root of the radius cubed, or $T \propto \sqrt{r^3}$. The greater the radius of a satellite's orbit, the slower it will travel and the longer it will take to complete one orbit.

Example

The Moon takes 27.3 days to orbit the Earth. Calculate its distance from the Earth. Take the mass of the Earth to be 5.98×10^{24} kg.

You're trying to find the radius of the orbit, r. Use the formula for period, T:

$$T = \sqrt{\frac{4\pi^2 r^3}{GM}}$$

And rearrange it for r^3:

$$T = \sqrt{\frac{4\pi^2 r^3}{GM}} \Rightarrow T^2 = \frac{4\pi^2 r^3}{GM} \Rightarrow r^3 = \frac{T^2 GM}{4\pi^2}$$

Then just put the numbers in:

$$r^3 = \frac{(2.35... \times 10^6)^2 \times (6.67 \times 10^{-11}) \times (5.98 \times 10^{24})}{4\pi^2}$$

$$= 5.6210... \times 10^{25}\ \text{m}^3$$

$$r = \sqrt[3]{5.6210... \times 10^{25}}$$

$$= 3.83 \times 10^5\ \text{km (to 3 s.f.)}$$

Tip: T is given in days, so you need to convert it to seconds first. 27.3 days is $2.35... \times 10^6$ s

Tip: Just take the cube root of r here — there's a button for it on your calculator ($\sqrt[3]{\square}$).

Tip: This is the distance from the centre of the Earth to the centre of the Moon.

Kinetic and potential energy of satellites

An orbiting satellite has kinetic and potential energy — its total energy (i.e. kinetic and potential) is always constant. In a circular orbit, a satellite's speed and distance above the mass it's orbiting are constant. This means that its kinetic energy and potential energy are also both constant.

In an elliptical orbit, a satellite will speed up as its height decreases (and slow down as its height increases). This means that its kinetic energy increases as its potential energy decreases (and vice versa), so the total energy remains constant.

Tip: Remember, kinetic energy, $E_k = \frac{1}{2}mv^2$, and gravitational potential energy $E_p = -\frac{GMm}{r}$ (see p. 41)

Tip: An elliptical orbit is like a squashed circle.

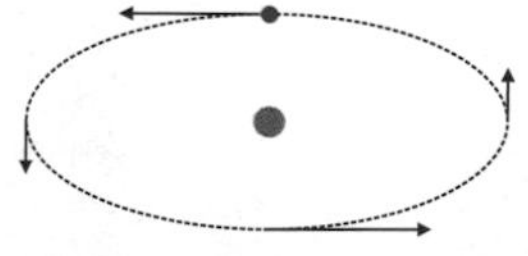

Geosynchronous Satellites

Geosynchronous satellites orbit directly over the equator and are always above the same point on Earth. A geosynchronous satellite travels at the same angular speed as the Earth turns below it. These satellites are really useful for sending TV and telephone signals — the satellite is stationary relative to a certain point on the Earth, so you don't have to alter the angle of your receiver (or transmitter) to keep up. Their orbit takes exactly one day.

Figure 2: *Syncom 2, the first geosynchronous communications satellite.*

Practice Questions — Fact Recall

Q1 How is the speed of a satellite related to the radius of its orbit?

Q2 How is the orbital period of a satellite related to the radius of its orbit?

Q3 In terms of energy, why does a satellite in an elliptical orbit move faster when its height, r, is small and slower when its height is large?

Q4 What's a geosynchronous satellite?

Q5 Why are geosynchronous satellites useful for transmitting TV and telephone signals?

5. Electric Fields

Electric fields are a lot like gravitational fields — you might think you're getting déjà vu over the next few pages. But although the concepts are similar, there are still some subtle differences, so make sure you follow carefully.

Learning Objectives:

- Know what an electric field is.
- Know that Coulomb's law can be used to calculate the force between point charges in a vacuum.
- Know that electric field strength is defined as the force per unit charge.
- Know how to represent an electric field using field lines.
- Be able to find the magnitude of the electric field in radial and uniform fields.

Specification Reference 3.4.3

Electric fields around charged objects

Electric fields can be attractive or repulsive, so they're different from gravitational ones (which are always attractive). It's all to do with charge. Any object with charge has an electric field around it — the region where it can attract or repel other charges.

Electric charge, Q, is measured in coulombs (C) and can be positive or negative. Oppositely charged particles attract each other, and like charges repel each other. If a charged object is placed in an electric field, then it will experience a force.

Coulomb's law

You can calculate the force on a charged object in an electric field using Coulomb's law. It gives the force of attraction or repulsion between two **point charges**, Q_1 and Q_2, in a vacuum:

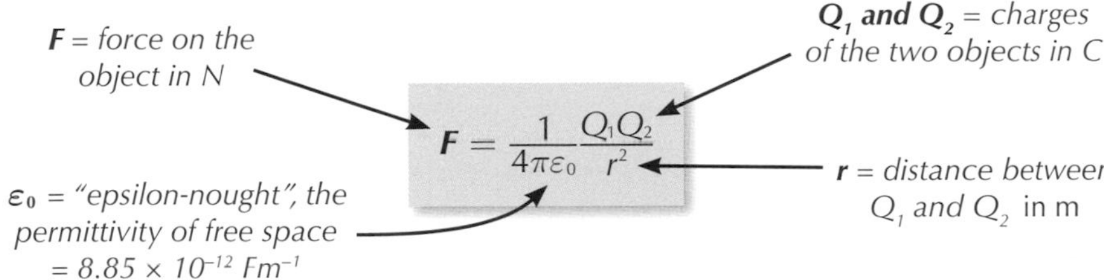

$F = \frac{1}{4\pi\varepsilon_0}\frac{Q_1Q_2}{r^2}$
F = force on the object in N
Q_1 and Q_2 = charges of the two objects in C
r = distance between Q_1 and Q_2 in m
ε_0 = "epsilon-nought", the permittivity of free space = 8.85×10^{-12} Fm^{-1}

Tip: ε_0 is a constant and its units are farads per metre (Fm^{-1}).

The force on Q_1 is always equal and opposite to the force on Q_2 — the direction depends on the charges.

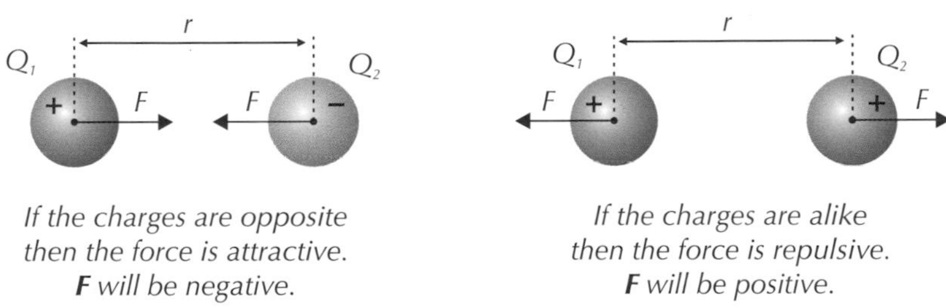

r
Q_1
Q_2
F
F
+
−
If the charges are opposite then the force is attractive. **F** will be negative.
r
Q_1
Q_2
F
F
+
+
If the charges are alike then the force is repulsive. **F** will be positive.

Figure 1: *The direction of the forces on two charged objects.*

Figure 2: *French physicist Charles Coulomb.*

Coulomb's law is another case of an inverse square law, so $F \propto \frac{1}{r^2}$ (page 35). The further apart the charges, the weaker the force between them. If the point charges aren't in a vacuum, then the size of the force **F** also depends on the permittivity, ε, of the material between them.

Tip: In this case you'd replace ε_0 in Coulomb's law with the ε of the material.

Exam Tip
Always assume the charges are in a vacuum if the question doesn't say otherwise.

Example

Find the acceleration experienced by a free electron 2.83 mm from a sphere carrying a charge of +0.510 μC. The charge of an electron is -1.60×10^{-19} C and the mass of an electron is 9.11×10^{-31} kg.

The acceleration of an object is given by $F = ma \Rightarrow a = \frac{F}{m}$.
You know the mass, so find the force using Coulomb's law:

$$F = \frac{1}{4\pi\varepsilon_0}\frac{Q_1Q_2}{r^2}$$

$$= \frac{1}{4\pi\varepsilon_0}\frac{(0.510 \times 10^{-6}) \times (-1.60 \times 10^{-19})}{(2.83 \times 10^{-3})^2}$$

$$= -9.161... \times 10^{-11} \text{ N}$$

Then use this to find the acceleration:

$$a = \frac{F}{m} = \frac{-9.161... \times 10^{-11}}{9.11 \times 10^{-31}}$$

$$= -1.01 \times 10^{20} \text{ms}^{-2} \text{ (to 3 s.f.)}$$

Tip: The acceleration is negative because it's towards the sphere.

Electric field strength

Electric field strength, ***E***, is defined as the force per unit positive charge. It's the force that a charge of +1 C would experience if it was placed in an electric field.

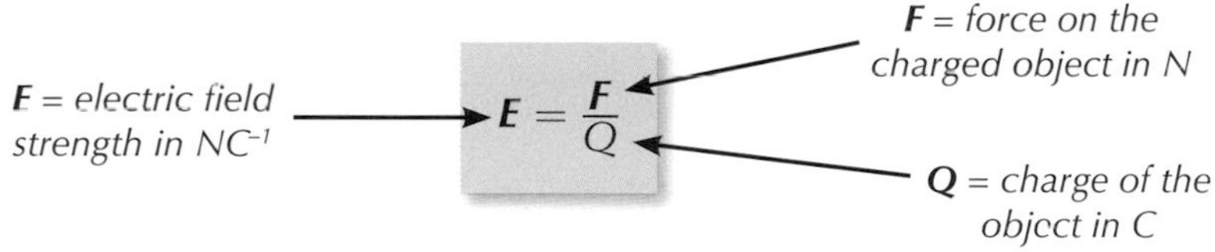

E is a vector pointing in the direction that a positive charge would move. The units of ***E*** are newtons per coulomb (NC^{-1}). Field strength usually depends on where you are in the field (see next page).

Tip: Remember, vector means it has a magnitude and a direction.

Example

Find the force acting on an electron in an electric field with a field strength of 5000 NC^{-1}. The charge on an electron is -1.60×10^{-19} C.

Just rearrange the equation for electric field strength and put in the numbers:

$$E = \frac{F}{Q} \Rightarrow F = E \times Q = 5000 \times (-1.60 \times 10^{-19})$$

$$= -8 \times 10^{-16} \text{ N}$$

Electric field lines

Electric fields are drawn to show the direction of the force that would act on a positive charge. Point charges have a radial field (see Figure 3).
For a positive point charge the field lines point away from the point charge, and for a negative point charge they point towards it. For parallel plates, the field lines point from the plate with the more positive voltage to the plate with the less positive voltage (see Figure 3).

Tip: For parallel plates, there won't necessarily be a positive plate and a negative plate.

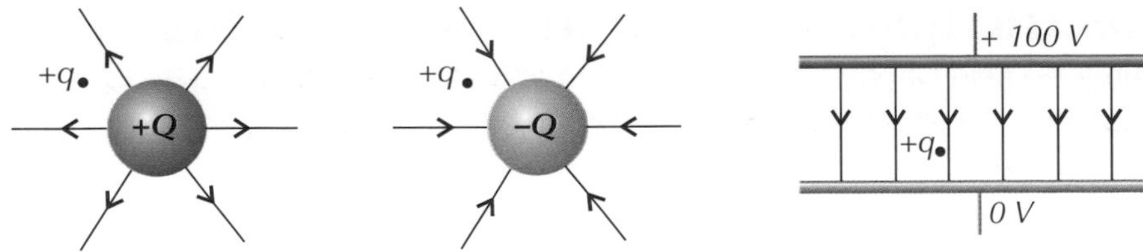

Figure 3: *Electric field lines for a positive point charge, a negative point charge and between two parallel plates.*

Figure 4: *Electric field lines between two plates shown by the alignment of pepper flakes in oil.*

Electric field strength in radial fields

A point charge — or any body that behaves as if all its charge is concentrated at the centre — has a radial field. In a radial field, the electric field strength, ***E***, depends on the distance *r* from the point charge *Q*:

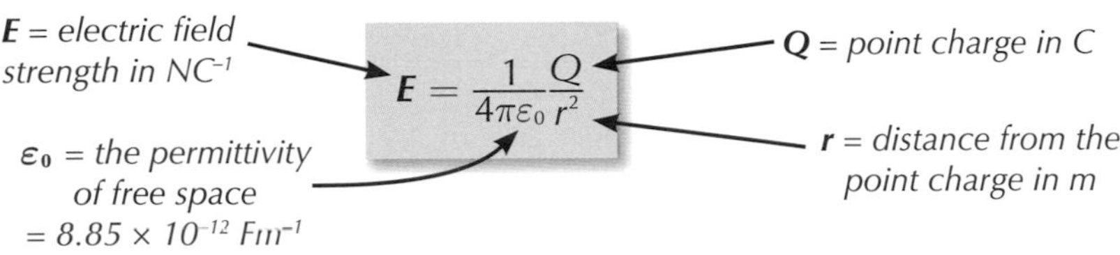

E = electric field strength in NC^{-1}
$E = \frac{1}{4\pi\varepsilon_0}\frac{Q}{r^2}$
Q = point charge in C
r = distance from the point charge in m
ε_0 = the permittivity of free space = 8.85×10^{-12} Fm^{-1}

Tip: *Q* is the point charge creating the radial field, not the charge experiencing a force inside the field.

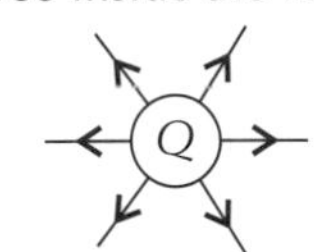

Example

The electric field strength 0.15 m away from a charged sphere is 44 000 NC^{-1}. What's the charge on the sphere?

You need to find *Q*, so make that the subject of the formula and then put the numbers in:

$$E = \frac{1}{4\pi\varepsilon_0}\frac{Q}{r^2} \Rightarrow Q = (4\pi\varepsilon_0 r^2)E$$

$$= 4\pi \times (8.85 \times 10^{-12}) \times 0.15^2 \times 44\,000$$

$$= 1.10 \times 10^{-7}\text{ C (to 3 s.f.)}$$

This is another case of the inverse square law — $E \propto \frac{1}{r^2}$. Field strength decreases as you go further away from *Q*.

On a diagram, the field lines get further apart, and if you plot the electric field strength against *r* you get the same shape as for gravitational field strength on page 38. If the charge isn't a point charge (e.g. a charged metal sphere), then the electric field strength inside the object will be zero.

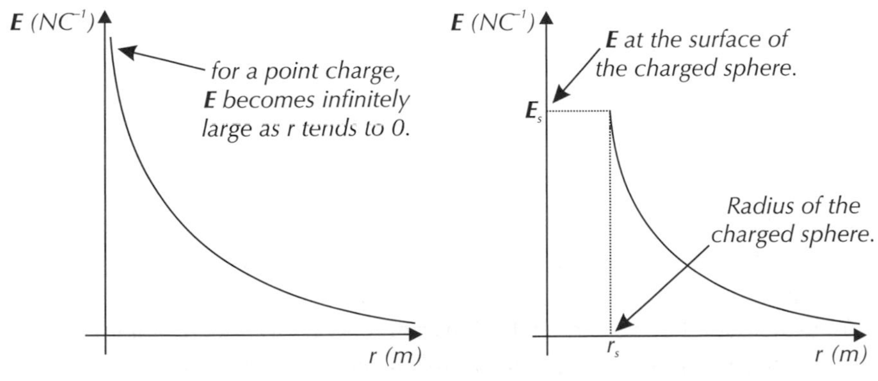

Figure 5: *Graphs of **E** against r for a point charge (left) and a charged sphere (right).*

Tip: Graphs of ***E*** against *r* usually only show the magnitude of ***E*** (so they're always positive). But if ***E*** was negative, the graph would just be reflected in the *x*-axis.

Electric field strength in uniform fields

A uniform field can be produced by connecting two parallel plates to the opposite poles of a battery — see Figure 6.

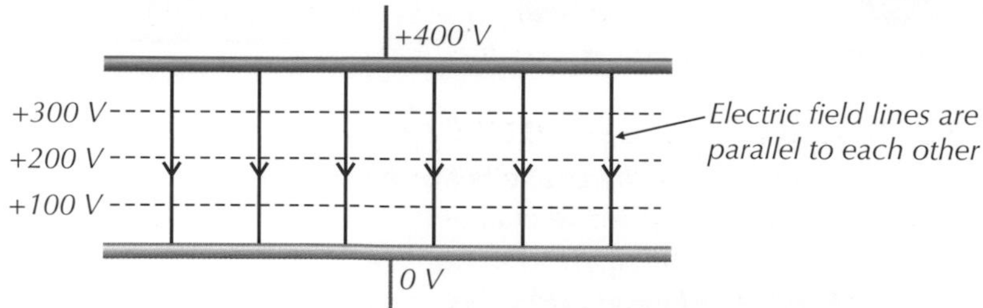

Figure 6: *Electric field lines between parallel plates.*

Field strength E is the same at all points between the two plates and is given by:

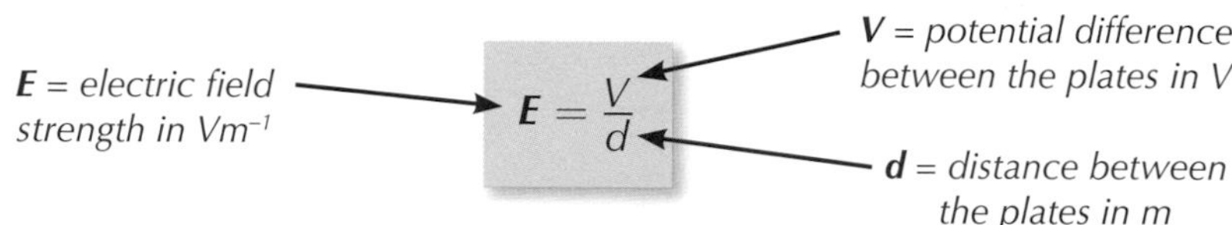

E = electric field strength in Vm⁻¹
E = V/d
V = potential difference between the plates in V
d = distance between the plates in m

$$E = \frac{V}{d}$$

Tip: Electric field strength can be measured in Vm^{-1} as well as NC^{-1}.

Note that here the potential difference between the plates is the same as the potential of the top plate. This is because the potential of the bottom plate is 0 V — this won't always be the case, so you might find it easier to think of it as ΔV.

Example

What's the electric field strength between two parallel plates 0.15 m apart with a potential of +650 V and +200 V respectively?

$$E = \frac{\Delta V}{d} = \frac{650 - 200}{0.15} = 3000\ Vm^{-1}$$

Practice Questions — Application

Q1 Two electrons are fired towards each other and reach a separation of 5.22×10^{-13} m. What's the force on each electron at this point?

Q2 The electric field generated by a charged sphere with charge 4.15 μC is measured as 15 000 NC^{-1}. How far from the sphere must the measuring instrument be?

Q3 An alpha particle with a charge of +2e and a mass of 6.64×10^{-27} kg is suspended freely between two parallel plates, as shown. How far apart are the plates if the alpha particle isn't moving?

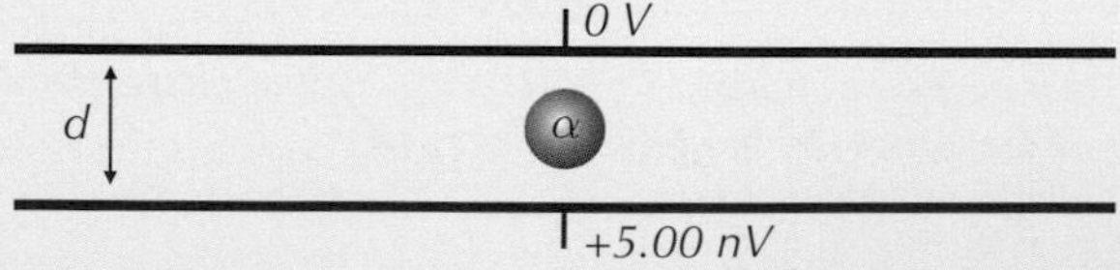

Tip: The charge on an electron, –e, is -1.60×10^{-19} C.

Tip: If the particle isn't moving, the upwards force from the electric field must equal the downwards force from gravity.

Tip: 1 nV = 1×10^{-9} V.

Practice Questions — Fact Recall

Q1 What is Coulomb's law?

Q2 What's E a measure of?

Q3 Draw the electric field generated by a positive point charge.

Q4 What kind of electric field is created by charged parallel plates?

6. Electric Potential

As you might have guessed, you can also find a charged object's electric potential. Because electric forces can be both attractive and repulsive, electric potential can be both positive and negative.

Learning Objectives:

- Understand the definition of electric potential.
- Be able to calculate the electric potential of a charged object in a radial electric field.
- Know that the electric potential tends to zero as the distance tends to infinity.
- Be able to sketch graphs of V against r for positive and negative point charges.
- Understand the idea of electric potential difference.
- Be able to calculate the work done in moving a charged object through an electric potential difference.

Specification Reference 3.4.3

What is electric potential?

All points in an electric field have an **electric potential**, V. This is the electric potential energy that a unit positive charge (+1 C) would have at that point. The electric potential of a point depends on how far it is from the charge creating the electric field and the size of that charge. In a radial field, electric potential is given by:

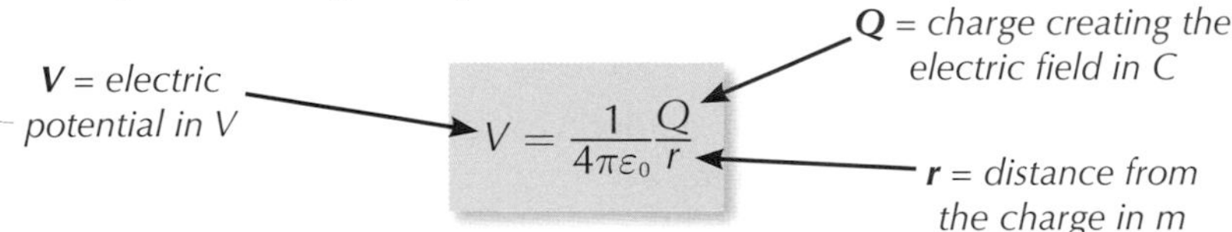

The sign of V depends on the charge Q — i.e. V is positive when Q is positive and the force is repulsive, and negative when Q is negative and the force is attractive. The absolute magnitude of V is greatest on the surface of the charge, and decreases as the distance from the charge increases — V will be zero at an infinite distance from the charge.

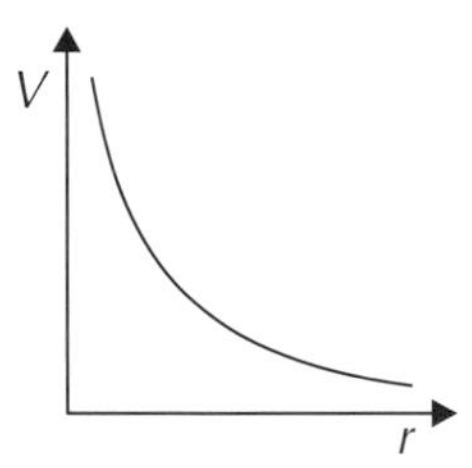

Repulsive force
V is initially positive and tends to zero as r increases towards infinity.

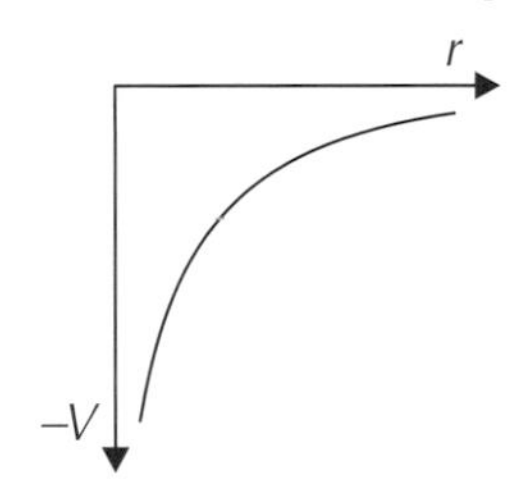

Attractive force
V is initially negative and tends to zero as r increases towards infinity.

Figure 1: *V changing with r for a positive charge (left) and a negative charge (right).*

The gradient of a tangent to either graph gives the field strength $\boldsymbol{E}$ at that point:

$$\boldsymbol{E} = \frac{\Delta V}{\Delta r}$$

Tip: You can see this link between $\boldsymbol{E}$ and V from the formula for field strength between parallel plates (see previous page).

Example

A positively charged particle is placed 0.035 m from a sphere with a charge of +3.1 μC. If the particle is then repelled by 0.19 m, what change in potential does it experience?

Change in potential = final potential – initial potential

$$= \frac{1}{4\pi\varepsilon_0}\frac{(3.1 \times 10^{-6})}{(0.035 + 0.19)} - \frac{1}{4\pi\varepsilon_0}\frac{(3.1 \times 10^{-6})}{0.035}$$

$= -6.73 \times 10^5$ V (to 3 s.f.)

Electric potential difference

Electric potential difference is the energy needed to move a unit charge. If two points in an electric field have a different potential, then there is an electric potential difference between them. To move a charge across a potential difference (i.e. from one electric potential to another) you need to use energy.

The amount of energy you need (or the work done) depends on the size of the charge you're moving and the size of the potential difference you want to move it across:

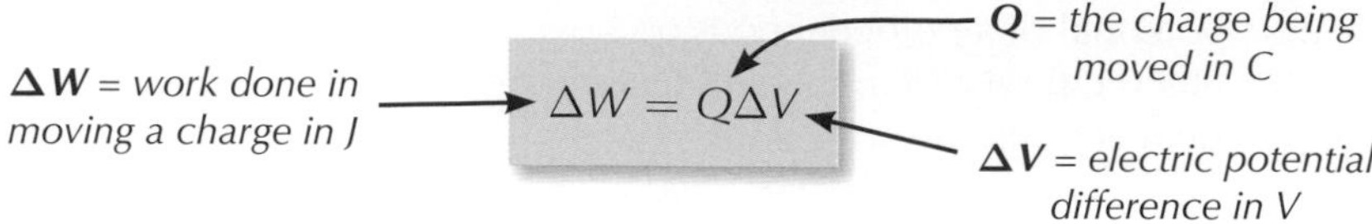

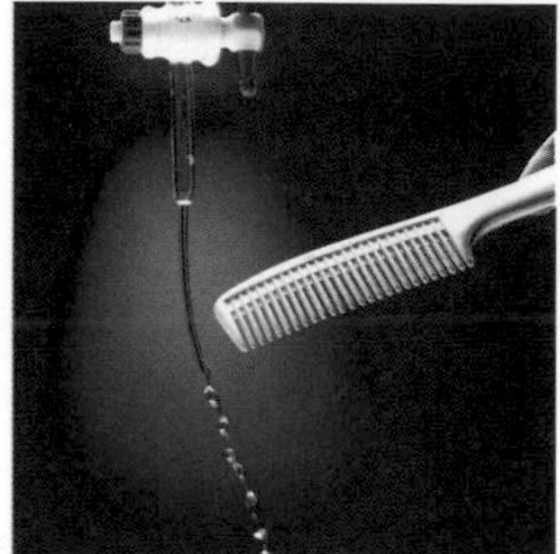

Figure 2: Static charge on a comb doing work against gravity to lift a trickle of water.

To see how this formula is derived, consider two parallel plates with a potential difference of ΔV across them, creating a uniform electric field.

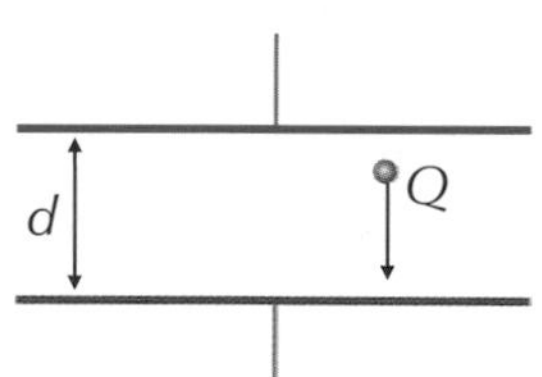

The field strength is given by: $E = \frac{\Delta V}{d} = \frac{F}{Q}$ ← *E defined as force per unit charge, page 46.*

↗ *E in a uniform field, page 48.*

This rearranges to give:

$$Q\Delta V = Fd$$

To move a charge Q from A to B:

$$\text{work done} = \text{force} \times \text{distance moved} = Fd$$

So the work done in moving a charge Q against a potential difference ΔV is given by:

$$\Delta W = Q\Delta V$$

Example

A strip of paper with a charge of –0.053 μC is resting on the lower of two horizontal parallel plates 2.8 cm apart. A potential difference of 350 V is applied across the plates and the strip of paper is lifted so that it's touching the top plate. Find the work done by the plates in lifting the strip of paper.

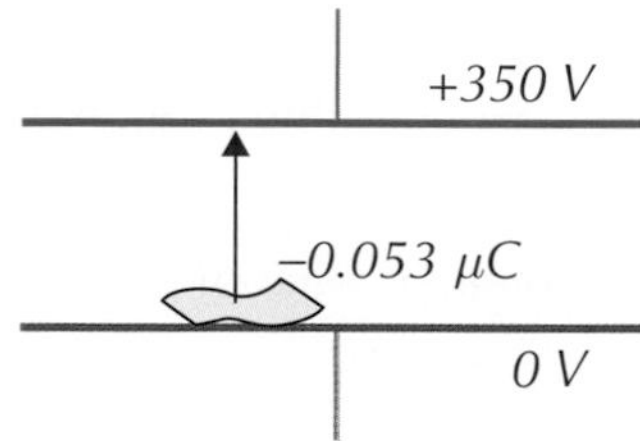

The paper moves through a potential difference of 350 V, so just put the numbers into the equation above:

$$\Delta W = Q\Delta V = (0.053 \times 10^{-6}) \times 350 = 1.9 \times 10^{-5} \text{ J (to 2 s.f.)}$$

Tip: Ignore the work done against gravity — assume the strip of paper is massless.

Tip: Work is always positive, so ignore any minus signs here.

Practice Questions — Application

Q1 A small metal sphere is being held stationary on a platform directly next to a charged metal sphere, as shown below.

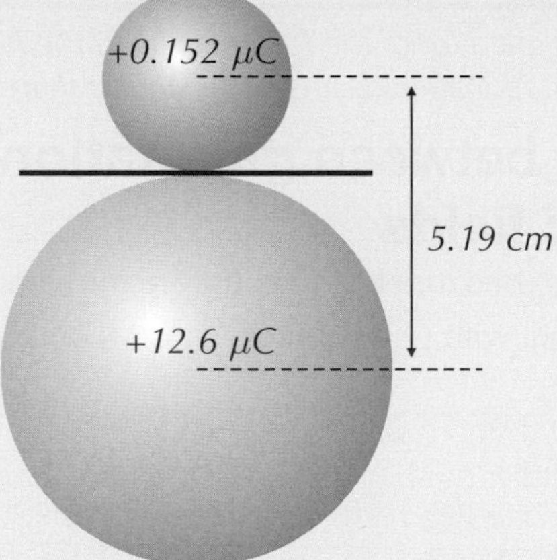

a) What's the electric potential at the centre of the smaller metal sphere?

b) The smaller sphere is released so that it can move freely, and is repelled by 12.9 cm before being stopped again. How much work is done in moving the sphere by this distance?

Q2 5.14 μJ of work is done to move a sphere with a charge of –83.1 nC from one parallel plate to another. Assuming no other forces are involved, what's the potential difference across the parallel plates?

Tip: Assume the smaller (green) sphere has a negligible radius.

Tip: The value of ε_0 is 8.85×10^{-12} Fm^{-1}.

Practice Questions — Fact Recall

Q1 What's electric potential?

Q2 Sketch the graph of electric potential V against distance r in a radial field for:

a) A positive point charge.

b) A negative point charge.

Q3 What's electric potential difference?

Q4 Say what each symbol represents in the equation $\Delta W = Q\Delta V$.

7. Comparing Electric and Gravitational Fields

You might have thought a lot of the formulas from the last topic looked familiar — electric and gravitational fields are more similar than you might think...

Similarities between gravitational and electric fields

A lot of the formulas used for electric fields are the same as those used for gravitational fields but with Q instead of m (or M) and $\frac{1}{4\pi\varepsilon_0}$ instead of G:

Tip: The graphs of $\boldsymbol{g}$ against r (p. 38) and V against r for gravitational fields (p. 40) are also very similar to the graphs of $\boldsymbol{E}$ against r (p. 47) and V against r for electric fields (p. 49).

Newton's law of gravitation:

$$\boldsymbol{F} = \frac{Gm_1m_2}{r^2}$$

Gravitational field strength for a radial field:

$$\boldsymbol{g} = \frac{GM}{r^2}$$

Gravitational potential:

$$V = -\frac{GM}{r}$$

Coulomb's law:

$$\boldsymbol{F} = \frac{1}{4\pi\varepsilon_0}\frac{Q_1Q_2}{r^2}$$

Electric field strength for a radial field:

$$\boldsymbol{E} = \frac{1}{4\pi\varepsilon_0}\frac{Q}{r^2}$$

Electric potential:

$$V = \frac{1}{4\pi\varepsilon_0}\frac{Q}{r}$$

There are four big similarities between electric and gravitational fields that it's useful to know:

Gravitational field strength, $\boldsymbol{g}$, is force per unit mass.	Electric field strength, $\boldsymbol{E}$, is force per unit positive charge.
Newton's law of gravitation for the force between two point masses is an inverse square law. $\boldsymbol{F} \propto \frac{1}{r^2}$	Coulomb's law for the electric force between two point charges is also an inverse square law. $\boldsymbol{F} \propto \frac{1}{r^2}$
The gravitational field lines for a point mass...	The electric field lines for a negative point charge... $-Q$
Gravitational potential, V, is potential energy per unit mass and is zero at infinity.	Electric potential, V, is potential energy per unit positive charge and is zero at infinity.

The important difference

Although gravitational and electric fields are similar, they're not the same — there's an important difference between them too. Gravitational forces are always attractive, whereas electric forces can be attractive or repulsive.

Practice Questions — Fact Recall

Q1 List four similarities between electric and gravitational fields.

Q2 Give one major difference between electric and gravitational fields.

Section Summary

Make sure you know...

- That a field is a region in which a body experiences a force.
- That gravity is an attractive force that acts between all matter (with mass).
- How to use Newton's law of gravitation to find the force between two point masses.
- What the gravitational constant, *G*, represents.
- How to represent radial and uniform gravitational fields using field lines.
- That the gravitational field strength, $\boldsymbol{g}$, is the force per unit mass in a gravitational field.
- How to find the value of $\boldsymbol{g}$ in radial gravitational fields.
- How to draw a graph of $\boldsymbol{g}$ against *r*.
- How to find the combined gravitational field strength of more than one object.
- That gravitational potential, *V*, is the gravitational potential energy that a unit mass would have at a specific point.
- That the gravitational potential becomes zero at an infinite distance from a point mass.
- How to draw a graph of gravitational potential, *V*, against *r*.
- How to calculate the gravitational potential at a given point in a gravitational field.
- That the gradient of a graph of *V* against *r* gives you the gravitational field strength $\boldsymbol{g}$ at that point.
- That gravitational potential difference is the energy needed to move a unit mass between two points.
- How to calculate the work done in moving a mass through a gravitational potential difference.
- How the orbital period and speed of an object are related to the radius of its orbit.
- That the combined potential and kinetic energy of an orbiting object is a constant.
- What a geosynchronous orbit is and its technological applications.
- How to use Coulomb's law to find the force between two point charges in a vacuum.
- That ε_0 is the permittivity of free space.
- That the electric field strength, $\boldsymbol{E}$, is defined as the force per unit positive charge in an electric field.
- How to represent radial and uniform electric fields using field lines.
- How to calculate the magnitude of $\boldsymbol{E}$ in radial and uniform electric fields.
- What a graph of $\boldsymbol{E}$ against *r* for a radial field looks like.
- That electric potential, *V*, is the potential energy that a unit positive charge would have at a specific point.
- That the electric potential becomes zero at an infinite distance from a point charge.
- How to calculate the electric potential at a given point in a radial electric field.
- What a graph of electric potential, *V*, against *r* looks like.
- That the gradient of a graph of *V* against *r* gives you the electric field strength $\boldsymbol{E}$ at that point.
- That electric potential difference is the energy needed to move a unit charge between two points.
- How to find the work done in moving a charge through an electric potential difference.
- The similarities and differences between gravitational and electric fields.

Exam-style Questions

Questions 1 to 4 are worth 1 mark each.

1 Which of the following statements is **incorrect**?

A Gravitational forces are always attractive.

B Gravitational potential increases with distance.

C Electric forces are always attractive.

D The electric field between charged parallel plates is uniform.

2 The diagram shows a (positively charged) alpha particle being fired in a straight line through charged parallel plates. Which of the following statements is **correct**?

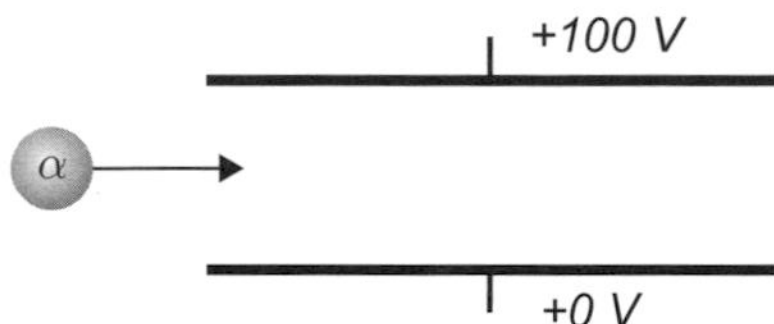

A The particle's path will be deflected downwards.

B The particle's path will be deflected upwards.

C The particle's path will not be deflected.

D The particle will be forced back in the direction it came.

3 Which of the following graphs shows how the gravitational field strength varies with distance from a spherical mass with a radius R.

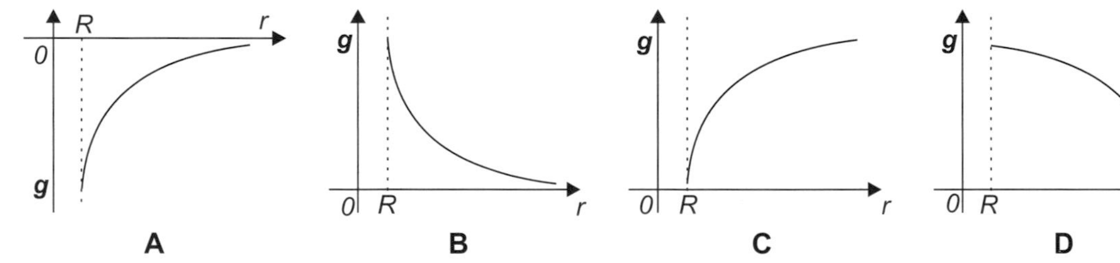

4 The diagram shows a point *T* halfway between two point masses with masses of m and 2m respectively. What's the gravitational field strength at *T*?

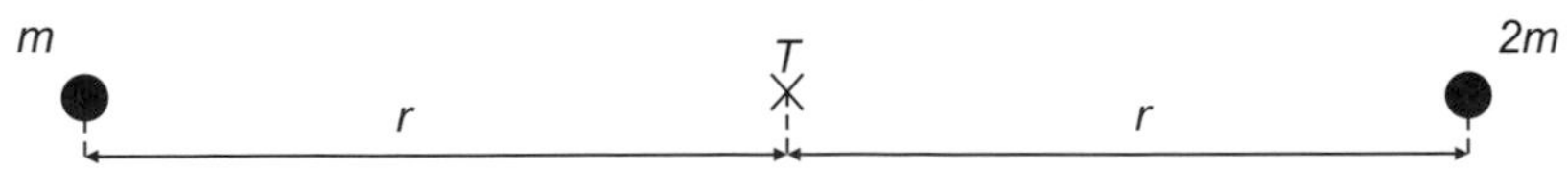

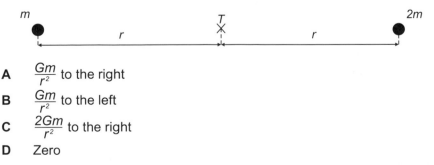

A $\frac{Gm}{r^2}$ to the right

B $\frac{Gm}{r^2}$ to the left

C $\frac{2Gm}{r^2}$ to the right

D Zero

5 (a) What is a force field?

(1 mark)

5 (b) A student is conducting an experiment to determine the local value of $\boldsymbol{g}$.
He finds $\boldsymbol{g}$ to be 9.83 Nm^{-1}, to 3 significant figures.

Another student conducts the same experiment and finds the value to be 6.31 Nm^{-1}. He claims his value is about 1/3 lower because his work bench is about 1/3 taller than the other student's.

5 (b) (i) Would this explain the difference in values for $\boldsymbol{g}$? Explain your answer.

(2 marks)

5 (b) (ii) If the radius of the Earth is 6370 km and its mass is 5.98×10^{24} kg, at what altitude would the local value of $\boldsymbol{g}$ be 6.31 Nm^{-1}? (Altitude is measured from sea level.)

(3 marks)

5 (c) A satellite is in orbit around Earth at a gravitational potential of –20.6 $MJkg^{-1}$.

5 (c) (i) Find the value of $\boldsymbol{g}$ at this point.

(3 marks)

5 (c) (ii) If the satellite has a mass of 2.53×10^3 kg, find the force of gravity acting on it.

(1 mark)

5 (d) Another satellite orbits the Earth once every 24 hours in the same plane as the equator. What type of orbit is this?

(1 mark)

6 (a) (i) Describe the field produced between two charged parallel plates with a potential difference across them.

(2 marks)

6 (a) (ii) Describe the field produced by a (positively charged) alpha particle.

(2 marks)

6 (b) In an experiment to demonstrate Rutherford scattering, alpha particles are fired at thin gold foil.

One alpha particle is fired directly at a gold nucleus so that it comes to a full stop 2.08×10^{-12} m from the nucleus, before being deflected backwards along its initial path.

Alpha particles carry a charge of $+2e$ ($e = 1.6 \times 10^{-19}$) and have a mass of 6.64×10^{-27} kg. A gold nucleus carries a charge of $+79e$.

6 (b) (i) Assuming the alpha particle started with zero electric potential, find the electric potential difference between its start position and where it came to a stop.

(2 marks)

6 (b) (ii) Find the speed at which the alpha particle is fired.
The kinetic energy of an object is given by $E_k = \frac{1}{2}mv^2$.

(4 marks)

7 A charged sphere carrying a charge of –34.7 μC is fixed to the bottom of a plastic tube. Another sphere, with a charge of –92.5 μC and a mass of 203 g, is dropped into the tube and allowed to move freely until it comes to a rest above the fixed sphere. This is shown in **Figure 1**.

Figure 1

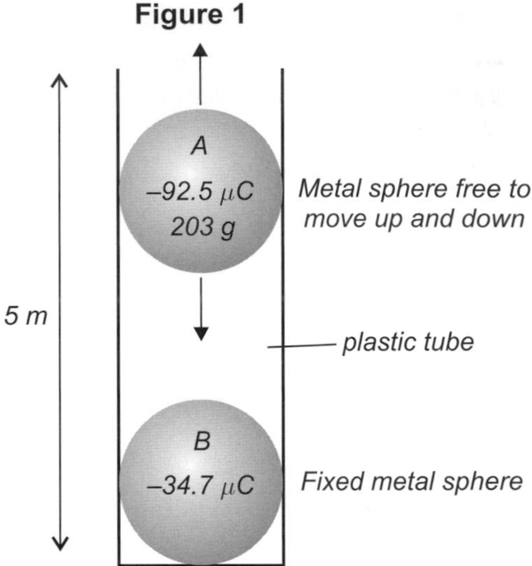

7 (a) Find the force due to gravity on sphere *A*. (Use $\mathbf{g}$ = 9.81 Nkg^{-1}.)

(1 mark)

7 (b) Assume the spheres have a negligible radius. How far apart will the centres of the spheres be when sphere *A* comes to rest?

(4 marks)

7 (c) The top sphere is now placed on a smooth, horizontal plane between two parallel plates, as shown (from above) in **Figure 2**. For this question, assume the sphere has a negligible radius.

Figure 2

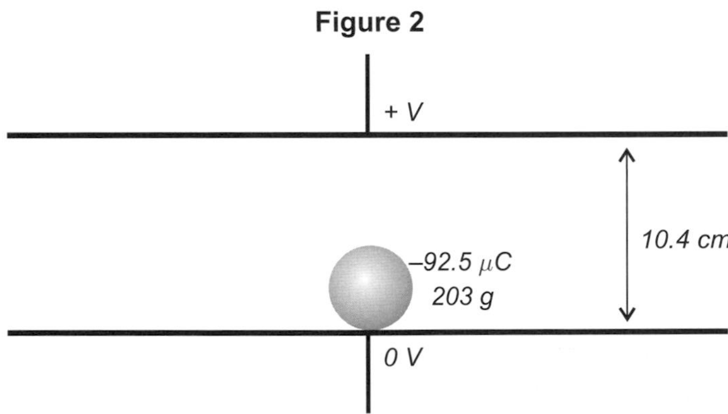

7 (c) (i) The electric field causes the sphere to roll from one plate to the other. If 18.5 mJ of work is done in moving the sphere, find the potential difference across the plates.

(2 marks)

7 (c) (ii) What is the electric field strength between the plates?

(1 mark)

Unit 4 Section 3: Capacitance

1. Capacitors

Capacitors are like big buckets. You can fill them up and empty them when you feel like it. The capacitance of a capacitor tells you how much charge it can hold. Almost all electrical products will contain one somewhere...

Learning Objectives:
- Know the definition of capacitance.
- Know that capacitance, $C = \frac{Q}{V}$.
- Know what a capacitor is and how it stores charge.

Specification Reference 3.4.4

Capacitance

The **capacitance** of an object is the amount of charge it is able to store per unit potential difference (p.d.) across it.

Capacitance is measured in **farads** — 1 farad (F) = 1 coulomb per volt (CV^{-1}).

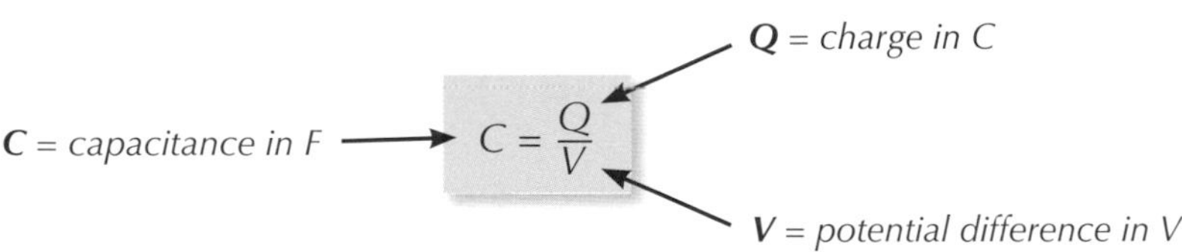

Tip: Remember, potential difference is also known as voltage and is measured in volts.

Capacitors

A **capacitor** is an electrical component that can store electrical charge. They are made up of two electrical conducting plates separated by an electrical insulator (a **dielectric**). The circuit symbol is two parallel lines:

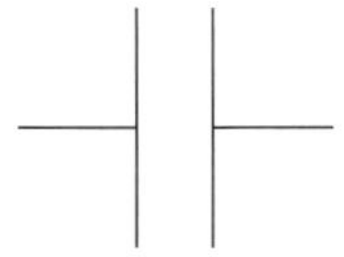

Figure 2: *Circuit symbol for a capacitor.*

Figure 1: *A disassembled capacitor, showing two sheets of aluminium foil with paper between them. The foil and paper are rolled up like a big Swiss roll.*

When a capacitor is connected to a direct current (d.c.) power source, charge builds up on its plates — one plate becomes negatively charged and one becomes positively charged (there's more on this on p. 62). The plates are separated by an electrical insulator, so no charge can move between them. This means that a potential difference builds up between the plates of the capacitor.

Tip: You can make your own simple capacitor using two pieces of aluminium separated by a piece of paper.

The capacitance of a capacitor is the charge that the capacitor can store per unit potential difference across it. The voltage rating of a capacitor is the maximum potential difference that can be safely put across it. A capacitor will only charge up to the voltage of the power source it is connected to.

A good way to think of a capacitor is as a bucket that can hold electrical charge. The capacitance (C) is the area of the bucket's base, and the height is equal to its voltage rating (V). Then the charge (Q) that it can store is $C \times V$ (a rearrangement of the equation above).

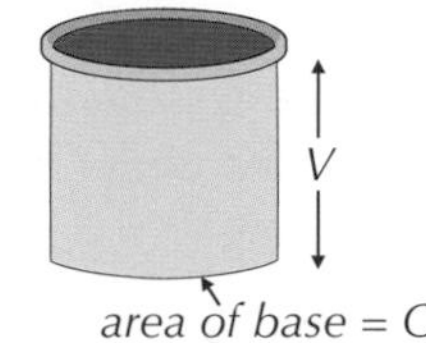

Figure 3: *A capacitor can be thought of as a charge bucket.*

Tip: Remember from AS physics... the potential difference between two points is the work done (energy transferred) in moving a unit charge between them.

Tip: In this formula, Q is the charge stored on each capacitor plate — the charge is just negative on one plate and positive on the other.

Tip: A farad is a huge unit so you'll usually see capacitances expressed in terms of:

μF — microfarads ($\times 10^{-6}$)

nF — nanofarads ($\times 10^{-9}$)

pF — picofarads ($\times 10^{-12}$)

Tip: This is the standard test circuit for testing the current through, and voltage across, a component. You should've seen it before when you learnt about electricity at AS level. Remember what each of the circuit symbols stands for:

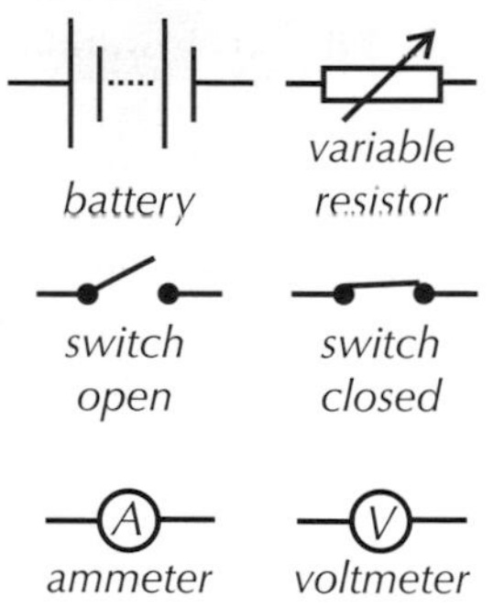

Tip: Remember the formula for charge from AS physics, $Q = It$.

Tip: There's more on why the current drops off like this on p. 62.

Examples

A 100 μF capacitor is charged to a potential difference of 12 V. How much charge is stored by the capacitor?

$C = \frac{Q}{V}$ so by rearranging, $Q = C \times V = (100 \times 10^{-6}) \times 12 = 1.2 \times 10^{-3}$ C

The voltage rating of the capacitor is 50 V. What is the maximum charge that the capacitor can store?

$Q = C \times V = (100 \times 10^{-6}) \times 50 = 5 \times 10^{-3}$ C

Investigating *V* and *Q*

$C = \frac{Q}{V}$ rearranged gives $Q = CV$, and since the capacitance of a capacitor is fixed, this means Q is directly proportional to V. You can investigate the relationship between the potential difference across, and the charge stored on, a capacitor experimentally by charging a capacitor using a constant current. First, set up a test circuit to measure current and potential difference:

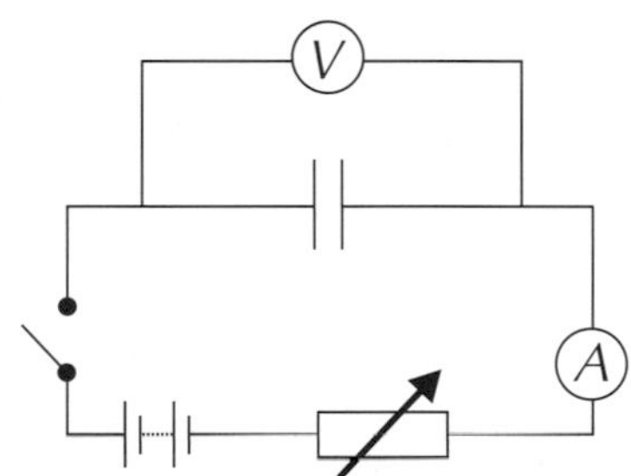

Figure 4: *Test circuit for a capacitor.*

After closing the switch, constantly adjust the variable resistor to keep the charging current constant for as long as you can (it's impossible when the capacitor is nearly fully charged). Record the p.d. at regular time intervals until it equals the battery p.d. Using the fixed charging current and the time taken to charge the capacitor you can plot the following graph:

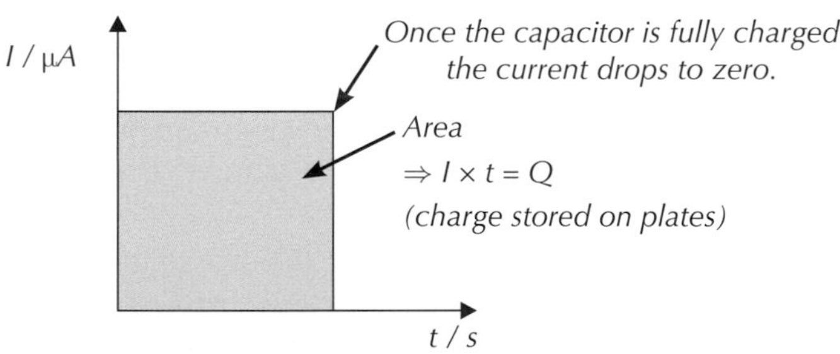

Figure 5: *Current-time graph for a capacitor.*

The area under the graph in Figure 5 is the charge stored on the capacitor. Using $Q = It$ you can calculate the charge stored on the capacitor at a given time. Plotting a graph of charge stored against potential difference across the capacitor at each recorded time interval gives the graph in Figure 6.

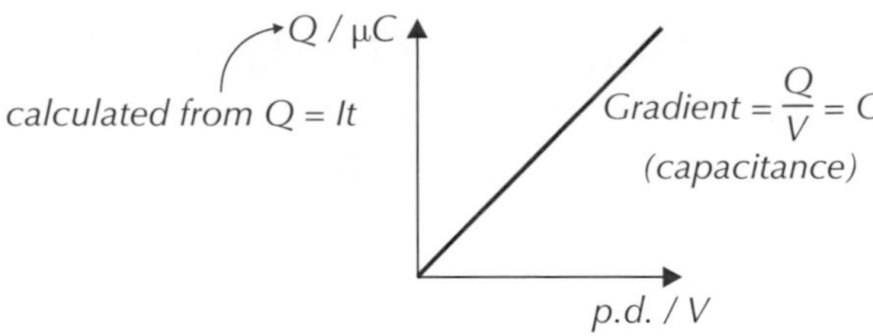

Figure 6: *Charge-p.d. graph for a capacitor.*

The graph in Figure 6 is a straight line through the origin — so this shows Q and V are directly proportional. You can use the same experiment to calculate the unknown capacitance of a capacitor, because the gradient of the graph in Figure 6 is the capacitance, C.

Exam Tip
They love asking questions about this graph in the exam. For example, what the gradient represents (they might flip the axes though, which would make the gradient the inverse of capacitance, so be careful...).

Uses of capacitors

Capacitors can only store small amounts of charge, therefore capacitors aren't used instead of batteries. To store the same energy as an AA battery, you'd need around 6000 farads. The capacitor would be absolutely massive. They also only provide power for a short amount of time.

But capacitors are still very useful because they can store charge until it's needed, and then discharge all of their charge in a fraction of a second, whereas a battery would take several minutes. For this reason, charged capacitors can be very dangerous. Capacitors in electronics in your home could contain enough charge to kill you.

One example of capacitor use is in a camera flash — the camera battery charges the capacitor over a few seconds, and then the entire charge of the capacitor is dumped into the flash almost instantly. This allows the camera flash to be very bright for a very short time. Some other applications of capacitors are:

- 'Ultracapacitors' (really big capacitors) can be used in back-up power supplies to provide reliable power for short periods of time.
- To smooth out variations in d.c. voltage supplies — a capacitor absorbs the peaks and fills in the troughs.

Tip: A one-farad capacitor would be something like the size of a one-litre drinks bottle — so they're a bit inconvenient if you need a large charge.

Figure 7: *An assortment of capacitors of different sizes and capacitances.*

Practice Questions — Application

Q1 A 0.1 F capacitor is used in a circuit as a back-up in case of a short interruption in the mains power supply. The p.d. supplied to the circuit is 230 V. How much charge can the capacitor store?

Q2 Explain why a capacitor would not be a good source for powering a portable media player.

Exam Tip
The formula for capacitance is given in the Data and Formulae booklet if you need a reminder in the exam.

Practice Questions — Fact Recall

Q1 Write down the definition of capacitance.

Q2 Write down the formula you would use to calculate the capacitance, C, of a capacitor that stores a charge, Q, at a voltage, V.

Q3 Draw the circuit symbol for a capacitor.

Q4 Explain how you could keep the current charging a capacitor constant.

Q5 Write down one application of a capacitor.

- Know how to derive $E = \frac{1}{2}QV$ using the area under a V-Q graph.
- Know how to use $E = \frac{1}{2}QV$ to derive the following expressions: $E = \frac{1}{2}CV^2$, $E = \frac{1}{2}\frac{Q^2}{V}$.

Specification Reference 3.4.4

Tip: There'll be more on exactly how a capacitor charges in the next topic (see p. 62).

Figure 2: Storm clouds store massive amounts of energy — forming huge natural capacitor plates. Particle collisions cause electrons to be knocked off atoms, giving the bottom of the cloud a charge. This induces a charge in the surface of the Earth. The air in between acts as the dielectric, and if the potential difference gets big enough, the dielectric breaks down and lightning bolts travel between the cloud and the Earth.

Exam Tip
This formula is given in the Data and Formulae booklet, but you need to understand where it comes from — remember it's the area under the V-Q graph.

2. Energy Stored by Capacitors

It takes energy to build up charge on the plates of a capacitor. This energy is stored by the capacitor and released when the charges are released.

Energy stored

Remember that when a capacitor charges, one plate becomes negatively charged while the other becomes positively charged (you'll see on p. 62 exactly how). Like charges repel, so when each plate of a capacitor becomes charged, the charges on that plate are being forced together 'against their will'. This requires energy, which is supplied by the power source and stored as electric potential energy for as long as the charges are held. When the charges are released, the electric potential energy is released.

Deriving the energy stored equations

You can find the energy stored by a capacitor by using the graph of potential difference against charge for the capacitor (see Figure 1).

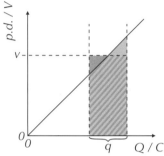

Figure 1: A V-Q graph showing the energy stored by a small increase in charge on the plates of a capacitor.

The p.d. across a capacitor is directly proportional to the charge stored on it, so the graph is a straight line through the origin (see page 59).

Consider a tiny increase in the charge on the plates during the charging process. The electric potential energy stored is the work done to move the extra charge onto the plates against the potential difference across the plates, given by $E = \Delta W = Q\Delta V$ (page 50). Let the small charge being moved be q. The average p.d. over that step is v. So in that small step, the energy stored is $E = qv$, which is given by the area of the red rectangle in Figure 1. The area of the green parallelogram in Figure 1 is the area under the graph over the charge difference q, and it is the same as the area of the red rectangle.

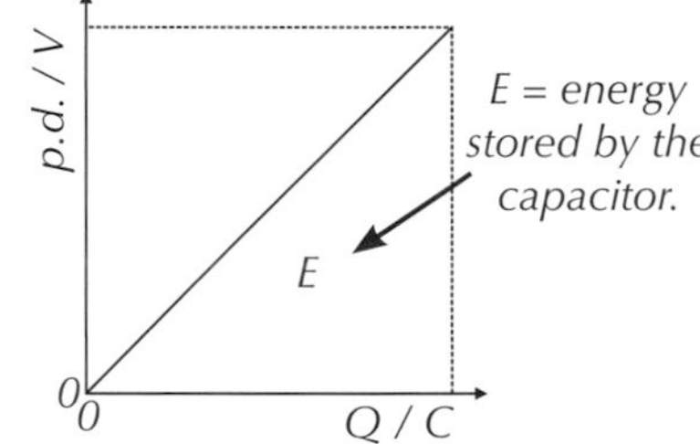

Figure 3: The area under a V-Q graph is the energy stored by a capacitor.

The total energy stored by the capacitor is the sum of all the energies stored in each small step increase in charge, until the capacitor is fully charged. So it's just the area under the graph of V against Q.

The area under the graph is just a triangle, and the area of a triangle is given by ½ × base × height, so the energy stored by the capacitor is:

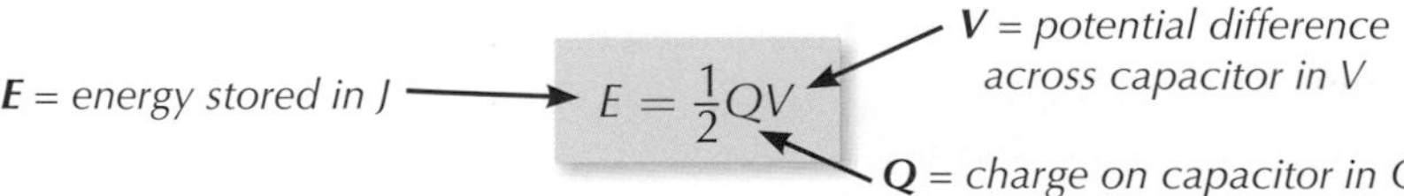

$$E = \frac{1}{2}QV$$

E = energy stored in J
V = potential difference across capacitor in V
Q = charge on capacitor in C

The energy supplied by the power source in charging a capacitor is equal to $\Delta W = V\Delta Q$, where V is the p.d. of the power source, so $E = QV$, which is double the energy stored by the capacitor (the rest is lost to the resistance in the circuit and internal resistance of the battery).

Example

A capacitor is charged to a potential difference of 12 V using a constant current of 5 mA over 30 seconds. Calculate the energy stored by it.

Using $Q = It$, $Q = 5 \times 10^{-3} \times 30 = 0.15$ C

So $E = \frac{1}{2}QV = \frac{1}{2} \times 0.15 \times 12 = 0.9$ J

Figure 4: Benjamin Franklin was one of the first people to store electrical energy, in the mid 1700s. He invented what he called a 'battery' by grouping together many Leyden jars (simple capacitors).

There are three expressions you need to know for the energy stored by capacitors:

- You know the first one already: $E = \frac{1}{2}QV$
- You know that $C = \frac{Q}{V}$, so $Q = CV$.
  Substitute that into the energy equation above: $E = \frac{1}{2}QV = \frac{1}{2}CV \times V$

$$E = \frac{1}{2}CV^2$$

- $C = \frac{Q}{V}$, so $V = \frac{Q}{C}$.
  Substituting into the first energy equation: $E = \frac{1}{2}QV = \frac{1}{2}Q \times \frac{Q}{C}$

$$E = \frac{1}{2}\frac{Q^2}{C}$$

Exam Tip
All of these equations are in the Data and Formulae booklet, but you need to know how to derive each one as shown here.

Example

A 900 μF capacitor is charged up to a potential difference of 240 V. Calculate the energy stored by the capacitor.

First, choose the best equation to use
— you've been given V and C, so you need $E = \frac{1}{2}CV^2$.

Substitute the values in:

$E = \frac{1}{2}CV^2 = \frac{1}{2} \times (900 \times 10^{-6}) \times 240^2 = 25.9$ J (to 3 s.f.)

Practice Questions — Application

Q1 A 40 mF capacitor is connected to a 230 V power source. When fully charged, how much energy will be stored by the capacitor?

Q2 A 5 μF capacitor is charged with a constant current of 0.025 mA for 45 s. Calculate the energy stored by the capacitor in this time.

Tip: Remember, $Q = It$.

Practice Questions — Fact Recall

Q1 Explain why a build-up of charge on a capacitor results in a build-up of energy.

Q2 What type of energy is stored in a capacitor?

Q3 Write down three equations that can be used to calculate the energy stored in a capacitor.

3. Charging and Discharging

You've seen how capacitors are used to store charge and energy, and how to calculate the energy stored by them — but now it's time to look at the physics of how they actually charge and discharge a little closer.

Learning Objectives:

- Be able to describe how charge is built up on the plates of a capacitor.
- Be able to represent the charging and discharging of capacitors through resistors graphically.
- Know that a voltage sensor and a datalogger can be used to plot discharge curves for a capacitor.
- Know that the charge on a discharging capacitor is given by: $Q = Q_0 e^{-\frac{t}{RC}}$.
- Know what the time constant of a charging or discharging capacitor is, and that it is given by $\tau = RC$.
- Be able to calculate the time constant of a charging or discharging capacitor, including from graphical data.

Specification Reference 3.4.4

Charging

When a capacitor is connected to a d.c. power supply (e.g. a battery), a current flows in the circuit until the capacitor is fully charged, then stops.

The electrons flow from the negative terminal of the supply onto the plate connected to it, so a negative charge builds up on that plate.

At the same time, electrons flow from the other plate to the positive terminal of the supply, making that plate positive. These electrons are repelled by the negative charge on the negative plate and attracted to the positive terminal of the supply.

The same number of electrons are repelled from the positive plate as are built up on the negative plate. This means an equal but opposite charge builds up on each plate, causing the potential difference between the plates. Remember that no charge can flow directly between the plates because they're separated by an insulator (dielectric).

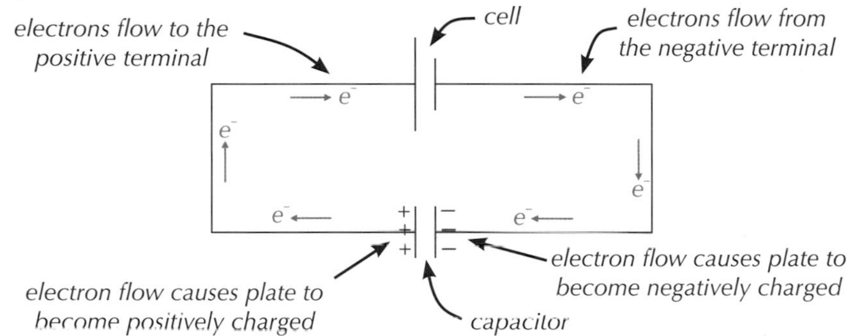

electrons flow to the positive terminal
cell
electrons flow from the negative terminal
e⁻
electron flow causes plate to become positively charged
capacitor
electron flow causes plate to become negatively charged

Figure 1: *Flow of electrons as a capacitor charges.*

Initially the current through the circuit is high. But, as charge builds up on the plates, electrostatic repulsion makes it harder and harder for more electrons to be deposited. When the p.d. across the capacitor is equal to the p.d. across the supply, the current falls to zero. The capacitor is fully charged.

Charging through a fixed resistor

If you charge a capacitor through a fixed resistor, as in Figure 2, the resistance of the resistor will affect the time taken to charge the capacitor.

Tip: The same is true for discharging a capacitor — see page 65.

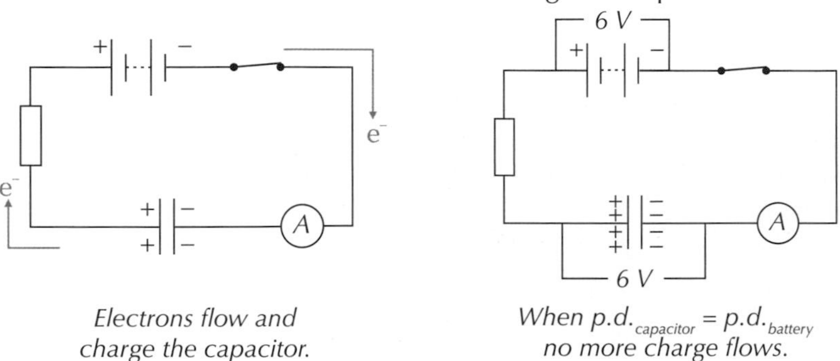

e⁻
A
6 V
Electrons flow and charge the capacitor.
When p.d.$_{capacitor}$ = p.d.$_{battery}$ no more charge flows.

Figure 2: *(Left) A capacitor charging through a resistor. (Right) A charged capacitor.*

As soon as the switch is closed, a current starts to flow. The potential difference across the capacitor is zero at first, so there is no p.d. opposing the current. The potential difference of the battery causes an initial relatively high current to flow equal to V/R (where V is the voltage of the power supply and R is the resistance of the resistor). As the capacitor charges, the p.d. across the resistor gets smaller (because the p.d. across the capacitor is getting bigger) and so the current drops. Charge (Q) is proportional to potential difference, so the Q-t graph is the same shape as the V-t graph. This results in the following graphs for charging a capacitor through a resistor:

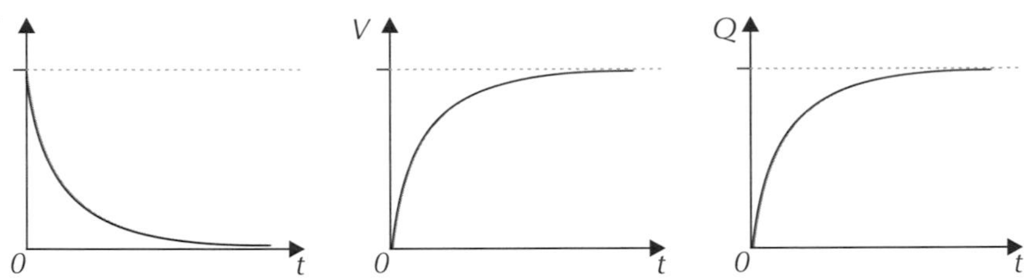

Figure 3: *Graphs to show charging current against time (left), potential difference against time (middle) and charge against time (right) for charging a capacitor through a fixed resistor.*

Tip: Remember, $V = IR$ so $I = V/R$.

Tip: Current is the odd one out here — while everything else increases, current decreases as the potential difference across the capacitor gets bigger.

Time to charge

The time to charge a capacitor through a resistor depends on two factors:

- The capacitance of the capacitor (C). This affects the amount of charge that can be transferred at a given voltage.
- The resistance of the circuit (R). This affects the current in the circuit.

Tip: There's lots more about the time taken to charge on page 65.

Discharging through a fixed resistor

To discharge a capacitor, take out the battery and reconnect the circuit. When a charged capacitor is connected across a resistor, the p.d. drives a current through the circuit. This current flows in the opposite direction from the charging current. The capacitor is fully discharged when the p.d. across the plates and the current in the circuit are both zero.

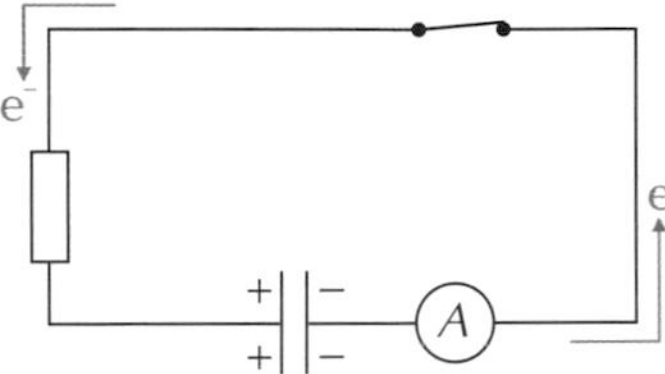

Figure 4: *Discharging a capacitor through a resistor.*

Tip: You need to reconnect the circuit to discharge a capacitor. If the capacitor isn't connected in a full circuit it will hold its charge.

Investigating capacitors discharging

If you connect a voltage sensor attached to a datalogger across the capacitor, you can plot a discharge curve for the capacitor (as shown in Figure 6). The V-t curve in Figure 6 shows how the voltage changes as the capacitor discharges.

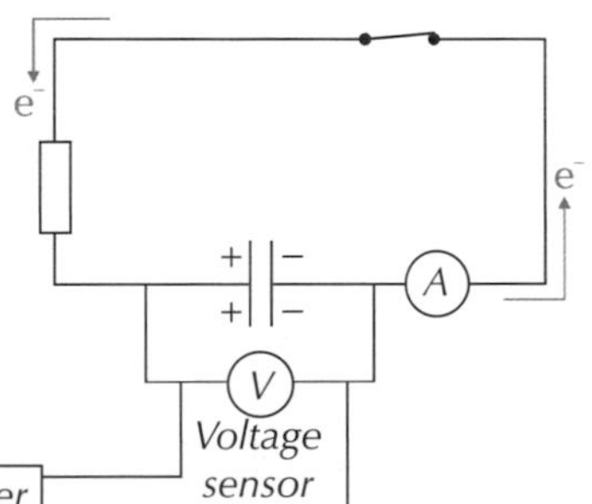

Figure 5: *Using a voltage sensor and datalogger to investigate the discharge for a capacitor.*

Tip: Dataloggers can be connected to a computer which will collect all your data for you and plot all sorts of graphs of it.

Tip: V is proportional to Q (see pages 58-59), so you always get the same shape graph whether you use V or Q on the y-axis.

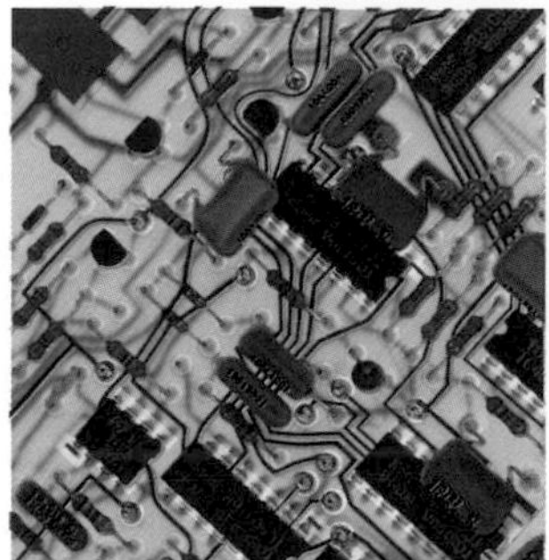

Figure 7: A circuit from a burglar alarm containing capacitors. They can be used with big resistors to create a time delay. When the door is opened the capacitor begins to discharge and when it has lost a certain amount of its charge the alarm goes off, giving you time beforehand to enter the code.

Exam Tip
The formula for charge is given in the Data and Formulae booklet.

Tip: Since V and Q are directly proportional, you can also use the equation $V = V_0 e^{-\frac{t}{RC}}$ if you're ever given an initial and final p.d. across a capacitor instead.

Tip: There's some help with logarithms and exponentials on pages 283-284. There should be a button on your calculator for 'e' that you can use for this calculation.

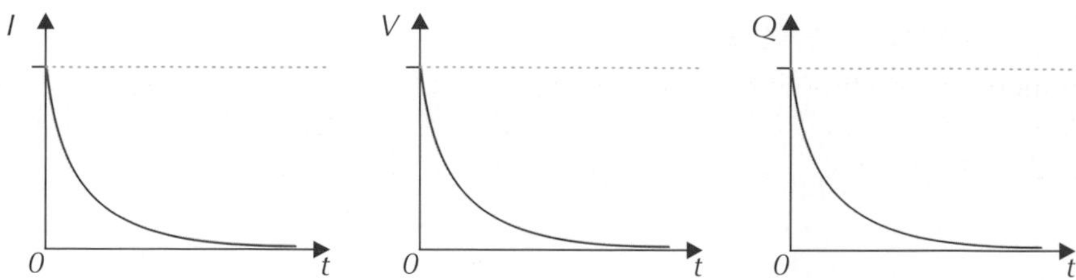

Figure 6: *Graphs to show discharging current against time (left), potential difference against time (middle) and charge against time (right) for discharging a capacitor through a fixed resistor.*

The I-t graph is the same as the one for charging (although the current is now flowing in the opposite direction). The current starts off relatively high and gradually decreases to zero. This is because the potential difference across the resistor decreases as the charge on the capacitor decreases.

When a capacitor is discharging, the amount of charge left on the plates falls exponentially with time. That means it always takes the same length of time for the charge to halve, no matter how much charge you start with — like radioactive decay (see p. 107).

The charge left on the plates of a capacitor discharging from full is given by the equation:

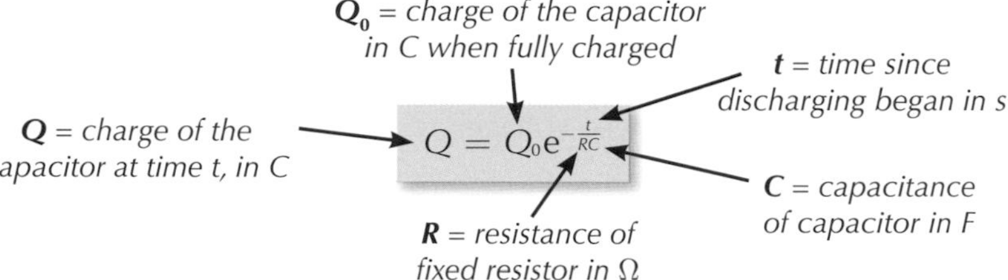

The graphs of V and I against t for charging (previous page) and discharging (above) are also exponential — but you don't need to know their equations.

Examples

A 0.20 mF capacitor was charged to a potential difference of 12 V and then discharged through a fixed 50 kΩ resistor. Calculate the charge on the capacitor after 1 second.

The question tells you $C = 0.20 \times 10^{-3}$ F, $V = 12$ V, $R = 50 \times 10^3$ Ω and $t = 1$.

First you need to calculate the initial charge.

$C = \frac{Q}{V}$ so $Q = CV$, so the initial charge is:

$Q_0 = CV = 0.20 \times 10^{-3} \times 12 = 2.4 \times 10^{-3}$ C

Then use the equation: $Q = Q_0 e^{-\frac{t}{RC}}$

$$= 2.4 \times 10^{-3} \times e^{-\frac{1}{(50 \times 10^3)(0.20 \times 10^{-3})}}$$
$$= 2.4 \times 10^{-3} \times e^{-0.1}$$
$$= 2.171... \times 10^{-3}$$
$$= 2.17 \times 10^{-3}\ \text{C (to 3 s.f.)}$$

Calculate the p.d. across the capacitor after 1 second.

The potential difference is found using:

$$V = \frac{Q}{C} = \frac{2.171... \times 10^{-3}}{0.20 \times 10^{-3}} = 10.9\ \text{V (to 3 s.f.)}$$

Time constant

Remember, the time it takes for a capacitor to charge through a fixed resistor depends on R and C (p. 63). The time to discharge depends on R and C too (see the formula for a discharging capacitor on the previous page).

When the discharge time t is equal to RC the equation becomes:

$$Q = Q_0 e^{-1}.$$

So when $t = RC$:

$$\frac{Q}{Q_0} = \frac{1}{e}, \text{ where } \frac{1}{e} \approx \frac{1}{2.718} \approx 0.37$$

The time $t = RC$ is known as the **time constant**, τ, and is the time taken for the charge on a discharging capacitor (Q) to fall to about 37% of Q_0. It's also the time taken for the charge of a charging capacitor to rise to about 63% of Q_0 (Figure 8).

The larger the resistance in series with the capacitor, the longer it takes to charge or discharge. In practice, the time taken for a capacitor to charge or discharge fully is taken to be about $5RC$ or 5τ.

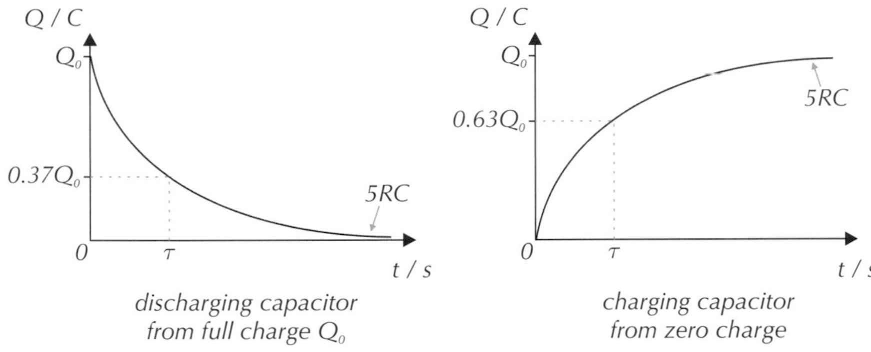

Figure 8: *Q-t graphs showing the time constant for discharging (left) and charging (right) a capacitor through a fixed resistor.*

> **Tip:** τ is the Greek letter 'tau'.

> **Tip:** Q is proportional to V, so the time constant is also the time taken for the voltage to decrease to 37% of the source voltage (or increase to 63% of the source voltage while charging).

Example

A capacitor was discharged from full through a 10 kΩ resistor. The graph below shows how the charge on the capacitor changed over the first 2 seconds. Calculate the time constant and the capacitance.

The initial charge is 12×10^{-4} C, and you want to find the time taken for the charge to decrease to 37% of that.

So $0.37 \times (12 \times 10^{-4}) = 4.4 \times 10^{-4}$ C.

Using the graph, the charge is 4.4×10^{-4} C when the time is 1.0 s, so the time constant, τ, is 1.0 s.

$\tau = RC$,

so, $C = \frac{\tau}{R}$

$= \frac{1}{10 \times 10^3}$

$= 1 \times 10^{-4}$ F $= 0.1$ mF

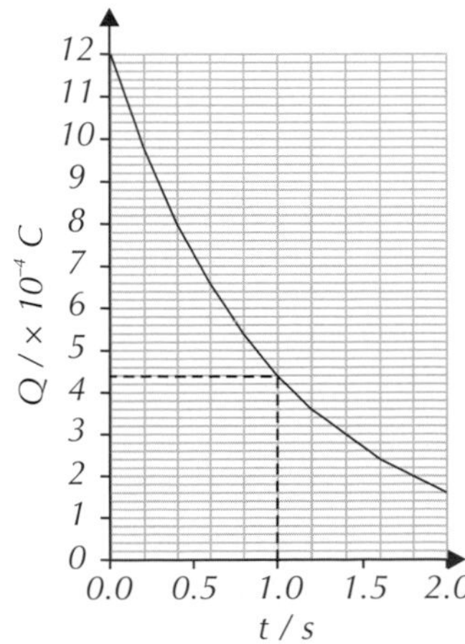

> **Tip:** You might be asked to find the time it takes for a capacitor to discharge (or charge) to a certain percentage of its total charge. Make sure that you remember that Q / Q_0 is the proportion of the charge on the plates, not the proportion of the charge that's been lost.

Practice Questions — Application

Q1 A capacitor discharged in series with a resistor can be used to create a time delay function in electronics. In a particular burglar alarm, the alarm goes off when a 15 μF capacitor discharged through a 400 kΩ resistor has lost 63% of its initial charge.

a) Calculate the time delay on the alarm.

The company want to increase the capacitance of the capacitor in order to make the time delay 60 seconds.

b) What capacitance would be needed for this time delay?

c) Explain why this might not be practical and suggest what other component they could replace instead.

Q2 Calculate the charge stored on a 15 nF capacitor, originally charged to a potential difference of 230 V and then discharged for 0.01 seconds through a 50 kΩ capacitor.

Q3 A discharging capacitor loses 70% of its initial charge, Q_0, in 20 seconds.

a) Write down the value of $\frac{Q}{Q_0}$ after 20 seconds.

b) Find the time constant of the capacitor-resistor circuit.

Tip: $\ln(e^x) = x$ because ln is the inverse of e. So if you take the natural log (ln) of an e^x, you'll just be left with the *x* bit. Use this to get $-\frac{t}{RC}$ on its own, and then rearrange.

Practice Questions — Fact Recall

Q1 Explain how negative charge is built up on the plate of a capacitor.

Q2 Draw curves showing how voltage, current and charge vary with time when a capacitor is charging through a fixed resistor.

Q3 What two factors affect the time taken to charge a capacitor through a fixed resistor?

Q4 How can you alter the circuit used to charge a capacitor so that the capacitor discharges?

Q5 Draw curves showing how voltage, current and charge vary with time when a capacitor is discharging through a fixed resistor.

Q6 Write the equation for the charge left on a discharging capacitor.

Q7 What is meant by the time constant when discharging a capacitor?

Section Summary

Make sure you know...

- That capacitance is defined as the amount of charge stored per unit potential difference, $C = \frac{Q}{V}$.
- The structure of a capacitor.
- The circuit symbol for a capacitor.
- That the charge on a capacitor and the potential difference across it are proportional.
- That the gradient of a graph of charge against p.d. is capacitance.
- Examples of how capacitors are useful in real-life applications.
- That electrical potential energy is stored by a charged capacitor.
- The equations for energy stored $E = \frac{1}{2}QV = \frac{1}{2}CV^2 = \frac{1}{2}\frac{Q^2}{C}$ and how to derive them.
- How charge is built up on the plates of a capacitor.
- How voltage, current and charge vary with time as a capacitor charges and discharges, and how to represent these relationships graphically.
- The equation for charge stored on a discharging capacitor: $Q = Q_0 e^{-\frac{t}{RC}}$.
- That the time constant is the time taken for a discharging capacitor to discharge to $\frac{1}{e}$ (about 37%) of its full charge, or the time taken for a charging capacitor to charge to about 63% of its full charge.
- That the time constant τ is equal to RC.

Exam-style Questions

Questions 1 to 4 are worth 1 mark each.

1 When the switch S in the circuit shown below is in position 1, the capacitor C is fully charged by the battery through resistor R. The switch is then moved to position 2 and the capacitor is allowed to discharge fully through the resistor.

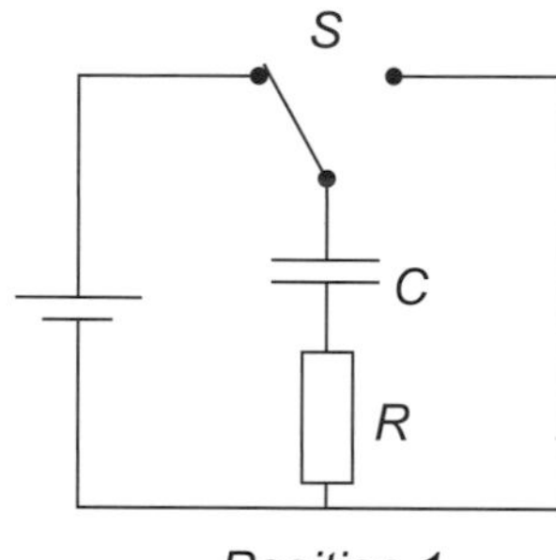

Position 1

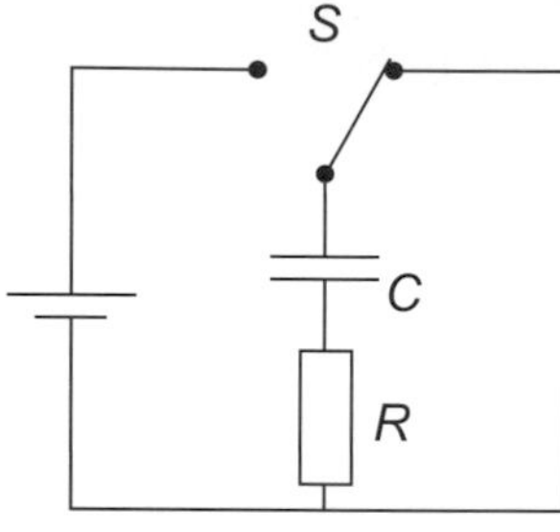

Position 2

Which graph correctly shows how the charge, Q, on the capacitor varies with time, *t*, during this process?

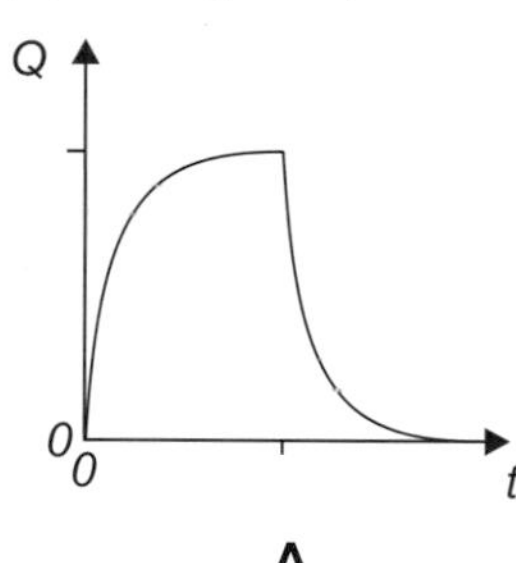

A

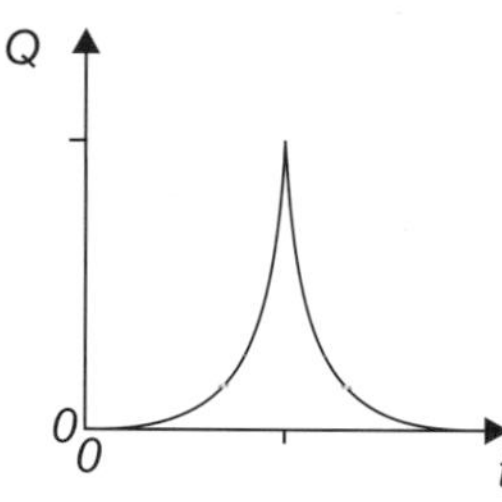

B

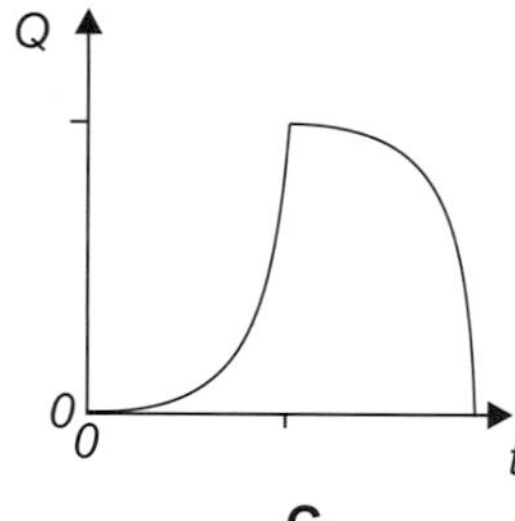

C

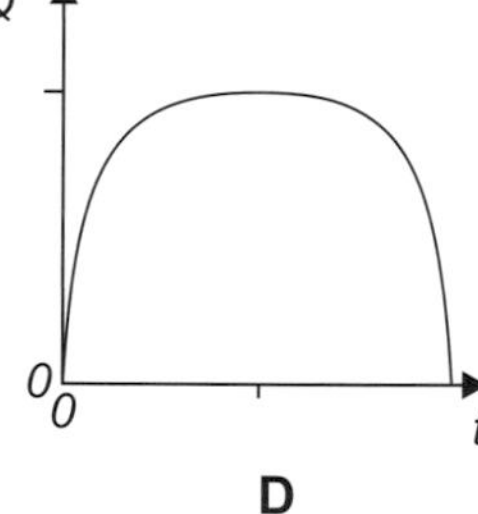

D

2 A capacitor discharging through a fixed 100 kΩ resistor loses 35% of its charge in 1 s. What is the approximate capacitance of the capacitor?

A 9.5×10^{-6} F

B 5.3×10^{-5} F

C 2.3×10^{-5} F

D 2.2×10^{-2} F

3 A 5 mF capacitor is charged to 24 V using a constant current for half a minute. What current is used to charge the capacitor?

A 4 A

B 0.24 A

C 4 mA

D 0.24 mA

4 A 20 μF capacitor is fully charged to a potential difference of 24 V through a variable resistor R using the circuit below. The charging current is constant and charging takes 10 s. Which of the following statements is **correct**?

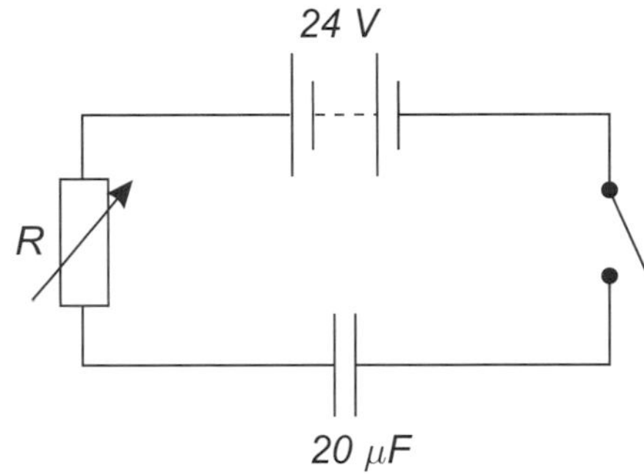

A The potential difference across the resistor is 20 V.

B The energy stored by the capacitor is 5.76 mJ.

C The total energy taken from the battery during charging is 5.76 mJ.

D The current supplied was 0.48 mA.

5 A student investigating capacitance charges a 0.1 F capacitor from a 12 V d.c. supply and uses a voltage sensor and a charge sensor connected to a data logger to measure the potential difference across the capacitor at regular intervals of charge stored by the capacitor. A computer is used to plot a graph of p.d. against charge.

5 (a) (i) Copy the axes below and sketch the graph obtained by the computer on the axes.

(1 mark)

5 (a) (ii) State what is represented by the gradient of the graph.

(1 mark)

5 (a) (iii) State what quantity the area enclosed by the line and the *x*-axis represents.

(1 mark)

5 (b) The student then discharges the capacitor through a light bulb, delivering a mean power of 15 W.

5 (b) (i) How long does the capacitor take to discharge?

(3 marks)

5 (b) (ii) Draw a graph showing how the current supplied to the light bulb varies over time as the capacitor discharges. You may assume the resistance of the light bulb remains constant.

(1 mark)

5 (b) (iii) Give one reason why a capacitor is not a suitable power source to power a light bulb.

(1 mark)

6 A 3×10^{-3} F capacitor charged to 50 V was discharged fully through a 2 kΩ resistor.

6 (a) During the charging, 7.5 J of energy was taken from the battery in total. Calculate how much energy was stored by the capacitor.

(1 mark)

6 (b) (i) Show that the time constant of the circuit is 6 s.

(1 mark)

6 (b) (ii) Show that the time taken for the capacitor to lose 90% of its charge is approximately 14 s.

(2 marks)

6 (b) (iii) Copy the axes below, and sketch a graph of charge against time for the first 14 seconds of the discharge of the capacitor described above.

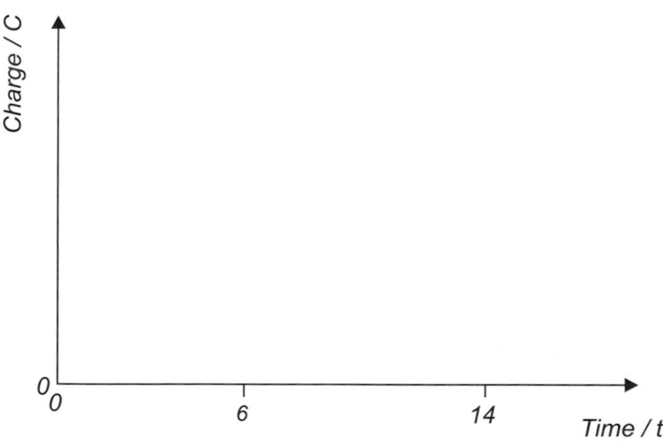

(1 mark)

Unit 4 Section 4: Magnetic Fields

1. Magnetic Flux Density

You've met gravitational fields, you've met electric fields, and now it's time for the final sort — magnetic fields. Magnetic fields, as you might expect, have a field strength, except in this case it's known as magnetic flux density.

Learning Objectives:
- Know that a force acts on a current-carrying wire in a magnetic field.
- Know Fleming's left-hand rule.
- Know what is meant by magnetic flux density and know it's measured in teslas.
- Be able to use $F = BIl$ to find the force acting on a current-carrying wire perpendicular to a magnetic field.

Specification Reference 3.4.5

Magnetic fields

A **magnetic field** is similar to a gravitational field (page 34) and an electric field (page 45) — it's a region in which a force acts. In a magnetic field, a force is exerted on magnetic or magnetically susceptible materials (e.g. iron). Magnetic fields can be represented by field lines. The closer together the field lines, the stronger the field. Magnetic field lines go from north to south (see Figure 1).

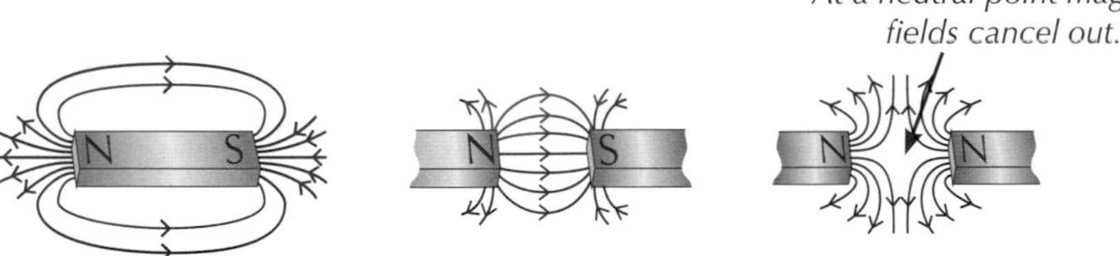

Figure 1: *The magnetic fields created by bar magnets.*

Magnetic fields around a wire

When current flows in a wire, a magnetic field is induced around the wire. The field lines are concentric circles centred on the wire. The direction of a magnetic field around a current-carrying wire can be worked out with the **right-hand rule**:

- Curl your right hand into a fist and stick your thumb up.
- Point your thumb in the direction of the current through the wire.
- Your curled fingers will then show the direction of the field.

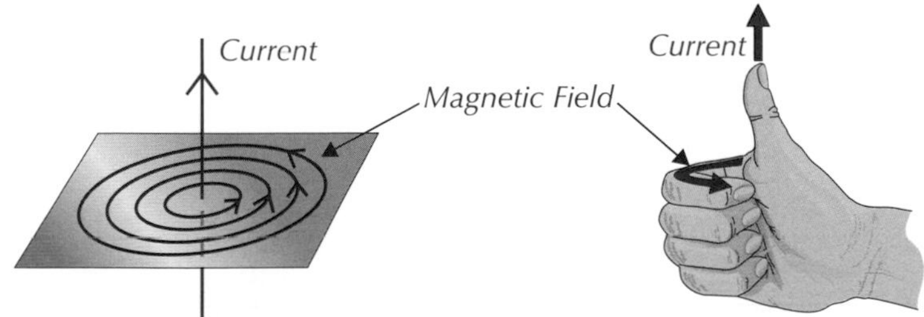

Figure 3: *Diagram to show how your right hand can be used to show the direction of magnetic field lines around a current-carrying wire.*

Figure 2: *A current-carrying wire induces a circular magnetic field around it — the needles of the small compasses follow a circle around the wire.*

Solenoids

If you loop a current-carrying wire into a coil, the field is doughnut shaped, while lots of coils (a **solenoid**) form a field like a bar magnet (see Figure 4).

Figure 5: A simple solenoid.

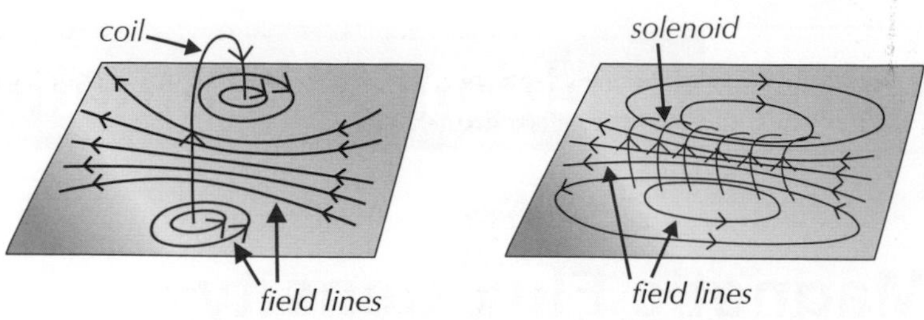

***Figure 4:** The magnetic fields created by a current-carrying wire in a coil (left) and in lots of coils (right).*

Force on a current-carrying wire

If you put a current-carrying wire into an external magnetic field (e.g. between two magnets), the field around the wire and the field from the magnets interact. The field lines from the magnet contract to form a 'stretched catapult' effect where the field lines are closer together (see Figure 6). This causes a force on the wire.

Tip: A solid dot like in Figure 6 (●) shows current flowing out of the page (or towards the reader). A circle with a cross (⊗) shows current flowing into the page (or away from the reader).

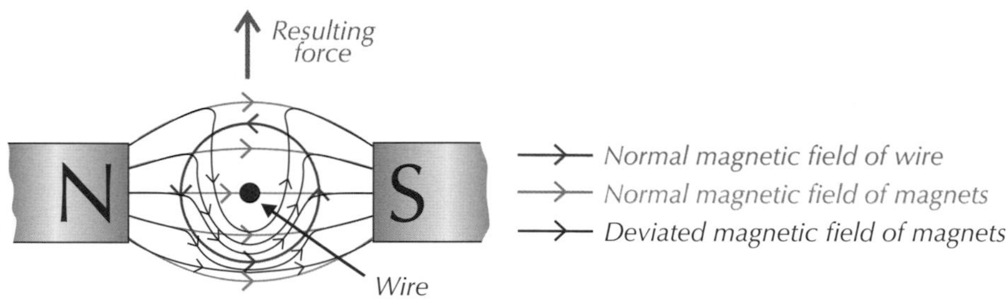

***Figure 6:** A current-carrying wire in a magnetic field experiences a force.*

If the current is parallel to the field lines, no force acts. The direction of the force is always perpendicular to both the current direction and the magnetic field — it's given by **Fleming's left-hand rule** (see below).

Fleming's left-hand rule

You can use your left hand to find the direction of the current, the direction of the magnetic field or the direction of the force on the wire (as long as you know the other two). Stretch your thumb, forefinger and middle finger out, as shown in Figure 7, and use the following rules:

- The **F**irst finger points in the direction of the uniform magnetic **F**ield.
- The se**C**ond finger points in the direction of the conventional **C**urrent.
- The thu**M**b points in the direction of the force (the direction of **M**otion).

Tip: Conventional current flows in the direction that a positive charge would flow, i.e. from positive to negative.

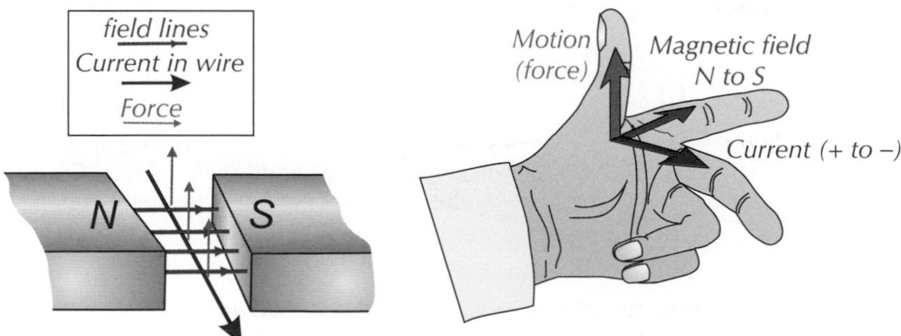

***Figure 7:** Fleming's left-hand rule for a current-carrying wire in a magnetic field.*

Example

A current-carrying wire runs between two magnets, as shown below. What direction will the force on the wire be?

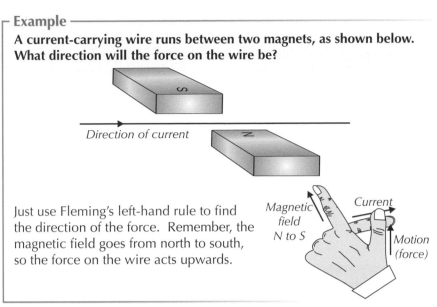

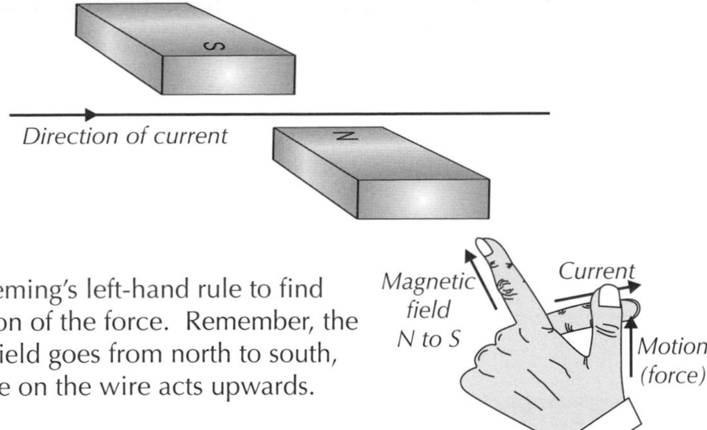

Just use Fleming's left-hand rule to find the direction of the force. Remember, the magnetic field goes from north to south, so the force on the wire acts upwards.

By passing an alternating current through a wire in a magnetic field, the wire can be made to vibrate. The direction of the force acting on the wire is perpendicular to the direction of the current — so when the current is reversed, the direction of the force is also reversed. The constant reversal of an alternating current means the force is constantly alternated too, resulting in vibration of the wire.

Figure 8: *British physicist John Ambrose Fleming.*

Magnetic flux density

The force on a current-carrying wire at a right angle to a magnetic field is proportional to the strength of the magnetic field. The magnetic field strength is called the **magnetic flux density**, ***B***, whose value is given by:

> The force on one metre of wire carrying a current of one amp at right angles to the magnetic field.

Magnetic flux density is a vector quantity with both a direction and a magnitude. It is measured in **teslas**, T. One tesla is equal to one weber per square metre:

$$1 \text{ tesla} = 1 \frac{\text{Wb}}{\text{m}^2}$$

Tip: Webers are the unit of magnetic flux (page 79).

Tip: It helps to think of flux density as the number of magnetic field lines (measured in webers, Wb) per unit area.

The size of the force, ***F***, on a current-carrying wire at right angles to a magnetic field is proportional to the current, *I*, the length of wire in the field, *l*, and the magnetic flux density, ***B***. This gives the equation:

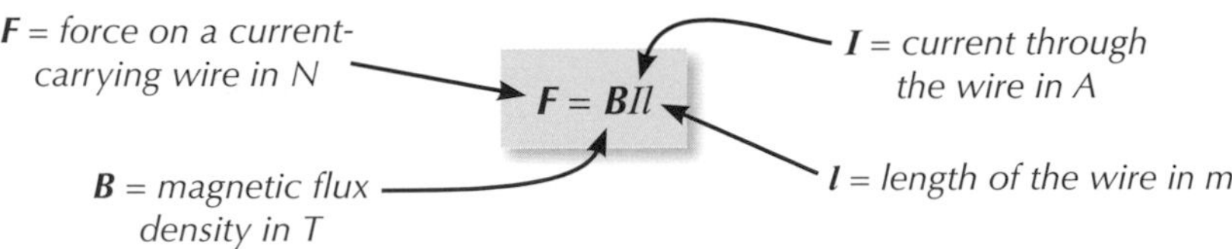

This equation gives the maximum force the wire could experience. A force still acts on the wire if it's not at right angles to the magnetic field (as long as they're not parallel), but it will be smaller.

Tip: There's more about this on page 80.

Tip: 1 mT (millitesla) is equal to 1×10^{-3} T.

Example

A section of wire carrying a current of 5.2 A is placed at right angles to a uniform magnetic field with a flux density of 19 mT. If the wire experiences a force of 1.2×10^{-2} N, what length of wire is inside the magnetic field?

Just rearrange the formula $\boldsymbol{F} = \boldsymbol{BI}l$ to make l the subject and then put in the numbers:

$$\boldsymbol{F} = \boldsymbol{BI}l \Rightarrow l = \frac{\boldsymbol{F}}{\boldsymbol{BI}}$$

$$= \frac{1.2 \times 10^{-2}}{(19 \times 10^{-3}) \times 5.2}$$

$$= 0.12\,\text{m (to 2 s.f.)}$$

Practice Question — Application

Q1 A student runs a steady 1.44 A current through a wire from a d.c. supply. A 2.51 cm section of the wire is fixed at two points and then placed in a uniform magnetic field with a flux density of 9.21 mT, as shown.

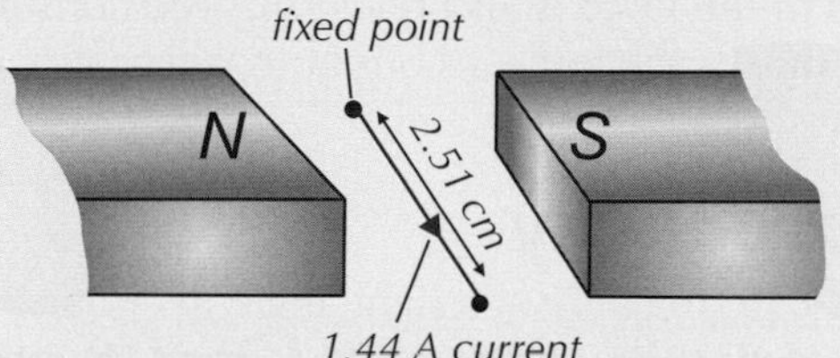

a) In what direction will the force on the section of wire act?

b) What's the size of the force that will act on the section of wire?

c) The student wants to make the wire vibrate. What part of the experimental set-up could he alter to achieve this?

Practice Questions — Fact Recall

Q1 a) Which hand can you use to find the direction of the force acting on a current-carrying wire at a right angle to a magnetic field?

b) Describe what each finger represents on this hand when using it to find the direction of the force.

Q2 Give the condition needed to use the equation $\boldsymbol{F} = \boldsymbol{BI}l$ to calculate the force on a current-carrying wire in a magnetic field.

Q3 What does $\boldsymbol{B}$ represent in the equation $\boldsymbol{F} = \boldsymbol{BI}l$, and what are its units?

2. Forces on Charged Particles

Magnetic fields don't just exert a force on current-carrying wires — they have the same effect on all charged particles.

Learning Objectives:

- Understand that a charged particle moving through a magnetic field experiences a force.
- Be able to calculate the force acting on a charged particle whose velocity is perpendicular to a uniform magnetic field with $\boldsymbol{F} = \boldsymbol{B}Q\boldsymbol{v}$.
- Know that a charged particle follows a circular path in a magnetic field, and the factors that affect the motion of the particle.
- Know what a cyclotron is and how it works.

Specification Reference 3.4.5

Charged particles in a magnetic field

A force acts on charged particles moving in a magnetic field. This is why a current-carrying wire experiences a force in a magnetic field (page 72) — electric current in a wire is the flow of negatively charged electrons.

- The force on a current-carrying wire in a magnetic field perpendicular to the current is given by $\boldsymbol{F} = \boldsymbol{B}Il$.
- Electric current, I, is the flow of charge, Q, per unit time, t. So $I = \frac{Q}{t}$.
- A charged particle which moves a distance l in time t has a velocity, $\boldsymbol{v} = \frac{l}{t}$. So $l = \boldsymbol{v}t$.

Putting all these equations together gives the force acting on a single charged particle moving through a magnetic field, where its velocity is perpendicular to the magnetic field:

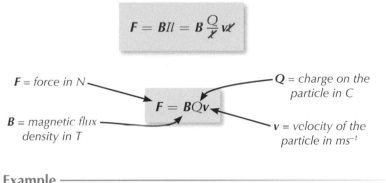

$$\boldsymbol{F} = \boldsymbol{B}Il = \boldsymbol{B}\frac{Q}{\cancel{t}}\boldsymbol{v}\cancel{t}$$

$$\boldsymbol{F} = \boldsymbol{B}Q\boldsymbol{v}$$

$\boldsymbol{F}$ = force in N

$\boldsymbol{B}$ = magnetic flux density in T

Q = charge on the particle in C

$\boldsymbol{v}$ = velocity of the particle in ms^{-1}

Exam Tip

In many exam questions, Q is the magnitude of the charge on the electron, which is 1.60×10^{-19} C.

Example

An electron travels at a velocity of 2×10^4 ms^{-1} perpendicular to a uniform magnetic field of strength 2 T. What is the force acting on the electron? (The magnitude of the charge on an electron is 1.6×10^{-19} C.)

Just use the equation $\boldsymbol{F} = \boldsymbol{B}Q\boldsymbol{v}$ and put the correct numbers in:

$$\boldsymbol{F} = \boldsymbol{B}Q\boldsymbol{v}$$
$$= 2 \times (1.6 \times 10^{-19}) \times (2 \times 10^4)$$
$$= 6.4 \times 10^{-15} \text{ N}$$

The circular path of particles

Charged particles in a magnetic field are deflected in a circular path. By Fleming's left-hand rule the force on a moving charge in a magnetic field is always perpendicular to its direction of travel. Mathematically, that is the condition for circular motion (page 15).

To use Fleming's left-hand rule for charged particles, use your second finger (normally current) as the direction of motion for a positive charge. If the particle carries a negative charge (i.e. an electron), either point your second finger in the opposite direction to its motion, or use your right hand instead.

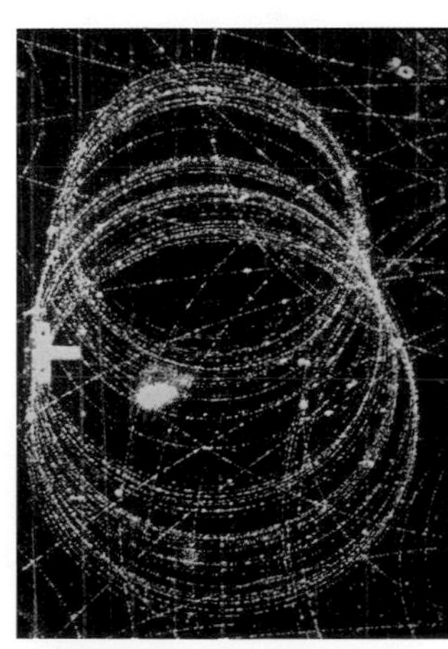

***Figure 1:** Circular tracks made by charged particles in a cloud chamber with an applied magnetic field.*

Tip: The acceleration is towards the centre of the circle — it is centripetal (see page 14).

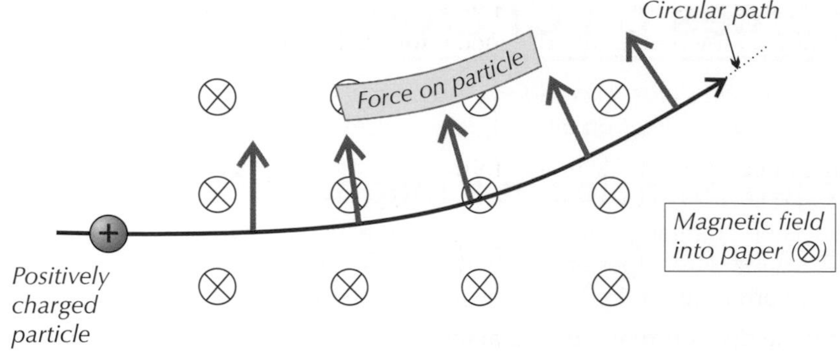

Figure 2: *A charged particle moving in a magnetic field follows a circular path.*

The force due to the magnetic field ($\boldsymbol{F} = BQv$) experienced by a particle travelling through a magnetic field is independent of the particle's mass, but the centripetal acceleration it experiences will depend on the mass — from Newton's 2nd law of motion.

Tip: Newton's laws of motion were covered in AS physics if you need a reminder.

- The particle's acceleration will be $\boldsymbol{a} = \frac{\boldsymbol{v}^2}{r}$ (see page 15).
- Combining this with Newton's 2nd law, $\boldsymbol{F} = m\boldsymbol{a}$, gives the force on a particle in a circular orbit $\boldsymbol{F} = \frac{m\boldsymbol{v}^2}{r}$.

The radius of the circular path followed by charged particles in a magnetic field can be found by combining the equations for the force on a charged particle in a magnetic field and for the force on a particle in a circular orbit.

Tip: A 'v' is cancelled from the top and bottom in the final rearrangement here.

$$\boldsymbol{F} = \frac{m\boldsymbol{v}^2}{r} \quad \text{and} \quad \boldsymbol{F} = \boldsymbol{B}Q\boldsymbol{v} \quad \Rightarrow \quad \frac{m\boldsymbol{v}^2}{r} = \boldsymbol{B}Q\boldsymbol{v}$$

$$\Rightarrow \quad r = \frac{m\boldsymbol{v}}{\boldsymbol{B}Q}$$

This means the radius of curvature increases (i.e. the particle is deflected less) if the mass or velocity of the particle increase. The radius of curvature decreases (i.e. the particle is deflected more) if the strength of the magnetic field or the charge on the particle increase.

Example

For each of the following, say which of the two particles would follow a circular path with the smaller radius in a magnetic field of flux density *B*.

a) **A carbon-12 nucleus with velocity *v*, relative mass of 12 and relative charge of +6, and a carbon-14 nucleus with velocity *v*, relative mass of 14 and relative charge of +6.**

The radius of the circular path followed by the particles is given by:

$$r = \frac{m\boldsymbol{v}}{\boldsymbol{B}Q}$$

In this case $\boldsymbol{v}$, $\boldsymbol{B}$ and Q are identical for both particles but m is larger for the carbon-14 nucleus. As r is directly proportional to m, the carbon-12 nucleus will follow the circular path with the smaller radius.

b) **A carbon-14 nucleus with velocity *v*, relative mass of 14 and relative charge of +6, and a nitrogen-14 nucleus with velocity v, relative mass of 14 and relative charge of +7.**

m, v and $\boldsymbol{B}$ are identical for both particles but Q is larger for the nitrogen nucleus. As r is inversely proportional to Q, the nitrogen nucleus will follow the circular path with the smaller radius.

- The frequency of rotation for an object in circular motion is given by its velocity ($\boldsymbol{v}$) divided by the distance it travels in each rotation ($2\pi r$):

$$f = \frac{\boldsymbol{v}}{2\pi r}$$

- You can combine this with the formula for r on the previous page to get an expression for the frequency of rotation in terms of $\boldsymbol{B}$, Q and m:

$$f = \frac{\boldsymbol{v}}{2\pi r} \quad \text{and} \quad r = \frac{m\boldsymbol{v}}{\boldsymbol{B}Q} \quad \Rightarrow \quad f = \frac{\cancel{\boldsymbol{v}}}{2\pi\left(\frac{m\cancel{\boldsymbol{v}}}{\boldsymbol{B}Q}\right)} = \frac{\boldsymbol{B}Q}{2\pi m}$$

So the frequency of rotation of a charged particle in a magnetic field is independent of its velocity. The time it takes a particle to complete a full circle depends only on the magnetic flux density and its mass and charge. Increasing a particle's velocity will make it follow a circular path with a larger radius, but it will take the same amount of time to complete it.

Tip: $2\pi r$ is the circumference of a circle with radius r.

Tip: For more on circular motion, see pages 11-16.

Particle accelerators

This effect is used in particle accelerators such as cyclotrons and synchrotrons. Cyclotrons have many uses, for example in medicine. Cyclotrons can be used to produce radioactive tracers or high-energy beams of radiation for use in radiotherapy.

A cyclotron is made up of two hollow semicircular electrodes with a uniform magnetic field applied perpendicular to the plane of the electrodes, and an alternating potential difference applied between the electrodes.

Tip: The electrodes are sometimes called "dees" because of their D-shape.

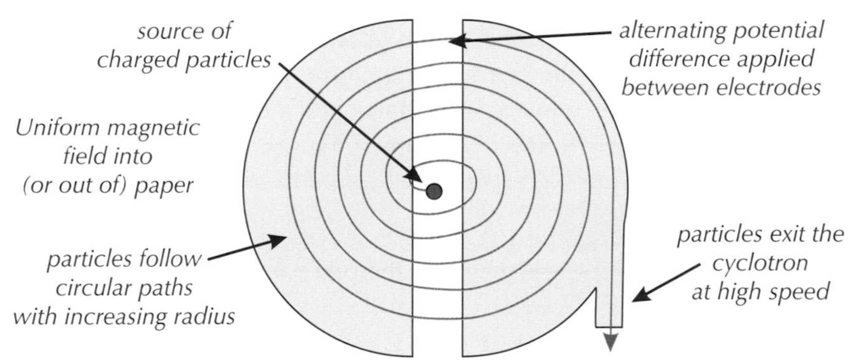

Figure 4: *The basic structure of a cyclotron.*

Figure 3: *A medical cyclotron used to produce radioactive tracers.*

Charged particles are produced and fired into one of the electrodes, where the magnetic field makes them follow a (semi)circular path and then leave the electrode. An applied potential difference between the electrodes then accelerates the particles across the gap until they enter the next electrode.

Because the particle's speed is slightly higher, it will follow a circular path with a larger radius (see page 12) before leaving the electrode again. At this point the direction of the potential difference will have been reversed and so the particle is accelerated again before entering the next electrode. This process repeats as the particle spirals outwards, increasing in speed, before eventually exiting the cyclotron.

Tip: If the potential difference wasn't alternating, the particle would slow down after leaving the second electrode.

Tip: Neutrons, along with protons, are one of the nucleons found in atoms. They have a mass of 1.67×10^{-27} kg and carry no charge.

Practice Questions — Application

Q1 Why would a neutron moving through a magnetic field perpendicular to its direction of motion not experience a force?

Q2 In which direction will the force due to the magnetic field act on the electron in the diagram below?

Q3 Find the force that acts on a particle with a charge of 3.2×10^{-19} C travelling at a velocity of 5.5×10^{3} ms^{-1} perpendicular to a magnetic field with a flux density of 640 mT.

Tip: See pages 11-16 for more on circular motion.

Q4 a) The force needed to keep an object in circular motion is given by $\boldsymbol{F} = \frac{mv^2}{r}$. Combine this with $\boldsymbol{F} = \boldsymbol{B}Q\boldsymbol{v}$ to find an expression for the magnetic flux density $\boldsymbol{B}$ needed to keep a charged particle in circular motion for a given radius r and orbital speed $\boldsymbol{v}$.

b) In a circular particle accelerator with a radius of 5.49 m, protons are accelerated to 1.99×10^{7} ms^{-1}. Find the magnetic flux density $\boldsymbol{B}$ that's required to keep the protons following the circular path of the accelerator. $m_p = 1.67 \times 10^{-27}$ kg and $Q_p = 1.60 \times 10^{-19}$ J.

Practice Questions — Fact Recall

Q1 If an electron is travelling through a uniform magnetic field perpendicular to its velocity, what shape will its path take? (Assume it has infinite space to move into.)

Q2 Briefly describe how high-speed charged particles are produced in a cyclotron.

3. Electromagnetic Induction

You might have come across electromagnetic induction before — it's the process at work in electromagnets, power generators, transformers, etc. It happens because of the force on charged particles in magnetic fields.

Learning Objectives:
- Understand that e.m.f. is induced across a straight conductor moving through a magnetic field.
- Know what is meant by magnetic flux and flux linkage.
- Be able to calculate the magnetic flux passing through an area normal to the magnetic flux density.
- Be able to calculate the flux linkage for a rectangular coil normal to the magnetic flux density with N turns cutting the flux.
- Be able to calculate the flux and flux linkage through a rotating coil at an angle to the magnetic field.

Specification Reference 3.4.5

Electromagnetic induction

If a conducting rod moves through a magnetic field its electrons will experience a force (see page 75), which means that they will accumulate at one end. This induces an **e.m.f.** (electromotive force) across the ends of the rod. If the rod is part of a complete circuit, then an induced current will flow through it — this is called electromagnetic induction.

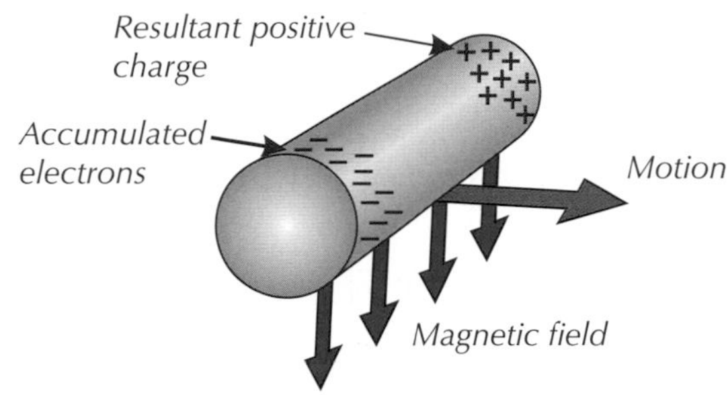

Figure 1: *A conducting rod moving through a magnetic field.*

An e.m.f. is induced when there is relative motion between a conductor and a magnet. The conductor can move and the magnetic field stay still or the other way round — you get an e.m.f. either way.

Flux cutting (i.e. moving a conductor through a magnetic field) always induces an e.m.f. but will only induce a current if the circuit is complete. Flux linking is when an e.m.f. is induced by changing the magnitude or direction of the magnetic flux (see below), e.g. by using an alternating current.

A change in flux of one weber per second will induce an electromotive force of 1 volt in a loop of wire.

Tip: E.m.f. is another way of saying voltage — you saw it in AS physics if you need a reminder. See pages 82-85 for more on induced e.m.f.

Magnetic flux

Magnetic flux density, $\boldsymbol{B}$, is a measure of the strength of the magnetic field per unit area (see page 73). The total magnetic flux, Φ, passing through an area, A, normal (perpendicular) to a magnetic field, $\boldsymbol{B}$, is given by:

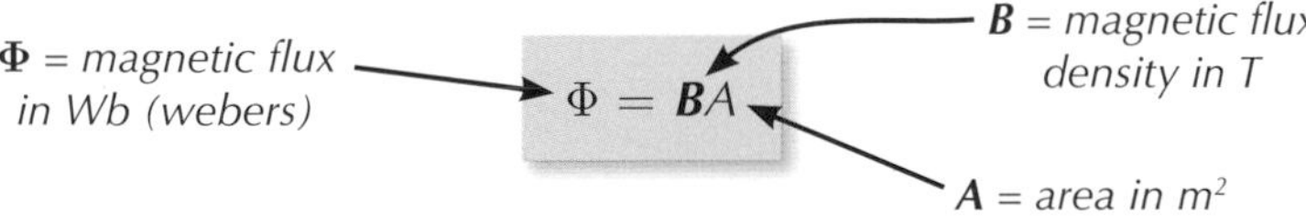

Tip: Think of magnetic flux as the total number of field lines.

Tip: You can only use this equation if $\boldsymbol{B}$ is normal to A — otherwise there's an extra term in the equation, which you'll see on the next page.

Example

A square with sides of length 4.5 cm is placed in a magnetic field, normal to the field's direction. Find the magnetic flux passing through the square if the magnetic flux density is 0.92 T.

Start by finding the area of the square, remembering to convert the units:

$$A = (4.5 \times 10^{-2}) \times (4.5 \times 10^{-2}) = 2.025 \times 10^{-3}\ \text{m}^2$$

Then just put the numbers into the equation above:

$$\Phi = \boldsymbol{B}A = 0.92 \times (2.025 \times 10^{-3}) = 1.9 \times 10^{-3}\ \text{Wb (to 2 s.f.)}$$

Tip: If you find the area in cm^2, you'll need to convert the units. 1 cm^2 = 1×10^{-4} m^2.

Tip: The diagram shows a side-on view of a rectangular coil normal to a magnetic flux density $\boldsymbol{B}$.

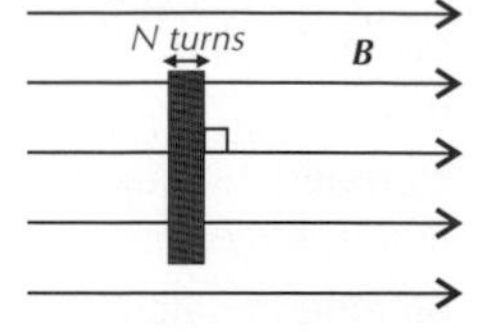

Tip: Even though N has no units, the word "turns" is usually added to the units for magnetic flux.

Tip: Don't be tempted to cancel down the 'N's here — consider the flux linkage, $N\Phi$, as a stand-alone term.

Flux linkage

When a wire coil is moved in a magnetic field, an e.m.f. (electromotive force) is induced across the coil (see previous page). The size of the e.m.f. induced depends on the magnetic flux passing through the coil, Φ, and the number of turns on the coil cutting the flux. The product of these is called the flux linkage, $N\Phi$. For a coil of N turns normal to $\boldsymbol{B}$, the **flux linkage** is given by:

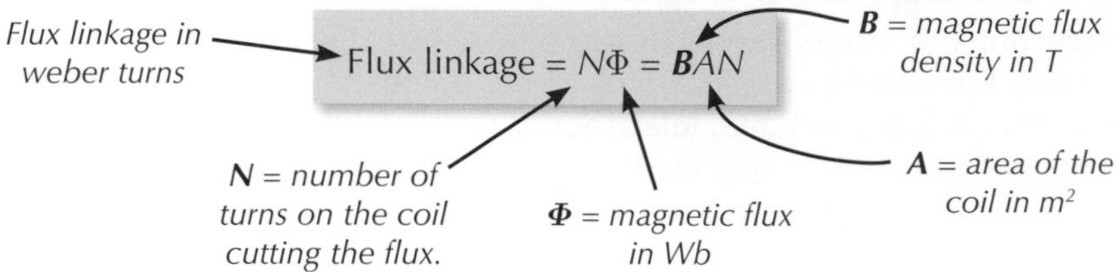

Example

The flux linkage of a coil with a cross-sectional area of 0.33 m² normal to a magnetic field of flux density 0.15 T is 4.0 Wb turns. How many turns are in the coil?

Just rearrange the equation for flux linkage to make N the subject and then put the numbers in:

$$[N\Phi] = \boldsymbol{B}AN \Rightarrow N = \frac{[N\Phi]}{\boldsymbol{B}A}$$

$$= \frac{4.0}{0.15 \times 0.33}$$

$$= 81 \text{ turns (to 2 s.f.)}$$

Flux linkage at an angle

Often, the wire coil is not normal to the direction of $\boldsymbol{B}$ — the normal to the coil makes an angle θ to the direction of the magnetic flux.

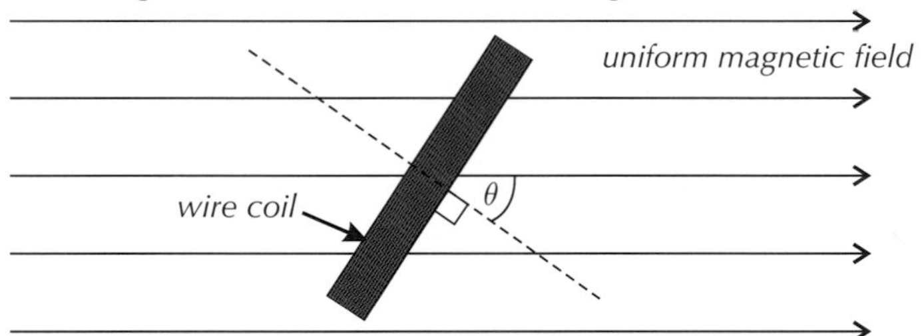

Figure 2: *A wire coil at an angle to a uniform magnetic field.*

In this case, you can find the magnetic flux through the coil with this equation:

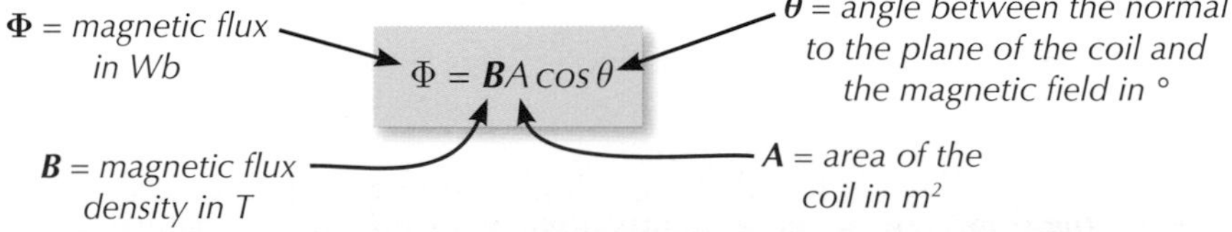

So for a coil with N turns, you can find the flux linkage with the equation:

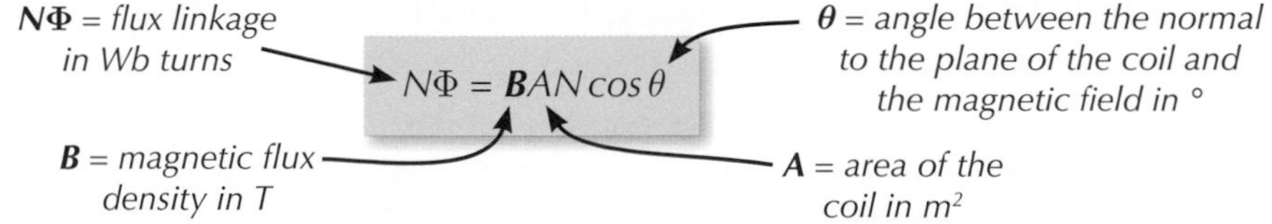

NΦ = flux linkage in Wb turns
NΦ = BAN cos θ
θ = angle between the normal to the plane of the coil and the magnetic field in °
B = magnetic flux density in T
A = area of the coil in m²

Example

A rectangular coil of wire with 200 turns and sides of length 5.00 cm and 6.51 cm is rotating in a magnetic field with $B = 8.56 \times 10^{-3}$ T. Find the flux linkage of the coil when it's at 29.5° to the magnetic field, as shown below.

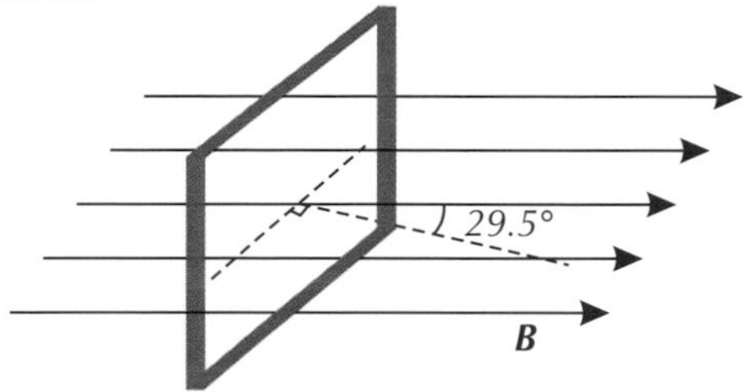

First find the area of the coil:

$$\text{Area} = (5.00 \times 10^{-2}) \times (6.51 \times 10^{-2}) = 3.255 \times 10^{-3}\ \text{m}^2$$

Then just put the numbers into the equation:

$$N\Phi = \boldsymbol{B}AN\cos\theta$$
$$= (8.56 \times 10^{-3}) \times (3.255 \times 10^{-3}) \times 200 \times \cos 29.5°$$
$$= 4.85 \times 10^{-3}\ \text{Wb turns (to 3 s.f.)}$$

Exam Tip
You'll only ever need to worry about a rectangular coil in the exam.

Practice Question — Application

Q1 Babatunde sets up an experiment to measure the strength of the Earth's magnetic field, ***B***. He does this by measuring the flux linkage of a rectangular wire coil.

a) Explain why the flux linkage of the coil changes when he rotates the coil.

b) Babatunde finds the highest value of flux linkage to be 1.3×10^{-6} Wb turns. If he used a coil with an area of 25 cm^2 and 10 turns, find the local value of ***B***.

c) Suggest two changes he could make to the coil to make his measurement of ***B*** more accurate.

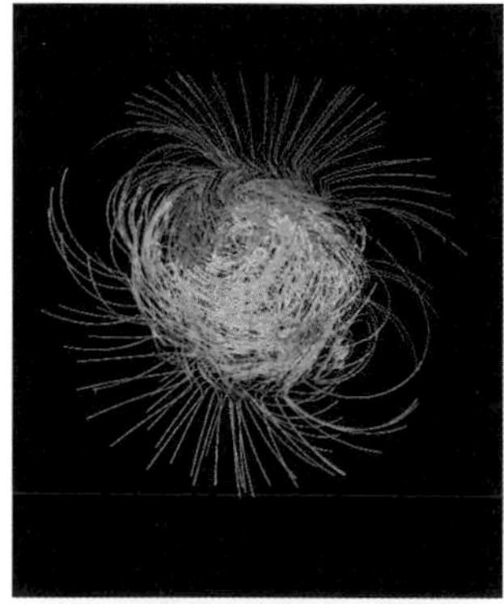

Figure 3: *A representation of the Earth's magnetic field.*

Tip: See page 288 for more on accuracy of measurements.

Practice Questions — Fact Recall

Q1 What's induced when a conductor moves through a magnetic field?

Q2 Write down the equation that links magnetic flux, magnetic flux density and an area *A*.

Q3 What are the units of flux linkage?

Q4 Write down the formula for flux linkage through a coil that is not perpendicular to the magnetic field, and briefly explain what each term represents.

Learning Objectives:

- Know Faraday's law.
- Know the magnitude of an induced e.m.f. is equal to the rate of change of flux linkage.
- Know Lenz's law.
- Be able to calculate the maximum induced e.m.f. in a coil rotating uniformly in a magnetic field.
- Be able to recognise and sketch the sinusoidal e.m.f. induced by a coil rotating uniformly in a magnetic field.

Specification Reference 3.4.5

Tip: Remember, a change in flux of 1 Wb per second will induce an electromotive force of 1 V in a loop of wire.

Figure 2: *British physicist Michael Faraday.*

Exam Tip
Finding the e.m.f. induced by the Earth's magnetic field across the wingspan of a plane is an exam favourite — think of it as a moving straight conducting rod.

Tip: There's only 1 'turn' in a conducting rod, so you can ignore the N in Faraday's law.

4. Faraday's Law and Lenz's Law

There's more electromagnetic induction coming up for you to sink your teeth into. In this topic, you'll see how Faraday and Lenz tried to explain the phenomenon better with the inventively named Faraday's law and Lenz's law.

Faraday's law

The results from the last topic can be summed up in **Faraday's law**:

> Induced e.m.f. is directly proportional to the rate of change of flux linkage.

Faraday's law also gives us the magnitude of the induced e.m.f.:

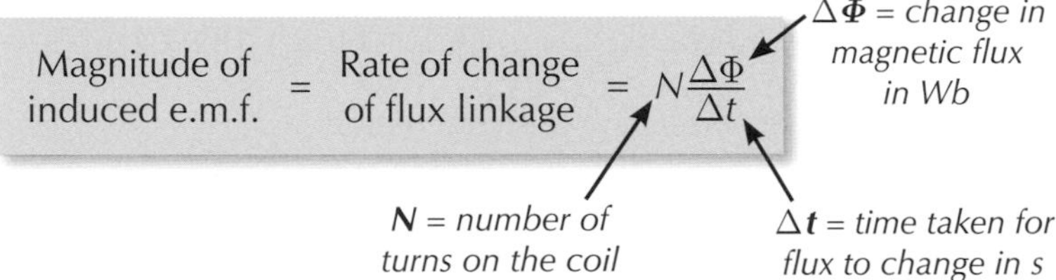

Magnitude of induced e.m.f. = Rate of change of flux linkage = $N\frac{\Delta\Phi}{\Delta t}$
$\Delta\Phi$ = change in magnetic flux in Wb
N = number of turns on the coil
Δt = time taken for flux to change in s

The magnitude of the e.m.f. is shown by the gradient of a graph of $N\Phi$ against time. The area under the graph of e.m.f. against time gives the flux change.

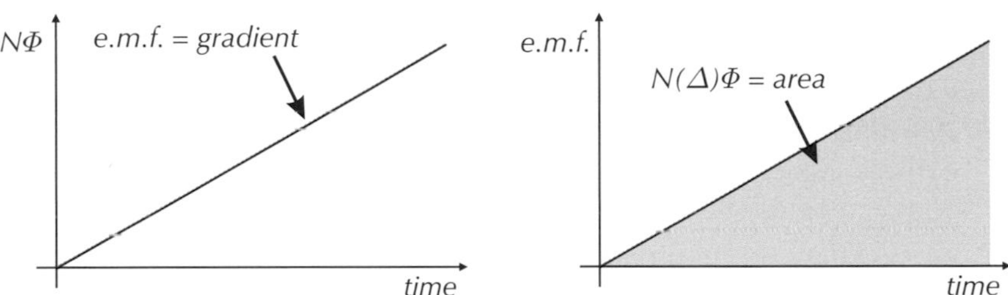

Figure 1: *Graphs of flux linkage against time (left) and e.m.f. against time (right) for a conductor moving through a magnetic field at a constant speed.*

Example

A conducting rod of length *l* moves through a perpendicular uniform magnetic field, *B*, at a constant velocity, *v*, as shown. Show that the e.m.f. induced in the rod is equal to *Blv*.

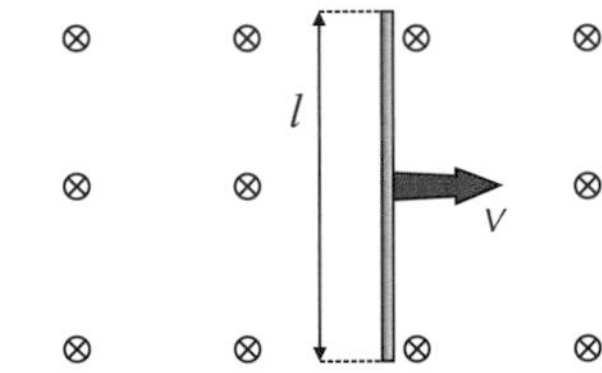

To use Faraday's law you need to know the flux the rod cuts through in time Δt. Flux Φ is given by $\Phi = BA$, so you need to find A. This is equal to the distance travelled in time $\Delta t \times$ the length of the rod (l).

Velocity = $\frac{\text{distance}}{\text{time}}$, so the distance travelled in time Δt is given by $v\Delta t$.

So the area of flux it cuts in this time is given by $lv\Delta t$.
$\Phi = BA$, so $\Phi = Blv\Delta t$.

Faraday's law states that e.m.f. = $\frac{\Delta\Phi}{\Delta t}$, so e.m.f. = $\frac{Blv\cancel{\Delta t}}{\cancel{\Delta t}} = Blv$

Lenz's law

The direction of the induced e.m.f. and current are given by **Lenz's law**:

> The induced e.m.f. is always in such a direction as to oppose the change that caused it.

The idea that an induced e.m.f. will oppose the change that caused it agrees with the principle of the conservation of energy — the energy used to pull a conductor though a magnetic field, against the resistance caused by magnetic attraction, is what produces the induced current.

Lenz's law can be used to find the direction of an induced e.m.f. and current in a conductor travelling at right angles to a magnetic field.

Example

Lenz's law says that the induced e.m.f. will produce a force that opposes the motion of the conductor — in other words a resistance. Picture a straight conductor being moved down through a magnetic field:

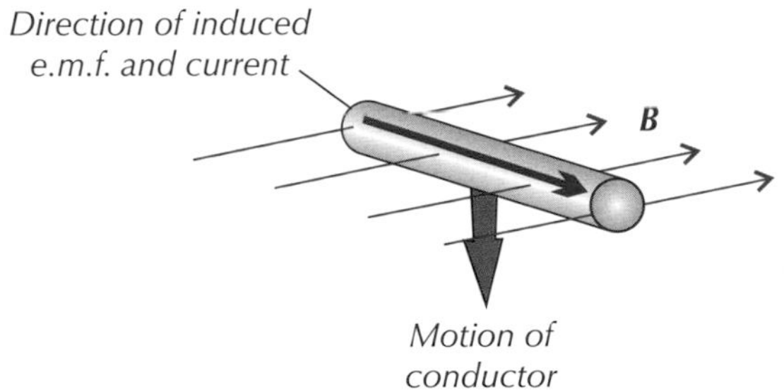

Using Fleming's left-hand rule (see page 72), point your first finger in the direction of the field and your second finger in the direction of the current. You'll see the induced force is in the opposite direction to the motion, causing a resistance.

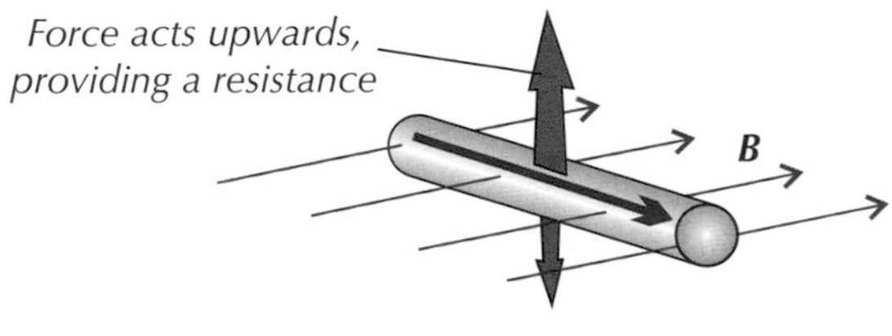

Tip: If the conductor is connected as part of a circuit, a current will be induced in the same direction as the induced e.m.f.

Tip: If you've forgotten which finger is which, here's a reminder:

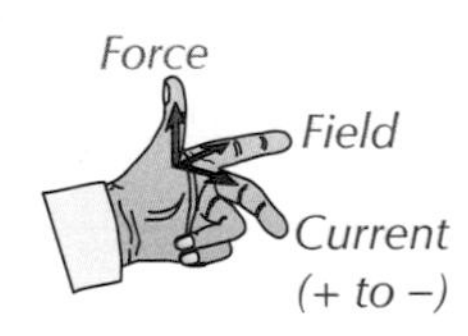

Induced e.m.f. in a rotating coil

When a coil rotates uniformly (at a steady speed) in a magnetic field, the coil cuts the flux and an alternating e.m.f. is induced. The amount of flux cut by the coil (flux linkage) is given by $N\Phi = \boldsymbol{B}AN\cos\theta$ (see page 80). As the coil rotates, θ changes so the flux linkage varies sinusoidally between $+\boldsymbol{B}AN$ and $-\boldsymbol{B}AN$.

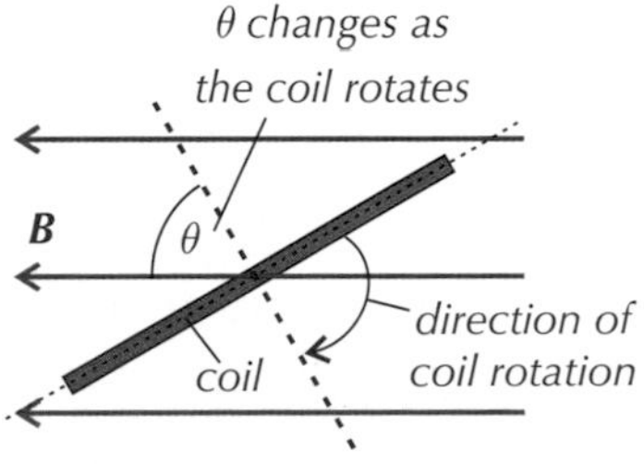

Figure 3: *The value of θ changes as the coil rotates.*

Tip: Note the axis of rotation is perpendicular to the magnetic field.

Tip: 'Sinusoidally' means it follows the same pattern as a sin (or cos) curve — see the next page for more.

How fast θ changes depends on the angular speed, ω, of the coil (see page 12), $\theta = \omega t$. So you can write:

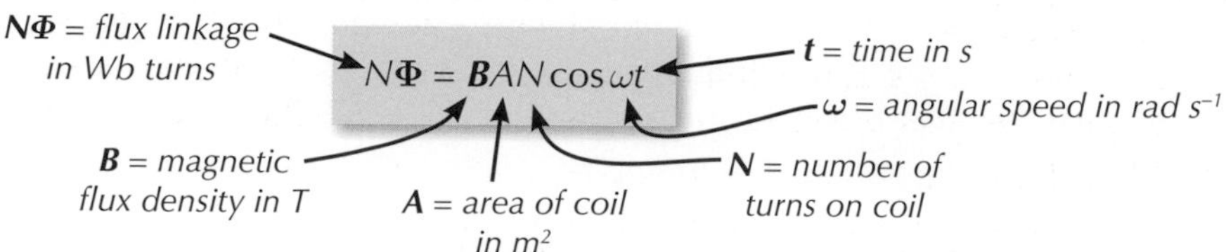

$$N\Phi = BAN\cos\omega t$$

Tip: 'rad' (short for radians) is just another unit for measuring angles. It's the one that's normally used in circular motion (page 11).

The induced e.m.f., ε, depends on the rate of change of flux linkage (Faraday's law), so it also varies sinusoidally. The equation for the e.m.f. at time t is:

ε = induced e.m.f. in V

$$\varepsilon = BAN\omega\sin\omega t$$

Tip: You might see induced e.m.f. given as E instead of ε.

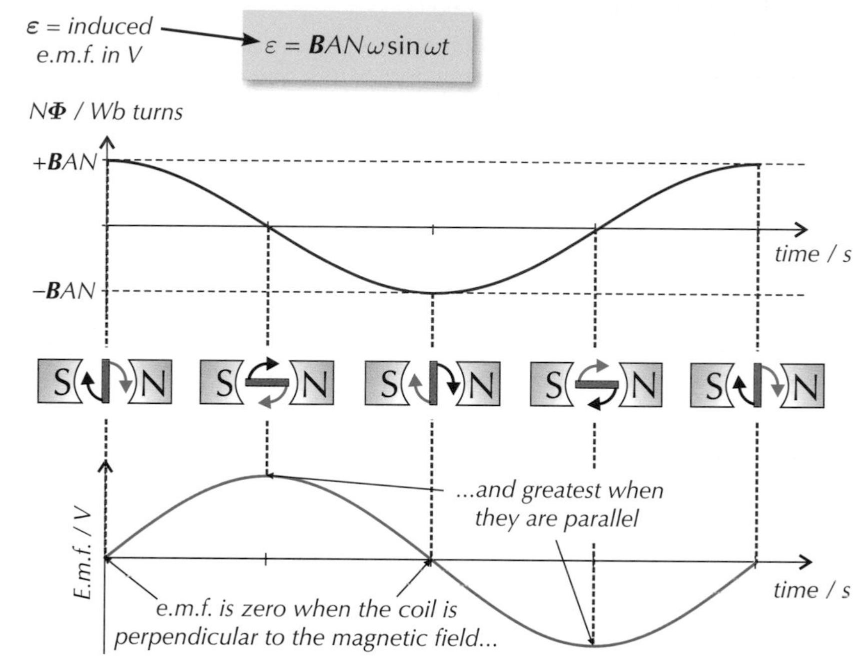

Figure 4: The sinusoidal graphs produced by plotting flux linkage and induced e.m.f. against time for a rotating coil in a magnetic field.

Tip: Flux linkage and induced e.m.f. are 90° out of phase.

Tip: Flux linkage is at a maximum at 0° and 180° and zero at 90° and 270°. E.m.f. is at a maximum at 90° and 270° and zero at 0° and 180°.

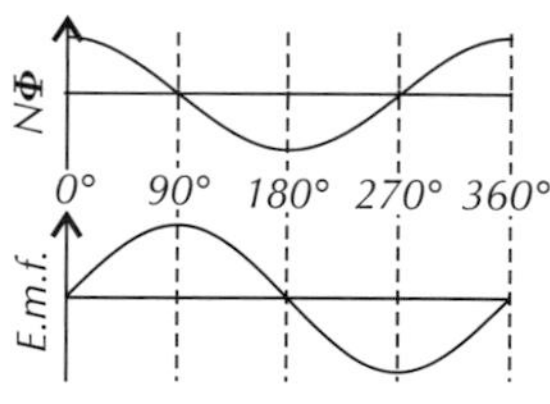

Example

A rectangular coil with 20 turns, and an area of 0.2 m², is rotated at 20 rad s⁻¹ with the axis of rotation perpendicular to a uniform 1.5 mT magnetic field. Calculate the maximum e.m.f. induced in the coil.

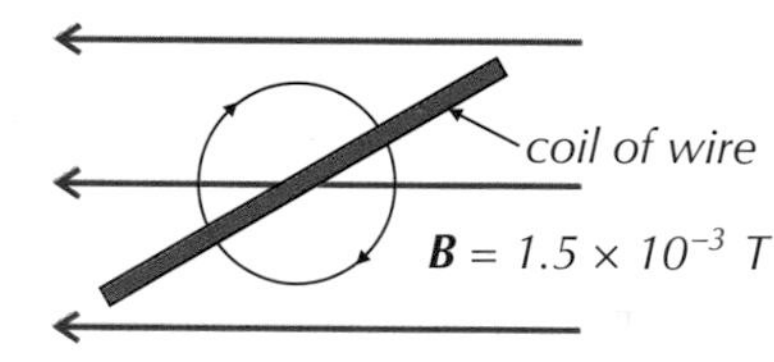

$\varepsilon = BAN\omega\sin\omega t$, so ε will be greatest when $\sin\omega t = \pm 1$. This gives:

$$\varepsilon = BAN\omega\sin\omega t$$
$$= (1.5 \times 10^{-3}) \times 0.2 \times 20 \times 20 \times \pm 1$$
$$= \pm 0.12 \text{ V}$$

Tip: $\sin\theta = \pm 1$ when $\theta = \frac{\pi}{2}, \frac{3\pi}{2}, \frac{5\pi}{2}$ etc.

The shape of the graph of induced e.m.f. can be altered by changing the speed of rotation or the size of the magnetic field:

- Increasing the speed of rotation will increase the frequency and increase the maximum e.m.f.
- Increasing the magnetic flux density B will increase the maximum e.m.f., but will have no effect on the frequency.

Tip: The changes are directly proportional — doubling the speed of rotation doubles the maximum e.m.f. and halving the speed halves the maximum e.m.f. etc.

Example

Below is a graph (in green) of induced e.m.f. against time for a coil, rotating with angular speed ω in a magnetic field with a flux density of B. Sketch, on the same axes, a graph of induced e.m.f. against time for the same coil rotating with angular speed 2ω in a magnetic field with a flux density of $0.25B$.

Doubling the speed will double the maximum e.m.f. and double the frequency. Dividing the flux density by 4 will have no effect on the frequency but will divide the maximum e.m.f. by 4. So the second graph (blue) will have double the frequency but half the amplitude of the first graph.

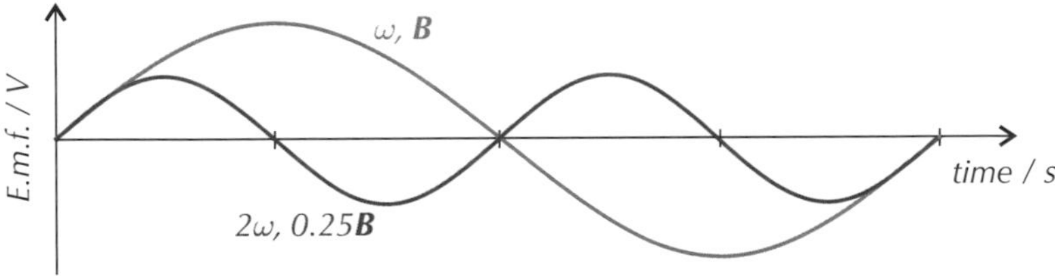

Tip: The amplitude is halved because it's doubled and then divided by 4.

Generators

Generators, or dynamos, convert kinetic energy into electrical energy — they induce an electric current by rotating a coil in a magnetic field.

Figure 5 shows a simple alternator — a generator of alternating current. It has slip rings and brushes to connect the coil to an external circuit. The output voltage and current change direction with every half rotation of the coil, producing an alternating current.

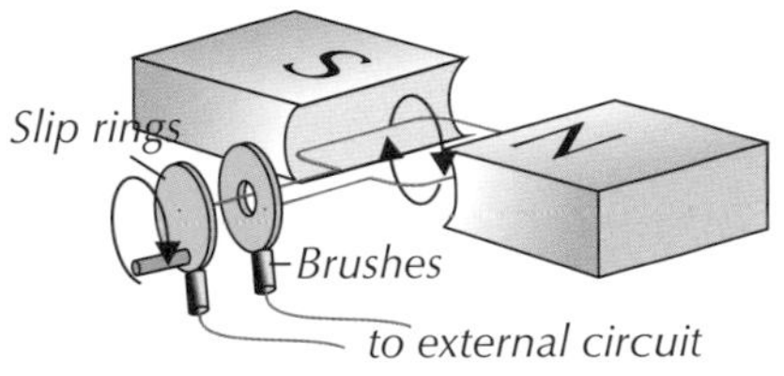

Figure 5: *A simple alternator.*

Figure 6: *Wind-up torches contain a simple electromagnetic generator.*

Practice Questions — Application

Q1 Why is an e.m.f. often induced across the wings of a moving plane?

Q2 A wire coil with 50 turns and an area of 0.24 m^2 is placed perpendicular to a magnetic field with flux density 1.5 T and rotated with a steady speed of 4π rad s^{-1}.

a) Find the maximum e.m.f. induced across the wire coil.

b) Sketch a graph of induced e.m.f. against time for the wire coil between 0 and 0.5 seconds.

c) The speed of the coil's rotation is doubled. Sketch a new graph of induced e.m.f. against time for the coil between 0 and 0.5 s.

Tip: There are 2π rad in 360°.

Practice Questions — Fact Recall

Q1 What's Faraday's law?

Q2 Write down an expression for rate of change of flux linkage.

Q3 What's Lenz's law?

Q4 Sketch a graph of flux linkage against time for:

a) A conductor moving in a straight line at a steady speed perpendicular to a uniform magnetic field.

b) A wire coil rotating at a steady speed inside a uniform magnetic field.

Learning Objectives:

- Understand what a transformer is and how it works.
- Be able to use the equation for an ideal transformer to find the number of turns or voltage on either coil.
- Understand why transformers cannot be 100% efficient and be able to suggest ways of improving efficiency.
- Be able to calculate the efficiency of a transformer and the energy lost.
- Understand how and why transformers are used to transmit power on the National Grid.

Specification Reference 3.4.5

Tip: A magnetically soft material is one whose magnetisation disappears after the current is removed.

Tip: The flux linkage will be higher in the coil with the most turns — it's proportional to the voltage in the coil.

Tip: In an ideal transformer, the flux through the secondary coil is the same as the flux through the primary coil and no energy is lost in the transfer.

Exam Tip
This is how the equation appears in your data and formulae booklet.

5. Transformers

Transformers are important in the transfer of electricity from power stations to the nation and are really useful in all sorts of electrical equipment. They're responsible for the buzzing you might have heard in chargers for laptops, speakers, and many more devices.

What's a transformer?

Transformers are devices that make use of electromagnetic induction to change the size of the voltage for an alternating current — see Figure 1.

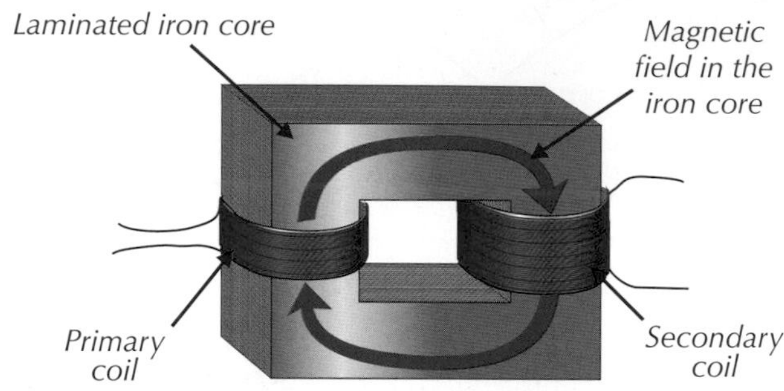

Figure 1: *The basic structure of a (step-up) transformer.*

An alternating current flowing in the primary (or input) coil causes the core to magnetise, demagnetise and remagnetise continuously in opposite directions. This produces a rapidly changing magnetic flux across the core. Because of this, a magnetically soft material is needed — usually iron or a special alloy.

The rapidly changing magnetic flux in the iron core passes through the secondary (or output) coil, where it induces an alternating voltage of the same frequency (but different voltage, assuming the number of turns is different). From Faraday's law (page 82), the voltage in both the primary and secondary coils can be calculated:

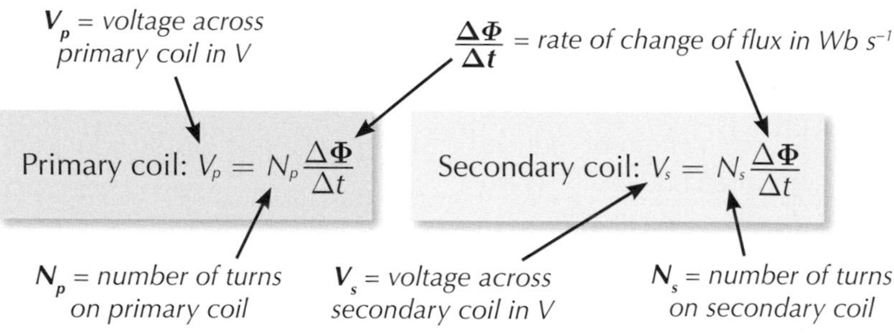

V_p = voltage across primary coil in V
$\frac{\Delta\Phi}{\Delta t}$ = rate of change of flux in Wb s^{-1}
Primary coil: $V_p = N_p \frac{\Delta\Phi}{\Delta t}$
Secondary coil: $V_s = N_s \frac{\Delta\Phi}{\Delta t}$
N_p = number of turns on primary coil
V_s = voltage across secondary coil in V
N_s = number of turns on secondary coil

These can be combined to give the equation for an ideal transformer:

$$V_p = N_p \frac{\Delta\Phi}{\Delta t} \Rightarrow \frac{V_p}{N_p} = \frac{\Delta\Phi}{\Delta t} \qquad V_s = N_s \frac{\Delta\Phi}{\Delta t} \Rightarrow \frac{V_s}{N_s} = \frac{\Delta\Phi}{\Delta t}$$

$$\Rightarrow \frac{V_p}{N_p} = \frac{V_s}{N_s} \quad \left(= \frac{\Delta\Phi}{\Delta t}\right)$$

Rearranging this gives:

$$\frac{N_s}{N_p} = \frac{V_s}{V_p}$$

Step-up transformers increase the voltage by having more turns on the secondary coil than the primary. **Step-down transformers** reduce the voltage by having fewer turns on the secondary coil.

Figure 2: An early version of a transformer.

Example

What is the output voltage for a transformer with a primary coil of 100 turns, a secondary coil of 300 turns and an input voltage of 230 V?

Just use the equation for an ideal transformer and rearrange it to make the output voltage (V_s) the subject:

$$\frac{N_s}{N_p} = \frac{V_s}{V_p} \Rightarrow V_s = \frac{V_p N_s}{N_p}$$

$$= \frac{230 \times 300}{100}$$

$$= 690 \text{ V}$$

Inefficiency in a transformer

If a transformer was 100% efficient the power in would equal the power out. However, in practice there will be small losses of power from the transformer, mostly in the form of heat.

The metallic core is being cut by the continuously changing flux, which induces an e.m.f. in the core. In a continuous core this causes currents called eddy currents, which cause it to heat up and energy to be lost. To reduce this effect the core can be laminated — this involves having layers of the core separated out by thin layers of insulator, so a current can't flow.

Heat is also generated by resistance in the coils. To reduce this, wires with a low resistance can be used. Thick copper wire is used for this, as copper has a low resistivity and a larger diameter means smaller resistance.

Energy is needed to magnetise and demagnetise the core, and this energy is wasted as it heats the core. To reduce this effect, a magnetically soft material that magnetises and demagnetises easily should be used (see previous page).

Ideally, all of the magnetic flux created by the primary coil would cut through the secondary coil, but in practice this isn't the case (especially if the two coils are far apart). To reduce this magnetic loss, a core design in which the coils are as close as possible can be used — this can include winding the coils on top of each other around the same part of the core (see Figure 3), rather than around different parts of the core (see Figure 1).

Tip: Resistivity is just a measure of how strongly a material opposes the flow of electric current.

Tip: Using low-resistance wires is particularly important in the secondary coil of a step-down transformer, or the primary coil of a step-up transformer, as they carry a higher current (see next page).

Figure 3: A transformer with both coils wrapped around the same core.

Calculating the efficiency of a transformer

Remember from AS physics the power transferred in a circuit is given by:

$$P = IV$$

P = power in W, *I* = current in A, *V* = voltage in V

So for an ideal transformer, where power in = power out:

$$I_p V_p = I_s V_s \quad \text{or} \quad \frac{V_p}{V_s} = \frac{I_s}{I_p}$$

Tip: You can combine the two ideal transformer equations (this one and the one from the bottom of the last page) to give:

$$\frac{V_p}{V_s} = \frac{N_p}{N_s} = \frac{I_s}{I_p}$$

However, because not all the power is transferred, you can find the efficiency of a transformer by calculating the ratio of power out to power in:

$$\text{efficiency} = \frac{I_s V_s}{I_p V_p}$$

I_s = current in secondary coil in A
V_s = voltage in secondary coil in V
V_p = voltage in primary coil in V
I_p = current in primary coil in A

Tip: This gives the efficiency as a decimal — to make it a percentage, just multiply it by 100.

Example

120 W of power is transferred to a transformer with 80% efficiency. If the current in the secondary coil is measured as 240 mA, what will the voltage be across the secondary coil?

Just rearrange the formula for efficiency to make V_s the subject, then put the numbers in:

$$\text{efficiency} = \frac{I_s V_s}{I_p V_p} \Rightarrow V_s = \frac{\text{efficiency} \times [I_p V_p]}{I_s}$$

$$= \frac{\left(\frac{80}{100}\right) \times 120}{(240 \times 10^{-3})}$$

$$= 400\ \text{V}$$

Tip: $P_p = I_p V_p$ is used here.

If a transformer isn't 100% efficient, it will lose energy (mostly through heat — see previous page). The power that isn't transferred to the secondary coil must be transferred to something else. You can find the energy 'lost' using the equation:

$$E = Pt$$

E = energy in J
P = power in W
t = time in s

Exam Tip
$E = Pt$ is given to you on the AS formula sheet in the form $P = \frac{\Delta W}{\Delta t}$ (remember, work done, W, and energy transferred are the same thing). You'll also find $P = VI$ on the AS formula sheet.

Example

A device charger contains a transformer which is 91% efficient. The supply voltage is 100 V and the supply current is 150 mA. If the device takes 2 hours to fully charge, how much energy is lost when the device is charged?

First find the power 'lost' when the charger is in operation.
If it's 91% efficient, (100 – 91 =) 9% of the power input is wasted:

$$\text{power wasted} = \frac{9}{100} \times I_p V_p$$

$$= 0.09 \times (150 \times 10^{-3}) \times 100$$

$$= 1.35\ \text{W}$$

Then find the energy wasted over 2 hours:

$$\text{energy wasted} = Pt$$

$$= 1.35 \times (2 \times 60 \times 60)$$

$$= 9.7\ \text{kJ (to 2 s.f.)}$$

Tip: Don't forget to convert the time to seconds.

Transformers in the National Grid

Transformers are an important part of the National Grid. Electricity from power stations is sent round the country in the National Grid at the lowest possible current. This is because a high current causes greater energy losses due to heating in the cables. The energy loss is proportional to I^2R — so if you double the transmitted current, you quadruple the power lost. Using cables with the lowest possible resistance can also reduce energy loss.

Since power = current × voltage, a low current means a high voltage for the same amount of power transmitted. Transformers allow us to step up the voltage to around 400 000 V for transmission through the National Grid.

High voltage raises safety and insulation issues, and has to be stepped back down to a safer 230 V before it can be used in homes. This is done in stages, with power transferred from overhead lines to underground wires.

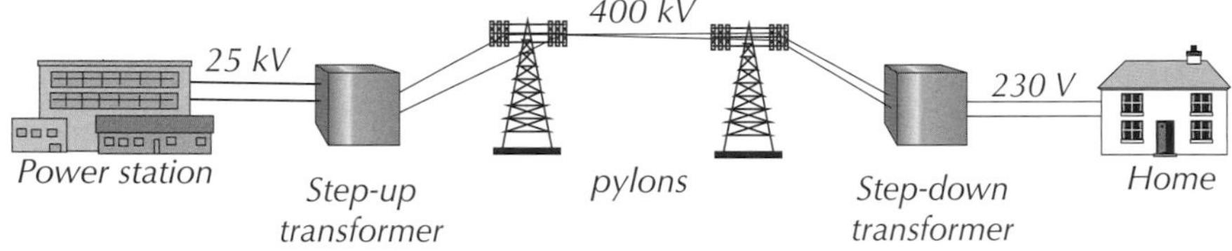

***Figure 4:** The power supply from a power station is stepped up to 400 kV before being stepped back down to 230 V for domestic use.*

Tip: Remember from AS that $P = I^2R$.

Tip: Although some energy is lost inside the transformers at each end, it's nowhere near as much as the energy that would be lost if the electricity were transmitted at 230 V.

Tip: Transformer efficiency was covered on pages 87-88.

Tip: Cables between pylons aren't insulated. This is because the air gap between the cables and the Earth or other cables is big enough to avoid sparks.

***Figure 5:** An electricity substation where the voltage is stepped down for domestic use.*

Tip: Mains electricity in the UK supplies 230 V.

Practice Questions — Application

Q1 Which of the answers a) to d) correctly completes this statement? If an ideal transformer has twice as many turns in the secondary coil as in the primary coil, the voltage across the secondary coil will be:

a) Double the voltage of the primary coil.

b) Half the voltage of the primary coil.

c) The same as the voltage of the primary coil.

d) Larger than the voltage in the primary coil, but by how much depends on the current in the primary coil.

Q2 What's the efficiency of a transformer with a power input of 65 W and a power output of 62 W?

Q3 Laptop chargers contain a transformer that reduces the voltage from the mains supply.

a) When in operation, the transformer heats up. Why does this happen? Give two reasons.

b) A laptop runs on a voltage of 19 V and consumes 120 W of power.

(i) Does the charger use a step-up or step-down transformer?

(ii) If the transformer has an efficiency of 0.85, how much current runs through the primary coil?

Practice Questions — Fact Recall

Q1 How does a transformer change the voltage of an electricity supply?

Q2 What's a transformer that reduces voltage called?

Q3 Give three ways of reducing energy loss in a transformer.

Q4 Why is a high voltage used to transmit power in the National Grid?

Section Summary

Make sure you know...

- What a magnetic field is.
- That a current-carrying wire produces a magnetic field around it.
- That a current-carrying wire in a magnetic field will experience a force.
- That the direction of the force acting on a current-carrying wire perpendicular to a magnetic field can be found using Fleming's left-hand rule.
- What magnetic flux density ($\boldsymbol{B}$) is, and that it's measured in teslas (T).
- How to calculate the force acting on a current-carrying wire perpendicular to a magnetic field.
- That a charged particle moving through a magnetic field will experience a force.
- How to calculate the force on a charged particle moving in a magnetic field when the magnetic field is perpendicular to the particle's velocity.
- That a charged particle moving perpendicular to a uniform magnetic field will follow a circular path.
- How to find the radius and frequency of rotation for a charged particle moving perpendicular to a uniform magnetic field by rearranging the equations of circular motion.
- How particle accelerators such as cyclotrons make use of the force that acts on charged particles moving perpendicular to a magnetic field.
- That an e.m.f. is induced across a conductor moving through a magnetic field, or a conductor inside a changing magnetic field.
- That if the conductor is connected to a complete circuit, a current will flow.
- What magnetic flux is, and how to calculate the value of magnetic flux when $\boldsymbol{B}$ is perpendicular to A.
- What flux linkage is, and how to calculate the flux linkage for a coil normal to $\boldsymbol{B}$ with N turns cutting the flux.
- How to calculate the magnetic flux in a rectangular coil when the coil is not normal to $\boldsymbol{B}$.
- How to calculate the flux linkage of a rectangular coil when the coil is not normal to $\boldsymbol{B}$.
- What Faraday's law is.
- That Faraday's law shows that the magnitude of the induced e.m.f. is equal to the rate of change of flux linkage in a conductor.
- What Lenz's law is.
- That the e.m.f. induced in a coil rotating uniformly in a magnetic field varies sinusoidally.
- The shape of the graphs of e.m.f. against time and flux linkage against time for a coil rotating uniformly in a magnetic field.
- How to calculate the maximum induced e.m.f. for a coil rotating uniformly in a magnetic field.
- Simple experimental applications of Faraday's law, such as generators and dynamos.
- What a transformer is and how it works.
- The different types of transformer (step-up and step-down).
- How to use the ideal transformer equation that links the number of turns and the voltage of the primary and secondary coils.
- What causes energy loss and inefficiency in a transformer, and ways to reduce this energy loss.
- How to calculate the efficiency of a transformer.
- How to calculate the power transfer and energy loss of a transformer.
- Why transformers are useful in transmitting power in the National Grid.
- How electrical power is transmitted in the National Grid.

Exam-style Questions

Questions 1 to 4 are worth 1 mark each.

1 Which of the following statements best describes Faraday's law?

A The induced e.m.f. is always in such a direction as to oppose the change that caused it.

B The induced e.m.f. is always in such a direction as to increase the change that caused it.

C The induced e.m.f. is directly proportional to the rate of change of flux linkage.

D The induced e.m.f. is inversely proportional to the rate of change of flux linkage.

2 The diagram shows a straight conductor moving perpendicular to a magnetic field. Which of the following statements is NOT true about the e.m.f. induced?

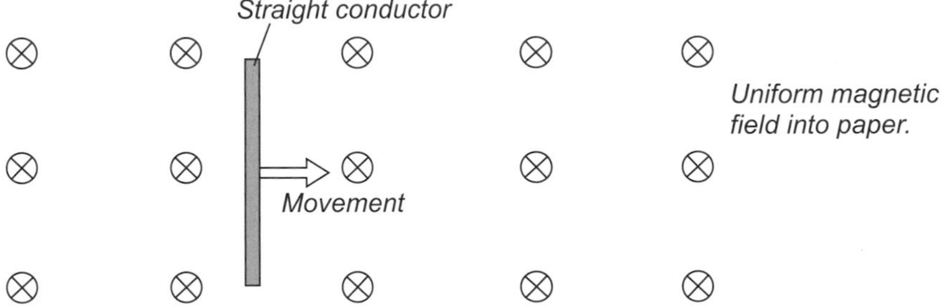

A The faster the conductor moves, the greater the induced e.m.f.

B The slower the conductor moves, the greater the induced e.m.f.

C The longer the conductor, the greater the induced e.m.f.

D The stronger the magnetic field, the greater the induced e.m.f.

3 Which of the following statements is true for a rectangular coil rotating in a uniform magnetic field?

A The magnitude of the induced e.m.f. is greatest when the coil is parallel to the magnetic field.

B Increasing the frequency of rotation increases the maximum induced e.m.f.

C The induced e.m.f. is independent of the area of the coil.

D A graph of induced e.m.f. against time would be linear.

4 Which of the following is NOT a way of improving transformer efficiency?

A Decreasing the thickness of the wires in the coils.

B Laminating the core.

C Reducing the distance between the two coils.

D Using a more magnetically soft material for the core.

5 (a) A wire carrying a current of 190 mA is fixed at points *P* and *Q*, perpendicular to a magnetic field with a flux density of 1.7 T. The wire experiences a force of 4.5×10^{-2} N. Calculate the length of the wire.

(2 marks)

5 (b) The experimental set-up is changed so that the wire is still attached to fixed points *P* and *Q*, but vibrates with a steady frequency. State two ways this could have been achieved.

(2 marks)

5 (c) The wire is wrapped into a rectangular coil with an area of 10 cm^2 and the points *P* and *Q* are free to rotate. The wire experiences a force that causes it to rotate in the clockwise direction, as shown:

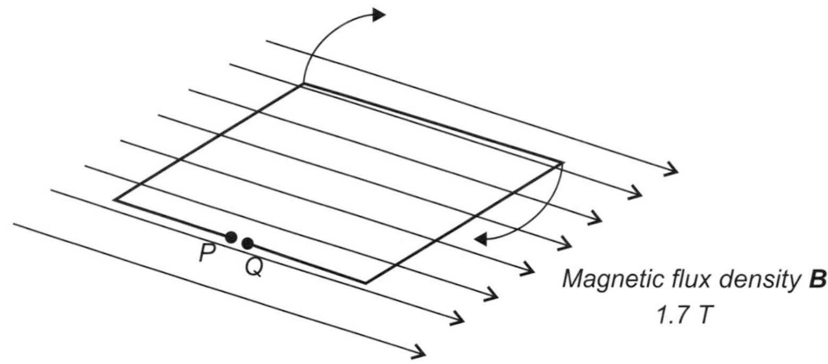

5 (c) (i) State in which direction current flows around the coil.

(1 mark)

5 (c) (ii) Calculate the flux linkage of the coil when the normal to the coil is at 41° to the magnetic field.

(2 marks)

5 (d) The current is removed and the ends of the wire at points P and Q are attached to slip rings. The coil is rotated with $\omega = 10\pi$ rad s^{-1} so that an alternating e.m.f. is induced across the coil.

5 (d) (i) Calculate the maximum e.m.f. induced across the coil.

(1 mark)

5 (d) (ii) On the axes below, show how the induced e.m.f. varies with angle θ during one complete rotation of the coil, starting at $\theta = 0$, where θ is the angle the normal to the coil makes to the field.

(2 marks)

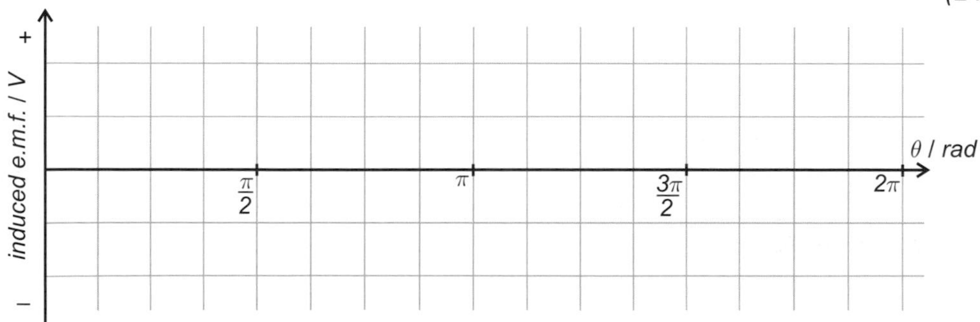

6 (a) If a moving charged particle enters a uniform magnetic field perpendicular to its velocity, what shape will the particle's path take?

(1 mark)

6 (b) An electron is fired into a uniform magnetic field with a flux density of 0.93 T at a speed of 8.1×10^7 m, as shown below.

Electron

Uniform magnetic field into paper.

6 (b) (i) Calculate the magnitude of the force the electron will experience, and state its direction.

(2 marks)

6 (b) (ii) An alpha particle of charge +2*e* is fired into the same magnetic field as the electron at the same speed. State the magnitude and direction of the force it will experience.

(2 marks)

7 (a) A wire coil is rotated at a steady rate in a uniform magnetic field, with the axis of rotation perpendicular to the field, so that an e.m.f. is induced across the coil.

7 (a) (i) State the values of θ at which the induced e.m.f. across the coil will be greatest, where θ is the angle the normal to the coil makes with the magnetic field.

(1 mark)

7 (a) (ii) The coil is rotated with a frequency of 5 Hz. Sketch a graph of the induced e.m.f. against time for $0 \leq t \leq 0.4$ s.

(3 marks)

7 (b) State which kind of current supply is required for a transformer.

(1 mark)

7 (c) Explain why it is important to use wires with as low a resistance as possible in the coils of a transformer.

(1 mark)

7 (d) (i) A transformer is 91% efficient and has a power input of 1.2 kW. Calculate the power output of the transformer.

(2 marks)

7 (d) (ii) If the transformer is in operation for 3 hours, calculate how much energy will be wasted.

(1 mark)

1. The Atomic Nucleus

Learning Objectives:
- Understand how Rutherford scattering of alpha particles demonstrates the existence of the atomic nucleus.
- Estimate the radius of a nucleus by calculating the distance of closest approach of an alpha particle.
- Be able to estimate the radius of a nucleus using electron diffraction.

Specification Reference 3.5.1

This topic is all about how you can 'look inside' an atom at the nucleus by firing particles at it. We'll begin with a sprinkle of history...

Rutherford scattering

HOW SCIENCE WORKS

At the start of the 20th century, physicists believed that the atom was a positively charged globule with negatively charged electrons sprinkled in it. This "plum pudding" model of the atom was known as the Thomson Model.

This all changed in 1909 when the **Rutherford scattering experiment** was done. In Ernest Rutherford's laboratory, Hans Geiger and Ernest Marsden studied the scattering of **alpha particles** by thin metal foils.

A stream of alpha particles from a **radioactive source** are fired at very thin gold foil. When alpha particles from a radioactive source strike a fluorescent screen a tiny visible flash of light is produced (see Figure 1).

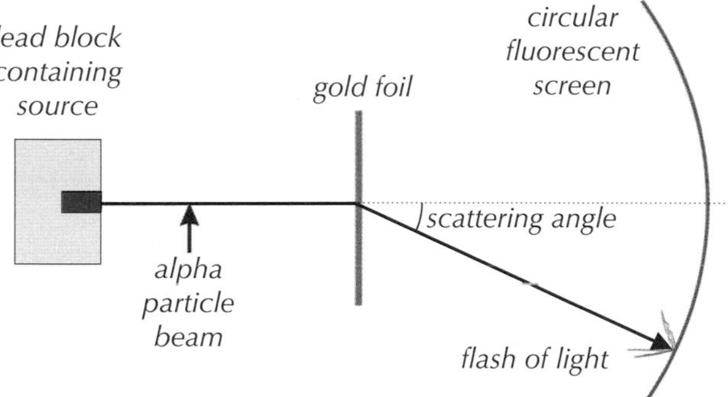

***Figure 1:** The Rutherford scattering experiment.*

Tip: Alpha particles are formed of two protons and two neutrons. They're positively charged, so they're repelled by other positive charges.

Geiger and Marsden recorded the number of alpha particles scattered at different angles. If the Thomson model was right, all the flashes should have been seen within a small angle of the beam. Most alpha particles passed straight through the gold film, but Geiger and Marsden observed that occasionally some alpha particles scattered at angles greater than 90°. This can only be possible if they're striking something more massive than themselves.

***Figure 2:** Ernest Rutherford, the New Zealand-born physicist who proposed the existence of the atomic nucleus.*

Conclusions from Rutherford scattering

Rutherford scattering shows that atoms must have a small, positively charged **nucleus** — see Figure 3.

- The nuclei must be positive to repel the positively charged alpha particles.
- The nuclei must be small since very few alpha particles are deflected by large angles — most just pass straight through the foil.
- Most of the mass and positive charge must be contained within the nucleus because most alpha particles pass straight through and only the few that pass close to the nucleus are deflected by large angles.

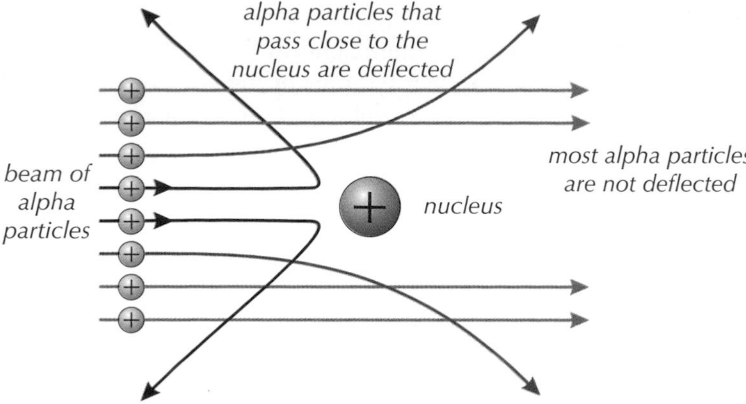

Figure 3: *Positively charged alpha particles deflected by an atomic nucleus.*

Tip: The conclusions from Rutherford scattering are really important — make sure you know them and understand how Rutherford arrived at them from the experimental evidence.

Closest approach of a scattered particle

An alpha particle that 'bounces back' and is deflected through 180° will have stopped a short distance from the nucleus (see Figure 4).

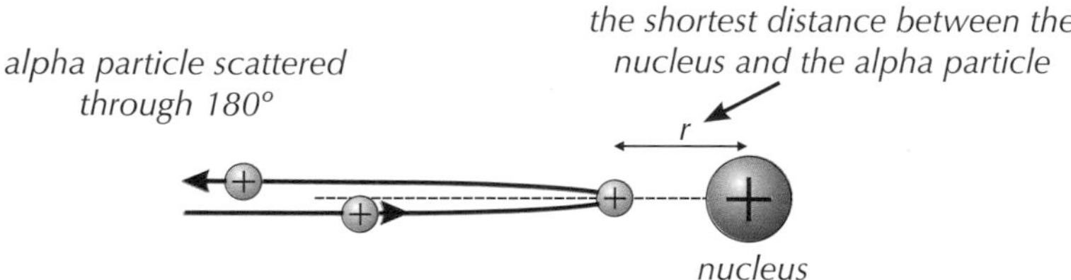

Figure 4: *The closest approach of a scattered alpha particle.*

It does this at the point where its electrical potential energy (see pages 49-50) equals its initial kinetic energy:

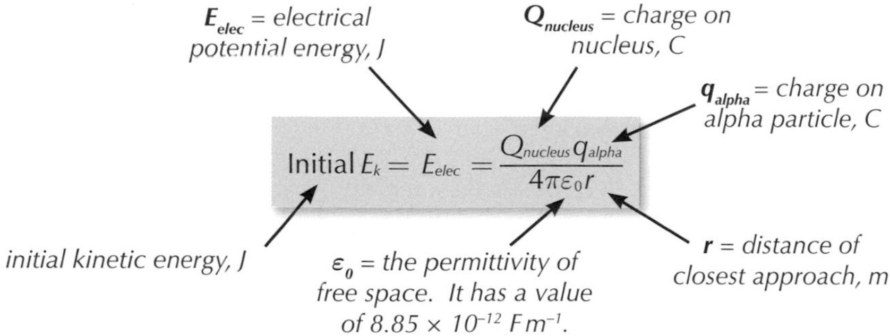

Exam Tip
The value of ε_0 will be in the data and formula book you'll be given in the exam, so don't worry about memorising it.

This is just conservation of energy — and if you know the initial kinetic energy of the alpha particle you've fired, you can use it to find how close the particle can get to the nucleus.

To find the charge of a nucleus you need to know the atom's **proton number**, Z — that tells you how many protons are in the nucleus (surprisingly). A proton has a charge of +e (where e is the magnitude of the charge on an electron), so the charge of a nucleus must be $+Ze$.

The distance of closest approach is an estimate of nuclear radius — it gives a maximum value for it. However electron diffraction (which you'll meet on the next page) gives much more accurate values for nuclear radii.

Tip: The magnitude of the charge on an electron, e, is 1.60×10^{-19} C, but an electron has a negative charge of $-e$.

Tip: Alpha particles contain 2 protons, so they have a charge of +2e.

Tip: To convert from electronvolts (eV) to joules (J), just multiply by the charge on an electron, *e*.

Exam Tip
Exam questions will normally give you particle energies in eV. Make sure you always convert from eV to joules before dropping the energy into this equation.

Example

An alpha particle with an initial kinetic energy of 6.0 MeV is fired at a gold nucleus. Estimate the radius of the nucleus by finding the closest approach of the alpha particle to the nucleus. (Z_{gold} = 79)

Initial particle energy $= 6.0\text{ MeV} = 6.0 \times 10^6\text{ eV}$

Convert energy into joules: $6.0 \times 10^6 \times 1.60 \times 10^{-19} = 9.6 \times 10^{-13}\text{ J}$

So initial $E_k = E_{elec} = \dfrac{Q_{gold}q_{alpha}}{4\pi\varepsilon_0 r}$

$= 9.6 \times 10^{-13}$ J at closest approach.

Rearrange to get $r = \dfrac{(+79e)(+2e)}{4\pi\varepsilon_0(9.6 \times 10^{-13})}$

$= \dfrac{2 \times 79 \times (1.60 \times 10^{-19})^2}{4\pi \times 8.85 \times 10^{-12} \times 9.6 \times 10^{-13}}$

$= 3.8 \times 10^{-14}$ m (to 2 s.f.)

Electron diffraction

Tip: Electrons are a type of particle called a lepton. Leptons don't interact with the strong nuclear force (whereas neutrons and alpha particles do).

As you may remember from your AS level, electrons show **wave-particle duality** — they can behave like both waves and particles. This is why electron beams can be diffracted. Electrons don't interact with the **strong nuclear force** — the interaction that binds nucleons together in nuclei. Because of this, **electron diffraction** is a very accurate method for getting a picture of a crystal's atomic structure.

A beam of moving electrons has an associated **de Broglie wavelength**, λ, which at high speeds is approximately:

Exam Tip
Don't worry about learning the value of Planck's constant — it's in the data and formulae booklet you get in the exam. The speed of light is also in there, but you should really know that by now.

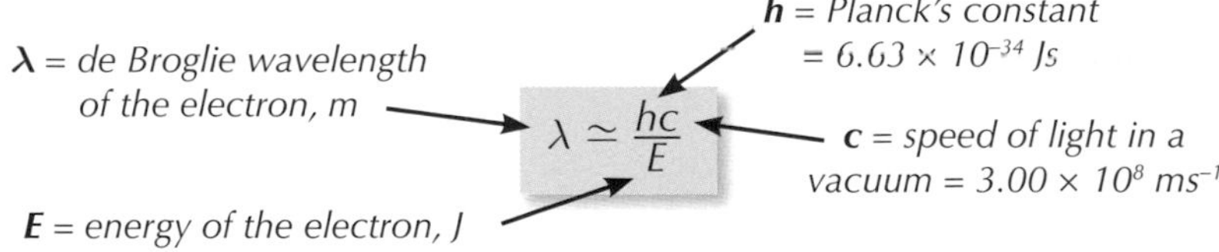

If a beam of high-energy electrons is directed onto a thin film of material in front of a screen, interference causes a diffraction pattern to be seen on the screen (see Figure 5) — similar to light diffraction patterns you saw at AS.

Tip: Each high-energy electron is diffracted by an individual nucleus. This is <u>not</u> the same as the electron diffraction covered at AS level, where the electrons diffracted through the gaps between the atoms, a bit like a diffraction grating. This is why the equation on the next page is for a minimum, not a maximum.

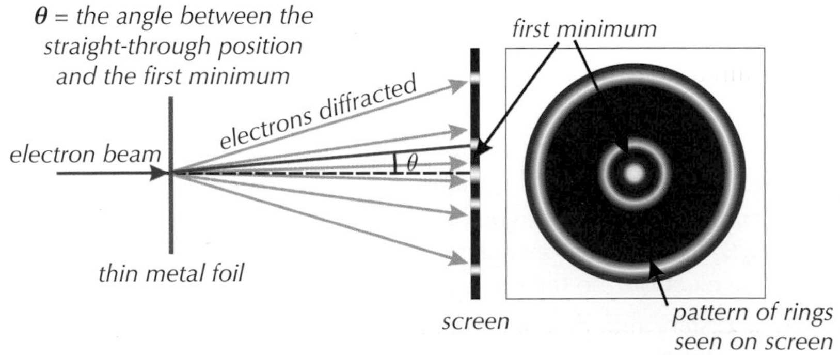

Figure 5: *Electron diffraction.*

The first minimum appears where:

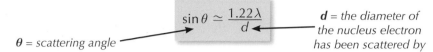

$$\sin\theta \simeq \frac{1.22\lambda}{d}$$

$\boldsymbol{\theta}$ = *scattering angle*

d = *the diameter of the nucleus electron has been scattered by*

Using measurements from this diffraction pattern, the size and spacing of the material's atomic nuclei can be worked out.

Example

A beam of 300 MeV electrons is fired at a piece of thin foil, and produces a diffraction pattern on a fluorescent screen. The first minimum of the diffraction pattern is at an angle of 30° from the straight-through position. Estimate the radius of the nuclei the electrons were diffracted by.

$E = 300 \text{ MeV} = 3.00 \times 10^{8} \times 1.60 \times 10^{-19} = 4.8 \times 10^{-11} \text{ J}$

$$\lambda \simeq \frac{hc}{E} = \frac{6.63 \times 10^{-34} \times 3.00 \times 10^{8}}{4.8 \times 10^{-11}} = 4.125 \times 10^{-15}\text{m}$$

$$\text{So } d \simeq \frac{1.22\lambda}{\sin\theta} = \frac{1.22 \times 4.125 \times 10^{-15}}{\sin 30^{\circ}} = 2 \times 1.22 \times 4.125 \times 10^{-15}$$

$$= 1.0 \times 10^{-14}\text{m}$$

So nuclear radius = $d \div 2 = 5.0 \times 10^{-15}$ m (to 2 s.f.)

Figure 6: *Louis de Broglie's wave-particle duality theory correctly predicted that electrons would form diffraction patterns.*

Practice Questions — Application

Q1 An alpha particle with an initial kinetic energy of 4.0 MeV is fired towards a lead nucleus. Calculate the distance of closest approach of the alpha particle to the nucleus.

Tip: The proton number of lead is 82.

Q2 If an alpha particle has an electrical potential energy of 1.0×10^{-13} J at its closest approach to a zinc nucleus. Use this information to estimate the size of the nuclear radius.

Tip: The proton number of zinc is 30.

Q3 What is the approximate de Broglie wavelength of an electron with an energy of 50 MeV?

Q4 A beam of 200 MeV electrons is fired towards a thin sheet of gold foil. If the first diffraction minimum is observed on a screen at an angle of 33° to the beam's original direction, calculate the radius of a gold nucleus.

Practice Questions — Fact Recall

Q1 Describe the Rutherford scattering experiment.

Q2 Explain how the Rutherford scattering experiment shows that atoms contain a small positive nucleus.

Q3 What equation would you use to calculate the distance of closest approach for an alpha particle scattered by an atomic nucleus?

Q4 Name a method that could be used for getting a very accurate picture of a crystal's atomic structure?

Q5 What is the relationship between the de Broglie wavelength of a fast-moving particle and its energy?

Q6 Give an equation for where the first minimum appears for the diffraction of an electron beam of wavelength λ around a nucleus of diameter d.

2. Nuclear Radius and Density

Learning Objectives:

- Know that the nucleus is much smaller than the whole atom.
- Know that nuclear radius increases with increasing nucleon number.
- Be able to calculate the radius of a nucleus from its nucleon number, *A*.
- Be able to calculate the density of a nucleus.
- Understand that most of an atom's mass is in the nucleus.

Specification Reference 3.5.1

Now you know how nuclear radii can be measured, it's time to see how they vary with nucleon number...

The size of the atom

By probing atoms using scattering and diffraction methods, we know that the radius of an atom is about 0.1 nm (1×10^{-10} m) and the diameter of the smallest nucleus is about 1 fm (1×10^{-15} m — pronounced "femtometres"). Basically, nuclei are really, really tiny compared with the size of the whole atom. To make this easier to visualise, try imagining a large Ferris wheel (which is pretty darn big) as the size of an atom. If you then put a grain of rice (which is rather small) in the centre, this would be the size of the atom's nucleus.

Molecules are just a number of atoms joined together. As a rough guide, the size of a molecule equals the number of atoms in it multiplied by the size of one atom.

Tip: You'll be expected to know the typical radius of a nucleus for your exam — it's around 10^{-15} m.

Nucleons

The particles that make up the nucleus (protons and neutrons) are called **nucleons**. The number of nucleons in an atom is called the **nucleon (mass) number**, *A*. As more nucleons are added to the nucleus, it gets bigger.

Tip: See page 111 for more on the nucleon (mass) number and how this is used to represent atomic structure in nuclide notation.

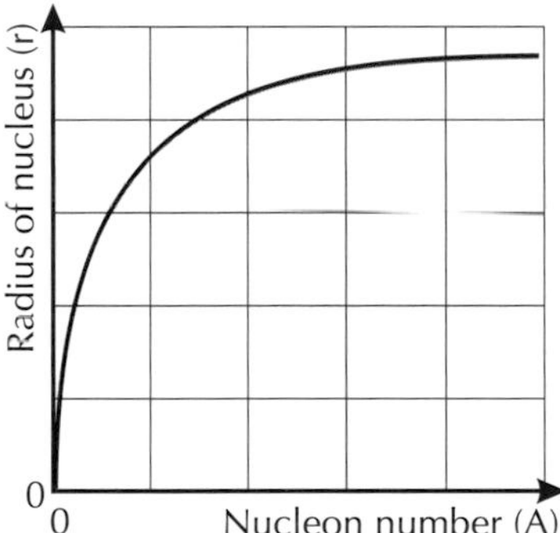

Figure 1: *A graph to show how nuclear radius increases with increasing nucleon number.*

In fact — as the straight-line graph below shows — the nuclear radius, *r*, increases roughly as the cube root of the nucleon number, *A*.

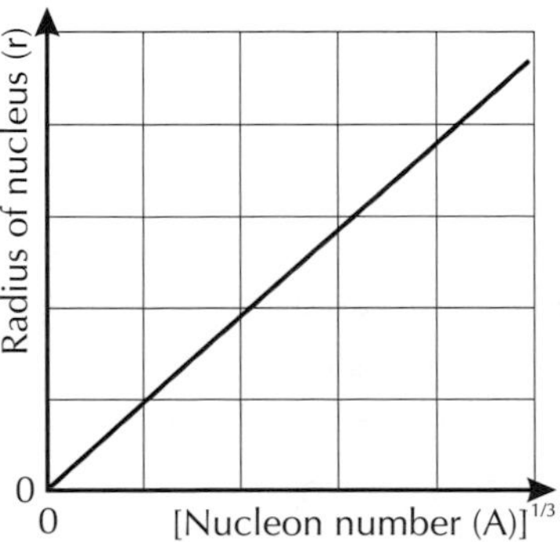

Figure 2: *A graph to show how nuclear radius is directly proportional to the cube root of the nucleon number.*

This relationship can be written as: $r \propto A^{1/3}$. You can make this into an equation by introducing a constant, r_0, giving:

$$r = r_0 A^{1/3}$$

Example

Calculate the radius of an oxygen nucleus containing 16 nucleons.

$r = r_0 A^{1/3} = (1.4 \times 10^{-15}) \times (16)^{1/3} = 3.5 \times 10^{-15}$ m = 3.5 fm (to 2 s.f.)

Nuclear density

The volume that each nucleon (a proton or a neutron) takes up in a nucleus is about the same. Because protons and neutrons have nearly the same mass, it means that all nuclei have a similar density, ρ. But nuclear matter is no ordinary stuff. Its density is enormous. A teaspoon of pure nuclear matter would have a mass of about five hundred million tonnes.

The following example shows how nuclear density is pretty much the same, regardless of the element.

Example

Show that a carbon nucleus (mass = 2.00×10^{-26} kg, A = 12) and a gold nucleus (mass = 3.27×10^{-25} kg, A = 197) have roughly the same density.

Carbon:

$$\text{Radius} = r = r_0 A^{1/3} = (1.4 \times 10^{-15}) \times (12)^{1/3} = 3.205... \times 10^{-15}\text{ m}$$

$$\text{Volume} = V = \frac{4}{3}\pi r^3 = 1.379... \times 10^{-43}\text{ m}^3$$

$$\text{Density} = \rho = \frac{m}{V} = \frac{2.00 \times 10^{-26}}{1.379... \times 10^{-43}} = 1.5 \times 10^{17}\text{ kg m}^{-3}\text{ (to 2 s.f.)}$$

Gold:

$$\text{Radius} = r = r_0 A^{1/3} = (1.4 \times 10^{-15}) \times (197)^{1/3} = 8.146... \times 10^{-15}\text{ m}$$

$$\text{Volume} = V = \frac{4}{3}\pi r^3 = 2.264... \times 10^{-42}\text{ m}^3$$

$$\text{Density} = \rho = \frac{m}{V} = \frac{3.27 \times 10^{-25}}{2.264 \times 10^{-42}} = 1.4 \times 10^{17}\text{ kg m}^{-3}\text{ (to 2 s.f.)}$$

Nuclear density is significantly larger than atomic density — this suggests three important facts about the structure of an atom:

- Most of an atom's mass is in its nucleus.
- The nucleus is small compared to the atom.
- An atom must contain a lot of empty space.

Tip: The constant r_0 is the value of r when A = 1, i.e. for a proton (hydrogen nucleus). The value of r_0 is about 1.4 fm (= 1.4×10^{-15} m).

Tip: Don't forget — something to the power of 1/3 is just the same as taking the cube root of that something.

Tip: Just to make you gasp in awe and wonder, out in space nuclear matter makes up neutron stars, which are several kilometres in diameter.

Tip: Remember that density, ρ, is just mass, m, divided by volume, V.

Tip: Here you need to assume that the nucleus is spherical. The volume of a sphere is $V = \frac{4}{3}\pi r^3$.

Tip: Sound familiar? These are some of the same conclusions made from Rutherford scattering (see page 94).

Practice Questions — Application

Q1 A nucleus is made up of 21 protons and 24 neutrons. Given that each nucleon has a mass of 1.7×10^{-27} kg, calculate the mass of the nucleus.

Q2 Phosphorus has a nucleon number of 31. Taking $r_0 = 1.4 \times 10^{-15}$ m, find its nuclear radius.

Q3 An unknown element has a nuclear radius of 4.2 fm. Estimate the element's nucleon number.

Q4 Calculate the volume of a nucleus containing 23 nucleons.

Q5 What is the density of a lead nucleus, given that it has a nucleon number of 207, and that each nucleon has a mass of 1.7×10^{-27} kg?

Tip: Remember — you can assume the nucleus is spherical.

Practice Questions — Fact Recall

Q1 What is the typical radius of:

a) The smallest atomic nucleus?

b) An atom?

Q2 What are nucleons?

Q3 Describe the relationship between nuclear radius and nucleon number.

Q4 Explain why nuclear density is approximately the same from element to element.

Q5 How would you calculate the density of a nucleus from its nucleon number?

3. Properties of Nuclear Radiation

There are four different types of nuclear radiation — each has different properties, and you can use these to identify what type a source is emitting.

Learning Objectives:

- Know the constituents and properties of each type of nuclear radiation.
- Know how to identify alpha, beta and gamma radiation.
- Know some applications of each type of radiation.

Specification Reference 3.5.1

Radiactive decay

If an atom is unstable, it will break down to become more stable. The atom decays by releasing energy and/or particles, until it reaches a stable form — this is called **radioactive decay**. An individual radioactive decay is random and can't be predicted.

Types of nuclear radiation

There are four types of **nuclear radiation** — **alpha**, **beta-minus**, **beta-plus** and **gamma** — and each is made up of different constituents. They are listed in Figure 1. The masses here have been given in atomic mass units (u) — one atomic mass unit = 1.661×10^{-27} kg, and is about the same as the mass of a proton or neutron (see page 344).

Radiation	Symbol	Constituent	Relative Charge	Mass (u)
Alpha	α	A helium nucleus — 2 protons & 2 neutrons	+2	4
Beta-minus (Beta)	β^- or β	Electron	–1	(negligible)
Beta-plus	β^+	Positron	+1	(negligible)
Gamma	γ	Short-wavelength, high-frequency electromagnetic wave.	0	0

Figure 1: *Types of nuclear radiation.*

Tip: You met positrons at AS level — they're the antiparticles of electrons.

Identifying nuclear radiation

Penetration of nuclear radiation

Different types of radiation have different penetrating powers. The more penetrating the type of radiation, the thicker or denser a material needs to be to absorb it.

- Alpha — absorbed by paper or a few centimetres of air.
- Beta-minus — absorbed by about 3 millimetres of aluminium.
- Gamma — absorbed by many centimetres of lead, or several metres of concrete.

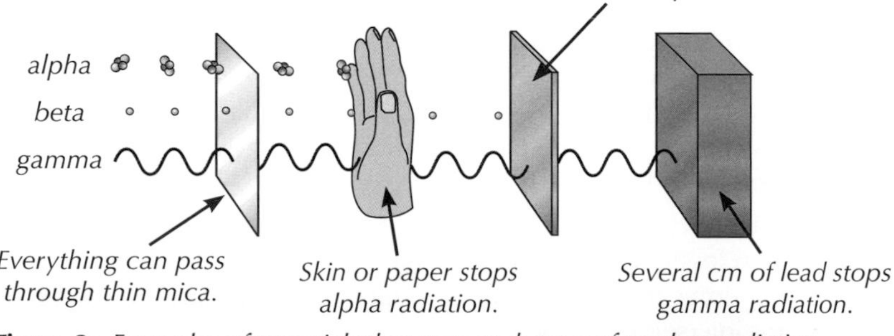
A few mm of aluminium stops beta radiation.
alpha
beta
gamma
Everything can pass through thin mica.
Skin or paper stops alpha radiation.
Several cm of lead stops gamma radiation.

Figure 2: *Examples of materials that stop each type of nuclear radiation.*

Tip: Both the thickness and the density of a material affect whether radiation will penetrate it — a very thick piece of aluminium could stop gamma radiation.

Beta-plus particles almost immediately annihilate with electrons, so they effectively have zero range.

You can identify the types of radiation emitted by a source by testing to see if they pass through various materials using the apparatus below.

Tip: A Geiger-Müller tube produces a 'count' in the form of an electrical pulse each time radiation enters it. The counter shows how many counts there are each second.

Figure 3: *Using different absorbers to experimentally identify radiation.*

Place a radioactive source in front of a **Geiger-Müller tube** connected to a counter (see Figure 3). When nothing is placed between the source and tube, the counter will record a high count. Insert different materials and different thicknesses of material between the source and tube, and record the count each time. If the count remains about the same, then the radiation can penetrate the material. If the count drops by a large amount, then the radiation is being absorbed and blocked by the material.

Magnetic fields

You can also identify types of radiation by looking at how they travel through magnetic fields. Charged particles moving perpendicular to a uniform magnetic field are deflected in a circular path. The direction in which a particle curves depends on the charge — if it's positive the particle will curve one way, if it's negative it'll curve the other way. The radius of curvature of its path can also tell you about its charge and mass — see pages 75-76 for more.

Tip: Gamma radiation isn't made up of charged particles, so it won't be deflected by a magnetic field.

Ionising radiation

When a radioactive particle hits an atom it can remove electrons, creating an ion — so radioactive emissions are also known as ionising radiation. Alpha, beta and gamma radiation have different ionising properties. What a radioactive source can be used for often depends on its ionising properties.

Alpha particles are strongly positive — so they can easily pull electrons off atoms. Ionising an atom transfers some of the energy from the alpha particle to the atom. The alpha particle quickly ionises many atoms (about 10,000 ionisations per alpha particle) and loses all its energy. This makes alpha sources suitable for use in smoke alarms because they allow current to flow, but won't travel very far.

The beta-minus particle has lower mass and charge than the alpha particle, but travels at a higher speed. This means it can still knock electrons off atoms. Each beta particle will ionise about 100 atoms, losing energy at each interaction. This lower number of interactions means that beta radiation causes much less damage to body tissue. It is used to treat some types of cancer by destroying the cancerous cells and is preferable to alpha radiation, as it can penetrate further into the cancerous tissue.

Gamma radiation is even more weakly ionising than beta radiation, so will do even less damage to body tissue. It is also more penetrating — these two properties make it useful for diagnostic techniques in medicine, e.g. PET scanning (see Figure 4).

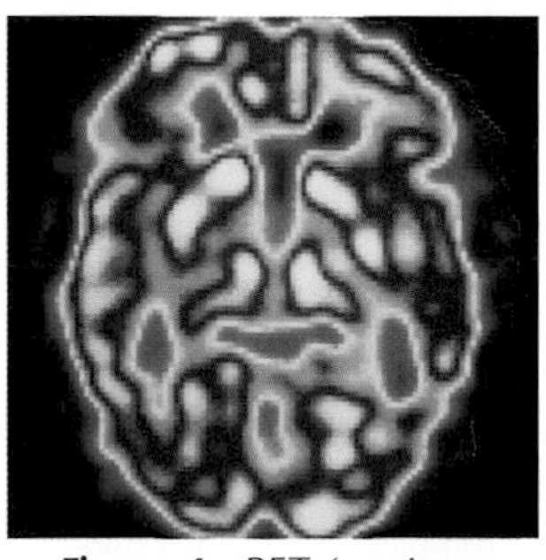

Figure 4: *PET (positron emission tomography) scanning uses a radioactive tracer injected into the bloodstream. Positrons emitted by the tracer annihilate with electrons in the body, producing gamma rays that are then detected by the scanner.*

Summary of properties

Here's a handy table of some of the properties of nuclear radiation:

Radiation	Symbol	Ionising power	Speed	Penetrating power	Affected by magnetic field
Alpha	α	Strong	Slow	Absorbed by paper or a few cm of air	Yes
Beta-minus (Beta)	β^- or β	Weak	Fast	Absorbed by ~3 mm of aluminium	Yes
Beta-plus	β^+	Annihilated by electron, so virtually zero range			
Gamma	γ	Very weak	Speed of light	Absorbed by many cm of lead, or several m of concrete	No

Figure 5: *Properties of nuclear radiation.*

Tip: Learn this table and the one at the start of the topic — they're packed full of useful information you need to know.

Practice Question — Application

Q1 A radioactive source emits an unknown type of radiation. Using a Geiger-Müller tube placed in front of the source, the count from the source was measured. There was no decrease in the count recorded when a few sheets of paper were placed between the source and Geiger-Müller tube. The count dropped to almost zero when the sheets of paper were replaced with a thin sheet of aluminium. Identify the type of radiation being emitted by the source.

Practice Questions — Fact Recall

Q1 What is radioactive decay?

Q2 List the four types of nuclear radiation and their constituents.

Q3 Give the relative ionising powers of alpha, beta and gamma radiation.

Q4 Give two methods of identifying types of nuclear radiation.

Q5 Describe a practical application for each of alpha, beta and gamma radiation, and explain why that form of radiation is used.

Learning Objectives:

- Know that the intensity of gamma radiation decreases with distance from a source according to the inverse square law.
- Know how the inverse square law can be experimentally verified.
- Be able to accurately eliminate background radiation.
- Know the sources of background radiation.

Specification Reference 3.5.1

4. Intensity and Background Radiation

The inverse square law describes how the intensity of gamma radiation falls off the further away you get from a source. Background radiation is nuclear radiation found everywhere and that comes from lots of different sources.

The inverse square law

A gamma source will emit gamma radiation in all directions. This radiation spreads out as you get further away from the source. The **intensity** of radiation is the amount of radiation per unit area — it will decrease the further you get from the source. If you took readings of intensity, I, at a distance, x, from the source you would find that it decreases by the square of the distance from the source (see Figure 1).

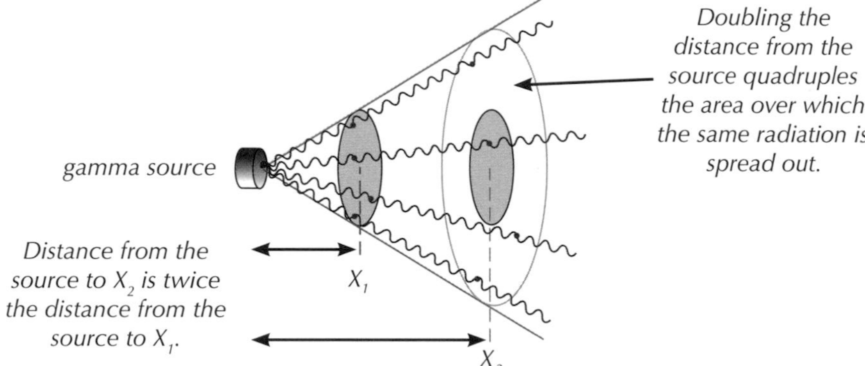

Doubling the distance from the source quadruples the area over which the same radiation is spread out.
gamma source
Distance from the source to X_2 is twice the distance from the source to X_1.
X_1
X_2

Figure 1: *How the intensity of radiation varies with distance from a source.*

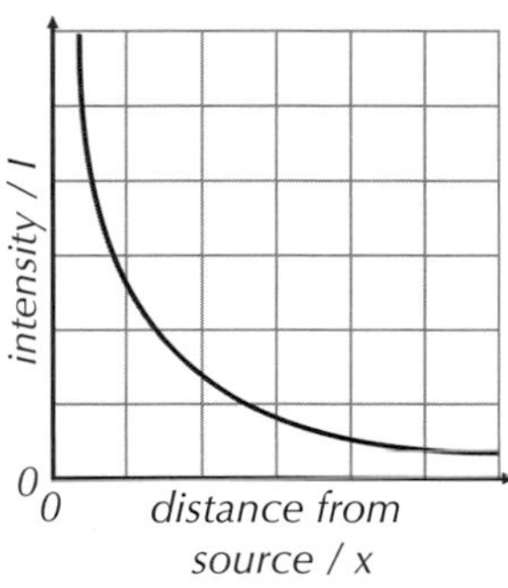

intensity / I
0
0
distance from source / x

Figure 2: *A graph of how the intensity varies with distance from a source.*

This can be written as the equation:

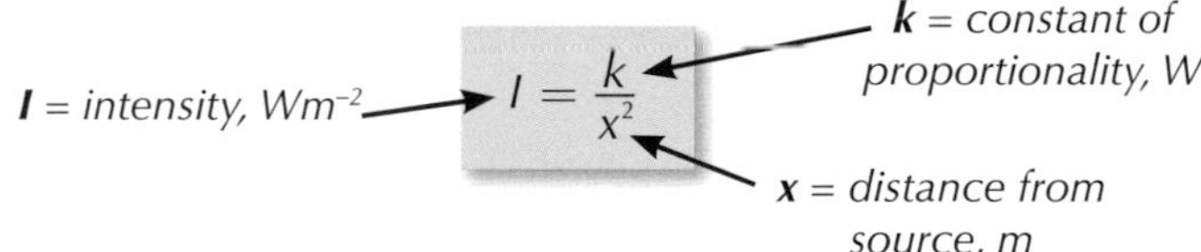

$I = \frac{k}{x^2}$
I = intensity, Wm^{-2}
k = constant of proportionality, W
x = distance from source, m

Tip: The $\frac{1}{x^2}$ term comes about because the gamma radiation spreads out over the surface of an imaginary sphere of area $A = 4\pi x^2$ (see pages 35-36).

Example

The intensity of radiation 0.5 m from a gamma source was measured as 2.5×10^{-10} Wm^{-2}. What intensity would be measured 1.5 m from the source?

Intensity at 0.5 m = $\frac{k}{0.5^2} = 2.5 \times 10^{-10}$

Therefore $k = 2.5 \times 10^{-10} \times 0.5^2 = 6.25 \times 10^{-11}$

So intensity at 1.5 m = $\frac{6.25 \times 10^{-11}}{1.5^2} = 2.8 \times 10^{-11}$ Wm^{-2} (to 2 s.f.)

This relationship can be proved by taking measurements of intensity at different distances from a gamma source, using a Geiger-Müller tube and counter (similar to the set-up used to identify types of radiation — see page 102). The 'counts' of radiation entering the Geiger-Müller tube will decrease according to the inverse square law (assuming no radiation has been absorbed along the way) — which shows that the radiation emitted must be decreasing in the same way.

That's why one of the safety precautions when handling a source is to hold it at arm's length, so you lessen the amount of radiation reaching you.

Tip: You can plot a graph of the different intensity readings against the inverse of the distance squared. If the data fits a straight line through the origin, then the inverse square law is verified.

Background radiation

Wherever you are, there's always a low level of radiation — this is called **background radiation**. When you take a reading from a radioactive source, you need to measure the background radiation separately and subtract it from your measurement. To do this accurately you should:

- Take three readings using a Geiger-Müller tube without a radioactive source present.
- Average these three readings.
- Subtract this average from each measurement you take of a radioactive source's count.

Sources of background radiation

There are many sources of background radiation, including:

- The air — radioactive radon gas is released from rocks. It emits alpha radiation. The concentration of this gas in the atmosphere varies a lot from place to place, but it's usually the largest contributor to the background radiation.
- The ground and buildings — nearly all rock contains radioactive materials.
- Cosmic radiation — cosmic rays are particles (mostly high-energy protons) from space. When they collide with particles in the upper atmosphere, they produce nuclear radiation.
- Living things — all plants and animals contain carbon, and some of this will be radioactive carbon-14.
- Man-made radiation — in most areas, radiation from medical or industrial sources makes up a tiny, tiny fraction of the background radiation.

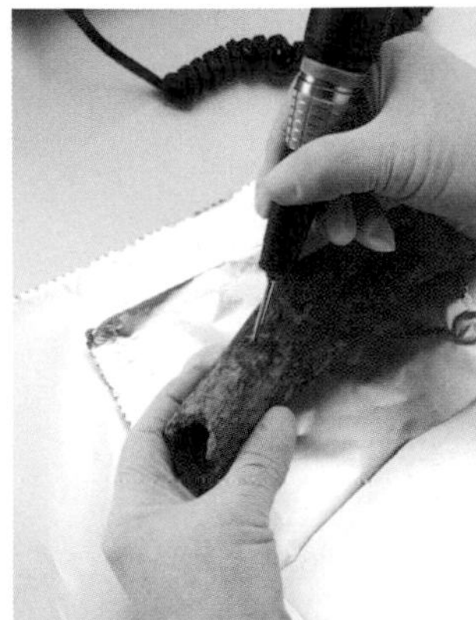

Figure 3: *Radiocarbon dating a human femur. The carbon-14 in living tissue decays after an organism dies. By measuring how much carbon-14 remains in dead tissue, the age of a sample can be estimated* *(see pages 108-109 for more).*

Practice Questions — Application

Q1 A Geiger-Müller tube placed 20 cm from a gamma source measures a count rate of 54 counts per second. Ignoring background radiation, calculate the expected count rate if the tube was placed 45 cm from the source.

Q2 The intensity of radiation from a gamma source is found to be 4.0×10^{-10} Wm^{-2} at a distance of 0.50 m from the source, and 1.8×10^{-10} Wm^{-2} at a distance of 0.75 m from the source. Use these measurements to show that the intensity of gamma radiation obeys the inverse square law.

Practice Questions — Fact Recall

Q1 What is the relationship between the intensity of gamma radiation and the distance from the source?

Q2 What experiment could you use to demonstrate this relationship?

Q3 Why should you hold radioactive sources at arm's length when you are handling them?

Q4 Describe how you would eliminate background radiation from counts of a radioactive source.

Q5 Give three sources of background radiation.

Learning Objectives:

- Know that radioactive decay is random.
- Know that a given nucleus has a constant probability of decay.
- Understand the meanings of activity, decay constant and half-life of an isotope.
- Be able to use the equations for activity, half-life and rate of change of N.
- Understand that the number of unstable nuclei, N, decreases exponentially with time: $N = N_0 e^{-\lambda t}$
- Be able to find the half-life from a decay curve.
- Understand how radioactive decay can have useful applications.

Specification Reference 3.5.1

Tip: You might see exam questions talking about N as the number of undecayed atoms — don't worry, it's just the same as the number of unstable nuclei.

Tip: This is how you'll get this equation in the exam — the minus sign has just been taken over to the other side by multiplying both sides by –1.

Tip: Don't get the decay constant confused with wavelength — they both use the symbol λ.

5. Exponential Law of Decay

The number of unstable nuclei that decay each second in a radioactive sample depends on how many unstable nuclei are left in the sample.

The rate of radioactive decay

Radioactive decay is completely random — you can't predict which atom will decay when. But although you can't predict the decay of an individual atom, if you take a very large number of atoms, their overall behaviour shows a pattern. **Isotopes** of an element have the same number of protons, but different numbers of neutrons in their nuclei. Any sample of a particular isotope has the same rate of decay — i.e. the same proportion of atoms will decay in a given time. Each unstable atom within the isotope will also have a constant decay probability.

The decay constant and activity

The **activity**, A, of a sample is the number of atoms that decay each second. It is proportional to the number of unstable nuclei in the sample, N. For a given isotope, a sample twice as big would give twice the number of decays per second. The **decay constant**, λ, is the constant of proportionality. It is the probability of a specific atom decaying per unit time, and is a measure of how quickly an isotope will decay — the bigger the value of λ, the faster the rate of decay. The decay constant has units s^{-1} and the activity is measured in becquerels (1 Bq = 1 decay per second).

$$A = \lambda N$$

A = activity, Bq; *N = number of unstable nuclei in sample*; *λ = decay constant, s^{-1}*

Because the activity, A, is the number of atoms that decay each second, you can write it as the change in the number of unstable nuclei, ΔN, during a given time (in seconds) Δt:

$$A = -\frac{\Delta N}{\Delta t}$$

There's a minus sign in this equation because ΔN is always a decrease. Combining these two equations for the activity then gives the rate of change of the number of unstable nuclei:

$$\frac{\Delta N}{\Delta t} = -\lambda N$$

$\frac{\Delta N}{\Delta t}$ = rate of change of number of unstable nuclei, s^{-1}; *N = number of unstable nuclei in sample*; *λ = decay constant, s^{-1}*

Example

A sample of a radioactive isotope contains 3.0 × 10¹⁹ nuclei. Its activity is measured to be 2.4 × 10¹² Bq. Calculate the isotope's decay constant.

Rearrange $A = \lambda N$ to give $\lambda = \frac{A}{N} = \frac{2.4 \times 10^{12}}{3.0 \times 10^{19}} = 8.0 \times 10^{-8}\ s^{-1}$

Example

A radioactive isotope has a decay constant of 1.2×10^{-4} s^{-1}. What is the rate of change of N for a sample containing 7.5×10^{20} nuclei?

$$\frac{\Delta N}{\Delta t} = -\lambda N = -(1.2 \times 10^{-4}) \times (7.5 \times 10^{20}) = -9.0 \times 10^{16}\ \text{s}^{-1}$$

Tip: So N decreases by 9.0×10^{16} nuclei every second.

Half-life

The **half-life** ($T_{½}$) of an isotope is the average time it takes for the number of unstable nuclei to halve. Of course, measuring the number of unstable nuclei isn't the easiest job in the world. In practice, half-life isn't measured by counting nuclei, but by measuring the time it takes the activity to halve. The longer the half-life of an isotope, the longer it takes for the radioactivity level to fall.

The number of unstable nuclei remaining, N, depends on the number originally present, N_0. The number remaining can be calculated using the equation:

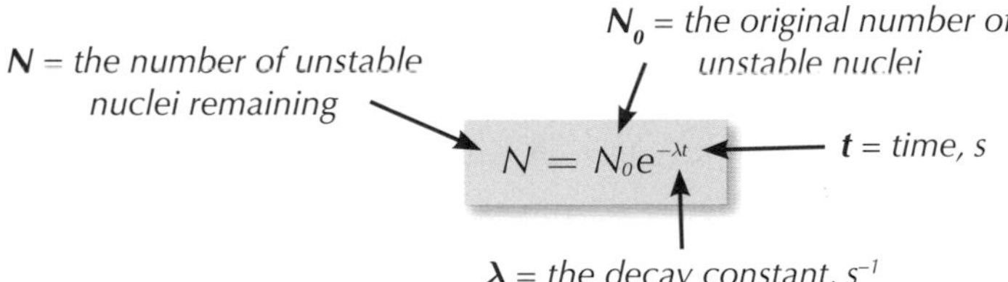
N = the number of unstable nuclei remaining
N₀ = the original number of unstable nuclei
N = N₀e^{-λt}
t = time, s
λ = the decay constant, s⁻¹

The number of unstable nuclei decreases **exponentially** with time (see Figure 1).

Tip: Exponential change is where the change in the amount of something is proportional to the amount of that something left.

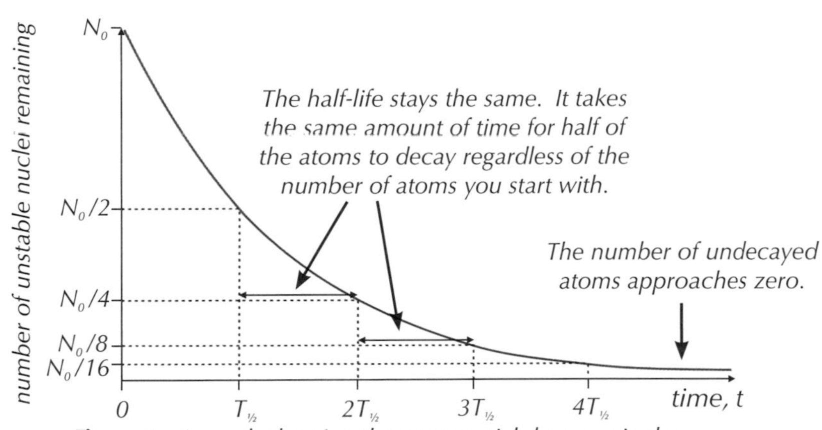
number of unstable nuclei remaining
N₀
N₀/2
N₀/4
N₀/8
N₀/16
0
T½
2T½
3T½
4T½
time, t
The half-life stays the same. It takes the same amount of time for half of the atoms to decay regardless of the number of atoms you start with.
The number of undecayed atoms approaches zero.

Figure 1: *A graph showing the exponential decrease in the number of unstable nuclei of a radioactive isotope.*

Tip: Make sure you check your units carefully when you're calculating half-life.

Here's how you'd calculate the half-life of an isotope from a graph:

- Read off the value of count rate, particles or activity when $t = 0$.
- Go to half the original number of unstable nuclei on the y-axis.
- Draw a horizontal line to the curve, then a vertical line down to the x-axis. Read off the half-life where the line crosses the x-axis.
- It's always a good idea to check your answer — repeat these steps for a quarter of the original value and divide your answer by two. That will also give you the half-life. Check that you get the same answer both ways.

Tip: When measuring the activity and half-life of a source, you've got to remember background radiation — it needs to be subtracted from the activity readings to give the source activity (see page 105).

Plotting the natural log (ln) of the number of undecayed atoms (or the activity) against time gives a straight-line graph.

> **Tip:** There's more on logs and log graphs on pages 283-284.

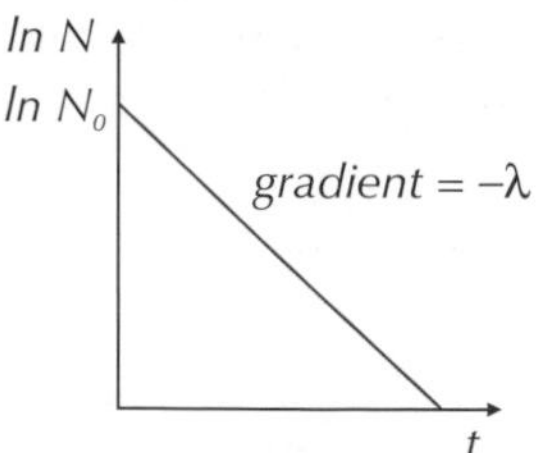

***Figure 2:** A graph showing the natural log of the number of unstable nuclei against time.*

The half-life can be calculated from the decay constant using the equation:

> **Tip:** This formula for the half-life comes from setting $N = \frac{1}{2}N_0$ in the previous formula for N — but don't worry, you don't need to know the derivation. Just make sure you know how to use the formula for $T_{1/2}$.

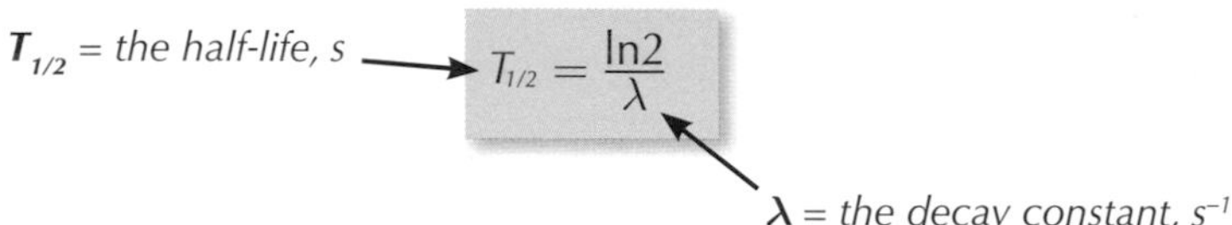

$$T_{1/2} = \frac{\ln 2}{\lambda}$$

The number of unstable nuclei decaying per second (the activity) is proportional to the number of nuclei remaining. As a sample decays, its activity goes down — there's an equation for that too:

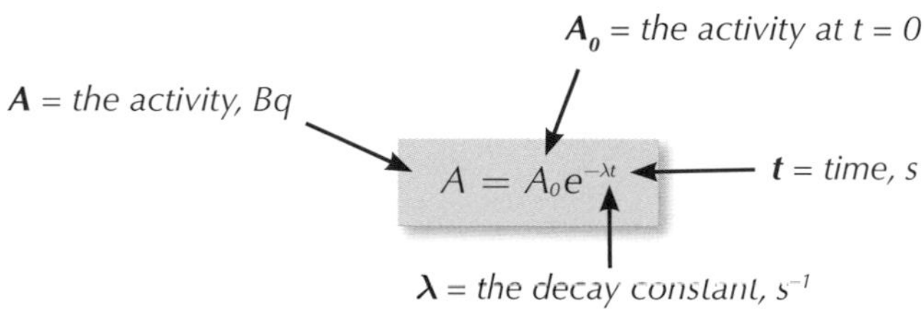

$$A = A_0 e^{-\lambda t}$$

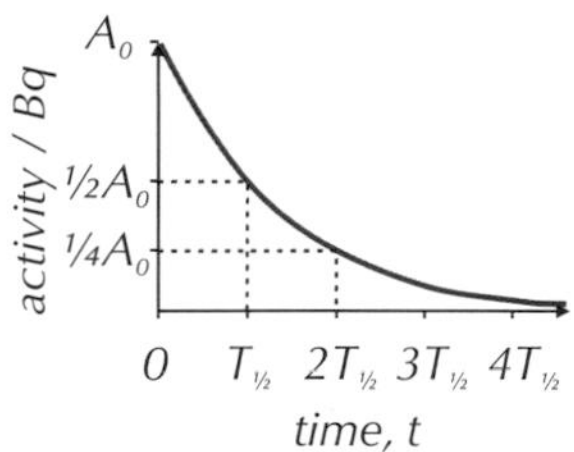

***Figure 3:** Graph showing the exponential decay of the activity against time.*

> **Tip:** Here it's fine to give the half-life in seconds. Some isotopes have much longer half-lives though, which are more sensible to give in years.

Example

A sample of the radioactive isotope ^{13}N contains 5.00×10^6 atoms. The decay constant for this isotope is 1.16×10^{-3} s^{-1}.

a) What is the half-life for this isotope?

b) How many atoms of ^{13}N will remain after 800 seconds?

a) $T_{1/2} = \frac{\ln 2}{\lambda} = \frac{\ln 2}{1.16 \times 10^{-3}} = 598$ s (to 3 s.f.)

b) $N = N_0 e^{-\lambda t} = (5.00 \times 10^6) \times e^{-(1.16 \times 10^{-3}) \times 800}$

$= 1.98 \times 10^6$ atoms (to 3 s.f.)

Applications of radioactive isotopes

Radioactive substances are extremely useful. You can use them for all sorts — to date organic material, diagnose medical problems, sterilise food, and in smoke alarms.

Radiocarbon dating

The radioactive isotope carbon-14 is used in **radiocarbon dating**. Living plants take in carbon dioxide from the atmosphere as part of photosynthesis, including the radioactive isotope carbon-14. When they die, the activity of carbon-14 in the plant starts to fall, with a half-life of around 5730 years. Archaeological finds made from once-living material (like wood) can be tested to find the current amount of carbon-14 in them, and date them.

Example

A sample of 6.5 × 10²³ carbon atoms is taken from a spear, and found to have an activity of 0.052 Bq. The ratio of radioactive carbon-14 to stable carbon-12 in living wood is 1 : 1.4 × 10¹², and the half-life of carbon-14 is 5730 years. How old is the wood the spear is made from?

The half-life of carbon-14 in seconds is

$T_{1/2} = 5730 \times (365 \times 24 \times 3600) = 1.8070... \times 10^{11}$ s

So the decay constant, $\lambda = \frac{\ln 2}{T_{1/2}} = \frac{\ln 2}{1.8070... \times 10^{11}} = 3.8358... \times 10^{-12}\ s^{-1}$

Rearrange and use the equation for activity to find the number of carbon-14 nuclei in the wood:

$N = \frac{A}{\lambda} = 0.052 \div (3.8358... \times 10^{-12}) = 1.3556... \times 10^{10}$

Use the ratio given in the question to calculate the expected number of carbon-14 nuclei in a sample of 6.5×10^{23} carbon atoms from living wood:

$N_0 = (1 \div 1.4 \times 10^{12}) \times 6.5 \times 10^{23} = 4.6428... \times 10^{11}$

N and N_0 are related by $N = N_0 e^{-\lambda t}$. You can rearrange this by dividing by N_0 and taking the natural log (ln) of both sides to make t the subject and find the age of the wood:

$$N = N_0 e^{-\lambda t} \rightarrow \frac{N}{N_0} = e^{-\lambda t} \rightarrow \ln\left(\frac{N}{N_0}\right) = \ln(e^{-\lambda t}) \rightarrow \ln\left(\frac{N}{N_0}\right) = -\lambda t$$

So $t = -\frac{1}{\lambda} \times \ln\left(\frac{N}{N_0}\right) = 9.2121... \times 10^{11}$ s = 29 000 years (to 2 s.f.)

Tip: $\ln(e^a) = a$, which is why $\ln(e^{-\lambda t})$ becomes $-\lambda t$ when you're rearranging to find t. For more help on logs, skip on over to pages 283-284.

However, it can be difficult to get a reliable age from radiocarbon dating as:

- For man-made objects crafted from natural materials like wood, you can only find the age of the material used — not the object itself.
- The object may have been contaminated by other radioactive sources.
- There may be a high background count that obscures the object's count.
- There may be uncertainty in the amount of carbon-14 that existed thousands of years ago.
- The sample size or count rate may be small, and so might be statistically unreliable.

Tip: If a house was built from wood from a tree cut down years ago, carbon dating would only give the length of time since the tree was cut down, not since the house was built.

Medical diagnosis

Technetium-99m is widely used in medical tracers — radioactive substances that are used to show tissue or organ function. The tracer is injected into or swallowed by the patient and then moves through the body to the region of interest. The radiation emitted is recorded and an image of inside the patient produced. Technetium-99m is suitable for this use because it emits γ-radiation, has a half-life of 6 hours (long enough for data to be recorded, but short enough to limit the radiation to an acceptable level) and decays to a much more stable isotope.

Storage of radioactive waste

Nuclear fission reactors use uranium-235 to generate electricity. The uranium decays into several different radioactive isotopes with different half-lives. These isotopes emit alpha, beta and gamma radiation, and must be stored carefully for hundreds of years until their activity has fallen to safe levels. This radioactive waste is a serious problem as it stays highly radioactive for a really long time. See pages 119-120 for more about nuclear fission reactors and their waste products.

Figure 4: *Spent nuclear fuel rods are stored in water for several years while the activity decreases. They are then stored underground for hundreds of years more.*

Tip: 1 kBq (kilobecquerel) is equal to 1000 Bq.

Practice Questions — Application

Q1 A sample contains 4.5×10^{18} atoms of a radioactive isotope. If it has a decay constant of 1.1×10^{-13} s^{-1}, what is the activity of the sample?

Q2 The activity of a radioactive sample fell from 2400 Bq to 75 Bq over a period of 24 hours. How long is the isotope's half-life?

Q3 An isotope has a half-life of 483 seconds. What is its decay constant?

Q4 A sample of a radioactive isotope has an activity of 3.2 kBq. If the isotope has a decay constant of 1.3×10^{-4} s^{-1}, what will the sample's activity be 6.5 hours later?

Q5 Protactinium-234m has a half-life of 1.17 minutes. If a sample initially contains 2.5×10^{15} unstable nuclei, how many will there be after 35 minutes?

Q6 A sample of carbon atoms from an ancient bone has an activity of 0.45 Bq. The same number of carbon atoms from a piece of living tissue has an activity of 1.2 Bq. Given that the half-life of carbon-14 is 5730 years, how old is the bone?

Practice Questions — Fact Recall

Q1 a) What is the decay constant of a radioactive isotope?

b) What is meant by the activity of a radioactive sample?

c) What is the half-life of an isotope?

Q2 Give the equation for the number of undecayed radioactive atoms as a function of time.

Q3 Describe how you would find an isotope's half-life from a graph showing its activity against time.

Q4 Give two applications of radioactive isotopes where the half-life is important.

6. Nuclear Decay

Nuclei are radioactive either because they have too few or too many neutrons, or too many nucleons altogether, making them unstable, or because they have too much energy.

Nuclide notation

The nuclide notation of an element summarises all the information about its atomic structure. Figure 1 shows the nuclide notation for carbon-12, with nucleon number A = 12 and proton number Z = 6:

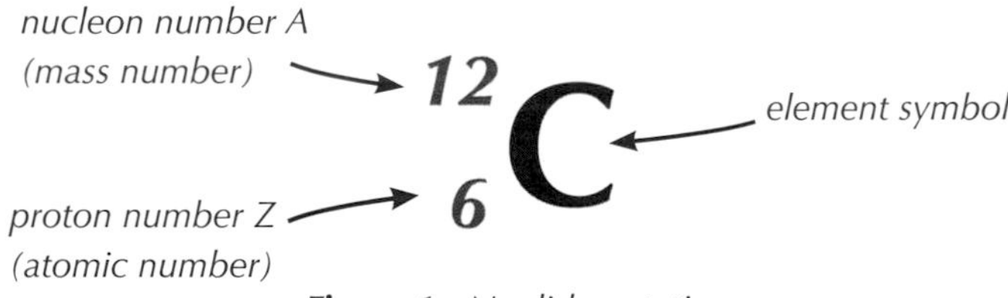

nucleon number A
(mass number)
12
C
element symbol
6
proton number Z
(atomic number)

Figure 1: *Nuclide notation.*

Learning Objectives:

- Be able to sketch the graph of N against Z for stable nuclei, and identify regions of particles that will undergo α and β decay.
- Know the four possible decay modes: α, β^-, β^+ and electron capture.
- Understand how proton and nucleon number change for each decay mode.
- Be able to write nuclear equations for each type of decay.
- Know that γ-rays can be emitted by nuclei in excited states.

Specification Reference 3.5.1

Nuclear stability

The nucleus is under the influence of the strong nuclear force holding it together and the electromagnetic force pushing the protons apart. It's a very delicate balance, and it's easy for a nucleus to become unstable.

A nucleus will be unstable if it has:

- too many neutrons
- too few neutrons
- too many nucleons altogether — i.e. it's too heavy
- too much energy

There are several types of decay or 'decay modes' that an unstable nucleus can undergo to make itself more stable. You can get a stability graph by plotting N (number of neutrons) against Z (proton number) — see Figure 2.

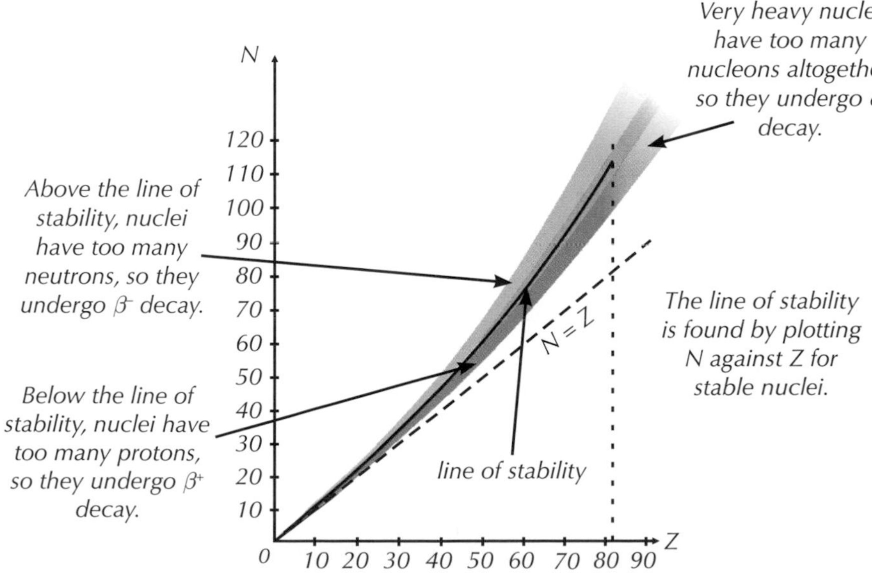

N
120
110
100
90
80
70
60
50
40
30
20
10
0
10 20 30 40 50 60 70 80 90
Z
Very heavy nuclei have too many nucleons altogether, so they undergo α decay.
Above the line of stability, nuclei have too many neutrons, so they undergo β⁻ decay.
Below the line of stability, nuclei have too many protons, so they undergo β⁺ decay.
N = Z
The line of stability is found by plotting N against Z for stable nuclei.
line of stability

Figure 2: *A graph showing stable and unstable nuclei.*

Tip: The sum of the proton number, Z, and neutron number, N, is the nucleon number, A.

Alpha emission

Alpha emission only happens in very heavy atoms (with more than 82 protons), like uranium and radium. The nuclei of these atoms are too massive to be stable. When an alpha particle is emitted, the proton number decreases by two, and the nucleon number decreases by four.

Example

Uranium-238 decays to thorium-234 by emitting an alpha particle:

nucleon number decreases by 4

$${}^{238}_{92}\text{U} \longrightarrow {}^{234}_{90}\text{Th} + {}^{4}_{2}\alpha$$

proton number decreases by 2

Tip: Isotopes that will undergo α decay have a large number of neutrons and protons. Emitting an alpha particle decreases Z by 2 and decreases N by 2, which moves the nucleus towards a more stable region on a graph of N against Z.

Beta emission

Beta-minus (usually just called beta) decay is the emission of an electron from the nucleus along with an antineutrino. Beta-minus decay happens in isotopes that are **neutron rich** (i.e. have many more neutrons than protons in their nucleus). When a nucleus ejects a beta-minus particle, one of the neutrons in the nucleus is changed into a proton — the proton number increases by one, and the nucleon number stays the same.

Example

Rhenium-188 decays to osmium-188 by emitting a beta-minus particle:

nucleon number stays the same

$${}^{188}_{75}\text{Re} \longrightarrow {}^{188}_{76}\text{Os} + {}^{0}_{-1}\beta + {}^{0}_{0}\bar{\nu}_e$$

proton number increases by 1

Tip: Remember that isotopes that will undergo β^- decay are above the line of stability on a graph of N against Z. Converting a neutron into a proton increases Z and decreases N, which brings the nucleus closer to the line of stability.

Tip: A beta-plus β^+ particle is a positron.

Beta-plus decay happens in isotopes that are **proton rich** (i.e. have a high proton to neutron ratio). When a nucleus ejects a beta-plus particle, a proton gets changed into a neutron — the proton number decreases by one, and the nucleon number stays the same. A neutrino is also emitted.

Example

Sodium-22 decays to neon-22 by emitting a beta-plus particle:

nucleon number stays the same

$${}^{22}_{11}\text{Na} \longrightarrow {}^{22}_{10}\text{Ne} + {}^{0}_{+1}\beta + {}^{0}_{0}\nu_e$$

proton number decreases by 1

Tip: Isotopes that will undergo β^+ decay are below the line of stability on a graph of N against Z. Converting a proton into a neutron increases N and decreases Z, which brings the nucleus closer to the line of stability.

Gamma emission

After alpha or beta decay, the nucleus often has excess energy — it's in an excited state. This energy is lost by emitting a gamma ray. During gamma emission, there is no change to the nuclear constituents — the nucleus just loses excess energy.

Another way that gamma radiation is produced is **electron capture**. This is when a nucleus captures and absorbs one of its own orbiting electrons, which causes a proton to change into a neutron. A neutrino is also released.

Exam Tip
You'll need to be able to write out (and complete) nuclear equations — so make sure you learn what changes with each decay. There's more coming up on how to tackle decay equations on the next page.

Electron capture has the same effect on the nucleon and proton numbers of the nucleus as beta-plus decay — both cause N to increase by 1 and Z to decrease by 1 in nuclei that are below the line of stability.

Example

Beryllium-7 decays to lithium-7 by electron capture:

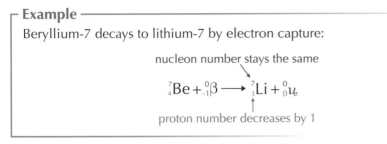

nucleon number stays the same

$$^{7}_{4}\text{Be} + ^{0}_{-1}\beta \longrightarrow ^{7}_{3}\text{Li} + ^{0}_{0}\nu_e$$

proton number decreases by 1

This makes the nucleus unstable and it emits gamma radiation.

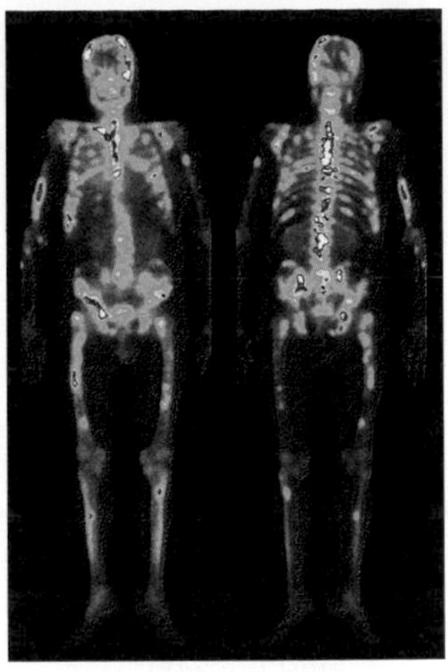

Figure 3: *The artificial isotope technetium-99m is formed in an excited state from the decay of another element. It is used as a tracer in medical imaging* *(see page 109).*

Conservation rules in nuclear reactions

In every nuclear reaction energy, momentum, charge, nucleon number and lepton number must be conserved. As you might remember from AS, electrons and neutrinos have a lepton number of +1. Positrons and antineutrinos have a lepton number of –1.

Example

Here's the nuclear equation for the beta-minus decay of rhenium-188, showing how nucleon number and charge are conserved:

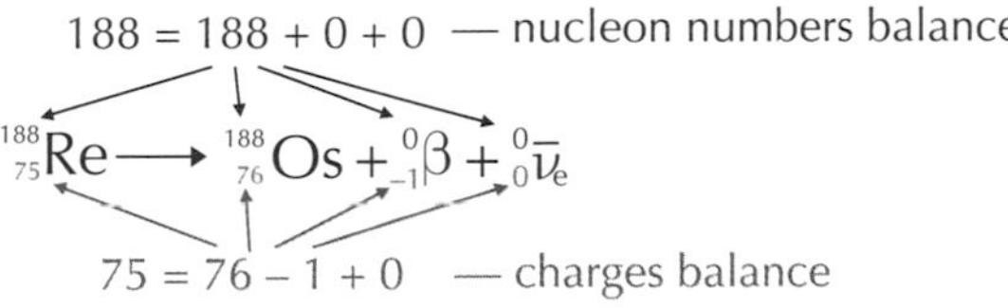

188 = 188 + 0 + 0 — nucleon numbers balance
$^{188}_{75}\text{Re} \longrightarrow ^{188}_{76}\text{Os} + ^{0}_{-1}\beta + ^{0}_{0}\overline{\nu}_e$
75 = 76 – 1 + 0 — charges balance

Tip: Momentum is always conserved in mechanics too — see page 5 for more.

Tip: When balancing equations, writing the charge of particles where the proton number would usually go helps you to make sure the charges are balanced.

Tip: Remember that the number in the name of an isotope is the nucleon number.

Practice Questions — Application

Q1 Complete the following nuclear equation for the beta-minus decay of caesium-137: $^{137}_{55}\text{Cs} \longrightarrow ^{?}_{?}\text{Ba} + ? + ?$

Q2 Write out the nuclear equation for the alpha decay of At-211 (Z = 85) to an isotope of bismuth. (The chemical symbol of bismuth is Bi.)

Q3 Rubidium-83 decays via electron capture to krypton. Write out the nuclear equation for this process. (The chemical symbol for rubidium is Rb, and the chemical symbol for krypton is Kr.)

Practice Questions — Fact Recall

Q1 Give four reasons why a nucleus might be unstable.

Q2 Sketch a graph of neutron number N against proton number Z, showing the line of stable nuclei, and indicating the regions of nuclei which will decay by α, β^- and β^+ decay.

Q3 Describe the particle(s) emitted and the change that occurs to the decayed nucleus for each of the following types of decay:

a) alpha b) beta-minus c) beta-plus

Q4 What causes a nucleus to emit a gamma ray?

Q5 Give three things that are always conserved in a nuclear reaction.

7. Mass Defect and Binding Energy

Learning Objectives:

- Know the definitions of the binding energy and mass defect of a nucleus, and that the two are equivalent.
- Know that a mass defect of 1 u is equivalent to a binding energy of 931.5 MeV.
- Be able to sketch the graph of binding energy per nucleon against nucleon number.

Specification Reference 3.5.2

The binding energy is a measure of how strongly a nucleus is held together — the greater the binding energy per nucleon, the more stable the nucleus.

Mass defect and binding energy

The mass of a nucleus is less than the mass of its constituent nucleons — the difference is called the **mass defect**. Einstein's equation says that mass and energy are equivalent:

$$E = mc^2$$

E *= energy in J*

c *= the speed of light in a vacuum in ms^{-1}*

m *= mass in kg*

So, as nucleons join together, the total mass decreases — this 'lost' mass is converted into energy and released. The amount of energy released is equivalent to the mass defect.

Tip: Remember atomic mass units from p. 101? $1\ u = 1.661 \times 10^{-27}$ kg.

Example

The mass of a nucleus of potassium, $^{40}_{19}K$, is 39.9536 u. The mass of a proton is 1.00728 u and the mass of a neutron is 1.00867 u. Calculate its mass defect in u.

Number of protons = 19, number of neutrons = (40 – 19) = 21
Mass of nucleons = (19 × 1.00728) + (21 × 1.00867) = 40.32039 u

So mass defect = mass of nucleons – mass of nucleus
= 40.32039 – 39.9536 = 0.3668 u (to 4 s.f.)

If you pulled the nucleus completely apart, the energy you'd have to use to do it would be the same as the energy released when the nucleus formed. The energy needed to separate all of the nucleons in a nucleus is called the **binding energy** (measured in MeV), and it is equivalent to the mass defect.

Example

Calculate the binding energy in MeV of the nucleus of a lithium-6 atom, $^{6}_{3}Li$, given that its mass defect is 0.0343 u.

Convert the mass defect into kg:
Mass defect = $0.0343 \times (1.661 \times 10^{-27}) = 5.697... \times 10^{-29}$ kg

Use $E = mc^2$ to calculate the binding energy:
$E = (5.697... \times 10^{-29}) \times (3.00 \times 10^{8})^2 = 5.127... \times 10^{-12}$ J
Convert to MeV:
$E = (5.127... \times 10^{-12}) \div (1.60 \times 10^{-19}) \div 10^6 = 32.0$ MeV (to 3 s.f.)

Tip: To convert from J to eV, you divide by the charge on an electron, $e = 1.60 \times 10^{-19}$ C. Then to convert to MeV you just divide by 10^6.

The binding energy per unit of mass defect is the same for all nuclei:

$$1\ u \approx 931.5\ MeV$$

Example

Using the mass defect calculated above, the binding energy in MeV of lithium-6 is:

$E = 0.0343\ u \times 931.5\ MeV = 31.950... = 32.0$ MeV (to 3 s.f.)

Exam Tip
Remember that 1 u ≈ 931.5 MeV — it'll be really useful for your exam.

Binding energy per nucleon

A useful way of comparing the binding energies of different nuclei is to look at the binding energy per nucleon.

$$\text{Binding energy per nucleon} = \frac{\text{Binding energy } (B)}{\text{Nucleon number } (A)}$$

Example

What is the binding energy per nucleon for a $^{6}_{3}Li$ nucleus?

You know from the previous page that binding energy = 32.0 MeV (to 3 s.f.)
Nucleon number of = $A = 6$
Binding energy per nucleon = $\frac{B}{A}$ = 31.943... ÷ 6 = 5.32 MeV (to 3 s.f.)

A graph of binding energy per nucleon against nucleon number, for all elements, shows a curve (Figure 1). Higher binding energy per nucleon means that more energy is needed to remove nucleons from the nucleus. Therefore, the higher the binding energy per nucleon, the more stable the nucleus. This means that the most stable nuclei occur around the maximum point on the graph — which is at nucleon number 56 (i.e. iron, Fe).

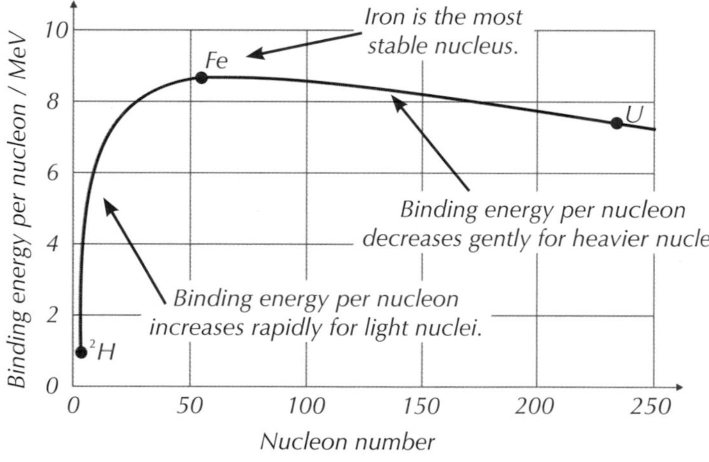

Figure 1: *Graph showing how the binding energy per nucleon varies with nucleon number.*

Exam Tip
Make sure you know this graph really well, including the units and axes — you could be asked to sketch it in an exam.

Practice Questions — Application

Q1 The mass defect of a carbon-12 nucleus is 0.0989 u. Calculate the binding energy of the nucleus.

Q2 Calculate the mass defect of a nucleus of $^{16}_{8}O$ (mass = 15.994915 u).

Q3 The binding energy per nucleon of a nucleus of iron-56 is 8.79 MeV. What is its mass defect in u?

Tip: The mass of a proton is 1.00728 u, and the mass of a neutron is 1.00867 u.

Practice Questions — Fact Recall

Q1 What is meant by the binding energy of a nucleus?

Q2 How many MeV equal 1 u?

Q3 Sketch the graph of the binding energy per nucleon against nucleon number. Label the key points on the graph.

8. Nuclear Fission and Fusion

Learning Objectives:

- Know that nuclear fission is the splitting of larger nuclei into smaller nuclei.
- Know that nuclear fusion is the combining of two smaller nuclei into one larger nucleus.
- Know that energy can be released during fission or fusion due to an increase in binding energy per nucleon.
- Be able to calculate the energy released during fission or fusion from nuclear masses.

Specification Reference 3.5.2

Radioactive decay isn't the only way that nuclei can change — they can also split into two smaller nuclei or fuse with other nuclei to form larger ones.

Fission

Large nuclei, with at least 83 protons (e.g. uranium), are unstable and some can randomly split into two smaller nuclei — this is called **nuclear fission**. This process is called spontaneous if it just happens by itself, or induced if we encourage it to happen.

Energy is released during nuclear fission because the new, smaller nuclei have a higher binding energy per nucleon (see page 115). The larger the nucleus, the more unstable it will be — so large nuclei are more likely to spontaneously fission. This means that spontaneous fission limits the number of nucleons that a nucleus can contain — in other words, it limits the number of possible elements.

Example

Fission can be induced by making a neutron enter a ^{235}U nucleus, causing it to become very unstable. Only low-energy neutrons can be captured in this way. A low-energy neutron is called a **thermal neutron**.

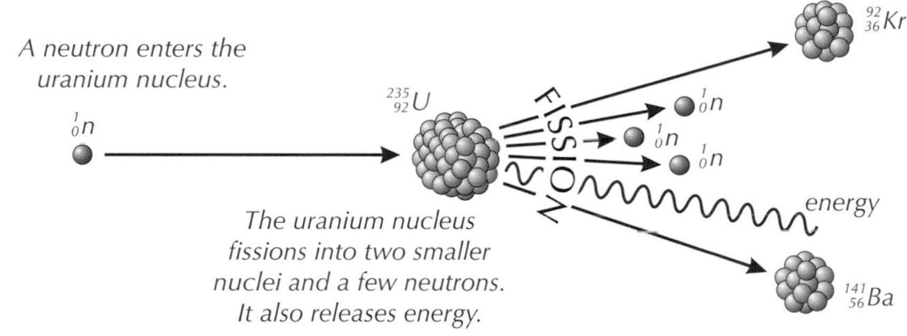

A neutron enters the uranium nucleus.
$^{1}_{0}n$
$^{235}_{92}U$
FISSION
$^{1}_{0}n$
$^{1}_{0}n$
$^{1}_{0}n$
energy
$^{92}_{36}Kr$
$^{141}_{56}Ba$
The uranium nucleus fissions into two smaller nuclei and a few neutrons. It also releases energy.

Figure 1: *A possible fission of a uranium-235 nucleus.*

Tip: Heavy nuclei don't always fission to form the same daughter nuclei — ^{235}U can split into lots of different pairs of nuclei (with nucleon numbers around 90 and 140).

Fusion

Two light nuclei can combine to create a larger nucleus — this is called **nuclear fusion**. A lot of energy is released during nuclear fusion because the new, heavier nuclei have a much higher binding energy per nucleon (as long as the lighter nuclei are light enough — see Figure 1 on p. 115).

Example

In the Sun, hydrogen nuclei fuse in a series of reactions to form helium. One of the reactions is: $^{2}_{1}\text{H} + ^{1}_{1}\text{H} \longrightarrow ^{3}_{2}\text{He} + \text{energy}$.

$^{2}_{1}H$
$^{1}_{1}H$
fusion
energy
$^{3}_{2}He$

Figure 3: *Two isotopes of hydrogen fuse to form helium.*

Figure 2: *Most of the energy emitted from the Sun has been released by the fusion of hydrogen nuclei.*

All nuclei are positively charged — so there will be an electrostatic (or Coulomb) force of repulsion between them (see Figure 4). Nuclei can only fuse if they overcome this electrostatic force and get close enough for the attractive force of the strong interaction to hold them both together. About 1 MeV of kinetic energy is needed to make nuclei fuse together — that's a lot of energy.

Low-energy nuclei are deflected by electrostatic repulsion.

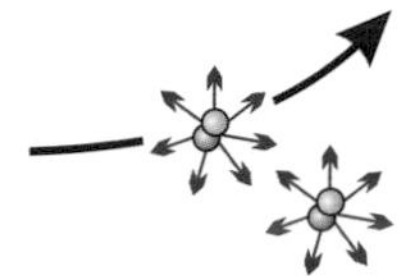

High-energy nuclei overcome electrostatic repulsion and are attracted by the strong interaction.

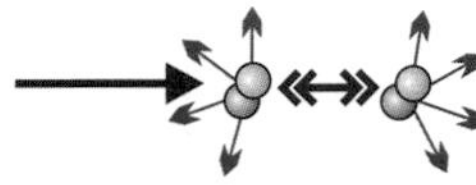

Figure 4: *Nuclei must overcome their mutual electrostatic repulsion to fuse together.*

Tip: The strong interaction can only attract nucleons together when they're less than a few femtometres apart — so the fusing nuclei must have enough energy to get very close to each other.

Energy released by fission and fusion

You can tell whether it is energetically favourable for an element to undergo fission or fusion by looking at the graph of binding energy per nucleon against nucleon number. Only elements to the right of ^{56}Fe can release energy through nuclear fission. Similarly only elements to the left of ^{56}Fe can release energy through nuclear fusion. This is because energy is only released when the binding energy per nucleon increases.

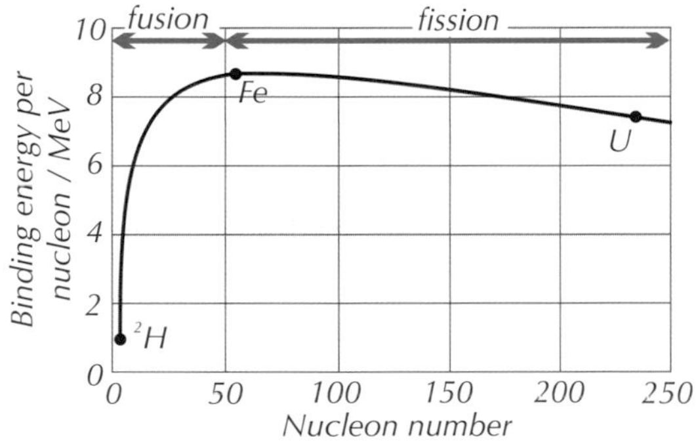

Figure 5: *Graph showing the regions where fusion and fission reactions are energetically favourable.*

Tip: Energetically favourable means that the fusion or fission will give out energy. These reactions can happen if they aren't energetically favourable — they'll just take in energy rather than release it.

The change in binding energy gives the energy released. The binding energy per nucleon graph can be used to estimate the energy released in nuclear reactions.

Example

Energy released through the nuclear fusion of ^{2}H and ^{3}H:

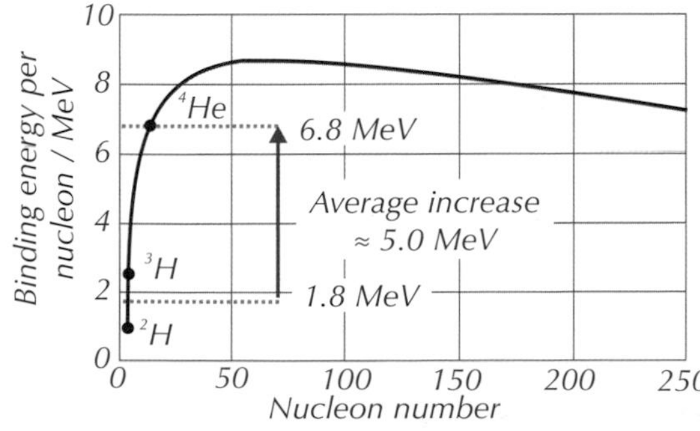

Figure 6: *Graph showing the energy released by the fusion of ^{2}H and ^{3}H.*

If ^{2}H and ^{3}H nuclei were fused together to form ^{4}He (and a neutron), the average increase in binding energy per ^{4}He nucleon would be about 5 MeV.

There are 4 nucleons in ^{4}He, so we can estimate the energy released as $4 \times 5.0 \approx 20$ MeV (to 2 s.f.).

Tip: To estimate the average increase in binding energy per nucleon, subtract the midpoint of the binding energies per nucleon of ^{2}H and ^{3}H from the binding energy per nucleon of ^{4}He. Then multiply by the nucleon number of ^{4}He. This estimate is really rough, but it gives you an idea.

Tip: This time, to estimate the average increase in binding energy per nucleon, subtract the binding energy per nucleon of the initial nucleus, ^{235}U, from the midpoint of the binding energies per nucleon of ^{92}Rb and ^{140}Cs. Then multiply by the nucleon number of ^{235}U.

Example

Energy released in the induced nuclear fission of ^{235}U:

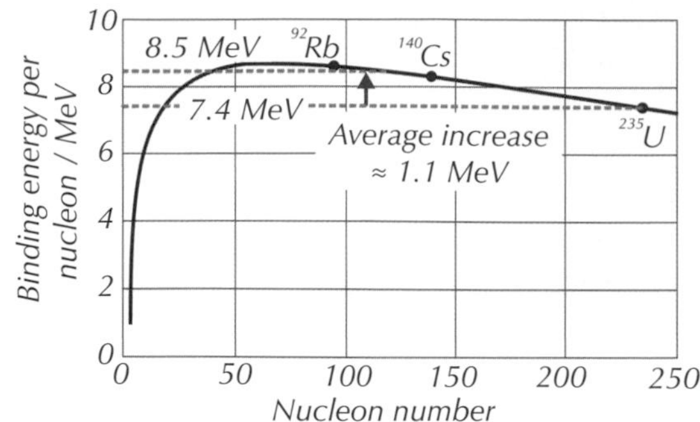

Figure 7: *Graph showing the energy released by the fission of ^{235}U.*

If a ^{235}U nucleus splits into ^{92}Rb and ^{140}Cs (plus a few neutrons) during nuclear fission, the average increase in binding energy per nucleon would be about 1.1 MeV.

There are 235 nucleons in ^{235}U, so we can estimate the energy released as $235 \times 1.1 \approx 260$ MeV (to 2 s.f.).

You can find the number of neutrons released per fission, x, by balancing the nucleon number on both sides of the reaction equation:

$^{235}_{92}U + ^{1}_{0}n \longrightarrow ^{92}_{37}Rb + ^{140}_{55}Cs + x^{1}_{0}n$

$235 + 1 = 232 + x$

So number of neutrons released per fission $= x = 236 - 232 = 4$

The energy released during a fission or fusion reaction can also be calculated using the equation $E = \Delta m \times c^2$, where Δm is the total difference in mass between the initial and final nuclei (as long as you take the neutrons released into account too).

Tip: Here the mass difference has been converted from u to MeV by multiplying by 931.5 MeVu^{-1} (see p. 114).

Example

Calculate the energy released by the following fission reaction using the data in Figure 8: $^{235}_{92}U + ^{1}_{0}n \longrightarrow ^{89}_{36}Kr + ^{144}_{56}Ba + 3^{1}_{0}n$

$\Delta m = m_{U\,235} + m_n - m_{Kr\,89} - m_{Ba\,144} - 3m_n$

$= 234.99333 + 1.00867 - 88.89783 - 143.89215 - (3 \times 1.00867)$

$= 0.18601$ u

In MeV: $0.18601 \times 931.5 = 173.3$ MeV (to 4 s.f.)

Isotope	Mass (u)
^{235}U	234.99333
^{89}Kr	88.89783
^{144}Ba	143.89215
^{139}Te	138.90613
^{94}Zr	93.88431
^{2}H	2.01355
proton	1.00728
neutron	1.00867
positron	0.00055
neutrino	0

Figure 8: *The masses of some nuclei and particles.*

Practice Questions — Application

Q1 Using the data in Figure 8, calculate the energy released during the fusion of two hydrogen nuclei: $^{1}_{1}p + ^{1}_{1}p \longrightarrow ^{2}_{1}H + ^{0}_{1}e + \nu$.

Q2 Calculate the energy released when a ^{235}U nucleus is hit by a neutron and fissions into ^{94}Zr and ^{139}Te and a number of neutrons.

Practice Questions — Fact Recall

Q1 What is nuclear fission?

Q2 What is the difference between spontaneous and induced fission?

Q3 What is nuclear fusion?

Q4 Why is fission/fusion only energetically favourable for certain nuclei?

Q5 Explain why light nuclei must have a lot of energy to fuse together.

Q6 Sketch the graph of binding energy per nucleon against nucleon number. Show on it what nuclear reaction elements on either side of the peak are most likely to undergo.

9. Nuclear Fission Reactors

You need to know all about the different bits and pieces that make up a nuclear reactor, as well as the potential problems that come from releasing energy in this way.

Learning Objectives:

- Know that thermal neutrons can induce fission in uranium nuclei and start a fission chain reaction.
- Understand the functions of the moderator, control rods and coolant in a nuclear reactor, and why certain materials are chosen for each of these.
- Know why control rods and shielding are important safety features.
- Know why fission waste products are dangerous, and how they are stored and disposed of.

Specification Reference 3.5.2

How reactors work

We can harness the energy released during nuclear fission reactions in a nuclear reactor (see Figure 1), but it's important that these reactions are very carefully controlled.

Chain reactions

Nuclear reactors use rods of uranium that are rich in ^{235}U (or sometimes plutonium rods rich in ^{239}Pu) as 'fuel' for fission reactions. (The rods also contain other isotopes, but they don't undergo fission.) These fission reactions produce more neutrons which then induce other nuclei to fission — this is called a **chain reaction**. The neutrons will only cause a chain reaction if they are slowed down, which allows them to be captured by the uranium nuclei — these slowed down neutrons are called thermal neutrons (see page 116).

Moderator

Fuel rods need to be placed in a **moderator** (for example, water or graphite) to slow down and/or absorb neutrons. You need to choose a moderator that will slow down some neutrons enough so they can cause further fission, keeping the reaction going at a steady rate. Choosing a moderator that absorbs more neutrons the higher the temperature will decrease the chance of meltdown if the reactor overheats — as it will naturally slow down the reaction.

control rods
concrete case
steam (to turbines)
fuel rods
coolant e.g. water
moderator e.g. water
pump

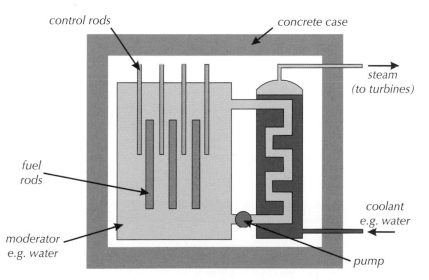

Figure 1: The key features of a nuclear reactor.

***Figure 2:** Fuel rods being lowered into the reactor at a nuclear power station. The core is surrounded by water which acts as a moderator.*

Control rods

You want the chain reaction to continue on its own at a steady rate, where one fission follows another. The amount of 'fuel' you need to do this is called the **critical mass** — any less than the critical mass (sub-critical mass) and the reaction will just peter out. Nuclear reactors use a supercritical mass of fuel (where several new fissions normally follow each fission) and control the rate of fission using **control rods**.

Tip: If the chain reaction in a nuclear reactor is left to continue unchecked, large amounts of energy are released in a very short time. Many new fissions will follow each fission, causing a runaway reaction which could lead to reactor meltdown and the release of radioactive material into the atmosphere.

Tip: See page 101 for more about materials that will block the different types of radiation.

Control rods control the chain reaction by limiting the number of neutrons in the reactor. They absorb neutrons so that the rate of fission is controlled. Control rods are made up of a material that absorbs neutrons (e.g. boron), and they can be inserted by varying amounts to control the reaction rate.

Coolant

Coolant is sent around the reactor to remove heat produced by fission. The material used should be a liquid or gas at room temperature, and be efficient at transferring heat. Often the coolant is the same water that is being used in the reactor as a moderator. The heat from the reactor can then be used to make steam for powering electricity-generating turbines.

Safety

Reactor shielding

The nuclear reactor is surrounded by a thick concrete case, which acts as shielding. This prevents radiation escaping and reaching the people working in the power station.

Emergency shut-down

In an emergency, the reactor can be shut down automatically by the release of control rods into the reactor. The control rods are lowered fully into the reactor, which slows down the reaction as quickly as possible.

Fuel and disposal of fission waste products

Unused uranium fuel rods emit only alpha radiation, which is weakly penetrating and so is easily contained. Spent fuel rods are more dangerous, since fission waste products usually have a larger proportion of neutrons than nuclei of a similar atomic number — this makes them unstable and radioactive. The fission waste products emit beta and gamma radiation, which are strongly penetrating.

The products can be used for practical applications such as tracers in medical diagnosis (see page 109). However, their handling and disposal needs great care since they are highly radioactive. When material is removed from the reactor, it is initially very hot, so it is placed in cooling ponds until the temperature falls to a safe level. The radioactive waste should then be stored underground in sealed containers until its activity has fallen sufficiently (see page 109).

Practice Questions — Fact Recall

Q1 What is meant by a nuclear chain reaction?

Q2 What properties do the materials used for each of the moderator and coolant need to have? Give an example material that each could be made of.

Q3 How are the control rods used to control the rate of reaction?

Q4 Give two safety features of a nuclear reactor, and explain how they are used.

Q5 Why are used fuel rods more dangerous than unused ones?

Q6 How are used fuel rods disposed of?

Section Summary

Make sure you know...

- What the Rutherford scattering experiment is, and how it demonstrates the existence of a small, positively-charged atomic nucleus.
- How to calculate the distance of closest approach of a scattered alpha particle to a nucleus, and that this distance can be used as an estimate for the nuclear radius.
- How to estimate a nuclear radius by diffracting electrons through a thin foil.
- That nuclear radius is proportional to the cube root of the nucleon number.
- How to calculate nuclear density, and that it is pretty much the same for all nuclei.
- That most of an atom's mass is in its nucleus.
- The four types of nuclear radiation: alpha, beta-plus, beta-minus and gamma, and their constituents.
- The relative ionising strengths and penetrating powers of the different types of nuclear radiation, and how they affect what the radiation can be used for.
- How to identify nuclear radiation from its penetrating power and its behaviour in a magnetic field.
- That the intensity of gamma radiation decreases with distance from a source by the inverse square law.
- How to verify the inverse square law by taking readings at different distances from a radioactive source.
- Where background radiation comes from, and how to remove it from readings of radioactive sources.
- That radioactive decay is random, but that an unstable nucleus has a constant probability of decay.
- What is meant by the activity, decay constant and half-life of a radioactive isotope.
- The equations describing the relationships between activity, half-life, decay constant, number of unstable nuclei and rate of change of number of unstable nuclei.
- How to calculate half-life from a graph of activity or number of unstable nuclei against time.
- That the number of unstable nuclei in a radioactive sample decreases exponentially, and the equation showing this.
- That radioactive isotopes can be used for radiocarbon dating and medical diagnosis.
- The graph of neutron number against proton number for stable and unstable nuclei.
- How proton and nucleon numbers change for each of α, β^- and β^+ decay, and electron capture.
- How to write nuclear equations for each of these decay modes using the conservation of nucleon number, charge and lepton number.
- That excited nuclear states can emit gamma radiation, and that gamma sources can be used as tracers in medical imaging.
- What is meant by mass defect and binding energy, and that the two are equivalent.
- That a mass defect of 1 u is equal to a binding energy of 931.5 MeV.
- How to sketch the graph of binding energy per nucleon against nucleon number.
- What is meant by nuclear fission and fusion, and that both processes can release energy due to an increase in binding energy per nucleon.
- How to calculate the energy released during fission and fusion reactions using nuclear masses.
- That a lot of energy is needed to overcome the repulsive electrostatic interaction of nuclei for fusion to happen.
- What is meant by a fission chain reaction.
- The functions of the moderator, coolant, control rods and shielding in a nuclear fission reactor.
- Examples of materials used for the moderator, coolant and control rods in a nuclear fission reactor.
- Why used fuel rods are more dangerous than unused ones, and how radioactive waste is stored and disposed of.

Exam-style Questions

1 (a) A beam of electrons each with an energy of 250 MeV is fired at a thin sheet of aluminium foil. Concentric bright and dark rings are seen on a luminescent screen behind the foil. The first minimum is at an angle of 57.4° to the beam's original path.

1 (a) (i) Estimate the de Broglie wavelength of the electron beam.

(3 marks)

1 (a) (ii) Use the results of the above experiment to calculate the radius of an aluminium nucleus.

(2 marks)

1 (b) ^{23}Na has a nuclear mass of 3.8×10^{-26} kg.

1 (b) (i) What is its nuclear radius, given that the radius of a hydrogen nucleus is 1.4×10^{-15} m?

(2 marks)

1 (b) (ii) Calculate the density of a nucleus of ^{23}Na.

(3 marks)

1 (c) Explain how observations from Rutherford's alpha scattering experiment led him to conclude that there is a small, positively charged nucleus at the centre of atoms.

(2 marks)

2 The diagram below shows the main features of a nuclear reactor.

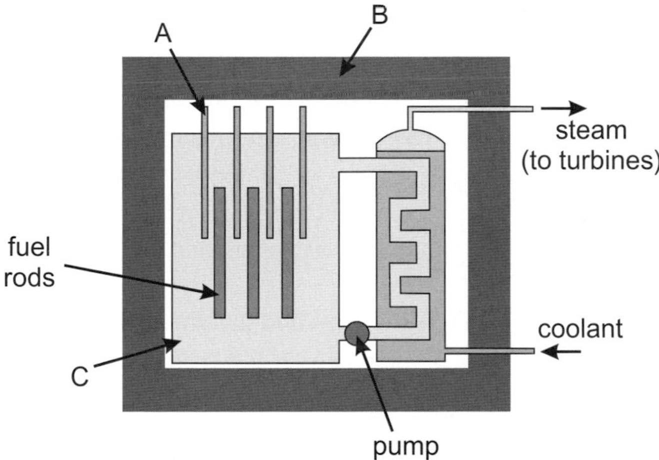

2 (a) Identify and explain the function of components *A*, *B* and *C* labelled in the diagram.
The quality of your written communication will be assessed in this question.

(7 marks)

2 (b) The mass of uranium used as fuel in the reactor is greater than the critical mass.
Explain what is meant by a critical mass and why this amount of fuel is used.

(2 marks)

2 (c) Describe what happens in an emergency shut-down of a nuclear reactor.

(2 marks)

3 (a) (i) What is meant by the term *binding energy*?

(1 mark)

3 (a) (ii) Sketch the graph of binding energy per nucleon against nucleon number. Indicate which nucleus is found at the peak of the graph, and give an approximate value for its binding energy per nucleon.

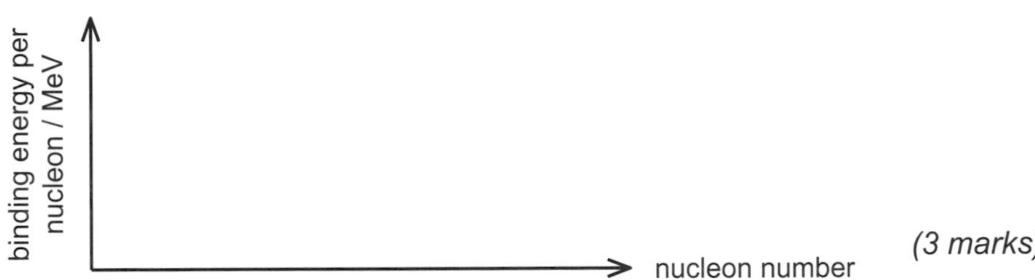

(3 marks)

3 (a) (iii) Calculate the binding energy per nucleon of zinc-66, given that it has a mass defect of 0.62065 u.

(1 mark)

3 (b) After absorbing a neutron, ^{235}U can fission into ^{94}Sr and ^{140}Xe, along with a number of neutrons:

$$^{235}_{92}U + ^{1}_{0}n \longrightarrow ^{140}_{54}Xe + ^{94}_{a}Sr + b^{1}_{0}n$$

3 (b) (i) Calculate the proton number of ^{94}Sr, *a*, and the number of neutrons produced, *b*.

(2 marks)

3 (b) (ii) Explain how the fission of heavy nuclei releases energy.

(1 mark)

3 (b) (iii) Calculate the energy released by this reaction.
(Nuclear masses: ^{235}U = 234.99333 u, ^{94}Sr = 93.89446 u,
^{140}Xe = 139.89194 u, ^{1}n = 1.00867 u.)

(3 marks)

4 (a) An isotope of phosphorus, ^{33}P, emits β^- radiation as it decays to an isotope of sulfur. ^{33}P has a half-life of 25.4 days, and a proton number of 15.

4 (a) (i) Write the nuclear equation for the decay of ^{33}P.

(3 marks)

4 (a) (ii) Calculate the decay constant of ^{33}P.

(2 marks)

4 (a) (iii) A sample of ^{33}P contains 1.6×10^{15} atoms. How long will it take for the size of the sample to fall to 7.0×10^{13} atoms?

(2 marks)

4 (b) Technetium-99m is a radioactive isotope that only emits γ radiation.

4 (b) (i) A Geiger-Müller tube records an intensity of 3.6×10^{-10} Jm^{-2} when 0.2 m from a sample of Te-99m. What would you expect the intensity to be 0.5 m from the source?

(2 marks)

4 (b) (ii) Technetium-99m is commonly used as a tracer for medical imaging. Describe how its properties make it useful for this purpose.

(2 marks)

Learning Objectives:
- Know that there is an 'absolute zero' of temperature, given as 0 K or –273 °C.
- Know the three gas laws for a fixed mass of ideal gas.
- Be able to sketch graphs of pressure, volume and temperature for a fixed mass of gas following the three gas laws.

Specification Reference 3.5.3

1. The Three Gas Laws

An 'ideal gas' follows the three gas laws, which describe how a fixed mass of gas behaves when you change its temperature, pressure or volume. Be careful though — they work on the Kelvin temperature scale, not traditional °C.

The absolute temperature scale

In thermal physics, temperature is measured using the Kelvin or absolute temperature scale. The unit of this scale is the kelvin (K).

There is a lowest possible temperature that any object can have called **absolute zero** — around –273 °C. Absolute zero is given a value of zero kelvins, written 0 K, on the absolute temperature scale. At 0 K all molecules have zero kinetic energy — everything theoretically stops. At higher temperatures, molecules have more energy. In fact, with the Kelvin scale, a molecule's energy is proportional to its temperature (see page 135).

The Kelvin scale is named after Lord Kelvin, who first suggested it. A change of 1 K equals a change of 1 °C. To change from degrees Celsius into kelvin you add 273 (or 273.15 if you need to be really precise).

Tip: You don't use the degrees sign (°) when writing temperatures in kelvins.

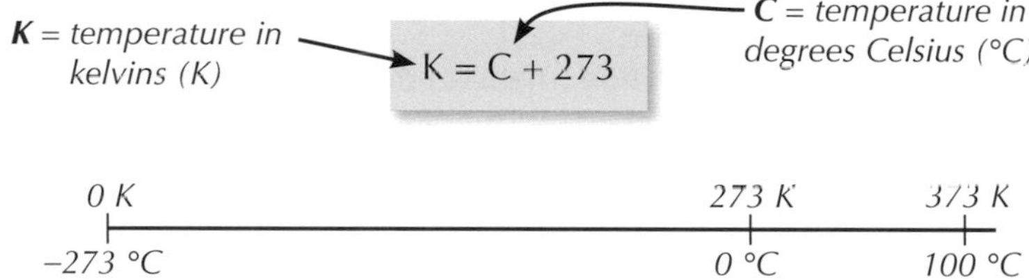

Figure 1: *Equivalent temperatures in the Kelvin and degrees Celsius scales.*

The three gas laws

There are three gas laws you need to know about. Each gas law was worked out independently by careful experiment. Each of the gas laws applies to a fixed mass of gas.

Boyle's law

Boyle's law states that:

> At a constant temperature the pressure p and volume V of a gas are inversely proportional.

Tip: If the pressure doubles, the volume halves, and so on.

A (theoretical) gas that obeys Boyle's law at all temperatures is called an **ideal gas**. Inversely proportional means that as one variable increases, the other decreases by the same proportion, i.e. $p \propto \frac{1}{V}$.

Tip: Most gases can usually be assumed to act as ideal gases — see pages 132-133.

Because of this, at any given temperature the product of p and V will always be the same:

$$pV = \text{constant}$$

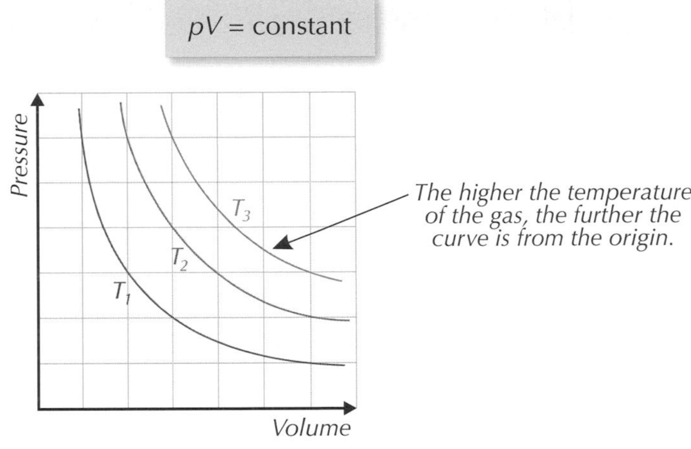

Figure 3: *Graphs of pressure against volume for an ideal gas at different temperatures.*

Figure 2: *Irish chemist and physicist Robert Boyle.*

Charles' law

Charles' law states that:

At constant pressure, the volume V of a gas is directly proportional to its absolute temperature T.

An ideal gas also obeys Charles' law. V and T are proportional, i.e. $V \propto T$. At the lowest possible temperature (0 K), the volume is zero. If Charles' law is obeyed, the volume divided by the temperature is a constant:

$$\frac{V}{T} = \text{constant}$$

Tip: If the temperature doubles, the volume doubles, and so on.

Tip: In practice a real (non-ideal) gas would condense before reaching 0 K.

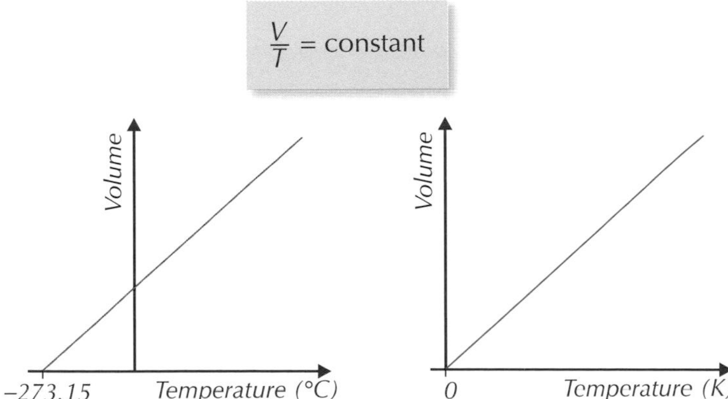

Figure 4: *Graphs of volume against temperature at constant pressure on the degrees Celsius scale and on the Kelvin scale.*

Figure 5: *French inventor, scientist, mathematician and balloonist Jacques Charles.*

The pressure law

The pressure law states that:

At constant volume, the pressure p of a gas is directly proportional to its absolute temperature T.

Tip: If the temperature doubles, the pressure doubles, and so on.

At absolute zero the pressure is also zero. If the pressure law is obeyed, the pressure divided by the temperature is a constant:

$$\frac{p}{T} = \text{constant}$$

Tip: The lines always reach the temperature axis at absolute zero.

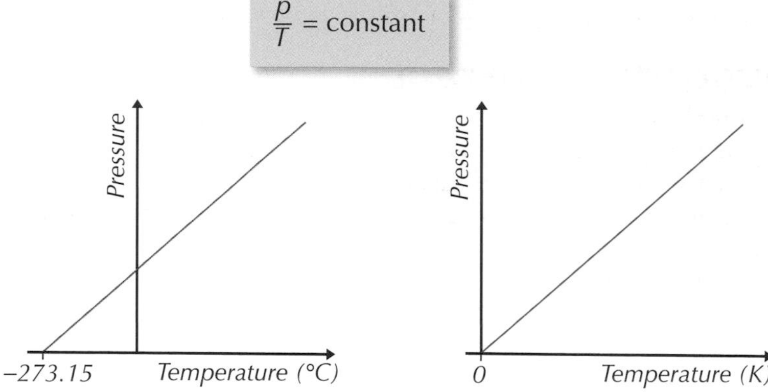

Figure 6: *Graphs of pressure against temperature at constant volume on the degrees Celsius scale and on the Kelvin scale.*

Tip: To convert from degrees Celsius to kelvins, add 273.

Practice Question — Application

Q1 A gas syringe is filled with 30 cm³ of an ideal gas at 27 °C and the pressure inside the syringe is measured as 1.4×10^5 Pa.

a) The syringe is pushed in so that its volume becomes 15 cm³. If the temperature remains constant, what will the pressure inside the syringe be?

b) The syringe is returned to its starting position and then cooled to –173 °C. Assuming the pressure inside the syringe remains constant, what will its new volume be?

Practice Questions — Fact Recall

Q1 What name is given to the lowest possible temperature an object can reach?

Q2 What's 0 °C in kelvins, to 3 significant figures?

Q3 What must be true of a gas's mass for it to obey the three gas laws?

Q4 a) What's Boyle's law?

b) Sketch a graph of pressure against volume for an ideal gas at fixed temperature *T*.

Q5 a) What's Charles' law?

b) Sketch a graph of volume against temperature (in °C) for an ideal gas at constant pressure *p*.

Q6 a) What's the pressure law?

b) Sketch a graph of pressure against temperature (in °C) for an ideal gas at constant volume *V*.

2. The Ideal Gas Equation

You can use the gas laws from the last topic to form the ideal gas equation. It's pretty important in thermal physics, so you'll probably see it quite a lot.

The Avogadro constant

Because gas molecules are tiny, it's easier to consider them in large groups when carrying out calculations. Amedeo Avogadro had an idea in the 19th century that a fixed volume of gas at a fixed temperature and pressure contains the same number of gas molecules, regardless of what type of gas it is. The mass, however, is proportional to its molecular mass, i.e. to the relative mass of the molecules of gas. So 1 g of hydrogen (^1_1H) and 16 g of oxygen ($^{16}_8O$) occupy the same volume at the same temperature and pressure.

This gave rise to the **Avogadro constant**, N_A, defined as the number of atoms in exactly 12 g of the carbon isotope $^{12}_6C$. This number gives the number of atoms (or molecules) in any volume of substance whose mass, in grams, is the same as its relative atomic (or molecular) mass. The value of Avogadro's constant is 6.02×10^{23} mol^{-1}.

Moles

A substance containing N_A atoms or molecules, all of which are identical, is defined as 1 **mole** of that substance. The **molar mass** of a substance is the mass that 1 mole of the substance would have (usually in grams), and is equal to its relative atomic or relative molecular mass — so the molar mass of helium (^4_2He) is 4 g, the molar mass of oxygen ($^{16}_8O$) is 32 g, and so on.

The number of moles in a substance is usually given by n, and its units are 'mol'. The number of molecules in a mass of gas is given by the number of moles, n, multiplied by Avogadro's constant. So the number of molecules, $N = nN_A$.

The ideal gas equation

The three gas laws from the last few pages can be used to derive the **ideal gas equation**. Start by combining the three laws to get:

$$\frac{pV}{T} = \text{constant}$$

Putting in values for 1 mole of an ideal gas at room temperature and atmospheric pressure gives the constant a value of 8.31 J K^{-1} mol^{-1}. This is the **molar gas constant**, R.

The value of $\frac{pV}{T}$ increases or decreases if there's more or less gas present — the more gas you have, the more space it takes up. The amount of gas is measured in moles, n, so the constant in the equation above becomes nR, where n is the number of moles of gas present. Plugging this into the equation gives:

$$\frac{pV}{T} = nR$$

Which can be rearranged to give the ideal gas equation:

$$pV = nRT$$

V *= volume in m^3*
n *= number of moles of gas*
T *= temperature in K*
p *= pressure in Pa*
R *= molar gas constant (= 8.31 J mol^{-1} K^{-1})*

Learning Objectives:

- Know what the Avogadro constant is.
- Know what is meant by relative molecular mass and molar mass.
- Know what the molar gas constant R and the Boltzmann constant k are.
- Be able to use the ideal gas equation and the equation of state of an ideal gas.

Specification Reference 3.5.3

Tip: For gases with only one type of element, the mass of one mole is often twice their relative atomic mass because many gases (e.g. oxygen) exist as molecules, which are two (or more) atoms bonded together. This is why the molar mass of oxygen (32 g) is twice its relative atomic mass (16). Helium exists as single atoms, so its molar mass is the same as its relative atomic mass. The gas laws all apply whether the gas is made up of molecules or atoms.

Tip: 1 mole of a gas at room temperature and atmospheric pressure (~101 kPa) takes up around 0.0224 m^3.

This equation works well (i.e., a real gas approximates to an ideal gas) for gases at low pressure and a fairly high temperature.

Tip: Don't forget to convert the units — remember the Kelvin scale is used for temperature in ideal gas calculations.

Example

What's the volume occupied by one mole of an ideal gas at room temperature (20 °C) and atmospheric pressure (10^5 Pa)?

First rearrange the ideal gas equation to make V the subject:

$$pV = nRT \Rightarrow V = \frac{nRT}{p}$$

Then put the correct numbers in:

$$V = \frac{nRT}{p} = \frac{1 \times 8.31 \times (20 + 273)}{10^5}$$
$$= 2.4 \times 10^{-2}\ \text{m}^3 \text{ (to 2 s.f.)}$$

Boltzmann's constant

Boltzmann's constant, k, is equivalent to $\frac{R}{N_A}$ — you can think of Boltzmann's constant as the gas constant for one molecule of gas, while R is the gas constant for one mole of gas. The value of Boltzmann's constant is 1.38×10^{-23} JK^{-1}.

Tip: Remember N is just the number of molecules in a mass of gas.

If you combine $N = nN_A$ (page 127) and $k = \frac{R}{N_A}$ you'll see that $Nk = nR$. First rearrange to make N_A the subject of the first equation:

$$N = nN_A \Rightarrow N_A = \frac{N}{n}$$

Then substitute this into the second equation:

$$k = \frac{R}{N_A} \Rightarrow k - \frac{R}{\left(\frac{N}{n}\right)} = \frac{nR}{N}$$
$$\Rightarrow nR = Nk$$

***Figure 1:** Austrian physicist Ludwig Boltzmann.*

Substituting this into the ideal gas equation (page 127) gives the **equation of state of an ideal gas**:

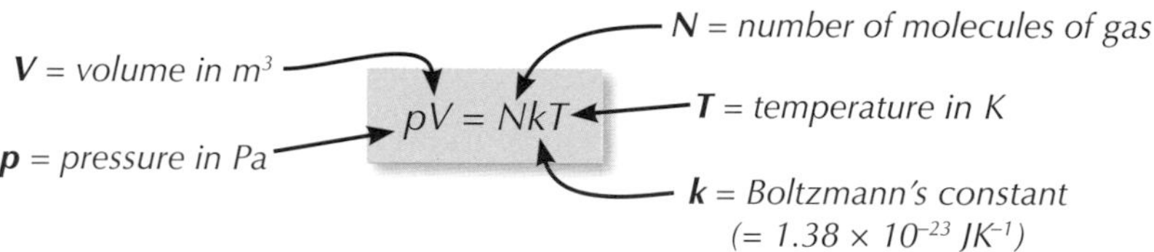

Example

An ideal gas at 303 K and 10^5 Pa occupies 23.2 litres. Find how many molecules of the gas are present.

Start by rearranging the equation to make N the subject:

$$pV = NkT \Rightarrow N = \frac{pV}{kT}$$

Then put the correct numbers in:

$$N = \frac{pV}{kT} = \frac{10^5 \times (23.2 \times 10^{-3})}{(1.38 \times 10^{-23}) \times 303}$$
$$= 5.55 \times 10^{23} \text{ (to 3 s.f.)}$$

Tip: There are 1000 litres in 1 m^3.

Practice Questions — Application

Q1 What's the molar mass of carbon dioxide (CO_2)?

Q2 Find the volume occupied by 23 moles of an ideal gas at 25 °C and a pressure of 2.4×10^5 Pa.

Q3 A sealed, airtight container with 8.21×10^{24} molecules of an ideal gas and with a fixed volume of 4.05 m^3 is heated to 500 K. What's the pressure inside the container?

Q4 A sealed, airtight container is filled with 1.44×10^{25} molecules of an ideal gas and kept at a constant pressure of 1.29×10^5 Pa. The container is heated so that its volume expands to 0.539 m^3. What temperature is the gas inside the container at this point?

Q5 A sealed, airtight container with a fixed volume of 0.39 m^3 is filled with 0.88 kg of an ideal gas whose molar mass is 44 g. The maximum pressure the container can withstand is 2.3×10^5 Pa.

a) How many moles of gas are inside the container?

b) What's the highest temperature the container can be heated to before the pressure on it would be too high?

Tip: A carbon dioxide molecule contains 1 carbon ($^{12}_{6}C$) atom and 2 oxygen ($^{16}_{8}O$) atoms.

Tip: $R = 8.31$ J mol^{-1} K^{-1} and $k = 1.38 \times 10^{-23}$ JK^{-1}.

Tip: Head to page 127 for a reminder on what the molar mass is.

Practice Questions — Fact Recall

Q1 What is the Avogadro constant?

Q2 What is the molar mass of a substance?

Q3 Write down the ideal gas equation, and state what each term in the equation represents.

Q4 What is Boltzmann's constant?

Q5 Write down the equation of state of an ideal gas, and state what each term in the equation represents.

3. The Pressure of an Ideal Gas

Learning Objectives:

- Know how the formula $pV = \frac{1}{3}Nm(c_{rms})^2$ is derived for an ideal gas.
- Know the assumptions made about an ideal gas in kinetic theory.
- Be able to explain why increasing the temperature of an ideal gas must cause an increase in its pressure or volume.

Specification Reference 3.5.3

The equation for the pressure exerted by an ideal gas can be derived by considering the individual molecules of the gas. The following few pages are rather tricky, so make sure you pay close attention.

Deriving the pressure of an ideal gas

You need to be able to derive the pressure of an ideal gas. Start by deriving the pressure on one wall of a box — in the x direction. Imagine a cubic box with sides of length *l* containing *N* molecules each of mass *m*.

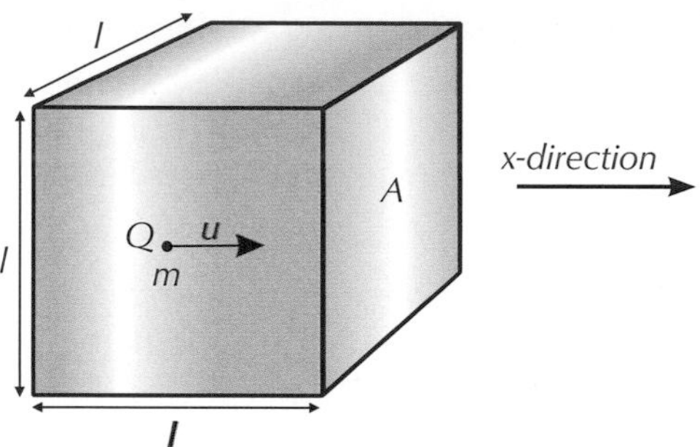

Figure 1: *A cubic box with sides of length l, containing N molecules each of mass m.*

Say molecule *Q* moves directly towards wall *A* with velocity $\boldsymbol{u}$. Its momentum approaching the wall is $m\boldsymbol{u}$. It strikes wall *A*. Assuming the collisions are perfectly elastic, the wall pushes back on the molecule so it rebounds and heads back in the opposite direction with momentum $-m\boldsymbol{u}$. So the change in momentum is:

$$m\boldsymbol{u} - (-m\boldsymbol{u}) = 2m\boldsymbol{u}$$

Tip: The wall pushes back because of Newton's third law of motion — every action has an equal and opposite reaction.

Assuming *Q* suffers no collisions with other molecules, the time between collisions of *Q* and wall *A* is $\frac{2l}{\boldsymbol{u}}$. The number of collisions per second is therefore $\frac{\boldsymbol{u}}{2l}$. This gives the rate of change of momentum as:

$$2m\boldsymbol{u} \times \frac{\boldsymbol{u}}{2l}$$

Tip: Time = $\frac{\text{distance}}{\text{speed}}$, and 2*l* is the distance a molecule would travel between collisions.

Force equals the rate of change of momentum (Newton's second law), so the force exerted on the wall by this one molecule is:

$$\frac{2m\boldsymbol{u}^2}{2l} = \frac{m\boldsymbol{u}^2}{l}$$

Tip: Check back on page 8 for more on this definition of Newton's second law.

Molecule *Q* is only one of many in the cube. Each molecule will have a different velocity $\boldsymbol{u}_1$, $\boldsymbol{u}_2$ etc. towards *A*. The total force, $\boldsymbol{F}$, of all these molecules on wall *A* is:

$$\boldsymbol{F} = \frac{m(\boldsymbol{u}_1^2 + \boldsymbol{u}_2^2 + \text{etc.})}{l}$$

You can define a quantity called the mean square speed, $\overline{\boldsymbol{u}^2}$ as:

$$\overline{\boldsymbol{u}^2} = \frac{\boldsymbol{u}_1^2 + \boldsymbol{u}_2^2 + \text{etc.}}{N}$$

If you put that into the equation before it, you get:

$$\boldsymbol{F} = \frac{Nm\overline{\boldsymbol{u}^2}}{l}$$

So, the pressure of the gas on end *A* is given by:

$$\text{pressure, } p = \frac{\text{force}}{\text{area}} = \frac{\left(\frac{Nm\overline{\boldsymbol{u}^2}}{l}\right)}{l^2} = \frac{Nm\overline{\boldsymbol{u}^2}}{l^3} = \frac{Nm\overline{\boldsymbol{u}^2}}{V}$$

V = volume of the cube in m^3

Tip: The volume of the cube is given by the length of the side cubed, i.e. l^3.

A gas molecule can move in three dimensions, so for the general equation you need to think about all 3 directions — *x*, *y* and *z*. You can calculate its speed, *c*, from Pythagoras' theorem: $c^2 = \boldsymbol{u}^2 + \boldsymbol{v}^2 + \boldsymbol{w}^2$ where ***u***, ***v*** and ***w*** are the components of the molecule's velocity in the *x*, *y* and *z* directions.

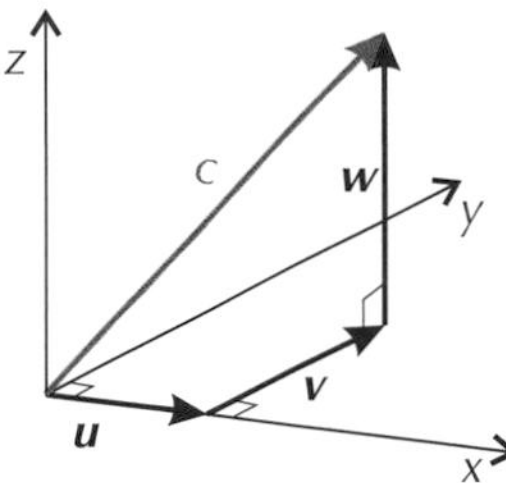

***Figure 2:** The speed of a molecule, c, can be found by using Pythagoras' theorem on its velocity in the x, y and z directions.*

Tip: You've probably met Pythagoras' theorem before in two dimensions, where $c^2 = a^2 + b^2$. It also works in 3 dimensions, as long as they're at right angles to each other.

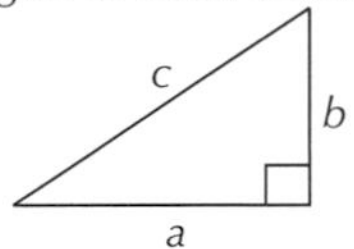

If you treat all *N* molecules in the same way, this gives an overall **mean square speed**, $(c_{rms})^2$, of:

$$(c_{rms})^2 = \overline{\boldsymbol{u}^2} + \overline{\boldsymbol{v}^2} + \overline{\boldsymbol{w}^2}$$

Since the molecules move randomly, $\overline{\boldsymbol{u}^2} = \overline{\boldsymbol{v}^2} = \overline{\boldsymbol{w}^2}$. So $(c_{rms})^2 = 3\overline{\boldsymbol{u}^2}$.
You can substitute this into the equation for pressure that you derived above:

$$p = \frac{Nm\overline{\boldsymbol{u}^2}}{V} \Rightarrow p = \frac{1}{3}\frac{Nm(c_{rms})^2}{V}$$

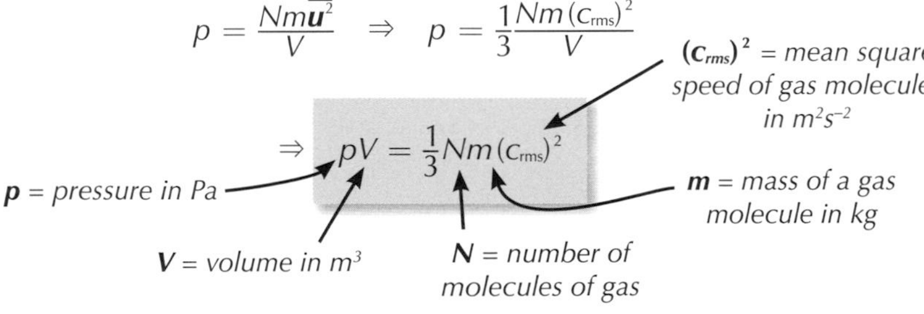

$$\Rightarrow pV = \frac{1}{3}Nm(c_{rms})^2$$

$(c_{rms})^2$ = *mean square speed of gas molecules in* m^2s^{-2}

***p** = pressure in Pa*

***V** = volume in* m^3

***N** = number of molecules of gas*

***m** = mass of a gas molecule in kg*

Tip: The mean square speed is the average of the squares of the speeds of molecules. The 'rms' stands for 'root mean square' — there's more on that on the next page.

Tip: Although this derivation assumed the container was cubic, the result is valid for any shape of container.

Example

1 mole of hydrogen gas occupies 2.5 × 10^{-2} m³ at a pressure 10^5 Pa. Find the mean square speed of the hydrogen molecules. The mass of a hydrogen molecule is 3.3 × 10^{-27} kg.

First find the number of hydrogen molecules present:

$$N = nN_A = 1 \times 6.02 \times 10^{23} = 6.02 \times 10^{23}$$

Then rearrange the formula to make $(c_{rms})^2$ the subject:

$$pV = \frac{1}{3}Nm(c_{rms})^2 \Rightarrow (c_{rms})^2 = \frac{3pV}{Nm}$$

And put in the correct numbers:

$$(c_{rms})^2 = \frac{3pV}{Nm} = \frac{3 \times 10^5 \times (2.5 \times 10^{-2})}{(6.02 \times 10^{23}) \times (3.3 \times 10^{-27})} = 3.8 \times 10^6 \text{ m}^2\text{s}^{-2} \text{ (to 2 s.f.)}$$

> **Tip:** Head to page 125 for a reminder of Charles' law and the pressure law.

Explaining Charles' law and the pressure law

You can use the derivation for the pressure of an ideal gas from the last two pages to explain why the volume or pressure must increase if the temperature of a fixed mass of ideal gas is increased.

Temperature is related to the kinetic energy of the molecules (page 135) — as the temperature increases, the average speed of the molecules increases. This means the rate of change of momentum of the molecules colliding with the walls of the container increases, and so the force on the walls of the container increases.

If the volume of the container is fixed, this will result in an increased pressure inside the container for two reasons:

- There will be more collisions between the molecules and the walls of the container in a given amount of time.
- On average, a collision will result in a larger change in momentum, and so exert a larger force on the walls of the container.

> **Tip:** There's a longer time between collisions because the walls are further apart, so a molecule takes longer to travel between them.

If the pressure inside the container remains constant, the volume of the container will increase to compensate for the temperature change for two reasons:

- If the volume is larger, there will be a longer time between molecule-wall collisions, and so the rate of change of momentum will be reduced.
- As the volume increases, the surface area of the walls increases. Pressure is defined as the force per unit area, and so increasing the area decreases the pressure.

Root mean square speed

As you saw on the previous page, it often helps to think about the motion of a typical molecule in kinetic theory. $(c_{rms})^2$ is the mean square speed and has units m^2s^{-2}. $(c_{rms})^2$ is the average of the squares of the speeds of molecules — the square root of it gives you the typical speed.

This is called the **root mean square speed** or, usually, the r.m.s. speed. The unit is the same as any speed — ms^{-1}.

$$\text{r.m.s. speed} = \sqrt{(c_{rms})^2} = c_{rms}$$

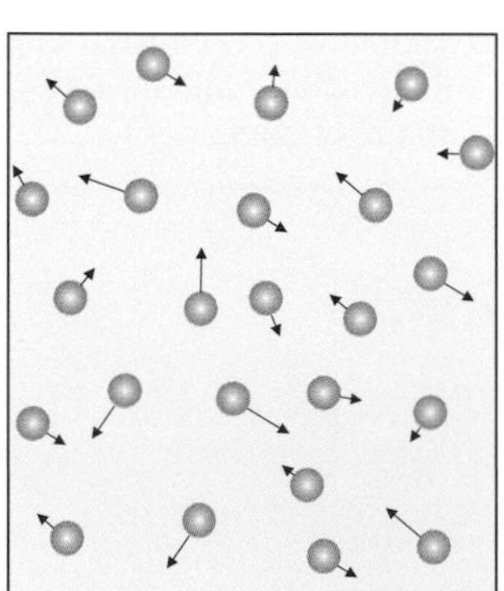

Figure 3: *A visual representation of an ideal gas. All molecules are identical, have negligible volume and move randomly.*

Assumptions in kinetic theory

In kinetic theory, physicists picture gas molecules moving at high speed in random directions. To get equations like the one derived earlier in this topic though, some simplifying assumptions are needed:

- All molecules of the gas are identical.
- The gas contains a large number of molecules.
- The molecules move rapidly and randomly.
- Newtonian mechanics apply (i.e. the motion of the molecules follows Newton's laws).
- Collisions between molecules themselves or at the walls of a container are perfectly elastic (i.e. kinetic energy is conserved).
- There are no forces between molecules except during collisions (i.e. they move with constant velocity in a straight line between collisions).

- The forces that act during collisions are instantaneous.
- The molecules have a negligible volume compared with the volume of the container (i.e. they act as point masses).

A gas obeying these assumptions is called an ideal gas. Real gases behave like ideal gases as long as the pressure isn't too big and the temperature is reasonably high (compared with their boiling point), so they're useful assumptions.

Practice Questions — Application

Q1 a) Show that the change in momentum of an ideal gas molecule colliding with the wall of a cubic container is equal to $2m\mathbf{u}$, where m is the mass of the molecule and $\mathbf{u}$ is its velocity normal to the wall.

b) Hence show that the force exerted on the wall of the container by the molecule of gas is equal to $\frac{m\mathbf{u}^2}{l}$, where l is the length of the edges of the container.

c) Hence show that the total force exerted by all the molecules of an ideal gas on one wall of a cubic container is equal to $\frac{Nm\overline{\mathbf{u}^2}}{V}$, where N is the number of molecules and $\overline{\mathbf{u}^2}$ is the mean square speed of the molecules in the direction normal to the wall.

d) Hence show that $pV = \frac{1}{3}Nm(c_{rms})^2$, where $(c_{rms})^2$ is the mean square speed of the molecules.

Q2 A sealed, rigid container with a volume of 1.44 m^3 is filled with 5 moles of an ideal gas. If the molecules of the gas have a mean square speed of 8.11×10^6 m^{2}s^{-2} and a mass of 5.31×10^{-26} kg, find the pressure inside the container.

Tip: Remember that the direction matters for velocity. In this case $\mathbf{u}$ is in the direction normal (at 90°) to the wall.

Practice Questions — Fact Recall

Q1 What does c_{rms} represent?

Q2 Give two reasons why increasing the temperature of a gas increases the force it exerts on the walls of its container.

Q3 A sealed container contains a fixed mass of an ideal gas. The temperature of the gas inside the container is increased, which causes another property of the gas to increase. Give two properties this could be.

Q4 State four assumptions made about an ideal gas in kinetic theory.

4. Energy and Temperature

The energy and temperature of gas molecules are closely linked — in fact, one can be used to work out the other. The specific heat capacity of any substance tells you how much energy is needed to raise its temperature by a given amount.

Learning Objectives:

- Know how the temperature of a gas and the speed of the gas molecules are linked.
- Know how energy is transferred between substances.
- Understand that heat transfer between substances occurs faster the bigger the difference in temperatures.
- Be able to find the average and total kinetic energy of gas molecules.
- Be able to find the energy transferred in a substance after a given change of temperature or change of state.

Specification Reference 3.5.3

Speed distribution of gas molecules

The speed distribution of gas molecules depends on the temperature. The molecules in a gas don't all travel at the same speed. Some molecules will be moving fast but others much more slowly. Most will travel around the average speed. The shape of the speed distribution depends on the temperature of the gas. As the temperature of the gas increases:

- The average molecule speed increases.
- The distribution curve becomes more spread out.

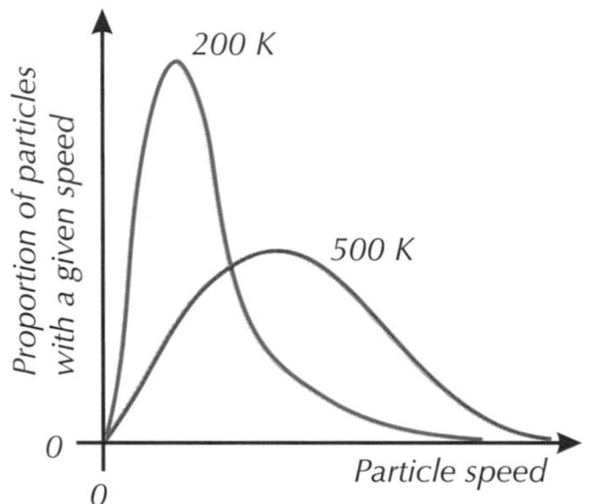

Figure 1: *The distribution of molecule speeds for a gas at 200 K and at 500 K.*

Energy changes between molecules

The molecules of a gas collide with each other all the time. Some of these collisions will be 'head-on' (molecules moving in opposite directions) while others will be 'shunts from behind' (molecules moving in the same direction). As a result of the collisions, energy will be transferred between molecules. Some molecules will gain speed in a collision and others will slow down.

Between collisions, the molecules will travel at constant speed. The energy of individual molecules changes at each collision, but the total energy of the system doesn't change. So, the average speed of the molecules will stay the same provided the temperature of the gas stays the same.

Figure 2: *The energy transfer from a hot drink to its surroundings can be monitored by measuring the temperature inside the cup.*

Heat transfer

Heat is always transferred from hotter substances to cooler substances. In particle terms, the particle with more energy transfers some energy to the particle with less energy. The higher the difference in temperature between two substances, the faster the heat transfer between substances will happen.

This is why ice will melt if you leave it out of the freezer — gas molecules collide with ice particles and transfer some energy to them. The hotter the room, the faster the ice will melt. The gas in the room will also get colder, but you don't notice the difference unless there's a huge amount of ice.

Heat is also transferred by radiation, and hotter substances radiate heat quicker than cooler substances.

Tip: The same is true for hot substances in a cooler room. A hot drink at 100 °C will transfer heat to the surrounding air molecules much quicker than a hot drink at 50 °C.

Average kinetic energy of gas molecules

There are two equations for the product pV of a gas — the ideal gas equation (page 127), and the equation involving the mean square speed of the molecules (page 131). You can equate these to get an expression for the average kinetic energy.

The ideal gas equation is:

$$pV = nRT$$

The equation given by kinetic theory is:

$$pV = \frac{1}{3}Nm(c_{rms})^2$$

Equating these two gives:

$$\frac{1}{3}Nm(c_{rms})^2 = nRT$$

Multiplying by $\frac{3}{2}$ gives:

$$\frac{3}{2} \times \frac{1}{3}Nm(c_{rms})^2 = \frac{3nRT}{2}$$

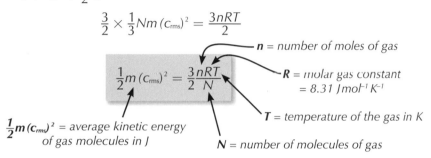

$$\frac{1}{2}m(c_{rms})^2 = \frac{3}{2}\frac{nRT}{N}$$

n = *number of moles of gas*

R = *molar gas constant* = $8.31\ Jmol^{-1}K^{-1}$

T = *temperature of the gas in K*

N = *number of molecules of gas*

$\frac{1}{2}m(c_{rms})^2$ = *average kinetic energy of gas molecules in J*

Tip: Remember n is the number of moles, N is the number of molecules, R is the molar gas constant, and $(c_{rms})^2$ is the mean square speed of the gas molecules. Head to pages 127 and 131 if you need a reminder on what all of these terms mean.

Tip: You might remember that the kinetic energy of a moving object is given by $\frac{1}{2}mv^2$. Here you just replace v^2 with the mean square speed of the gas molecules, $(c_{rms})^2$.

You can substitute Nk for nR, where k is the Boltzmann constant (see page 128), to show that the average kinetic energy of a molecule is directly proportional to T (the absolute temperature). You can use kT as an approximation for the average kinetic energy of the molecules in any substance.

$$\frac{1}{2}m(c_{rms})^2 = \frac{3}{2}kT$$

k = *Boltzmann's constant* = $1.38 \times 10^{-23}\ JK^{-1}$

Tip: The N cancels on the top and bottom.

Finally, the Boltzmann constant is equivalent to $\frac{R}{N_A}$ (see page 128), so you can substitute this for k in the equation above, to get:

$$\frac{1}{2}m(c_{rms})^2 = \frac{3RT}{2N_A}$$

N_A = *Avogadro's constant* = $6.02 \times 10^{23}\ mol^{-1}$

Tip: You can also get to this equation by substituting N_A for $\frac{N}{n}$ in the first equation.

Example

What's the average kinetic energy of the molecules in an ideal gas at 100 °C?

Just put the numbers into the equation above, making sure to convert the temperature to an absolute temperature first.

$$\frac{1}{2}m(c_{rms})^2 = \frac{3}{2}kT$$

$$= \frac{3}{2} \times (1.38 \times 10^{-23}) \times (100 + 273)$$

$$= 7.72 \times 10^{-21}\ \text{J (to 3 s.f.)}$$

Total kinetic energy of gas molecules

Once you've found the average kinetic energy of the molecules in a gas, you can find the total kinetic energy of the molecules as long as you know how many there are. Just multiply the average kinetic energy by the total number of molecules present.

Exam Tip
You can use any of the formulas on page 135 to calculate the average kinetic energy of gas molecules.

Example

What's the total kinetic energy of 3 moles of an ideal gas at 341 K?

First find the average kinetic energy of the molecules:

$$\frac{1}{2}m(c_{rms})^2 = \frac{3}{2}\frac{RT}{N_A}$$
$$= \frac{3}{2}\frac{8.31 \times 341}{6.02 \times 10^{23}}$$
$$= 7.06... \times 10^{-21}\,\text{J}$$

Then multiply this by the number of molecules of gas:

$$\text{total kinetic energy} = n \times N_A \times (7.06... \times 10^{-21})$$
$$= 3 \times (6.02 \times 10^{23}) \times (7.06... \times 10^{-21})$$
$$= 12\,800\,\text{J (to 3 s.f.)}$$

Tip: Look back to page 127 for the relationship between N, n and N_A.

Specific heat capacity

When you heat something, its particles get more kinetic energy and its temperature rises.

Tip: The specific latent heat of a substance changes slightly depending on its temperature.

The **specific heat capacity** (c) of a substance is the amount of energy needed to raise the temperature of 1 kg of the substance by 1 K (or 1°C).

Or put another way:

energy change = mass × specific heat capacity × change in temperature

$$\Delta Q = mc\Delta T$$

Δ*Q* = *energy change in J*

m = *mass of substance in kg*

c = *specific heat capacity in* $Jkg^{-1}K^{-1}$ *or* $Jkg^{-1}°C^{-1}$

Δ*T* = *temperature change in K or °C*

Tip: You might see ΔT written as $\Delta\theta$.

Example

The specific heat capacity of water is 4180 J kg⁻¹ K⁻¹. If 172 kJ of energy is supplied to 5 kg of water at 300 K, what will its final temperature be?

First find the value of ΔT:

$$\Delta Q = mc\Delta T \Rightarrow \Delta T = \frac{\Delta Q}{mc}$$
$$= \frac{172 \times 10^3}{5 \times 4180}$$
$$= 8.22...\,\text{K}$$

Then add this to the initial temperature:

$$\text{final temperature} = 300 + 8.22...$$
$$= 308\,\text{K (to 3 s.f.)}$$

Tip: Energy is supplied to the water, so the temperature goes up.

Specific latent heat

To melt a solid or boil or evaporate a liquid, you need energy to break the bonds that hold the particles in place. The energy needed for this is called latent heat. The larger the mass of the substance, the more energy it takes to change its state. That's why the **specific latent heat** is defined per kg:

> The specific latent heat (l) of fusion or vaporisation is the quantity of thermal energy required to change the state of 1 kg of a substance.

Which gives:

> energy change = specific latent heat × mass of substance changed

$$\Delta Q = ml$$

ΔQ = *energy change in J*

m = mass of substance in kg

l = specific latent heat in J kg^{-1}

Tip: The specific latent heat of fusion is used when a substance is melting or freezing. The specific latent heat of vaporisation is used when a substance is boiling or condensing.

Tip: You'll usually see the latent heat of vaporisation written l_v and the latent heat of fusion written as l_f.

Tip: Water turns to steam at 100 °C.

Example

Find the energy needed to turn 1 kg of water at 90 °C to 1 kg of steam at 110 °C. c_{water} = 4210 J kg^{-1} K^{-1}, c_{steam} = 1890 J kg^{-1} K^{-1}, and the latent heat of vaporisation of water is 2.26 × 10^6 J kg^{-1}.

First find the energy needed to heat the water by 10 °C:

$$\Delta Q = mc\Delta T = 1 \times 4210 \times 10 = 42100 \text{ J } (= 42.1 \text{ kJ})$$

Then find the energy needed to turn the water to steam:

$$\Delta Q = ml = 1 \times (2.26 \times 10^6) = 2.26 \times 10^6 \text{ J } (= 2260 \text{ kJ})$$

Then find the energy needed to heat the steam by 10° C:

$$\Delta Q = mc\Delta T = 1 \times 1890 \times 10 = 18900 \text{ J } (= 18.9 \text{ kJ})$$

Then just add all these numbers together:

Energy needed = 42.1 + 2260 + 18.9 = 2320 kJ (to 3 s.f.)

Figure 3: *When boiling water, the vast majority of the energy you supply goes into turning the water into steam (only a small proportion heats the water).*

Practice Questions — Application

Q1 What's the average kinetic energy of the molecules of an ideal gas at 112 K?

Q2 2.44 moles of an ideal gas are heated from 250 K to 290 K. Find how much energy is supplied to the gas to cause this heating, assuming all of the energy is converted to kinetic energy of the gas molecules.

Q3 A bowl containing 100 g of water at 25 °C is placed in a freezer. A few hours later, all of the water has become ice at –5 °C.

a) Find how much energy the water lost to its surroundings. c_{water} = 4180 J kg^{-1} K^{-1}, c_{ice} = 2110 J kg^{-1} K^{-1}, l_f = 334 000 J kg^{-1}.

b) The freezer temperature is increased from –20 °C to –10 °C and an identical bowl of water is placed inside the freezer. After the same amount of time, not all of the water has frozen. Why is this?

Practice Questions — Fact Recall

Q1 a) Sketch a graph to show the speed distribution of the molecules of a gas at 100 K and at 250 K.

b) State two ways in which increasing the temperature of a gas affects the speed of the gas molecules.

Q2 How is energy transferred between gas molecules?

Section Summary

Make sure you know...

- That temperature can be measured on the Kelvin (or absolute) scale.
- That absolute zero temperature is equal to 0 K or –273 °C.
- Boyle's law, which states that for an ideal gas at constant temperature the pressure p and volume V of a gas are inversely proportional.
- Charles' law, which states that for an ideal gas at constant pressure the volume V is directly proportional to the absolute temperature T.
- The pressure law, which states that for an ideal gas at constant volume, the pressure p is directly proportional to its absolute temperature T.
- How to sketch graphs of pressure, volume and temperature for a fixed mass of gas following the three gas laws.
- That the Avogadro constant N_A is the number of atoms in exactly 12 g of the carbon isotope ${}^{12}_{6}C$.
- What is meant by molecular mass and molar mass.
- What the molar gas constant R and the Boltzmann constant k are.
- How to use the ideal gas equation and the equation of state of an ideal gas.
- How to derive the equation for the pressure exerted by an ideal gas.
- The assumptions made about an ideal gas in kinetic theory.
- Why increasing the temperature of a fixed mass of an ideal gas causes either its volume or the pressure inside its container (or both) to increase.
- How the temperature of a gas is linked to the speed of the molecules in the gas.
- That (heat) energy can be transferred between substances by the collision of particles.
- That (heat) energy transfer between substances occurs quicker if there is a greater difference in temperature between the substances.
- How to calculate the average kinetic energy of the molecules in an ideal gas.
- How to calculate the total kinetic energy of the molecules in an ideal gas.
- How to find the energy transferred when a substance changes temperature by a given amount.
- How to find the energy transferred when a substance changes state.

Exam-style Questions

1 (a) The graph below shows the relationship between pressure and volume for an ideal gas with a fixed temperature T_1. On the same axes, sketch a pressure-volume curve for two more ideal gases with fixed temperatures T_2 and T_3, where $T_2 > T_1$ and $T_3 < T_1$.

(2 marks)

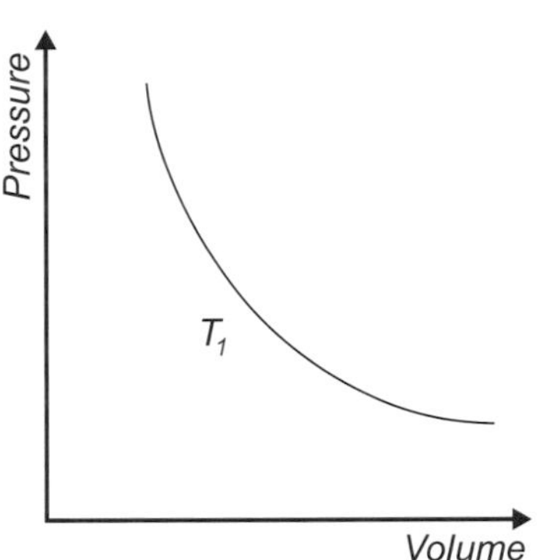

1 (b) A sealed container with a fixed volume of 0.51 m^3 is filled with an ideal gas at low temperature. The gas is heated so that the pressure inside the container increases. At 0 °C the pressure inside the container is 8.1×10^5 Pa.

1 (b) (i) Explain why increasing the temperature of the gas increases the pressure inside the container.

(3 marks)

1 (b) (ii) Using the axes below, show how the pressure of the gas varies with temperature between –273 °C and 100 °C.

(2 marks)

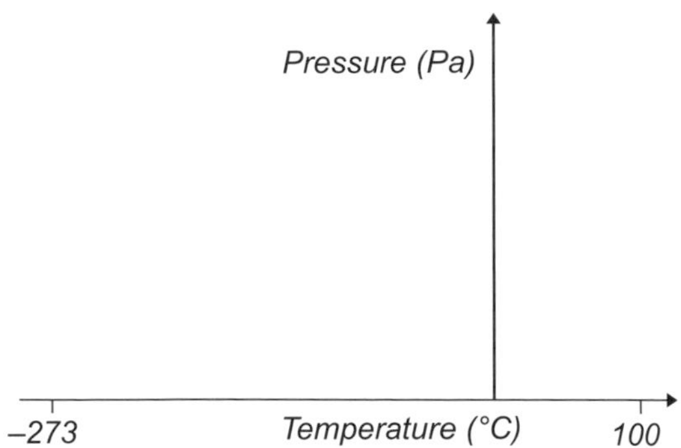

1 (b) (iii) Calculate the number of molecules of gas present in the container.

(2 marks)

1 (b) (iv) The specific heat capacity of the gas is 2.2×10^3 J kg^{-1}K^{-1} and the mass of a molecule of the gas is 2.7×10^{-26} kg. If the gas was heated from –150 °C to 0 °C, calculate the energy transferred to the gas.

(2 marks)

1 (c) State three assumptions that are made about an ideal gas in kinetic theory.

(3 marks)

2 (a) A glass beaker contains a cylindrical block of ice at –25 °C. A heating element is placed inside the block of ice and turned on, supplying energy at a rate of 50 $J s^{-1}$. The ice has a mass of 92 g, a specific heat capacity of 2110 $J kg^{-1} K^{-1}$ and a specific latent heat of fusion of 3.3×10^5 $J kg^{-1}$.

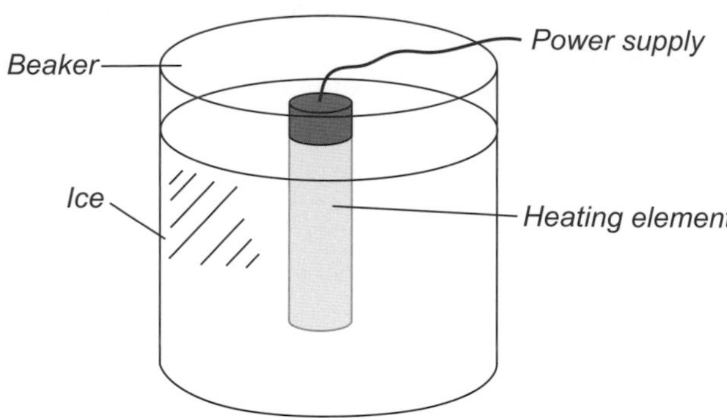

2 (a) (i) Calculate the energy needed to heat the ice from –25 °C to its melting point, 0 °C.

(1 mark)

2 (a) (ii) Calculate the energy needed to melt all of the ice once it reaches 0 °C.

(1 mark)

2 (a) (iii) Assuming the ice is heated uniformly and there is no heat transfer between the ice and the surroundings, calculate how long it will take for all of the ice to melt.

(2 marks)

2 (b) If the experiment in part (a) is being carried out in a room with air temperature of 25 °C, would insulating the beaker speed up or slow down the melting of the ice? Explain your answer.

(2 marks)

3 (a) Briefly describe what is meant by the following terms.

3 (a) (i) Absolute zero temperature

(1 mark)

3 (a) (ii) The Avogadro constant N_A

(1 mark)

3 (a) (iii) Molar mass

(1 mark)

3 (b) A sealed container with a fixed volume of 4.18 m^3 is filled with 54.0 moles of an ideal gas.

3 (b) (i) Calculate the total number of molecules of gas in the container.

(1 mark)

3 (b) (ii) Calculate the temperature of the gas at atmospheric pressure (10^5 Pa).

(2 marks)

3 (b) (iii) Calculate the total kinetic energy of the gas molecules at this temperature.

(3 marks)

1. Lenses

A lot of what we know about astrophysics was discovered by looking at objects in space. One way of doing this is to use optical telescopes to collect light from space. Some optical telescopes use lenses, so you need to start with a bit of lens theory before we get onto the really cool bits.

Learning Objectives:
- Understand what the principal focus and the focal length of a converging lens are.
- Understand how images are formed by a converging lens.
- Be able to draw ray diagrams and use them to work out where an image will be formed by a converging lens.
- Understand and use the lens equation: $\frac{1}{f} = \frac{1}{u} + \frac{1}{v}$.

Specification Reference A.1.1

Converging lenses

Lenses change the direction of light rays by **refraction**. **Converging lenses** are convex (thicker across the middle than at the edges) and cause rays of light to bend towards each other. In Figure 1, the horizontal axis through the centre of a lens is called the **principal axis** and the vertical axis is called the **lens axis**.

Rays parallel to the principal axis of the lens are known as **axial rays**. Axial rays passing through the lens will converge on a point called the **principal focus** (see Figures 1 and 3). Rays that aren't parallel to the principal axis are called **non-axial rays**. A converging lens will cause parallel non-axial rays to converge somewhere else on the **focal plane** — the plane perpendicular to the principal axis that contains the principal focus (see Figure 2).

The **focal length** of the lens, *f*, is the perpendicular distance between the lens axis and the focal plane.

Tip: You should hopefully remember a bit of this lens theory from GCSE.

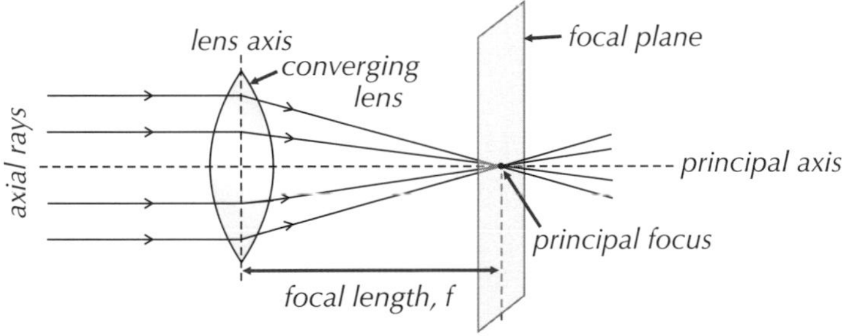

***Figure 1:** Axial rays passing through a lens converging at the principal focus.*

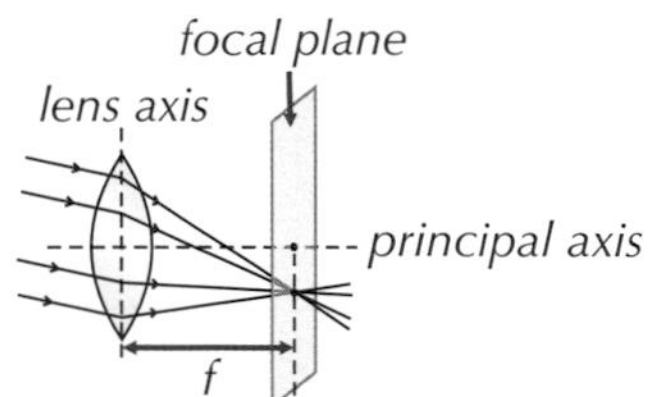

***Figure 2:** Parallel non-axial rays will converge on the focal plane.*

Images

When light rays from an object pass through a lens, an image is formed where the rays meet. To work out where an image will appear, you can draw a **ray diagram**.

Ray diagrams

A ray diagram shows how light rays travel from an object through a lens. Draw all the rays coming from the top of the object, and where they meet each other is where the top of the image will be formed.

You only need to draw two rays from the top of the object to work out where the top of the image will be: one parallel to the principal axis (an axial ray) that passes through the principal focus, and one passing through the centre of the lens that doesn't get refracted at all — see Figure 4. If an object sits on the principal axis, the bottom of the image will be on the principal axis.

If an object doesn't sit on the principal axis you'll also need to draw two rays from the bottom of the object to find where the bottom of the image will be formed.

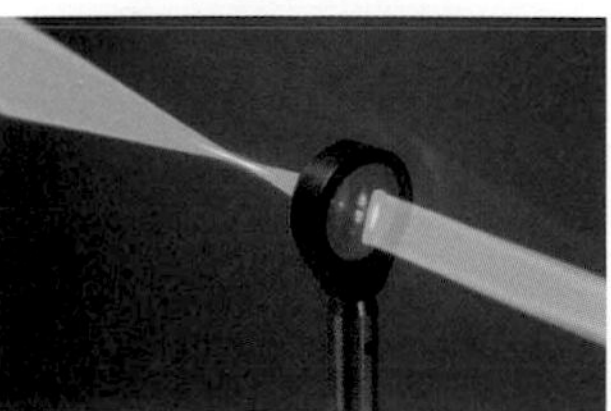

***Figure 3:** A converging lens focusing axial rays onto the principal focus.*

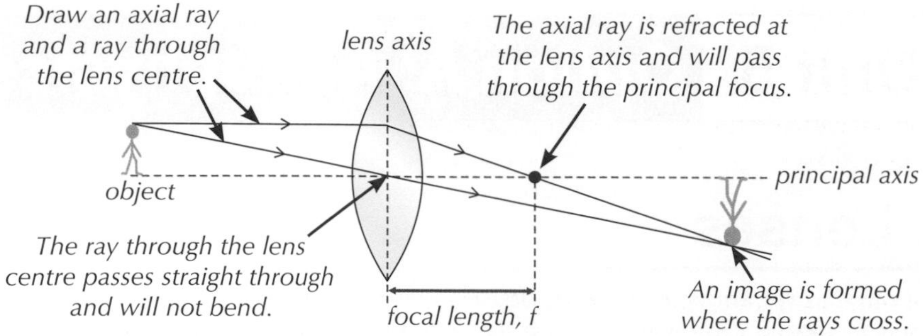
Draw an axial ray and a ray through the lens centre.
lens axis
The axial ray is refracted at the lens axis and will pass through the principal focus.
principal axis
object
The ray through the lens centre passes straight through and will not bend.
focal length, f
An image is formed where the rays cross.

Figure 4: *How to draw a ray diagram for light passing through a converging lens.*

Tip: In reality the ray through the lens centre will refract one way as it enters the lens, and then back again when it leaves. The overall direction won't be changed, so in ray diagrams you can just draw it as a straight line.

A ray diagram can also tell you whether the image is diminished (smaller than the object), the same size, or magnified. If the image is further from the lens axis than the object, then it's magnified, if it's closer it's diminished, and if it's the same distance away, then it's the same size. (See page 145 for more on magnification.)

Figure 5: *When you look into a mirror, you see a virtual image. Surprisingly, there's not really a bird behind the mirror — it just looks like the light rays are coming from behind the mirror.*

Real and virtual images

Images can be real or virtual. A **real image** is formed when light rays from a point on an object are made to pass through another point in space. The light rays are actually there, and the image can be captured on a screen. A **virtual image** is formed when light rays from a point on an object appear to have come from another point in space. The light rays aren't really where the image appears to be, so the image can't be captured on a screen.

Converging lenses can form both real and virtual images, depending on where the object is. If the object is further than the focal length away from the lens, the image is real and inverted. If the object's closer, the image is virtual. The ray diagrams in Figures 7 and 8 show how real and virtual images are formed by a converging lens.

Figure 6: *The garden is further from the converging lens than the focal point of the lens, so the image formed is real and inverted (upside down).*

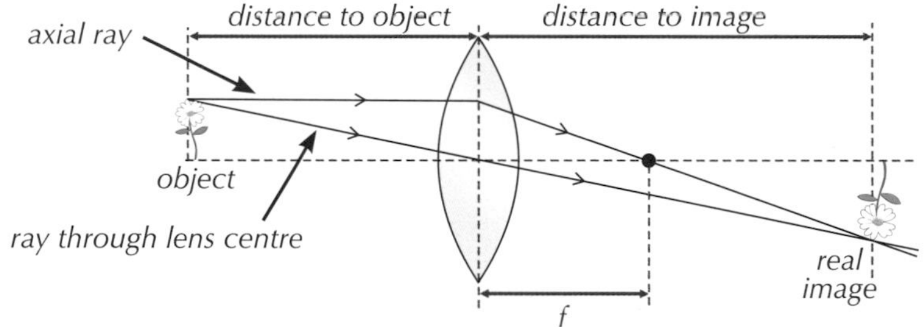
axial ray
distance to object
distance to image
object
ray through lens centre
real image
f

Figure 7: *A real image of an object is formed by a converging lens when the object is further from the lens than the focal length.*

Tip: If the image is formed on the same side of the lens as the object, it's a virtual image. Otherwise, it's a real image.

The image is formed where the rays meet. Here you have to extend the rays back to where they appear to meet — this is where the virtual image is formed.

distance to image

distance to object

virtual image

object

f

Figure 8: *A virtual image of an object is formed by a converging lens when the object is closer to the lens than the focal length.*

The lens equation

The distance between the object and the lens axis is known as u, and the distance between image and the lens axis in known as v (positive if image is real, negative if image is virtual). The values u, v and f are related by the lens equation:

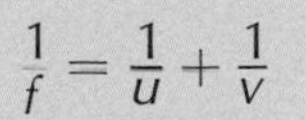

$$\frac{1}{f} = \frac{1}{u} + \frac{1}{v}$$

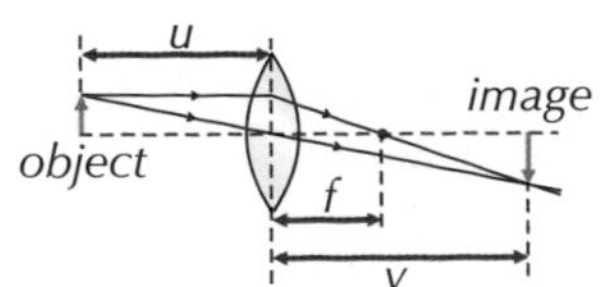

***Figure 9:** The positions of u and v for a real image formed by a lens with a focal length f.*

Tip: If you place an object at exactly double the focal length ($2f$) from the lens axis, the lens equation will tell you that the image will also be $2f$ from the lens axis. The image will not be magnified — it will be exactly the same size as the object.

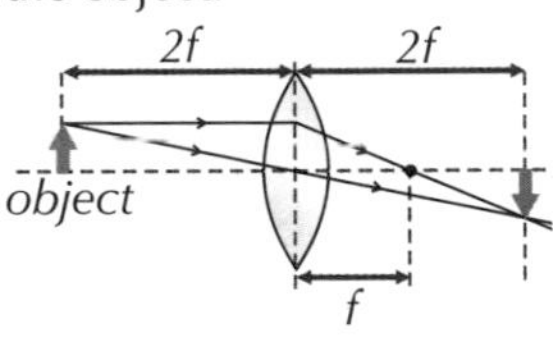

Example

An object is placed 3.0 metres away from a converging lens with a focal length of 1.2 m. At what distance from the lens will an image be produced? Will the image be real or virtual?

$u = 3.0$ and $f = 1.2$ m, substituting into the lens equation gives

$\frac{1}{1.2} = \frac{1}{3.0} + \frac{1}{v} \Rightarrow \frac{1}{v} = \frac{1}{1.2} - \frac{1}{3.0} = \frac{1}{2.0}$, so $v = 2.0$ m.

The value of v is positive, so the image is real. (The object is further than the focal length away from the lens, so this also tells you it'll be real.)

Practice Question — Application

Q1 A magnifying glass made from a converging lens is used to look at a screw closely. The magnifying glass is placed at a distance shorter than its focal length, f, to the screw.

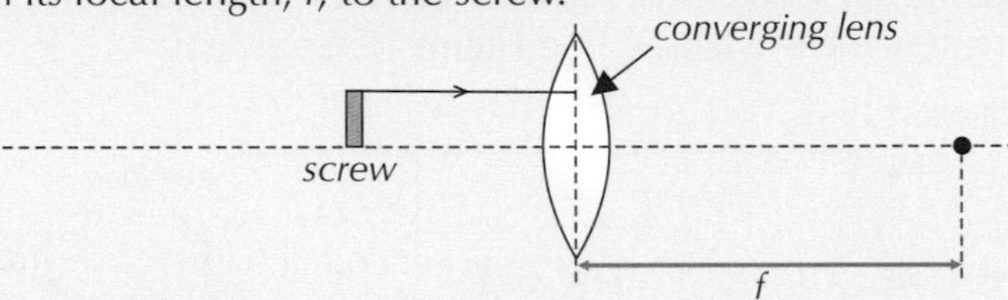

a) Copy the diagram and label the following:
(i) lens axis (ii) principal axis (iii) principal focus

b) Complete the ray diagram to show where the image will be formed.

c) State three properties of the image formed.

d) As the magnifying glass is moved away, the image of the screw seen through the magnifying glass appears to flip upside down. Why does the image flip upside down?

e) When the object is 20 cm from the lens axis, a real image that is the same distance from the lens axis is produced. What is the focal length of the magnifying lens?

Exam Tip

If you're asked for the properties of an image — think about whether it'll be real or virtual, inverted or upright, and its size in comparison to the object.

Practice Questions — Fact Recall

Q1 Name the point that axial rays converge on when passed through a converging lens.

Q2 What is the focal plane of a converging lens?

Q3 What is the focal length of a converging lens?

Q4 What is a real image? Explain how a real image is formed by light rays passing through a converging lens.

Q5 What is a virtual image? Explain how a virtual image is formed by light rays passing through a converging lens.

Q6 Write down the lens equation.

2. Optical Telescopes

This topic's all about the two main types of optical telescope — refracting telescopes and reflecting telescopes. You need to know their set-up and how they're used with CCDs to detect and record images of objects in space.

Learning Objectives:

- Be able to draw a ray diagram of an astronomical refracting telescope forming an image in normal adjustment.
- Be able to calculate the magnification of an astronomical refracting telescope using M = (angle subtended by image at eye) / (angle subtended by object at unaided eye) or $M = f_o / f_e$.
- Know what is meant by the focal point of a concave mirror.
- Know the Cassegrain arrangement for a reflecting telescope and be able to draw a ray diagram showing the path of rays through the telescope as far as the eyepiece.
- Understand the structure and operation of CCDs.
- Know that the number of electrons released by a CCD is proportional to the intensity of light on it.

Specification Reference A.1.1

Astronomical refracting telescopes

Ray diagram in normal adjustment

An **astronomical refracting telescope** is usually made up of two converging lenses. The objective lens converges the rays from the object to form a real image inside the telescope. The eye lens (confusingly this is part of the telescope — not the lens inside your eye) acts as a magnifying glass on this real image to form a magnified virtual image, which the observer can then view.

When you're viewing an object from space, the object is so far away that you can assume it is at infinity and the rays from each point of it are parallel to each other. When viewed with an astronomical refracting telescope, a real image is formed on the focal plane of the objective lens.

A telescope that is in normal adjustment is set up so that the principal focus of the objective lens is in the same position as the principal focus of the eye lens (see Figure 1). This means the rays from the real image come out of the eye lens parallel and the final magnified image appears to be at infinity. The length of the telescope is the focal length of the objective lens, f_o, added to the focal length of the eye lens, f_e (see Figure 2).

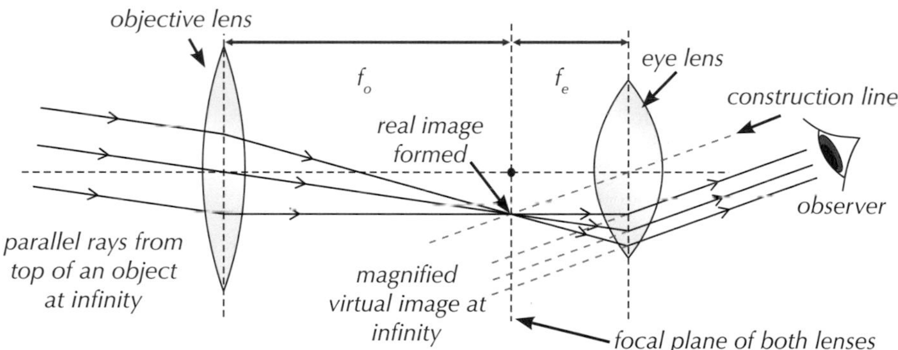

Figure 1: *Light rays from a distant object passing through an astronomical refracting telescope in normal adjustment.*

Tip: An objective lens (or mirror) is the first lens (or mirror) that the light from an object hits.

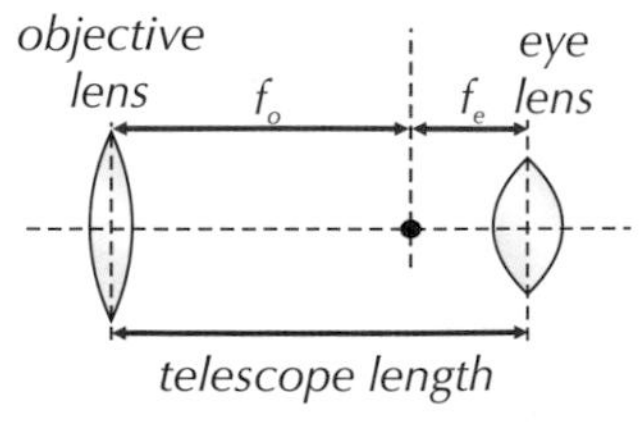

Figure 2: *The length of a telescope is the sum of the focal lengths of the lenses.*

You need to know how to draw a ray diagram for an astronomical telescope in normal adjustment (see Figure 1). Here's how to go about it:

- Start by drawing a straight non-axial ray that passes through the centre of the objective lens and ends at the eye lens axis.
- Draw a non-axial ray on either side of the ray you've just drawn, making sure both rays are parallel to the original ray and end at the objective lens axis. Draw a straight line from where each of these rays meet the objective lens axis, so that all of the rays cross at the same point on the focal plane and reach the eye lens axis. A real image is formed where these three rays intersect.
- Draw a dotted line that passes through the point the rays cross and the centre of the eye lens — this is a construction line. Continue the three rays drawn so they are refracted at the eye lens axis and leave the lens parallel with the construction line (and each other). You can show a virtual image is formed at infinity by extending these lines backwards using dotted lines.

Angular magnification

The magnification, M, of the telescope can be calculated in terms of angles, or the focal length. The **angular magnification** is the angle subtended by the image at the eye divided by the angle subtended by the object at the unaided eye:

$$M = \frac{\textit{angle subtended by image at eye}}{\textit{angle subtended by object at unaided eye}}$$

Tip: It doesn't matter what the units are for the angles used in this formula, as long as both angles are in the same units.

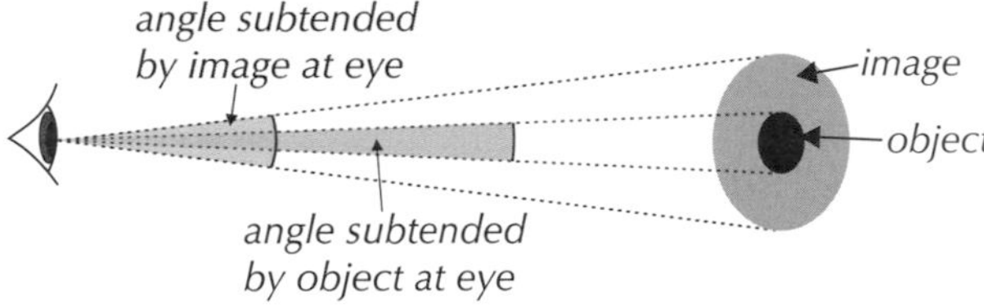

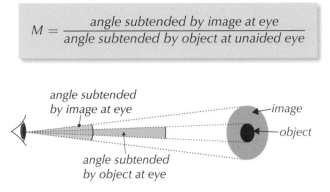

Figure 3: *Calculating the angular magnification of a refracting telescope.*

Example

A galaxy subtends an angle of 9.5×10^{-3} rad at the eye when viewed from Earth. The image seen through an astronomical refracting telescope subtends an angle of 0.71 rad at the eye.
Calculate the angular magnification of the telescope.

$$M = \frac{\text{angle subtended by image at eye}}{\text{angle subtended by object at unaided eye}}$$

$$= \frac{0.71}{9.5 \times 10^{-3}} = 75 \text{ (to 2 s.f.)}$$

The angular magnification of an astronomical refracting telescope in normal adjustment can also be calculated from the focal lengths of the objective and eye lenses (f_o and f_e respectively):

$$M = \frac{f_o}{f_e}$$

Figure 4: *Refracting telescopes have to be very long to get a good magnification (see p.149). This one at the Yerkes Observatory is the largest one currently in operation.*

Example

Calculate the focal length of the objective lens in an astronomical refracting telescope in normal adjustment with an angular magnification of 50 and a total length of 0.8 m.

- You know the angular magnification $M = \frac{f_o}{f_e} = 50$.
- The length of the telescope is the sum of the focal lengths of the lenses: $0.8 = f_o + f_e$, so $f_e = 0.8 - f_o$.
- Substituting this value for f_e into the magnification equation gives: $\frac{f_o}{0.8 - f_o} = 50$
- Rearrange and solve to find: $f_o = 50(0.8 - f_o) = 40 - 50f_o \Rightarrow 51f_o = 40$
  $\Rightarrow f_o = \frac{40}{51} = 0.78 \text{ m (to 2 s.f.)}$

Tip: Notice that 0.78 m of the 0.8 m telescope is made up of the focal length of the objective lens — the focal length of the eye lens is tiny in comparison.

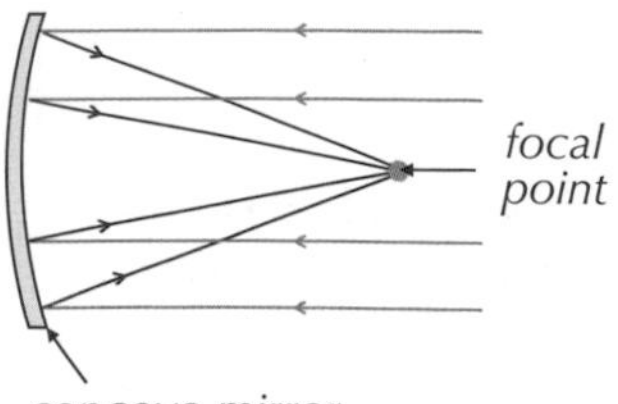

Figure 5: The focal point of a parabolic concave mirror.

Tip: Some reflecting telescopes' principal mirrors are hyperbolic, or another shape — you only need to know about when they are parabolic.

Figure 7: Reflecting telescopes can be much shorter than refracting ones because the light 'doubles back' on itself inside.

Tip: Light intensity is just how bright the light is.

Tip: The potential wells aren't physically there — they're actually electric fields that trap the electrons.

Figure 9: A CCD chip in a circuit.

Reflecting telescopes

Reflecting telescopes use mirrors to reflect and focus light. A parabolic concave primary mirror converges parallel axial rays from an object at its **focal point**, forming a real image (see Figure 5). An eye lens magnifies this image in the same way as in a refracting telescope.

The focal point of the primary mirror is in front of the mirror. If you tried to observe the light from that side of the mirror, you'd be in the way of the rays coming in. So an arrangement needs to be devised where the observer doesn't block out the incoming light. A set-up called the Cassegrain arrangement, which uses a convex secondary mirror, is a common solution to this problem — see Figure 6.

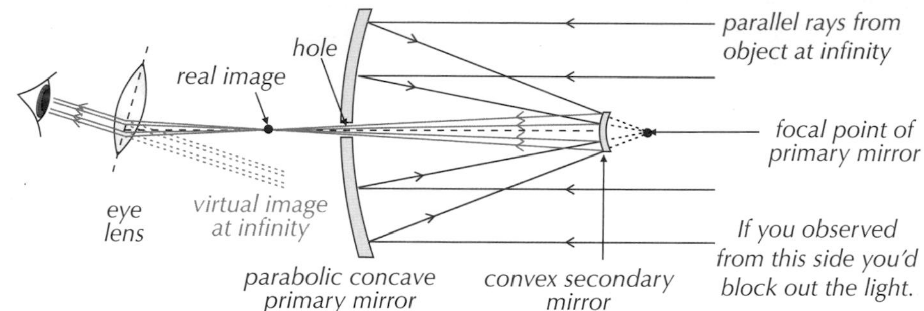

Figure 6: The Cassegrain reflecting telescope arrangement.

Charge-coupled devices (CCDs)

Astronomers use sensitive light detectors called **CCDs** to capture images digitally. CCDs are silicon chips about the size of a postage stamp, divided up into a grid of millions of identical picture elements (pixels).

Silicon is a semiconductor so it doesn't usually have many free electrons. When light shines on a pixel, electrons are released from the silicon, with the number of electrons released being proportional to the brightness/intensity of the light. Underneath each pixel is a potential well (a kind of controllable electrical bucket), which traps the electrons.

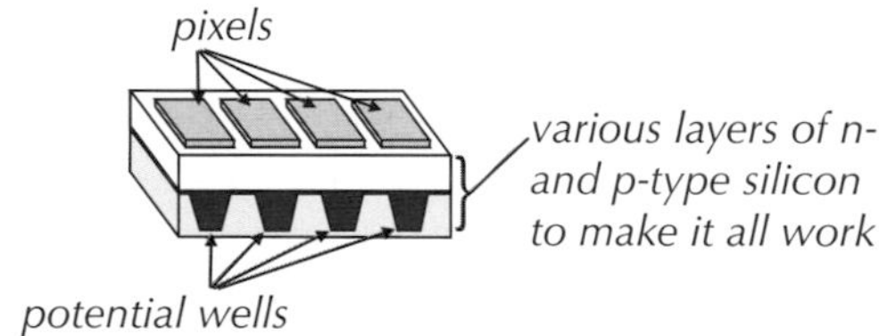

Figure 8: A diagram showing the pixels and potential wells on a CCD chip.

The electrons released build up in the potential wells, creating a pattern identical to the image formed on the CCD chip. Once the chip has been exposed to light for the desired time, the charge is processed and converted into a digital signal that can be sent to computers anywhere in the world.

Quantum efficiency

Quantum physics tells us that electromagnetic radiation is formed in discrete packets of energy called **photons**. The incoming photons release electrons in the silicon of the CCD due to the photoelectric effect.

Electrons are released by more than 70% of the photons that hit a pixel, so the quantum efficiency of a CCD is greater than 70%. In comparison, on average, a cell in the eye needs about 100 photons before it responds and so has a quantum efficiency of about 1%. The quantum efficiency of a photographic emulsion is about 4%.

Tip: You've seen the photoelectric effect before in AS physics.

Practice Question — Application

Q1 The telescope shown in Figure 10 is used to observe distant galaxies. $f_o = 0.52$ m and $f_e = 0.001$ m.

a) Calculate the magnification of the telescope.

b) The image formed of a distant galaxy by the telescope subtends an angle of 2.08 rad at the eye.
Calculate the angle subtended by the galaxy at the unaided eye.

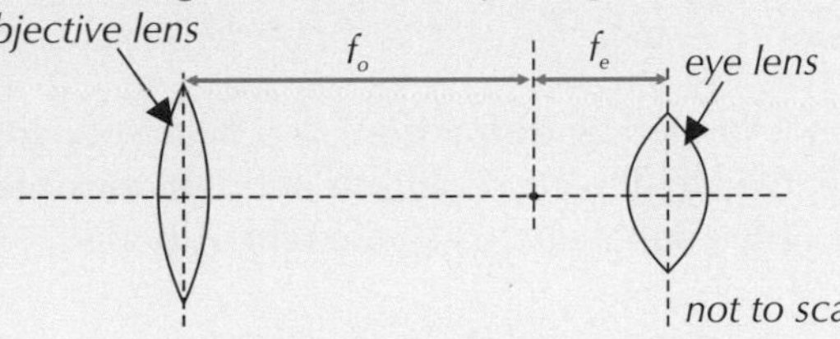

***Figure 10:** A refracting telescope.*

Exam Tip
There are two formulas for calculating linear magnification — just look at the quantities you're given in the question to work out which one you should use.

Practice Questions — Fact Recall

Q1 a) What assumption can be made about the light rays reaching Earth from a distant object in space?

b) Draw a ray diagram of an astronomical refracting telescope in normal adjustment showing the paths of three non-axial rays from a distant object passing through the telescope and forming a virtual image at infinity.

c) What type of image is viewed by the observer looking through the eye lens?

Q2 Give an equation for the magnification of an astronomical refracting telescope in terms of the focal lengths of the lenses.

Q3 Explain why astronomical refracting telescopes have to be very long to produce a highly magnified image.

Q4 Draw a ray diagram of a Cassegrain reflecting telescope showing the path of rays as they pass through the telescope and form a virtual image at infinity.

Q5 a) Describe how light incident on a CCD produces a digital image.

b) What is meant by the quantum efficiency of a CCD?
What is its value?

Exam Tip
Make sure you can draw ray diagrams for the two types of optical telescopes to show how light passes through them.

3. Comparing Telescopes

Telescopes come in all sorts of different sizes and set-ups. Different ones will perform better in different situations so it's important to choose the right one. Your decision may also be based on factors such as how much space you have, or how much money you have.

Learning Objectives:
- Know the diffraction pattern produced by a circular aperture.
- Understand what the resolving power of a telescope is and be able to calculate it using the Rayleigh criterion: $\theta \approx \frac{\lambda}{D}$.
- Know the relative merits of using reflecting and refracting telescopes, including the problems of spherical and chromatic aberration.

Specification Reference A.1.1

Resolving power of a telescope

The **resolving power** of a telescope is just a measure of how much detail you can see. It's very important when choosing a telescope — you could have a huge magnification, but if your resolving power's low, you'll just see a big blurry image.

The resolving power of an instrument is the smallest angular separation at which it can distinguish two points.

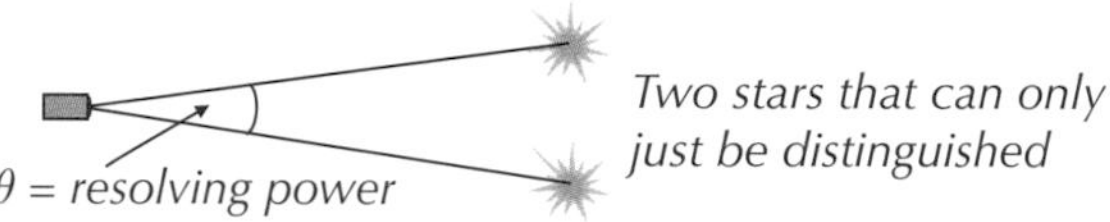

Figure 1: *Finding the resolving power of a telescope.*

Resolution is limited by **diffraction**. If a beam of light passes through a circular aperture, then a diffraction pattern of bright maxima and dark minima is formed. The central circle is called the Airy disc.

Tip: When light passes through a circular aperture, it spreads out. This is called diffraction. The light interferes constructively and destructively to produce a diffraction pattern, which you met in AS physics.

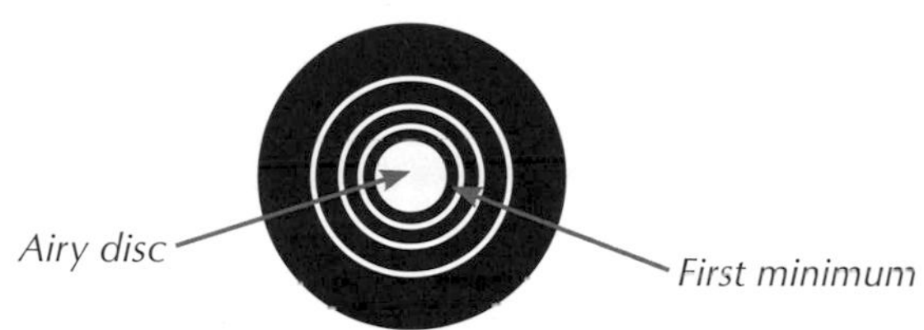

Figure 2: *Diffraction pattern through a circular aperture.*

The Rayleigh criterion

Two light sources can just be distinguished if the centre of the Airy disc from one source is at least as far away as the first minimum of the other source (i.e. their Airy discs do not touch) — see Figure 3.

Figure 3: *Two light sources can be resolved if the Airy discs of their diffraction patterns do not touch.*

This observation led to the **Rayleigh criterion**:

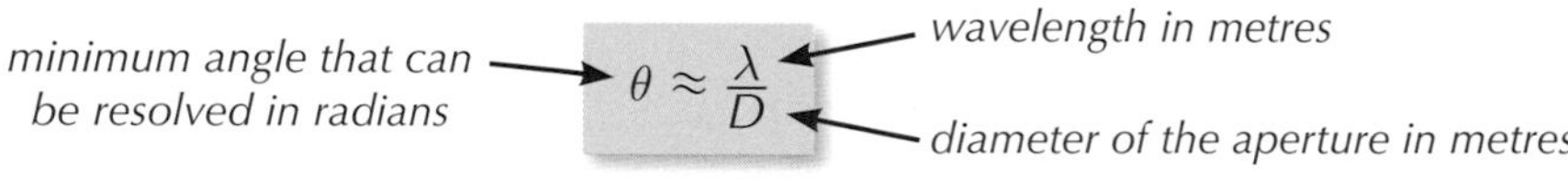

$$\theta \approx \frac{\lambda}{D}$$

For telescopes, D is the diameter of the objective lens or the objective mirror. So very large lenses or mirrors are needed to see fine detail.

Tip: $\theta \propto \lambda$, so the resolving power of a telescope is different for every wavelength of light — it's not a fixed value for the telescope. The lower the angle, the better the resolving power.

Example

Find the diameter of lens needed to resolve radiation with a wavelength of 900 nm from two objects that are 1.7 × 10⁻⁶ rad apart in the sky.

Rearrange the Rayleigh criterion:

$$D = \frac{\lambda}{\theta} = \frac{900 \times 10^{-9}}{1.7 \times 10^{-6}} = 0.53 \text{ m (to 2 s.f.)}$$

Reflectors or refractors?

There are disadvantages and difficulties to using both refracting and reflecting telescopes.

Refracting telescopes

- Glass refracts different colours of light by different amounts and so the image for each colour is in a slightly different position. This blurs the image and is called **chromatic aberration**.

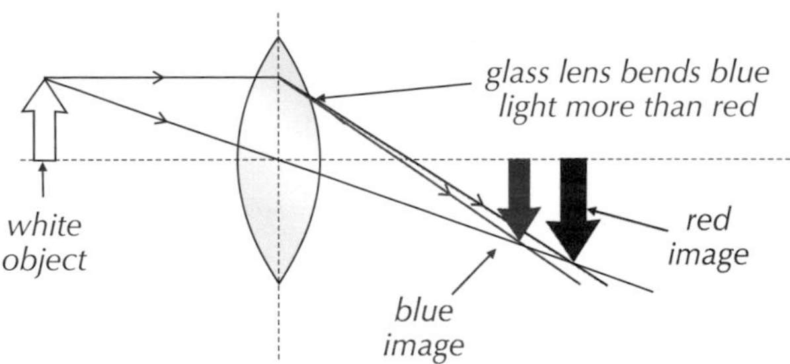

Figure 4: *Chromatic aberration.*

Tip: Different colours of light have different wavelengths, and different wavelengths of light are refracted different amounts.

- Any bubbles or impurities in the glass absorb and scatter some of the light, which means that very faint objects aren't seen. Building large lenses that are of a sufficiently good quality is difficult and expensive.
- Large lenses are very heavy and can only be supported from their edges, so their shape can become distorted.
- For a large magnification, the objective lens needs to have a very long focal length. This means that refracting telescopes have to be very long, leading to very large, expensive buildings being needed to house them.

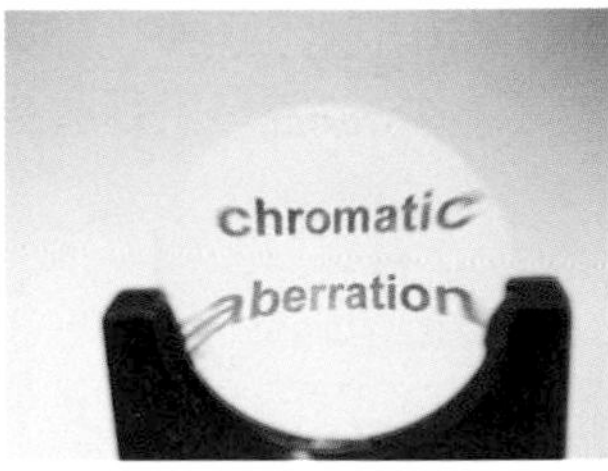

Figure 5: *Different wavelengths of light are refracted by different amounts by the lens, which causes the blurred fringe effect seen here.*

Reflecting telescopes

Large mirrors of good quality are much cheaper to build than large lenses. They can also be supported from underneath so they don't distort as much as lenses.

Mirrors don't suffer from chromatic aberration but can have **spherical aberration**. If the shape of the mirror isn't quite right, parallel rays reflecting off different parts of the mirror do not all converge onto the same point.

Tip: When the Hubble Space Telescope was launched it suffered from spherical aberration. They had to find a way round the problem before it could be used.

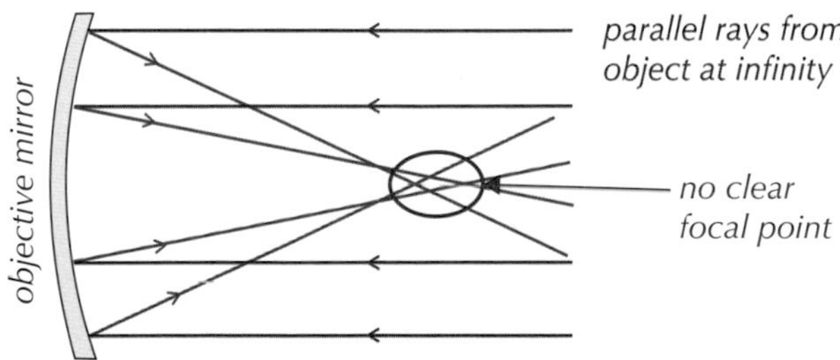

Figure 6: *Spherical aberration.*

The secondary mirror in a Cassegrain telescope can also cause problems. Some incoming light will be blocked by the secondary mirror and mirror supports, and some of the light reflected from the primary mirror will diffract round the secondary mirror — both leading to a decrease in image clarity.

Tip: See p.146 if you need a recap on the Cassegrain telescope.

Tip: Remember, the resolving power of a telescope is actually an angle.

Practice Questions — Application

Q1 Telescope A has a dish diameter of 3 m, and Telescope B has a dish diameter of 2.5 m. Which will have a higher resolving power for a given wavelength of radiation?

Q2 A reflecting telescope with an aperture of diameter 3.2 m is used to detect light with a wavelength of 650 nm.

a) Calculate the resolving power of the telescope at this wavelength.

b) The light detected is emitted by two sources, separated by an angle of 1.99×10^{-7} rad. Calculate the maximum wavelength of light these sources would need to emit to be distinguished as two sources by the telescope.

Practice Questions — Fact Recall

Q1 What is the resolving power of a telescope?

Q2 What sort of pattern is produced when light passes through a circular aperture? What is the central part of this pattern called? What effect does this have on the resolution of a telescope?

Q3 Write down the Rayleigh criterion.

Q4 a) Describe the problem of chromatic aberration when using refracting telescopes.

b) Give two more examples of the problems with using refracting telescopes.

Q5 Give two advantages of using a reflecting telescope rather than a refracting telescope with the same resolution power and magnification.

Q6 The mirror of an old reflecting telescope has become slightly distorted and now creates images that are slightly blurred.
Name this effect and describe how this problem occurs.

4. Non-optical Telescopes

Astronomers aren't only interested in the visible electromagnetic (EM) radiation coming from space — they also detect and analyse EM radiation that is not visible — like radio waves, I-R, U-V and X-rays.

Learning Objectives:

- Understand how the following telescopes work: single-dish radio telescopes, I-R telescopes, U-V telescopes and X-ray telescopes.
- Understand the similarities and differences between optical telescopes and the telescopes listed above — to include the structure, where they should be positioned, and how they are used.
- Be able to compare the resolving powers and collecting powers of optical, single-dish radio, I-R, U-V and X-ray telescopes.

Specification Reference A.1.2

Radio telescopes

Radio telescopes are similar to optical telescopes in some ways. The most obvious feature of a radio telescope is its parabolic dish. This works in exactly the same way as the objective mirror of an optical reflecting telescope. Instead of a polished mirror, a wire mesh can be used since the long wavelength radio waves don't notice the gaps. EM radiation is reflected and focused by the dish and an antenna is used as a detector at the focal point. There is no equivalent to the eye lens of an optical telescope.

A preamplifier amplifies the weak radio signals without adding too much noise to the signal. The signal is then amplified further by a second amplifier before being passed through a tuner to filter out any unwanted wavelengths. A computer creates something called a false-colour image of the detected radio signals. Different colours are assigned to different wavelengths or intensities to produce false-colour images of non-visible EM radiation.

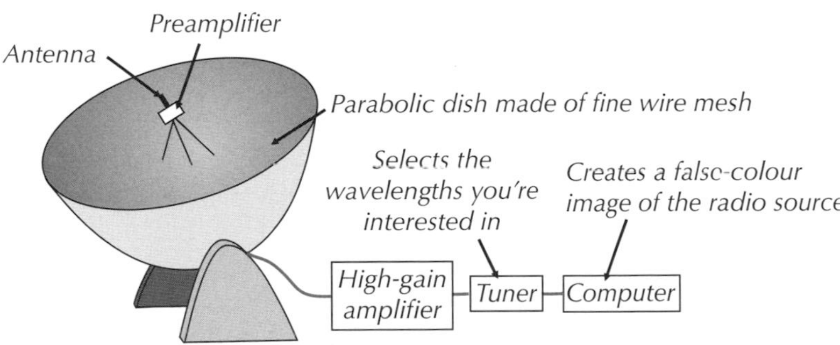

Figure 1: *A radio telescope focuses a signal onto an antenna. The signal is amplified, filtered and analysed to produce a digital image.*

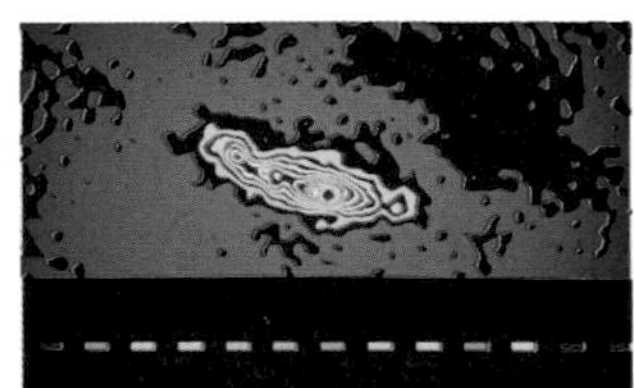

Figure 2: *A false-colour radio image of a galaxy.*

Most radio telescopes are manoeuvrable, allowing the source of the waves to be tracked (in the same way as by optical telescopes). The telescope moves with the source, stopping it 'slipping out of view' as the Earth rotates.

Resolving power

The wavelengths of radio waves are about a million times longer than the wavelengths of light. The Rayleigh criterion (see p.148) gives the resolving power of a telescope as $\theta \approx \frac{\lambda}{D}$.

So for a radio telescope to have the same resolving power as an optical telescope, its dish would need to be a million times bigger (about the size of the UK for a decent one). The resolving power of a radio telescope is worse than the unaided eye.

Radio astronomers get around this by linking lots of telescopes together. Using some nifty computer programming, their data can be combined to form a single image. This is equivalent to one huge dish the size of the separation of the telescopes. Resolutions thousands of times better than optical telescopes can be achieved this way.

Figure 3: *The Very Large Array (VLA) in New Mexico consists of 27 radio dishes, each with a 25 m diameter.*

Benefits of radio telescopes

Radio telescopes are much easier to make than optical telescopes...

- Being able to make the radio telescope's dish using a wire mesh makes their construction much easier and cheaper than optical reflectors.
- The longer the wavelength of the radiation being detected, the less it's affected by imperfections in the shape of the dish or mirror collecting it. So for radio telescopes, the dish doesn't have to be anywhere near as perfect as the mirrors and lenses used in optical telescopes to avoid problems like spherical aberration.

Tip: Forgotten all about spherical aberration? Pop back to p.149.

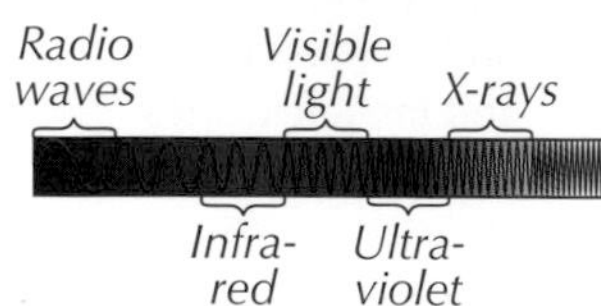

Figure 4: *The positions of types of radiation on the EM spectrum — the wavelength increases from right to left.*

I-R and U-V telescopes

Infrared (I-R) and ultraviolet (U-V) telescopes are very similar to optical reflecting telescopes. They use the same parabolic mirror set-up to focus the radiation onto a detector. In both cases, CCDs (see p.146) or special photographic paper are used as the radiation detectors, just as in optical telescopes.

The longer the wavelength of the radiation, the less it's affected by imperfections in the mirror (see above). So the mirrors in infrared telescopes don't need to be as perfectly shaped as in optical telescopes. But because U-V waves have a shorter wavelength, the mirrors in U-V telescopes have to be even more precisely made (see Figure 4).

I-R telescopes have the added problem that they produce their own infrared radiation due to their temperature. They need to be cooled to very low temperatures using liquid helium, or refrigeration units.

Tip: Infrared is produced by anything that's hot (or even moderately warm) — so if an infrared telescope isn't cooled it'll produce its own infrared radiation which will be mixed up with the radiation being observed.

X-ray telescopes

X-ray telescopes have a different structure from other telescopes. X-rays don't reflect off surfaces in the same way as most other EM radiation. Usually X-ray radiation is either absorbed by a material or it passes straight through it.

X-rays do reflect if they just graze a mirror's surface though. By having a series of nested mirrors, you can gradually alter the direction of X-rays enough to bring them to a focus on a detector. This type of telescope is called a grazing telescope.

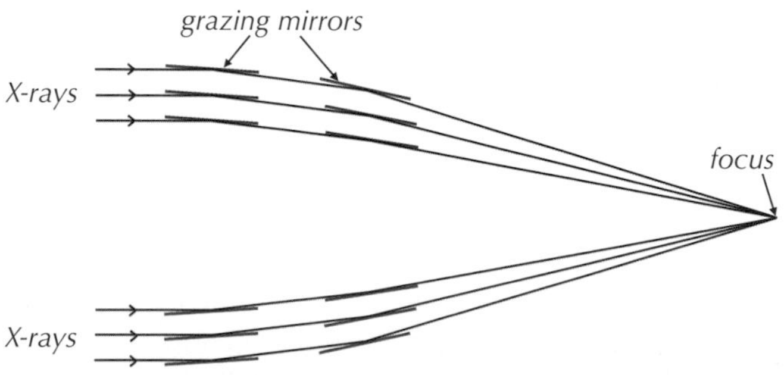

Figure 5: *Grazing mirrors focusing X-rays in an X-ray telescope.*

The X-rays can be detected using a modified Geiger counter or a fine wire mesh. Modern X-ray telescopes such as the XMM-Newton telescope use highly sensitive X-ray CCD cameras.

Figure 6: *The XMM-Newton telescope actually contains three separate X-ray telescopes, each with 58 mirrors which gradually alter the direction of the X-rays.*

Telescope positioning

One of the big problems with doing astronomy on Earth is trying to look through the atmosphere. Our atmosphere only lets certain wavelengths of electromagnetic radiation through and is opaque to all the others. Figure 7 shows how the transparency of the atmosphere varies with wavelength.

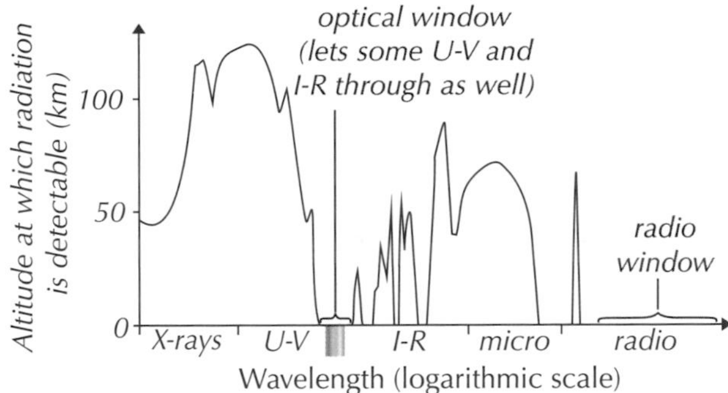

Figure 7: *The transparency of the Earth's atmosphere to different wavelengths of EM radiation.*

We can use optical and radio telescopes on the surface of the Earth because the atmosphere is transparent to these wavelengths. Observing other wavelengths can be a bit more tricky.

A few wavelengths of infrared radiation can reach the Earth's surface, but most are absorbed by water vapour in the atmosphere. On Earth, the best way to observe I-R radiation is to set up shop in high and dry places, like the Mauna Kea volcano in Hawaii.

Most ultraviolet, X-rays and the other wavelengths of infrared radiation are absorbed higher up in the atmosphere, so being on a mountain doesn't help.

One way to get round this problem is to strap U-V, X-ray and I-R telescopes to high-altitude weather balloons or aeroplanes. They can take the telescope high enough into the atmosphere to detect the radiation.

The ideal situation is to get your telescope above the atmosphere altogether, by launching it into space and setting it in orbit around the Earth (see Figure 6 on the previous page).

Figure 8: *The UK Infra-Red Telescope (UKIRT) is one of twelve telescopes around the summit of the Mauna Kea volcano.*

Figure 9: *The Stratospheric Observatory for Infrared Astronomy's (SOFIA) airborne observatory — a telescope embedded in a plane.*

Resolving power

You need to be able to compare resolving powers of various non-optical telescopes with that of an optical telescope. The resolving power of a telescope is limited by two main factors:

- The Rayleigh criterion (see page 148):
  This depends on the wavelength of the radiation and the diameter of the objective mirror or dish. So, for the same size of dish, a U-V telescope has a much better resolving power than a radio telescope, as the radiation it detects has a much shorter wavelength.
- The quality of the detector:
  The resolving power of a telescope is limited by the resolving power of the detector. That can be how many pixels there are on a CCD, or for a wire mesh X-ray detector, how fine the wire mesh is.

Tip: Remember, the Rayleigh criterion is: $\theta \approx \frac{\lambda}{D}$.

A lower value of θ means a better resolving power.

Collecting power

The **collecting power** of a telescope is proportional to its collecting area. For a radio, optical, U-V or I-R telescope, this is the area of the objective mirror or dish. For X-ray telescopes, it's the size of the opening through which X-rays can enter the telescope. In general, X-ray telescopes have a much lower collecting power than other types of telescope.

A bigger dish or mirror collects more energy from an object in a given time. This gives a more intense image, so the telescope can observe fainter objects. The collecting power (energy collected per second) is proportional to the area:

$$\textit{collecting power} \propto \textit{dish diameter}^2$$

Practice Question — Application

Q1 The VISTA (Visible and Infrared Survey Telescope for Astronomy) is positioned at an altitude of 2500 m in the Atacama Desert in Chile. The telescope has a mirror diameter of 4.1 m.

a) How many times greater is the collecting power of VISTA than that of the largest astronomical refracting telescope with an objective lens of diameter 1.02 m?

b) The resolving power of this telescope is found to be better in the visible light region than in the infrared region.
Suggest a reason for this.

c) The Atacama desert is one of the driest places on Earth and the telescope is at an altitude of around 2500 m. Why is this a good location?

d) Give an example of how the resolving power of the telescope for a particular wavelength of light could be increased without changing the size of the dish.

Practice Questions — Fact Recall

Q1 Describe the structure of a radio telescope and how it is designed to detect radio waves.

Q2 Why is the resolving power of a radio telescope much lower than that of a similar sized optical telescope?

Q3 Explain how radio telescopes are used to get resolutions much higher than optical telescopes.

Q4 Give two reasons why building a large radio telescope is easier than building a large optical telescope.

Q5 Why do the mirrors of U-V telescopes have to be made more precisely than optical telescopes?

Q6 Explain why I-R telescopes must be cooled to very low temperatures.

Q7 Why do X-ray telescopes use grazing mirrors?

Q8 Suggest a suitable location for:

a) an X-ray telescope,

b) an I-R telescope.

Q9 What's the relationship between collecting power and diameter?

5. Parallax and Parsecs

The distances to stars can be difficult to calculate. Astronomers have several methods to work them out — but not all of the methods work for all distances. Astronomers also use a few different units to measure distance.

Learning Objective:
- Understand parsecs and light years as distance measurements.

Specification Reference A.1.3

Parallax

Imagine you're in a moving car. You see that (stationary) objects in the foreground seem to be moving faster than objects in the distance. This apparent change in position is called **parallax**.

The distance to nearby stars can be calculated by observing how they move relative to stars that are so distant that they appear not to move at all — background stars. This is done by comparing the position of the nearby star in relation to the background stars at different parts of the Earth's orbit.

Parallax is measured in terms of the angle of parallax. If you observe the position of the star at either end of the Earth's orbit (6 months apart), the angle of parallax is half the angle that the star moves in relation to the background stars. The greater the angle, the nearer the object is to you.

Tip: Very distant stars appear not to move as we orbit the Sun because the angle by which they move is too tiny for us to measure.

Tip: You can see parallax at work by holding your hand out in front of your face and closing just your right eye, followed by just your left eye. Your hand will move in relation to the background. The closer your hand is to your face, the more it moves in relation to the background.

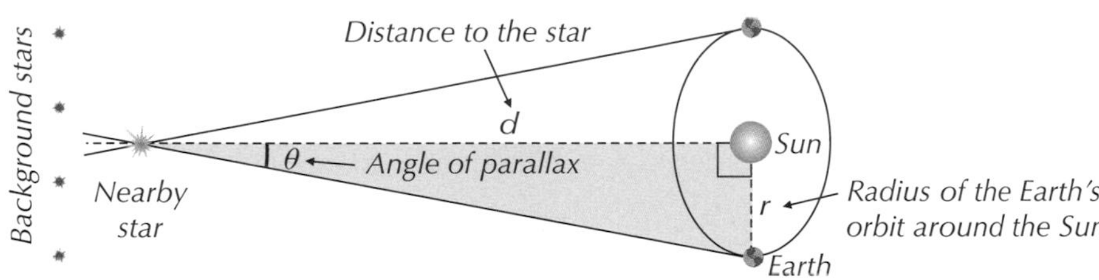

Figure 1: *The distance of a nearby star can be calculated by measuring the angle of parallax and knowing the diameter of the Earth's orbit.*

Using the triangle in Figure 1, you can calculate the distance to the nearby star, d, using trigonometry, if you know the angle of parallax and the radius of the Earth's orbit:

$$\tan\theta = \frac{r}{d}$$

$$\Rightarrow d = \frac{r}{\tan\theta}$$

Tip: Remember, trigonometry says that $\tan\theta = \frac{\text{opposite side}}{\text{adjacent side}}$.

For small angles $\tan\theta \approx \theta$, where θ is in radians. Because the angles used in astronomy are so tiny, you can assume this for calculations of parallax (as long as you're working in radians). So:

Tip: You've seen small angle approximations before on page 25.

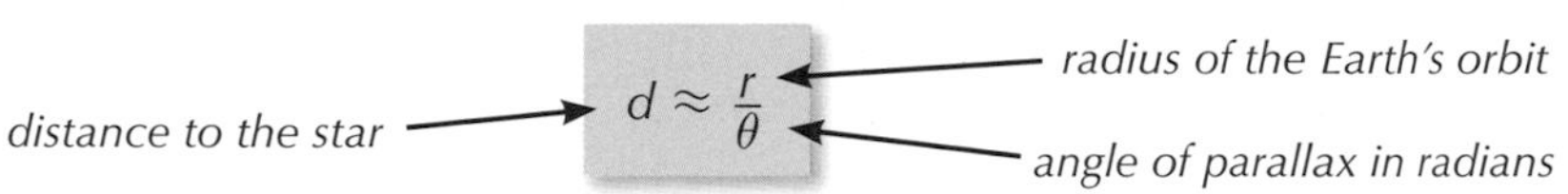

Tip: If you use this formula in the exam, make sure you tell them that you're assuming that θ is small.

Remember, the angle in radians = angle in degrees × $\frac{2\pi}{360}$ (see page 11).

Parsecs

Parallax gives a unit of distance called a **parsec** (pc).

A star is exactly one parsec (pc) away if the angle of parallax, $\theta = 1 \text{ arcsecond} = \left(\frac{1}{3600}\right)^\circ$

Tip: An arcsecond is just a measure of angle like degrees and radians. It's equivalent to $\left(\frac{1}{3600}\right)^\circ$, so it's useful when measuring the really small distances that astronomers use.

The distances measured in astronomy are usually huge — even the nearest large galaxy to the Milky Way is 780 000 parsecs away. Astronomers often use parsecs (pc) or megaparsecs (Mpc) to measure these large distances. You need to be able to use these conversions:

$1 \text{ pc} = 3.08 \times 10^{16} \text{ m}$ $\quad$ $1 \text{ Mpc} = 1 \times 10^6 \text{ pc}$

Exam Tip
This conversion between parsecs and metres will be in the exam Data and Formulae Booklet, so don't worry about learning it. (Confusingly, 1 pc is more accurately 3.085... ×10^{16} m, but you must use the value given in your exam.)

Example

Proxima Centauri has an angle of parallax of 0.77 arcseconds. Calculate the distance to Proxima Centauri in parsecs. The average radius of the Earth's orbit is 1.50 × 10^{11} m.

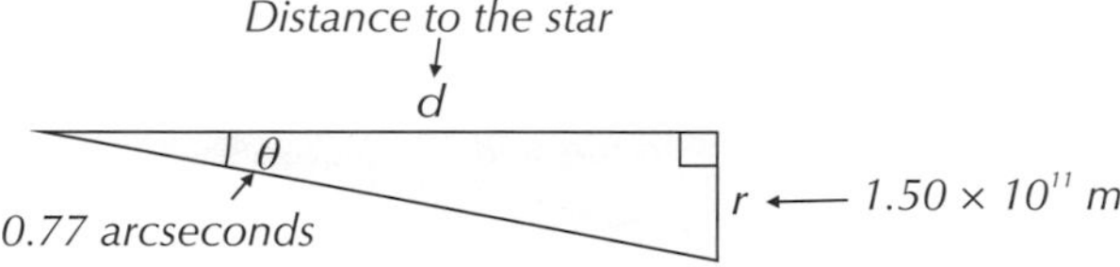

- Convert the angle to degrees, and then into radians:

$$0.77 \text{ arcseconds} = 0.77 \times \left(\frac{1}{3600}\right)^\circ = 2.138... \times 10^{-4\,\circ}$$
$$2.138... \times 10^{-4\,\circ} \times \frac{2\pi}{360} = 3.73... \times 10^{-6} \text{ rad}$$

- $$d \approx \frac{r}{\theta} = \frac{1.50 \times 10^{11}}{3.73... \times 10^{-6}} = 4.018... \times 10^{16} \text{ m}$$

- Convert this into parsecs by dividing by 3.08×10^{16}:

$$d = 4.018... \times 10^{16} \text{ m}$$
$$= (4.018... \times 10^{16} \text{ m}) \div (3.08 \times 10^{16})$$
$$= 1.3 \text{ pc (to 2 s.f.)}$$

Tip: Astronomers sometimes use a unit called the astronomical unit (AU). 1 astronomical unit is defined as the average distance between the Earth and the Sun: 1 AU = 1.50 × 10^{11} m

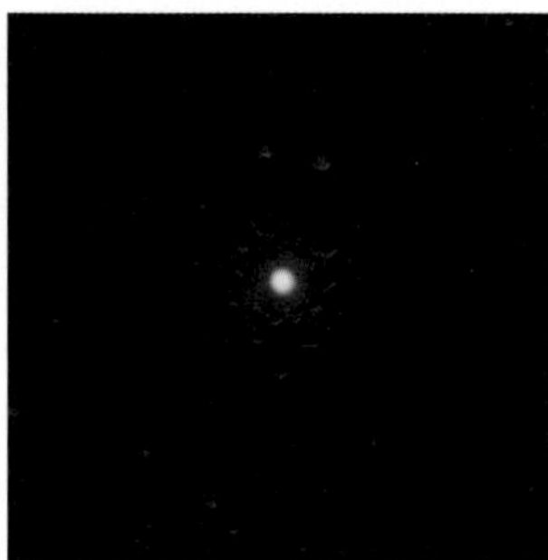

Figure 2: An X-ray image of Proxima Centauri.

Light years (ly)

All electromagnetic waves travel at the speed of light, c, in a vacuum (where $c = 3.00 \times 10^8 \text{ ms}^{-1}$). The distance that electromagnetic waves travel through a vacuum in one year is called a **light year** (ly).

If we see the light from a star that is, say, 10 light years away then we are actually seeing it as it was 10 years ago. The further away the object is, the further back in time we are actually seeing it.

$1 \text{ light year} = 9.46 \times 10^{15} \text{ m}$

$1 \text{ parsec} = 3.26 \text{ light years}$

Exam Tip
Both of these conversions will be given to you in the Data and Formulae Booklet in the exam.

Examples

- Light from the Sun takes around 8 minutes to reach Earth, so the light that we see from the Sun actually left the Sun 8 minutes earlier.
- Proxima Centauri is 1.3 pc away from Earth (see previous example), so it is $1.3 \times 3.26 = 4.238 = 4.2$ (to 3 s.f.) light years away.

  So the light from Proxima Centauri will take just under 4 years and 3 months to reach us.

The light from very distant galaxies has taken billions of years to reach us. Astronomers search for distant galaxies so that they can 'look into the past' at what the Universe was like billions of years ago.

Tip: So the X-ray image in Figure 2 actually shows the X-rays emitted from Proxima Centauri 4 years, 3 months before the image was taken.

Angle subtended

If you know the diameter of an object, you can measure the angle subtended by it in the sky and use these values to work out the distance to the object.

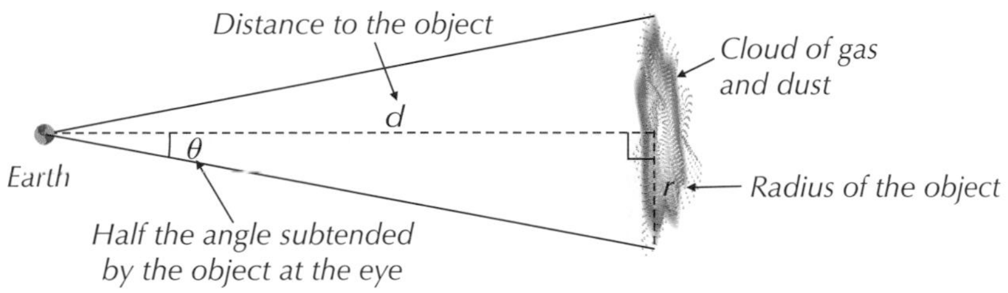

Figure 3: *The distance of an object can be calculated by measuring the angle it subtends in the sky and knowing the actual diameter of the object.*

Tip: You might need to use this method to find the magnification of a telescope (see p.145). If you're given the distance to and the size of an object, you can use this method to work out the angle the object subtends in the sky. If you know the angle the image subtends, you can work out the magnification.

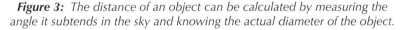

As long as the angle is small, you can use the formula on page 155 to calculate the distance to the object, or the angle subtended:

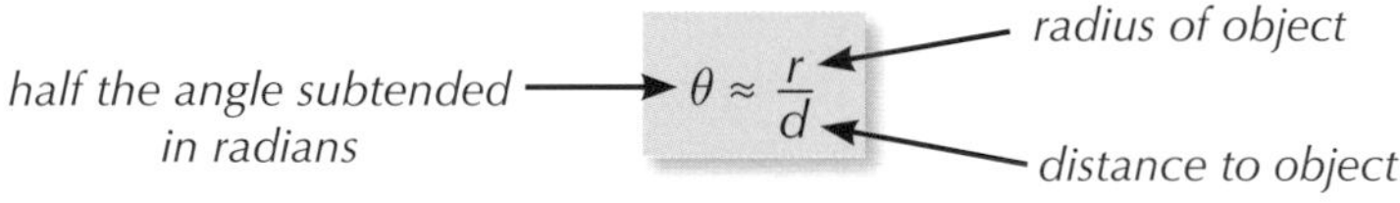

Tip: Don't forget to work with angles in radians when using the small angle approximation.

Example

A satellite in orbit around the Earth has a radius of 6.6 m. Given that it is in orbit at 569 km from Earth, find the angle subtended by it as viewed from Earth.

Half the angle subtended $= \theta \approx \frac{r}{d} = \frac{6.6}{569 \times 10^3} = 1.159... \times 10^{-5}$ rad

So the angle subtended $= 1.159... \times 10^{-5} \times 2 = 2.3 \times 10^{-5}$ rad (to 2 s.f.)

Tip: $\frac{r}{d}$ is just a ratio, so the two distances just need to be in the same units — it doesn't matter which.

You can only use parallax to measure distance for nearby objects, and using the angle subtended only works if you already know the object's size, which is not very likely if you don't know its distance.

There are lots of other ways of measuring distance that astronomers can use, including standard candles (page 161), redshift (pages 180-183) and quasars (page 189).

It's important for astronomers to have several ways of measuring distance. Measuring the same distance using different methods makes the measurement more reliable (see page 288), and some methods only work for certain distances.

Practice Questions — Application

Q1 The star Alpha Tauri in the constellation Taurus is 20 pc away. Calculate this distance in light years.

Q2 An observatory is studying the star Sirius from Earth. One image of Sirius is captured, and another is captured 6 months later. The angle of parallax is recorded to be 0.37 arcseconds.

a) Why does the observatory take two images, 6 months apart, to measure the parallax of Sirius?

b) The average radius of the Earth's orbit is 1.50×10^{11} m. Calculate the distance to Sirius in metres.

c) How long will it take for light from Sirius to reach Earth in years and months?

Q3 An astronomer wants to calculate the distance to Mars from Earth. He knows the following information about Mars:

Radius: 3389.5 km

Mass: 6.4185×10^{23} kg

Volume: 1.6318×10^{11} km^3

a) He measures the angle subtended by Mars in the sky. Which of the measurements above does he also need to know to calculate the distance to Mars?

b) The angle subtended by Mars in the sky was measured as 5 arcseconds. Calculate the distance to Mars at the time the measurement was taken.

Tip: The distance from Earth to Mars isn't always the same — it varies depending on where the two planets are in their orbits of the Sun.

Practice Questions — Fact Recall

Q1 What is meant by the angle of parallax?

Q2 What is a parsec?

Q3 What is the definition of a light year?

Q4 Why does it take time for light emitted by the Sun to reach us? How long does it take?

Q5 What formula would you use to calculate the distance to an object if you knew the size of the object, and the angle subtended by the object in the sky. What assumption needs to be made?

Q6 Why is it important for astronomers to have several different methods of calculating distances to objects in space?

6. Magnitude

There are a few properties that are used to classify stars. Some stars in the sky look a lot brighter than others — this could be because they're actually a lot brighter, or just much closer. When classifying stars by their brightness you can either talk about how bright they appear, or how bright they actually are.

Power output

Stars can be classified according to their **luminosity** — that is, the total amount of energy emitted in the form of electromagnetic radiation each second (see p.165). Luminosity is also known as the **power output** of a star, as it's just a rate of energy transfer, and is measured in watts (W). The Sun's luminosity is about 4×10^{26} W. The most luminous stars have a luminosity about a million times that of the Sun.

The **intensity**, I, of an object that we observe is the power received from it per unit area at Earth. This is the effective **brightness** of an object.

Apparent magnitude

The brightness of a star in the night sky depends on two things — its power output and its distance from us (if you ignore weather and light pollution, etc.). So the brightest stars will be close to us and have a high luminosity. The **apparent magnitude**, m, of an object is a measure of the brightness (or intensity) of the object.

The ancient Greeks invented a system where the very brightest stars were given an apparent magnitude of 1 and the dimmest stars an apparent magnitude of 6, with other levels catering for the stars in between. In the 19th century, the scale was redefined using a strict logarithmic scale:

A magnitude 1 star has an intensity 100 times greater than a magnitude 6 star.

In other words, 5 magnitudes difference corresponds to a difference in intensity of 100 times. This means a difference of one magnitude corresponds to a difference in intensity of $100^{1/5} \approx 2.5$ times.

Example

A magnitude 1 star is about 2.5 times brighter than a magnitude 2 star and $2.5 \times 2.5 = 2.5^2$ times brighter than a magnitude 3 star.

You can calculate the brightness ratio between two stars using:

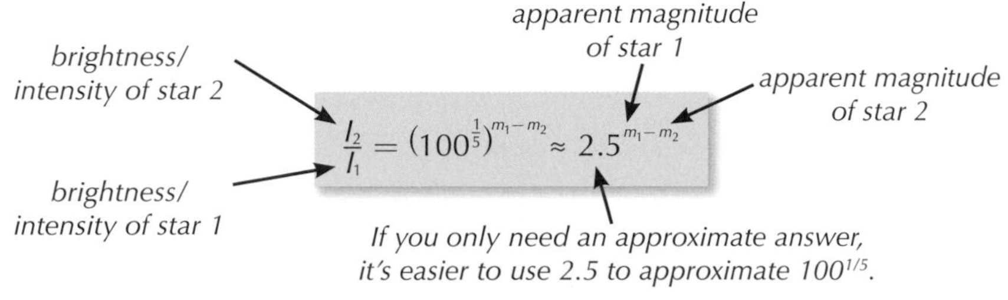

Learning Objectives:

- Understand how stars can be classified by their luminosity (or power output).
- Know what is meant by apparent magnitude, m.
- Know the relationship between brightness and apparent magnitude.
- Know what is meant by absolute magnitude, M.
- Understand how M and m are related by the formula: $m - M = 5 \log \frac{d}{10}$
- Understand how type 1a supernovae can be used as standard candles to determine distances.

Specification Reference A.1.3

Tip: Don't get confused between brightness and luminosity. Luminosity is the power emitted by the star. Brightness is the power received at Earth per unit area.

Tip: It's important to know that the magnitude scale isn't linear. The intensity difference between a magnitude 1 and a magnitude 2 star isn't the same as it is between a magnitude 2 and a magnitude 3 star. Only the ratios of the intensities are the same.

Tip: The apparent magnitude of any object, m, is related to the intensity, I, by:
$m = -2.5 \log I + \text{constant}$
But don't worry — you won't need to use this equation.

The scale is continuous — an object can have an apparent magnitude of any value, including decimals.

Example

Star A has an apparent magnitude of 3.44 and star B has an apparent magnitude of 5.72. Show that star A appears around 8 times brighter than star B.

- Find the difference in apparent magnitude:

$$m_B - m_A = 5.72 - 3.44 = 2.28$$

- So brightness/intensity ratio is approximately:

$$\frac{I_A}{I_B} = 2.5^{2.28} = 8.1 \text{ (to 2 s.f.)}$$

- So star A appears around 8 times brighter than star B.

Tip: Make sure you substitute in the right apparent magnitude values. If you get them the wrong way round you'll get the wrong ratio.

At the same time as the logarithmic scale was introduced, the range was extended in both directions, with the very brightest objects in the sky having negative apparent magnitude. The Sun has an apparent magnitude of –26.7, and the dimmest objects observed by the Hubble Space Telescope have an apparent magnitude of around 30. The whole scale is tied to a star called Vega, which is defined to have an apparent magnitude of 0.

Tip: The Moon isn't actually very bright, but it's very close. Its apparent magnitude during a full moon is about –12.7 and it's by far the brightest object in the night sky. Have a look — it's lovely.

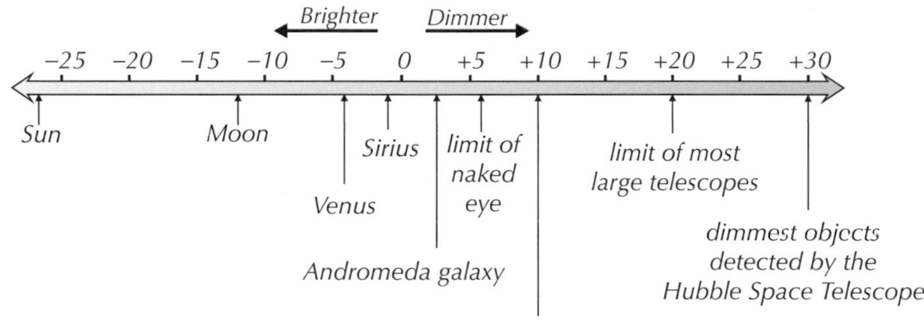

***Figure 1:** The apparent magnitude scale and the positions of some key features.*

Absolute magnitude

The **absolute magnitude** of an object, M, is based only on the power output of the object. It does not depend on its distance from Earth. It is defined as what its apparent magnitude would be if it were 10 parsecs away from Earth.

The relationship between M and m is given by the following formula:

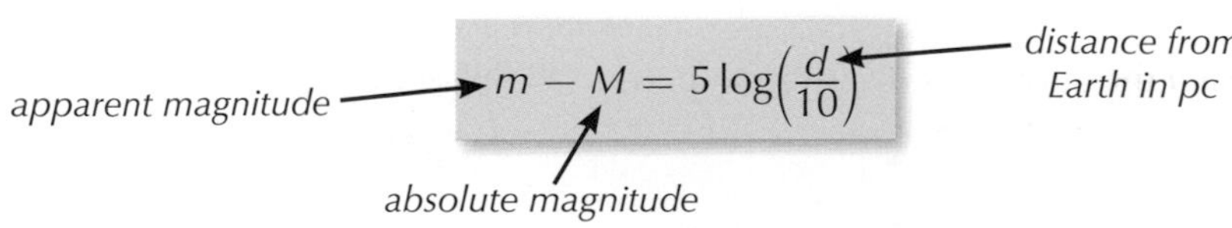

$$m - M = 5\log\left(\frac{d}{10}\right)$$

Tip: The absolute magnitude of the Sun is 4.83, so if we put it 10 parsecs away, we'd only just be able to see it with the naked eye.

Tip: The logarithm here is to the base 10 — don't get it confused with the natural logarithm 'ln'.

For more on logs, see pages 283-284.

Example

The star Aludra in the constellation Canis Major has an apparent magnitude of 2.5 and is 3200 light years from Earth. Calculate the absolute magnitude of Aludra.

- Convert the distance to parsecs:

  3200 light years = 3200 ÷ 3.26 = 981.5... pc

- You know the apparent magnitude so use the formula $m - M = 5\log\left(\frac{d}{10}\right)$ to find the absolute magnitude.

- So $M = m - 5\log\left(\frac{d}{10}\right)$

  $= 2.5 - 5\log\left(\frac{981.5...}{10}\right)$
  $= -7.459...$
  $= -7.5$ (to 2 s.f.)

If you know the absolute magnitude of an object, you can use this equation to calculate its distance from Earth. This is really handy, since the distance to most stars is too big to measure using parallax (see page 155).

Tip: Just like with apparent magnitude, you can get negative absolute magnitudes. The more negative, the brighter the star.

Standard candles

You can also use the absolute magnitude formula to calculate the distance to distant objects using **standard candles**. Standard candles are objects that you can calculate the brightness of directly, e.g. **type 1a supernovae**. All type 1a supernovae have the same peak in absolute magnitude. If you find a type 1a supernova within a galaxy, you can work out how far that galaxy is from us by looking at how bright the supernova appears in comparison to how bright you know it really is, then use the formula on page 160.

Tip: Supernovae occur when stars much more massive than the Sun explode — see p.176 for more.

Figure 2: *A type 1a supernova (the bright dot) within the galaxy NGC 4526. The brightness is known, so its distance can be calculated (around 55 million light years).*

Example

A type 1a supernova in a distant galaxy has a peak absolute magnitude of –19.3, and a peak apparent magnitude of –2.2. Calculate the distance to the galaxy in parsecs.

Rearrange the equation for absolute magnitude to get $\log\left(\frac{d}{10}\right)$ on its own on one side of the equation.

$m - M = 5\log\left(\frac{d}{10}\right)$

$\Rightarrow \frac{m - M}{5} = \log\left(\frac{d}{10}\right)$

You want to find d, so you need to get rid of the log in the equation. To do that, raise each side of the equation to the power 10:

$10^{\frac{m-M}{5}} = 10^{\log\left(\frac{d}{10}\right)} \Rightarrow 10^{\frac{m-M}{5}} = \frac{d}{10}$

Make d the subject and substitute in the values for m and M:

$d = 10 \times 10^{\frac{m-M}{5}}$

So $d = 10 \times 10^{\frac{-2.2-(-19.3)}{5}} = 10 \times 10^{\frac{17.1}{5}}$
$= 26\ 302.6...$ pc
$= 26\ 000$ pc (to 2 s.f.)

Tip: It's really handy to remember log rules like $10^{\log x} = x$ in calculation questions. For more on log rules, see pages 283-284.

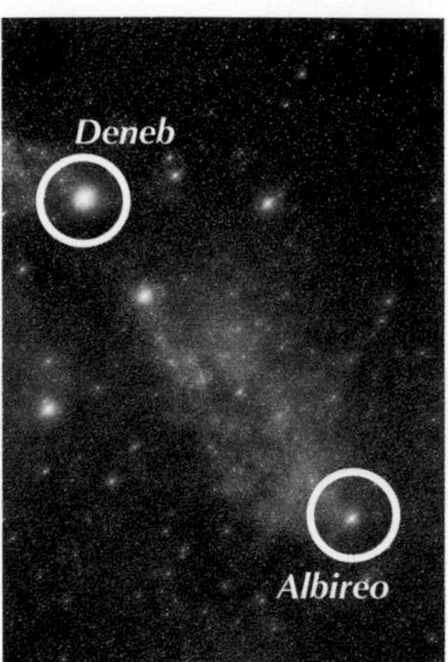

Figure 3: *The constellation Cygnus. Deneb is one of the brightest stars in the sky, despite being around 1000 parsecs away. This means it must be one of the largest and brightest stars known. Albireo consists of three stars — one of which is Albireo B.*

Tip: Remember (p.159), brightness and intensity are the same thing.

Tip: The Hubble constant (see p.184) was worked out using standard candles.

Practice Questions — Application

Q1 Albireo B and Deneb are stars in the constellation Cygnus. Albireo B has an apparent magnitude of 5.1 and Deneb has an apparent magnitude of 1.25.

a) Approximately how much brighter is Deneb than Albireo B?

b) Deneb is 975 parsecs from Earth.
Calculate the absolute magnitude of Deneb.

Q2 The following table shows some information about two stars in the constellation of Orion.

	Alnilam	*Bellatrix*
Apparent magnitude, m		*1.64*
Absolute magnitude, M	*–6.39*	
Distance from Earth, pc	*413 pc*	*75 pc*

a) Calculate the apparent magnitude of Alnilam.

b) Calculate the absolute magnitude of Bellatrix.

c) Which star appears to be brighter?

d) Which star would appear brighter from 10 pc away?

Q3 Type 1a supernovae all have the same peak in absolute magnitude of –19.3. A type 1a supernova occurs in a galaxy 3.4 Mpc away. Calculate the peak apparent magnitude of the supernova.

Practice Questions — Fact Recall

Q1 What is another name for the power output of a star?

Q2 What two quantities affect the brightness of a star in the night sky?

Q3 Describe what is meant by the apparent magnitude of a star.

Q4 Roughly how much brighter is a magnitude 1 star than a magnitude 2 star?

Q5 Write down the equation that links the brightness and apparent magnitudes of two stars, including the approximation.

Q6 What does it mean if a star has a negative apparent magnitude value?

Q7 Define the absolute magnitude of a star.

Q8 Write down the equation linking apparent magnitude and absolute magnitude.

Q9 What is a standard candle? Why are type 1a supernovae used as standard candles?

7. Stars as Black Bodies

Astronomers can estimate a star's temperature by assuming that stars are perfect absorbers and emitters — something known as a black body...

Black body radiation

All objects that are hotter than **absolute zero** emit electromagnetic radiation due to their temperature. At room temperature, this radiation lies mostly in the infrared part of the spectrum (which we can't see) — but heat something up enough and it'll start to glow and emit visible light. This is because the wavelengths of radiation emitted depend on the temperature of the object.

A **black body** is an object with a pure black surface that emits radiation strongly and in a well-defined way. It absorbs all light incident on it — we call them black bodies because they don't reflect any light.

> A black body is a body that absorbs all electromagnetic radiation of all wavelengths and can emit all wavelengths of electromagnetic radiation.

Because they emit all wavelengths of electromagnetic radiation, they emit a continuous spectrum of electromagnetic radiation. We call it black body radiation. A graph of radiation power output against wavelength for a black body varies with temperature, but they all have the same general shape (as shown in Figure 1). They're known as black body curves:

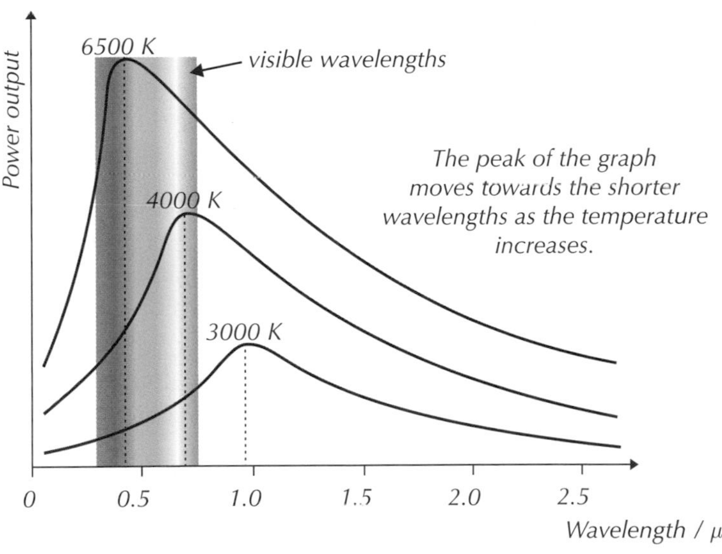

Figure 1: *Black body radiation curves for black bodies at 3000 K, 4000 K and 6500 K.*

There is no such thing as a perfect black body, but to a reasonably good approximation stars (and some other astronomical sources) behave as black bodies. We can use black body radiation curves to make estimations about an object's temperature and other properties.

Learning Objectives:

- Understand what is meant by a black body.
- Know the general shape of black body radiation curves.
- Know that it can be assumed that a star is a black body.
- Understand Wien's displacement law: $\lambda_{max}T = 2.9 \times 10^{-3}$ m K and be able to use it to estimate the black-body temperature of a source.
- Understand Stefan's law: $P = \sigma AT^4$ and be able to use it to estimate the area needed for a source to have the same power output as the Sun.
- Know and understand how to use the inverse square law for intensity: $I = \frac{P}{4\pi d^2}$
- Know what assumptions are made when applying the inverse square law.

Specification Reference A.1.3

Tip: Remember, power output is the energy emitted per second.

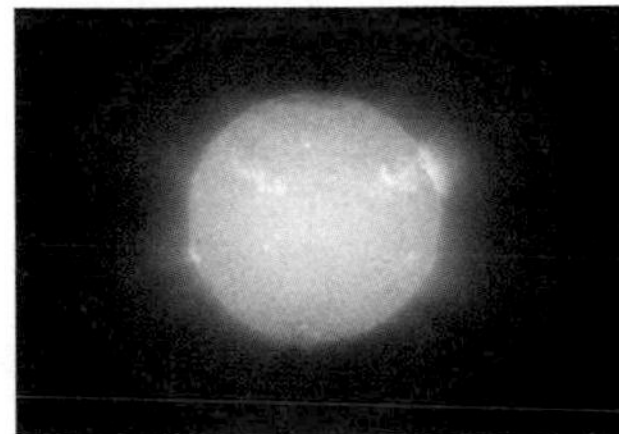

Figure 2: *The Sun can be assumed to be a black body. It absorbs almost all of the light incident on it, and emits the most intense radiation in the yellow part of the visible region of the electromagnetic spectrum.*

Wien's displacement law

All black body spectra have a peak intensity. The wavelength that this peak occurs at is called the peak wavelength, λ_{max}. The higher the surface temperature of a star, the shorter the wavelength, λ_{max}.

λ_{max} is related to the temperature by **Wien's displacement law**:

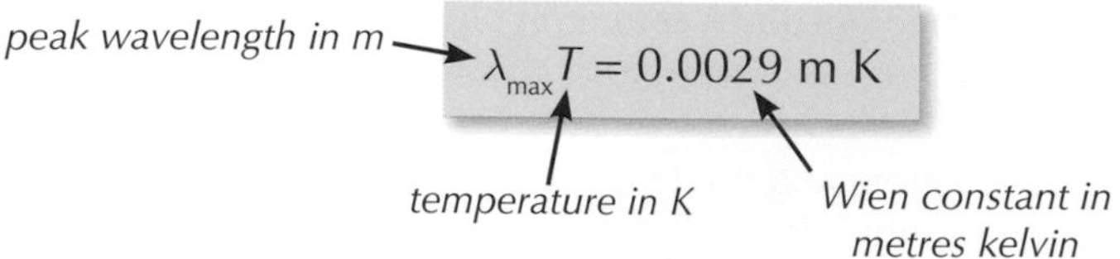

peak wavelength in m
$\lambda_{max}T = 0.0029$ m K
temperature in K
Wien constant in metres kelvin

A hotter black body will emit more radiation at shorter wavelengths than a cooler one, as well as having a higher total power output (assuming it has the same surface area) — see Figure 4.

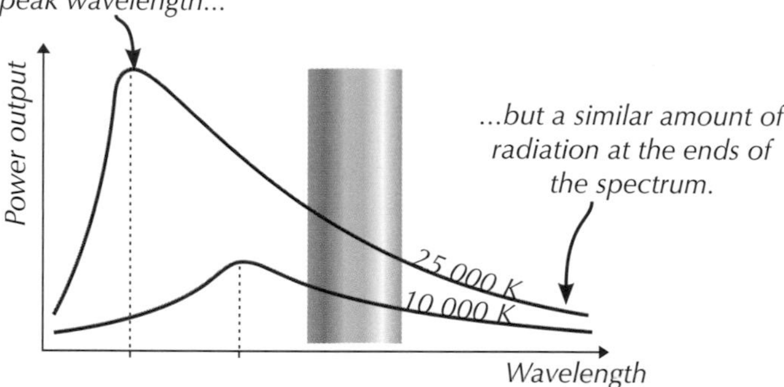

The hotter star emits a lot more radiation near its peak wavelength...
Power output
...but a similar amount of radiation at the ends of the spectrum.
25 000 K
10 000 K
Wavelength

Figure 4: *Black body curves to show the different range and intensity of wavelengths of radiation emitted by stars of different temperatures.*

Tip: This is because hotter stars emit radiation with higher energies. The energy of a photon is given by $E = \frac{hc}{\lambda}$ (as you'll have seen in AS physics), and so the radiation must have a lower wavelength if it has a higher energy.

Figure 3: *Wilhelm Wien was a German physicist who was awarded the 1911 Nobel Prize in physics for his work on black bodies.*

Tip: You can approximate stars as black bodies — but you need to assume that they have a uniform surface temperature.

A hotter star may not appear as bright as a cooler one, as it may mostly emit radiation that isn't in the visible part of the electromagnetic spectrum. If a cooler star emits more radiation in the visible region than a hotter one, it will appear brighter (see p.159 for more on brightness).

If you assume that a source acts as a black body, you can use Wien's displacement law to estimate the surface temperature of the source using measurements of its peak wavelength. The temperature you calculate is the source's black-body temperature.

Exam Tip
Wien's displacement law and the Wien constant are both given to you in the Data and Formulae booklet in the exam.

Tip: This temperature is only an estimate of the surface temperature because you've assumed that the star is a perfect black body.

Example

An astronomer observed radiation from a star and recorded the peak wavelength to be in the visible light region at 520 nm. Assuming that the star behaves as a black body, estimate the temperature of the star in kelvin.

- The peak wavelength in metres is $\lambda_{max} = 520 \times 10^{-9}$ m.
- Rearranging Wien's displacement law: $T = \frac{0.0029}{\lambda_{max}}$
- So $T = \frac{0.0029}{520 \times 10^{-9}} = 5576.9... \text{ K} = 5600 \text{ K}$ (to 2 s.f.)

Stefan's law

As you probably remember from p.159, the power output of a star is the total energy it emits per second and is related to the surface temperature of the star and its surface area. The power output is proportional to the fourth power of the star's temperature and is directly proportional to the surface area.

This is **Stefan's law**:

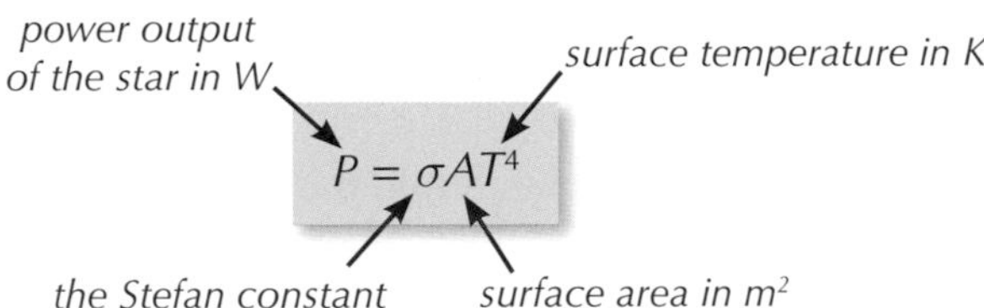

Measurements give the Stefan constant as $\sigma = 5.67 \times 10^{-8}\ \text{W m}^{-2}\,\text{K}^{-4}$.

Exam Tip
Stefan's law and the Stefan constant are given in the Data and Formulae booklet.

Example

The Sun has a black-body temperature of 5800 K. What surface area would a star have if it had a black-body temperature of 3000 K but the same power output as the Sun?

- Start by calculating the surface area of the Sun. Assuming the Sun is a sphere, the surface area is given by $4\pi r^2$, where r is the radius of the Sun:
  $A_{Sun} = 4 \times \pi \times (6.96 \times 10^8)^2 = 6.08... \times 10^{18}\ \text{m}^2$
- $P = \sigma A T^4$. The power outputs of the star and the Sun are the same, so:
  $\sigma A_{Sun}(T_{Sun})^4 = \sigma A_{star}(T_{star})^4$
  $\Rightarrow A_{star} = \dfrac{A_{Sun}(T_{Sun})^4}{(T_{star})^4}$ *(cancelling σ from both sides and rearranging)*
  $\Rightarrow A_{star} = \dfrac{(6.08... \times 10^{18})(5800)^4}{(3000)^4}$
  $= 8.50... \times 10^{19} = 8.50 \times 10^{19}\ \text{m}^2$ (to 3 s.f.)

Exam Tip
The formula for the area of a sphere, $A = 4\pi r^2$, and the value of the mean radius of the Sun, 6.96×10^8 m, are both given in the Data and Formulae booklet in the exam.

Tip: A cooler star needs to be a lot bigger to have the same power output.

Inverse square law

From Earth, we can measure the intensity of a star. The intensity is the power of radiation per square metre, so as the radiation spreads out and becomes diluted, the intensity decreases. If the energy has been emitted from a point or a sphere (like a star, for example) then it obeys the inverse square law:

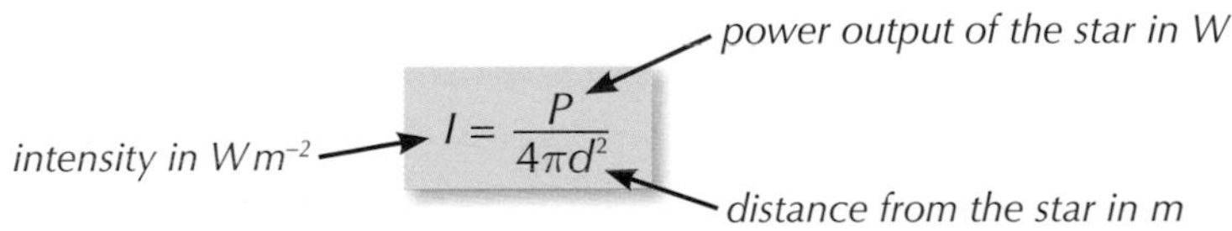

To use the inverse square law, you need to assume that the star is spherical, and that it gives out an even amount of power in every direction.

You can use Wien's displacement law, Stefan's law and the inverse square law to work out all sorts of things about stars, as long as you assume that stars behave as black bodies.

Tip: There's a full explanation of the inverse square law on pages 35-36.

Exam Tip
You won't be given the inverse square law in the exam. You'll need to remember it.

Tip: The inverse square law means that if you moved a star 3 times further away, it'd be $3^2 = 9$ times less intense.

> **Tip:** The Stefan constant: $\sigma = 5.67 \times 10^{-8}$ Wm^{-2}K^{-4}

> **Tip:** Speed of light in a vacuum: $c = 3.0 \times 10^{8}$ ms^{-1}

Example

The star Sirius B has a surface area of 4.1×10^{13} m^2 and produces a black body spectrum with a peak wavelength of 115 nm. The intensity of the light from Sirius B when it reaches Earth is 1.12×10^{-11} Wm^{-2}.
How long does the light from Sirius B take to reach Earth?

- First, find the temperature of Sirius B using Wien's displacement law:
  $\lambda_{max}T = 0.0029$ m K,
  so $T = 0.0029 \div \lambda_{max} = 0.0029 \div 115 \times 10^{-9} = 25\,217.39...$ K.
- Now, you can use Stefan's law to find the power output:
  $P = \sigma AT^4 = (5.67 \times 10^{-8}) \times (4.1 \times 10^{13}) \times (25\,217.39...)^4$
  $= 9.40... \times 10^{23}$ W
- Then use $I = \frac{P}{4\pi d^2}$ to find the distance of Sirius B from Earth:
  $d = \sqrt{\frac{P}{4\pi I}} = \sqrt{\frac{9.40... \times 10^{23}}{4\pi \times 1.12 \times 10^{-11}}} = 8.17... \times 10^{16}$ m
- Finally, use $c = d \div t$ to find the time taken
  $t = d \div c = 8.17... \times 10^{16} \div 3.0 \times 10^{8} = 272426013.2$ s ≈ 8.6 years

Practice Questions — Application

Q1 Sunspots are cooler spots on the Sun's surface that have a temperature of around 3000-4500 K, compared with the average surface temperature of 5800 K on the rest of the Sun's surface.
Use this information to explain why calculations using the inverse square law for the Sun might be inaccurate.

Q2 The data in the table below gives some of the properties of the star Rigel in the constellation of Orion.

Surface temperature / K	*11 000*
Distance / ly	*773*
Intensity of light / W m^{-2}	*3.7×10^{-8}*

a) Calculate the wavelength of the peak in the black body radiation curve of Rigel, λ_{max}.
b) Sketch the black body radiation curve for Rigel, labelling λ_{max}.
c) Calculate the surface area of Rigel in metres squared.

Practice Questions — Fact Recall

Q1 What is a black body?
Q2 Draw the general shape of a graph of wavelength against intensity for a black body.
Q3 What does the peak wavelength of radiation emitted by a black body depend on?
Q4 Write down Wien's displacement law linking black-body temperature and peak wavelength.
Q5 Write down Stefan's law linking power, temperature and surface area.
Q6 Write down the law linking intensity and distance.

8. Stellar Spectral Classes

You can classify stars using their light spectra as well as by their power output. One way astronomers analyse the light emitted from stars is by splitting the light received from them using a prism or diffraction grating.

Line spectra

You've seen line spectra at AS level, but for A2 you need to know about line absorption spectra in a bit more detail...

Energy levels in atoms

Electrons in an atom can only exist in certain well-defined energy levels. Each level is given a number. n = 1 represents the lowest energy level an electron can be in — the ground state. An atom is said to be excited when one or more of its electrons is in an energy level higher than the ground state.

Electrons can move up an energy level by absorbing a photon. Since these transitions are between definite energy levels, the energy of each photon absorbed can only take a certain allowed value. The energy of a photon is given by $E = hf$ (h = Planck's constant and f = frequency), so only certain frequencies, and so certain wavelengths, of light can be absorbed by electrons.

Line absorption spectra

If you split the light from a star using a prism or diffraction grating, you get a spectrum. Stars are approximately black bodies (see page 163), so they emit a continuous spectrum of electromagnetic radiation. You get **absorption lines** in the spectrum when radiation from the star passes through a cooler gas e.g. in the star's atmosphere.

At low temperatures, most of the electrons in the gas atoms will be in their ground states (n = 1). Photons of particular wavelengths are absorbed by the electrons to excite them to higher energy levels. When the electrons de-excite, the same wavelength of light is emitted and radiated in all directions. This means the intensity of radiation with this wavelength reaching Earth is reduced, which is shown by dark lines in the otherwise continuous spectrum, corresponding to the absorbed wavelengths.

The intensity of an absorption line is how dark it is — don't get this confused with the intensity of radiation. The more intense the absorption line at a particular wavelength, the more radiation of that wavelength has been absorbed.

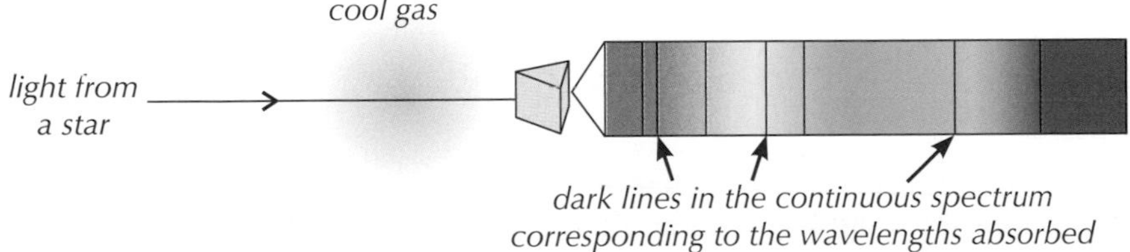

Figure 1: *An absorption spectrum of a cool gas.*

Hydrogen Balmer absorption lines

The wavelengths corresponding to the visible part of hydrogen's line absorption spectrum are caused by the electrons in atomic hydrogen moving between the first excitation level (n = 2) and higher energy levels. This leads to a series of lines called the **Balmer series**.

Learning Objectives:

- Know how stars can be classified according to their spectra.
- Know the seven spectral classes used to classify stars: O, B, A, F, G, K, M.
- Be able to classify stars into one of the seven spectral classes from their colour, temperature, or prominent absorption lines.
- Understand how astronomers can use Hydrogen Balmer absorption lines to determine stellar surface temperature.

Specification Reference A.1.3

Tip: You learnt about diffraction gratings in AS physics — they are just thin slides that contain lots of equally spaced slits very close together. They are often used to diffract light.

These lines are seen in stellar spectra where light emitted by the star has been absorbed by hydrogen atoms in the stellar atmosphere as the light passes through it.

Tip: Remember, when we talk about the intensity of an absorption line, we mean how dark it is. The more intense an absorption line is, the darker it is — don't confuse this with light intensity where more intense means brighter.

Determining stellar temperatures

For a hydrogen absorption line to occur in the visible part of a star's spectrum, electrons in the hydrogen atoms already need to be in the n = 2 state. This happens at high temperatures, where collisions between the atoms give the electrons extra energy.

If the temperature is too high, though, the majority of the electrons will reach the n = 3 level (or above) instead, which means there won't be so many Balmer transitions. So, the intensity of the Balmer lines depends on the temperature of the star (see Figure 2).

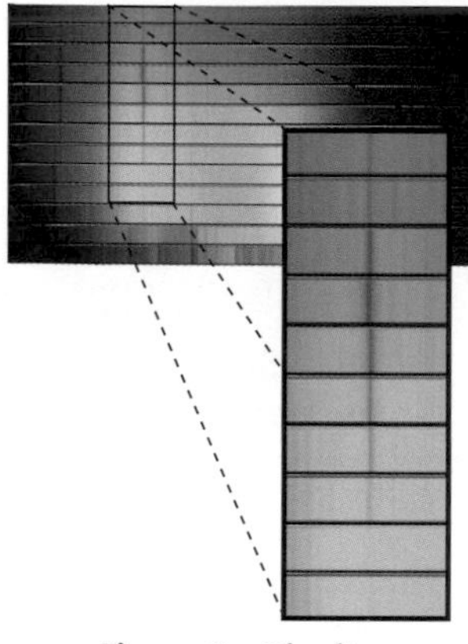

Figure 3: *The line absorption spectra of several stars of decreasing temperature (top to bottom). The close-up shows a Hydrogen Balmer absorption line, and how its intensity varies with temperature.*

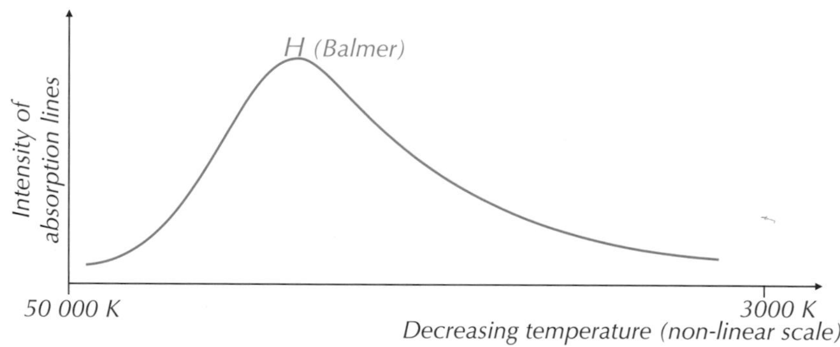

Figure 2: *The intensity of Balmer lines in the hydrogen line absorption spectrum of a star depends on the temperature of the star.*

You can use the intensity of Balmer lines to find the temparature of a star. For a particular intensity of the Balmer lines, two temperatures are possible. Astronomers get around this by looking at the absorption lines of other atoms and molecules as well.

Spectral classes

Stars are classified into groups called **spectral classes**. The spectral class of a star depends on the relative strength of certain absorption lines. There are seven main spectral classes that we classify stars into — here they are in order of decreasing temperature:

O, B, A, F, G, K and **M**

O class stars are the hottest and appear blue in colour. M class stars are the coolest and appear red in colour. All the in-between classes cover the temperatures and colours in between. The Sun is a G class star.

Remember... the spectral classification system is all to do with the spectra of stars — properties like magnitude, distance and apparent brightness don't affect it.

Tip: Use a mnemonic to remember the order. You might hear:

Oh **B**e **A** **F**ine **G**irl, **K**iss **M**e.

But you can make up your own — just make sure you remember it! How about...

Only **B**ad **A**stronomers **F**orget **G**enerally **K**nown **M**nemonics.

Figure 4 shows how the intensity of the visible spectral lines changes with temperature, and how the spectral classes are split up:

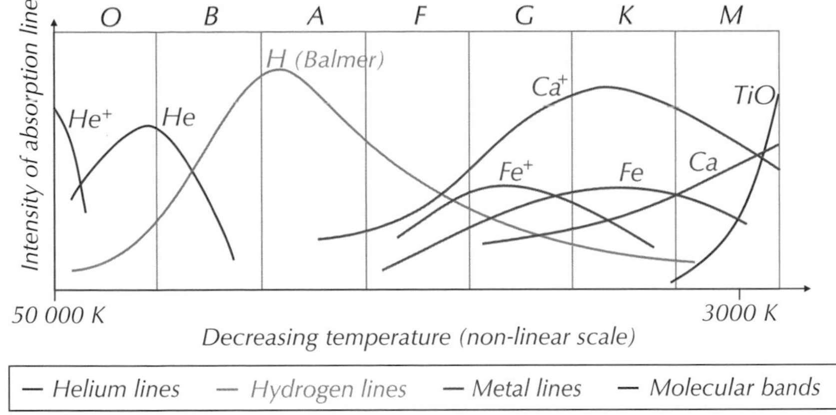

Figure 4: *A graph showing how the intensity of absorption lines in the visible region of stellar spectra changes with stellar temperature (and spectral class).*

Tip: Hot stars only have absorption lines corresponding to a few different elements (mostly hydrogen and helium), whereas cooler stars will have absorption lines corresponding to many more elements — see the table below.

Tip: This type of diagram, and the H-R diagram which you'll see on page 171, tend to be drawn with spectral class along the horizontal axis. The relationship between spectral class and temperature isn't linear or logarithmic.

The visible spectral characteristics of spectral classes

The seven spectral classes of stars all have different characteristics, e.g. colour, temperature and line absorption spectra, that you need to know...

Spectral Class	*Colour*	*Temperature / K*	*Absorption lines*
O	*Blue*	*25 000 – 50 000*	*The strongest spectral lines are helium-plus ion (He^+) and helium atom (He) absorptions, since these need a really high temperature. They have weak hydrogen (H) Balmer lines too.*
B	*Blue*	*11 000 – 25 000*	*These spectra show strong helium atom (He) and hydrogen (H) absorptions.*
A	*Blue-white*	*7500 – 11 000*	*Visible spectra are governed by very strong Hydrogen Balmer (H) lines, but there are also some metal ion absorptions.*
F	*White*	*6000 – 7500*	*These spectra have strong metal ion absorptions.*
G	*Yellow-white*	*5000 – 6000*	*These have both metal ion and metal atom absorptions.*
K	*Orange*	*3500 – 5000*	*Spectral lines are mostly from neutral metal atoms.*
M	*Red*	*< 3500*	*Spectral lines are from neutral atoms, as well as molecular band absorptions from compounds like titanium oxide (TiO), since these stars are cool enough for molecules to form.*

Only cooler stars contain atoms with electrons in low enough energy levels to bond and form molecules, and therefore show molecular bands in their absorption line spectra.

Exam Tip
You'll need to be able to work out what spectral class a star belongs to given its characteristics, so make sure you know all the information in this table off by heart.

Tip: Spectral class A stars have the strongest absorption lines.

Tip: Spectral classes used to be ordered alphabetically according to the strength of their Balmer lines, but when astronomers realised that this didn't work, they just rearranged them into this funny order. Useful.

Tip: The colour goes from blue to red as the temperature decreases, because the peak wavelength increases ($\lambda_{max}T$ = constant) and so moves towards the red end of the spectrum.

Practice Question — Application

Q1 Figure 5 shows the line absorption spectra of two stars, with some absorption lines labelled with the elements or molecules that are responsible for them.

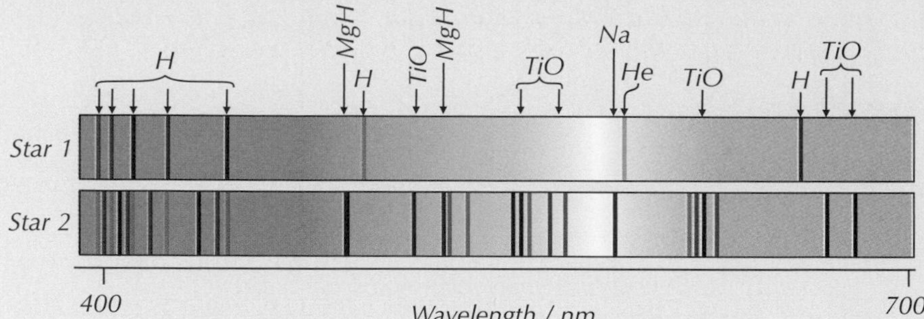

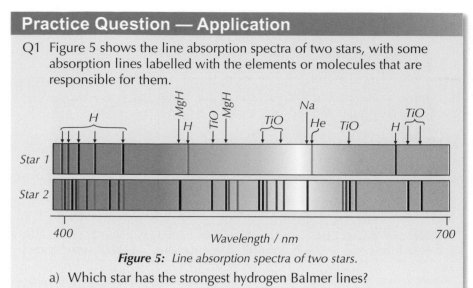

Figure 5: *Line absorption spectra of two stars.*

a) Which star has the strongest hydrogen Balmer lines?

b) Which star would you expect to have the lower temperature? Give one reason for your answer.

c) Which of the two stars would you expect to be in spectral class B? Give a reason for your answer.

d) Suggest a spectral class for the other star and explain your answer.

e) Give a range of temperatures in which you'd expect to find Star 1.

Practice Questions — Fact Recall

Q1 Why do absorption lines only appear at particular wavelengths in the spectra of stars?

Q2 Why do hydrogen atoms need to have electrons in the n = 2 energy level for hydrogen Balmer lines to be seen?

Q3 Sketch a graph showing how the intensity of hydrogen Balmer absorption lines varies with temperature.

Q4 Write down the seven spectral classes of stars in order of decreasing temperature.

Q5 Which would you expect to be hotter, a blue star or a white star?

Q6 Briefly state what ions, atoms or molecules cause the strongest absorption lines in the line absorption spectrum of a star in spectral class:

a) G b) M c) O d) K

Q7 What spectral class would a white star be in?

Q8 What spectral class would you expect a star with metal ion absorption lines and very strong hydrogen Balmer lines to be in?

9. The Hertzsprung-Russell Diagram

This whole section is about one diagram... but it's a pretty important one. It's also very pretty — so think of this part of the book as a bit of light relief.

The diagram

Independently, Hertzsprung and Russell noticed that a plot of absolute magnitude (see p.160) against temperature (or spectral class) didn't just throw up a random collection of stars but showed distinct areas.

This diagram ended up being really important for studying how stars evolve (p.173-175). A graph of absolute magnitude vs temperature/spectral class for stars became know as the **Hertzsprung-Russell** (H-R) **diagram** (Figure 1).

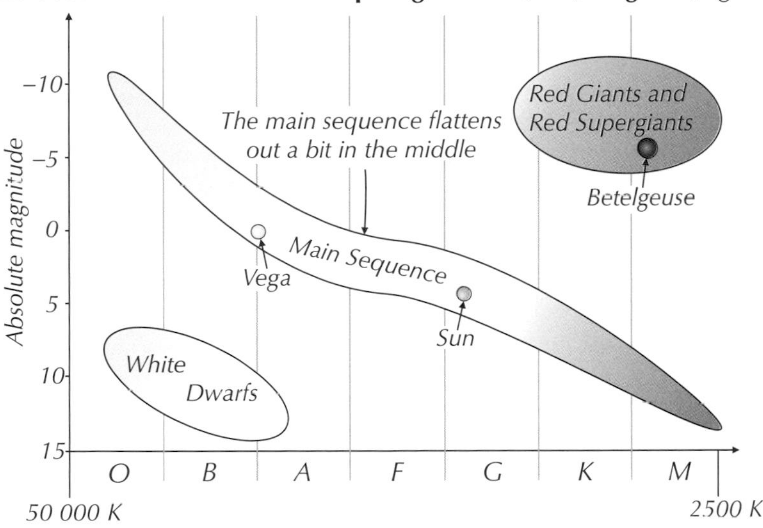

***Figure 1:** The Hertzsprung-Russell diagram with the positions of the Sun and the stars Vega and Betelgeuse labelled.*

Distinct areas of the H-R diagram

The three distinct areas in which stars fall on the H-R diagram correspond to three main types of stars:

- The long, diagonal band is called the **main sequence**. Main sequence stars are in their long-lived stable phase where they are fusing hydrogen into helium. The Sun is a main sequence star.
- Stars that have a high luminosity and a relatively low surface temperature must have a huge surface area because of Stefan's law (page 165). These stars are called **red giants** and are found in the top-right corner of the H-R diagram. Red giants are stars that have moved off the main sequence, and fusion reactions other than hydrogen to helium are also happening in them (see pages 173-174).
- Stars that have a low luminosity but a high temperature must be very small, again because of Stefan's law. These stars are called **white dwarfs** and are about the size of the Earth. They lie in the bottom-left corner of the H-R diagram. White dwarfs are stars at the end of their lives, where all of their fusion reactions have stopped and they are just slowly cooling down (see page 174).

Learning Objectives:

- Know the general shape of the Hertzsprung-Russell (H-R) diagram, including the position of the main sequence, dwarf and giant stars.
- Know that the absolute magnitude axis on an H-R diagram ranges from –10 to 15.
- Know that the *x*-axis on an H-R diagram either shows temperature ranging from 50 000 K to 2500 K, or the spectral classes OBAFGKM.

Specification Reference A.1.3

Tip: Remember... stars with negative values of absolute magnitude are brighter (page 160).

Tip: The temperature scale's a bit weird because of how the spectral classes (O-M) are defined. Remember, temperature goes the "wrong way" along the *x*-axis — from hotter to cooler.

Tip: In several billion years, the Sun will become a red giant (see page 173). It will expand to be around 20% larger than the Earth's current orbit and shine 3000 times brighter than it does now.

***Figure 2:** A white dwarf is a small hot blue or white star about the size of the Earth.*

Practice Question — Application

Q1 Star 1 is a spectral class B star and has an absolute magnitude of 10. Star 2 is also in spectral class B, but has an absolute magnitude of –4.

a) Which star you would expect to be bigger, and why?

b) What type of star is Star 1?

c) What type of star is Star 2?

d) Which star is further along in its evolution sequence?

Exam Tip
Make sure you've learnt the axis scales off by heart — you might need to draw an H-R diagram in your exam.

Practice Questions — Fact Recall

Q1 What quantity is shown by the vertical axis of an H-R diagram? What range of values does this axis have?

Q2 What two quantities can be plotted on the horizontal axis of an H-R diagram?

Q3 Copy the axes below and draw the H-R diagram. Mark on your diagram the main sequence, the red giants, the white dwarfs and the position of the Sun. Label values of temperature and the spectral classes on the *x*-axis.

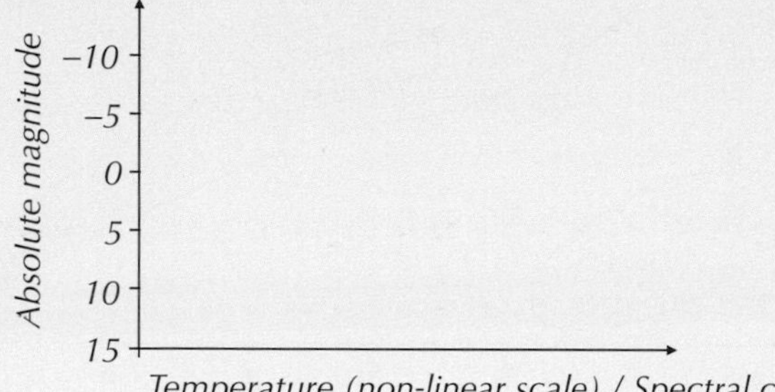

Q4 What process is occurring in the core of a main sequence star?

10. Evolution of Sun-like Stars

Stars like our Sun go through several different stages in their lives and move around the H-R diagram as they go (see p. 171). The Sun is on the main sequence right now, but it's still got a long way to go.

Learning Objectives:

- Understand the stellar evolution of a Sun-like star from formation to white dwarf.
- Understand how a Sun-like star moves around the H-R diagram as it evolves.

Specification Reference A.1.3

Formation

All stars are born in a cloud of dust and gas, most of which was left when previous stars blew themselves apart in supernovae (see page 176). The denser clumps of the cloud contract (very slowly) under the force of gravity.

When these clumps get dense enough, the cloud fragments into regions called protostars, that continue to contract and heat up. Eventually the temperature at the centre of the protostar reaches a few million degrees, and hydrogen nuclei start to fuse together to form helium (see page 116).

This releases an enormous amount of energy and creates enough pressure (radiation pressure) to stop the gravitational collapse. The star has now reached the main sequence (see page 171) and will stay there, relatively unchanged, while it fuses hydrogen into helium.

Figure 1: *The 'Pillars of Creation' photographed by the Hubble Space Telescope. These pillars of gas and dust in the Eagle Nebula are thought to be areas of star formation. Nebulae are clouds of interstellar gas and dust and are often star-forming regions.*

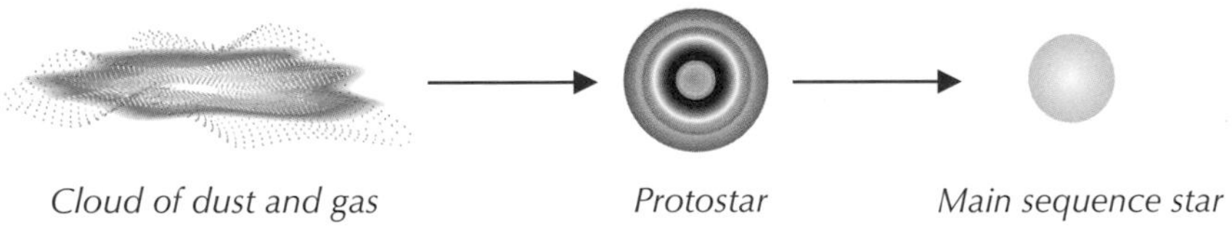

Cloud of dust and gas *Protostar* *Main sequence star*

Figure 2: *A star in the early stages of its stellar evolution.*

Core and shell burning sequence

Stars spend most of their lives as main-sequence stars. The pressure produced from hydrogen fusion in their core balances the gravitational force trying to compress them. This stage is called core hydrogen burning.

When the hydrogen in the core runs out nuclear fusion stops, and with it the outward pressure stops. The core contracts and heats up under the weight of the star. As a result, the outer layers expand and cool, and the star becomes a red giant.

The material surrounding the core still has plenty of hydrogen. The heat from the contracting core raises the temperature of this material enough for the hydrogen to fuse. This is called shell hydrogen burning. (Very low-mass stars stop at this point. They use up their fuel and slowly fade away...)

The core continues to contract until, eventually, it gets hot enough and dense enough for helium to fuse into carbon and oxygen. This is called core helium burning. This releases a huge amount of energy, which pushes the outer layers of the star further outwards.

When the helium runs out, the carbon-oxygen core contracts again and heats a shell around it so that helium can fuse in this region — shell helium burning.

Figure 4 shows a summary of the stages a star goes through between the main sequence and becoming a red giant.

Tip: As a star contracts, the temperature increases due to conservation of energy — gravitational potential energy is converted to thermal energy.

Tip: The cooling of the outer layers of the star makes the star's colour change to become redder — this is why we call them red giants.

Tip: This process is just a load of contracting, heating and fusing of successively bigger nuclei.

Main sequence star

1) H → He core burning

H → He

H in core runs out, core burning stops, core contracts and heats up.

Red giant

2) H → He shell burning

Heat from the core heats up a shell of H surrounding it enough that H fuses to He in the shell. The He core continues to contract and heat up.

H → He

He

Core contraction causes the shells and outer layers to expand and cool — the star becomes a red giant.

Eventually the core heats up enough for He to fuse.

3) He → C and O core burning

He → C and O

H → He

He in the core eventually runs out. Core burning stops and the core contracts and heats up.

4) He → C and O shell burning

H → He

C and O

He → C and O

Heat from contracting core causes He to begin fusing in this shell.

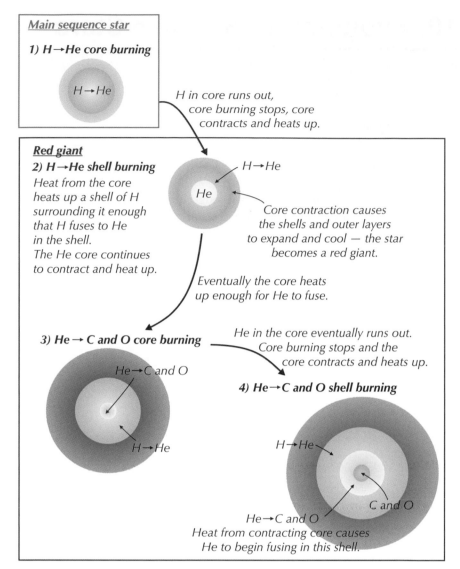

Figure 4: *The helium and hydrogen burning sequence of a star transitioning from a main sequence star to a red giant.*

Figure 3: *A red giant with a radius of around 1 billion km.*

Tip: Red giants are... well... reddy-orangey. They're usually K or M class stars — see the H-R diagram (p.171).

Tip: Some stars are of such a low mass that they may never even reach the main sequence.

White dwarfs

In low-mass stars, like our Sun, the carbon-oxygen core won't get hot enough for any further fusion and so it continues to contract under its own weight. Once the core has shrunk to about Earth-size, electrons exert enough pressure (**electron degeneracy pressure**) to stop it collapsing any more (fret not — you don't have to know how).

The helium shell becomes more and more unstable as the core contracts. The star pulsates and ejects its outer layers into space as a **planetary nebula**, leaving behind the dense core.

The star is now a very hot, dense solid called a white dwarf, which will simply cool down and fade away.

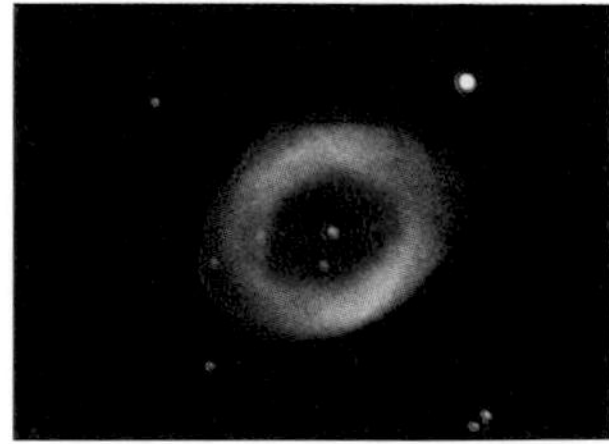

Figure 5: *When a low-mass red giant cools down, the shells are ejected and create a beautiful planetary nebula, like this one, leaving a white dwarf at the centre.*

Stellar evolution and the H-R diagram

As a Sun-like star evolves through its life, it moves in a certain path on the H-R diagram:

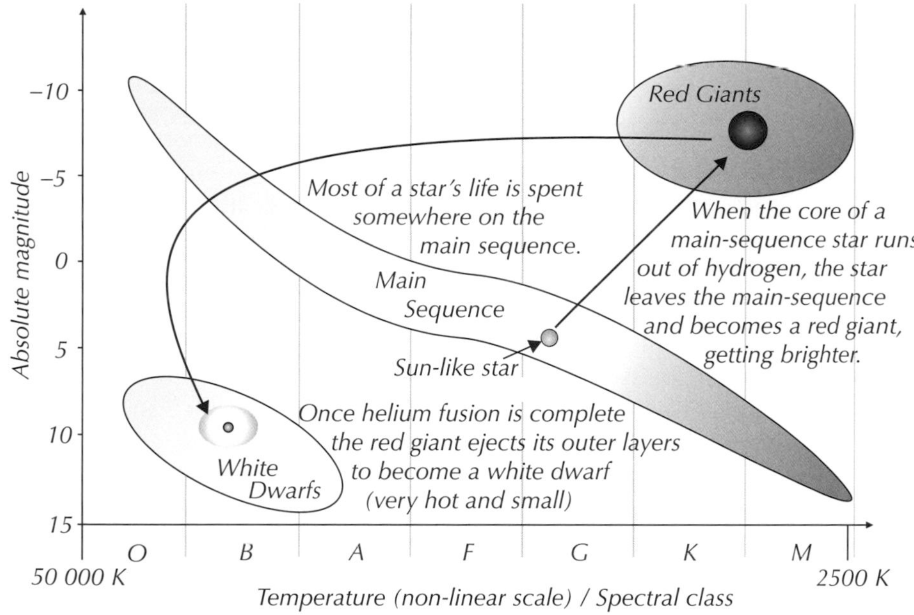

Figure 6: *The movement of a Sun-like star on the H-R diagram as it evolves.*

Tip: Stars begin as a cloud of dust and gas — as they contract and get hotter they appear in the M spectral class on the H-R diagram and move across to the main sequence as they get hotter. They reach the main sequence when fusion starts in their cores.

Tip: Most of the stars on the main sequence will eventually leave the main sequence and become a red giant. The path they take on the H-R diagram is actually a bit more wiggly than the one shown for the yellow star in Figure 6 — but you just need to know the basic shape.

Practice Question — Application

Q1 Five stars ***a***, ***b***, ***c***, ***d*** and ***e*** are plotted on the graph below.

a) Which star is a red giant? Which is the hottest main-sequence star?

b) Which star could be the Sun?

c) Write down a sequence of letters that represents the evolution of the Sun from its current position until it becomes a white dwarf.

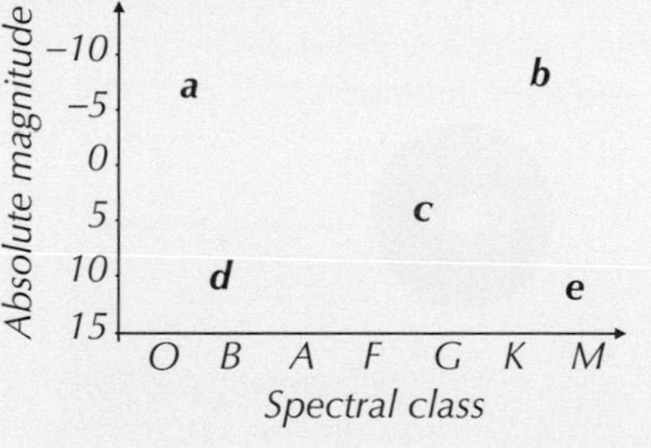

Practice Questions — Fact Recall

Q1 What causes a cloud of dust and gas to contract and form a star?

Q2 In what stage of evolution does a star spend most of its life?

Q3 Explain how the process of core hydrogen burning stops a main sequence star from compressing under the gravitational force.

Q4 What happens to the core of a star when it runs out of hydrogen? What effect does this have on the hydrogen layer surrounding the core of the star?

Q5 What causes a main-sequence star to become a red giant?

Q6 How is a white dwarf formed?

Q7 What is a planetary nebula?

11. Supernovae, Neutron Stars and Black Holes

Learning Objectives:

- Know the defining properties of supernovae, including a rapid increase in apparent magnitude.
- Understand how neutron stars and black holes are formed.
- Know the composition and density of a neutron star.
- Know that a black hole is an object that has an escape velocity greater than the speed of light, c.
- Know that astronomers believe that there is a supermassive black hole at the centre of every galaxy.
- Know that the event horizon of a black hole is called the Schwarzschild radius (R_s), and be able to calculate it using $R_s = \frac{2GM}{c^2}$.

Specification Reference A.1.3

Eventually the Sun will become a white dwarf and slowly fade away — but stars a lot more massive than our Sun end their lives in much more exciting and spectacular ways...

Supernovae

High-mass stars have a shorter life and a more exciting death than lower-mass stars like the Sun. Even though stars with a large mass have a lot of fuel, they use it up more quickly and don't spend so long as main-sequence stars.

When they are red giants the 'core burning to shell burning' process can continue beyond the fusion of helium, building up layers in an onion-like structure. For really massive stars this can go all the way up to iron. Nuclear fusion beyond iron isn't energetically favourable though, so once an iron core is formed then very quickly it's goodbye star.

When the core of a star runs out of fuel, it starts to contract — forming a white dwarf core (see page 174). If the star is massive enough, though, electron degeneracy can't stop the core contracting. This happens when the mass of the core is more than 1.4 times the mass of the Sun.

The core of the star continues to contract, and as it does, the outer layers of the star fall in and rebound off the core, setting up huge shockwaves. These shockwaves cause the star to explode cataclysmically in a **supernova**, leaving behind the core, which will either be a **neutron star** or (if the star was massive enough) a **black hole**.

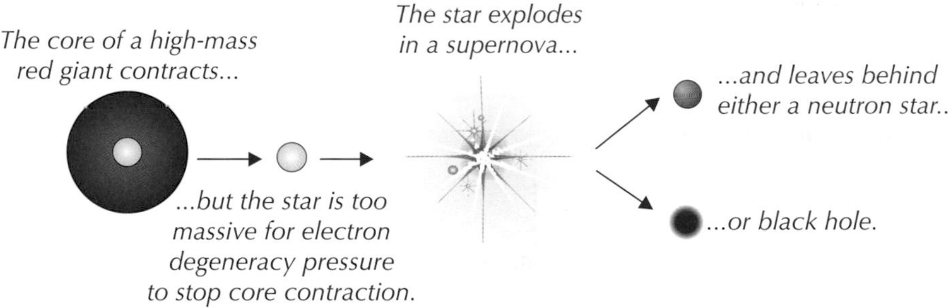
The core of a high-mass red giant contracts...
...but the star is too massive for electron degeneracy pressure to stop core contraction.
The star explodes in a supernova...
...and leaves behind either a neutron star...
...or black hole.

***Figure 1:** The possible evolution paths of a high-mass star from its red-giant phase.*

Tip: One type of supernova can be used as standard candles to calculate galactic distances (see page 161).

When the star explodes in a supernova, it will experience a brief and rapid increase in absolute magnitude (see page 160). The light from a supernova can briefly outshine an entire galaxy, before fading over the next few weeks or months.

***Figure 2:** The Crab Nebula — a supernova remnant with a pulsar (rotating neutron star) in the centre.*

Neutron stars

As the core of a massive star contracts, the electrons in the core material get squashed onto the atomic nuclei and combine with protons to form neutrons and neutrinos. If the star's core is between 1.4 and 3 solar masses, this is as far as the star can contract — the core suddenly collapses to become a neutron star made of neutrons. The outer layers of the star fall onto the neutron star, which causes shockwaves in these layers and leads to a supernova. After the supernova, the neutron star is left behind.

Neutron stars are incredibly dense (about 4×10^{17} kg m^{-3}). They're very small, typically about 20 km across, and they can rotate very fast (up to 600 times a second).

They emit radio waves in two beams as they rotate. These beams sometimes sweep past the Earth and can be observed as radio pulses rather like the flashes of a lighthouse. These pulsing neutron stars are called pulsars.

Tip: When I say 'incredibly' dense I mean it... if you squashed the entire population of the Earth into the size of an average sugar cube — it still wouldn't quite be as dense as a neutron star. Good luck getting your head around that.

Black holes

If the core of the star is more than 3 times the Sun's mass, the core will contract until neutrons are formed, but now the gravitational force on the core is greater — the neutrons can't withstand this gravitational force. There's nothing left to stop the core collapsing to an infinitely dense point. At that point, the laws of physics break down completely.

The **escape velocity** is the velocity that an object would need to travel at to have enough kinetic energy to escape a gravitational field. When a massive star collapses into an infinitely dense point, a region around it has such a strong gravitational field that it becomes a **black hole** — an object whose escape velocity is greater than the speed of light, *c*. If you enter this region, there's absolutely no escape — not even light can escape it.

Tip: Remember, the kinetic energy of an object is given by $E_k = \frac{1}{2}mv^2$.

Tip: Nothing can travel faster than the speed of light, *c*.

The boundary of the region around the infinitely dense point in which the escape velocity is greater than *c* is called the **event horizon**. It is the distance at which the escape velocity is equal to *c*, so light has just enough kinetic energy to overcome the gravitational pull.

The event horizon of a black hole is called the **Schwarzschild radius** — it is thought of as being the radius of a black hole. Inside the Schwarzschild radius, everything, including light, can do nothing but travel further into the black hole.

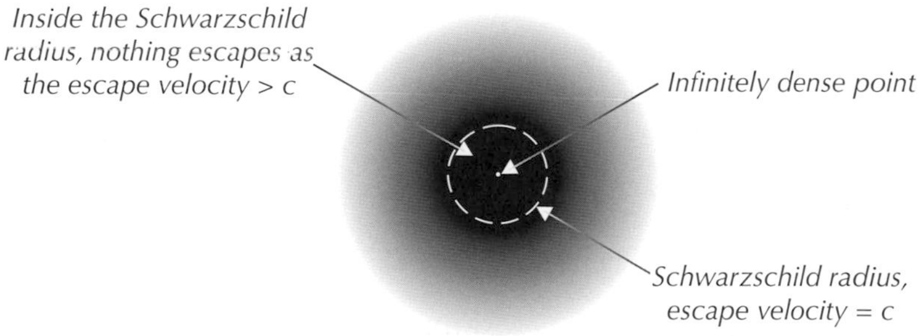

Inside the Schwarzschild radius, nothing escapes as the escape velocity > c

Infinitely dense point

Schwarzschild radius, escape velocity = c

Figure 3: *The structure of a black hole.*

Astronomers now believe that there is a **supermassive black hole** (more than 10^6 times more massive than our Sun) at the centre of every galaxy. As they consume stars close to them, they produce intense radiation, making the centre of galaxies very bright (see pages 189-190 for more).

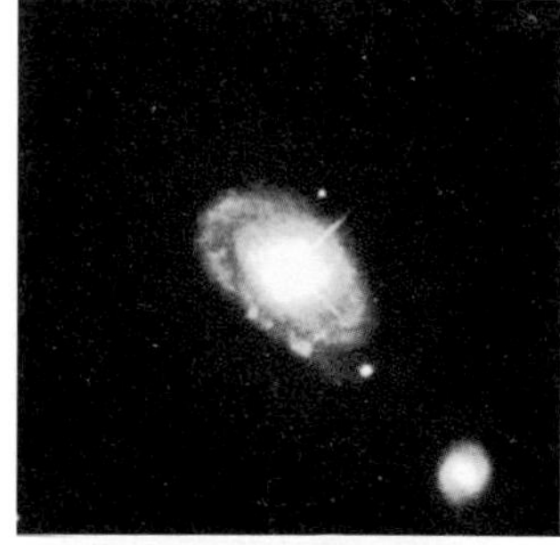

Figure 4: *Astronomers think the intense radiation seen at the centre of galaxies is caused by matter falling onto a supermassive black hole.*

Deriving the Schwarzschild radius

The size of the Schwarzschild radius for a black hole with a given mass can be found by thinking about the energy needed to move an object from a distance of *r* from the centre to infinity.

Tip: The gravitational constant, G, is 6.67×10^{-11} Nm^{2}kg^{-2}. It'll be given in the Data and Formulae booklet in the exam.

Consider a black hole with a mass of M. Assuming that its entire mass is at the centre, it is a point mass and the gravitational potential, V, at a distance of r from it is given by the formula (page 40):

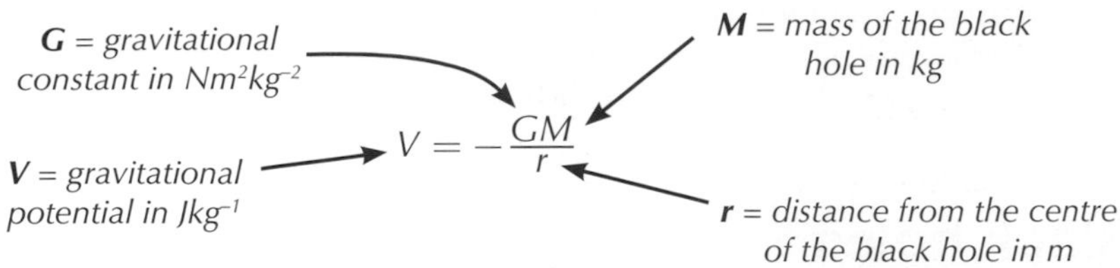

Tip: This doesn't quite work in such strong gravitational fields. You really need to use Einstein's general relativity, but that's way too complicated for A level and it just so happens that this method still gives the right answer — hooray.

The gravitational potential energy (E_p) of an object with mass m is (page 41):

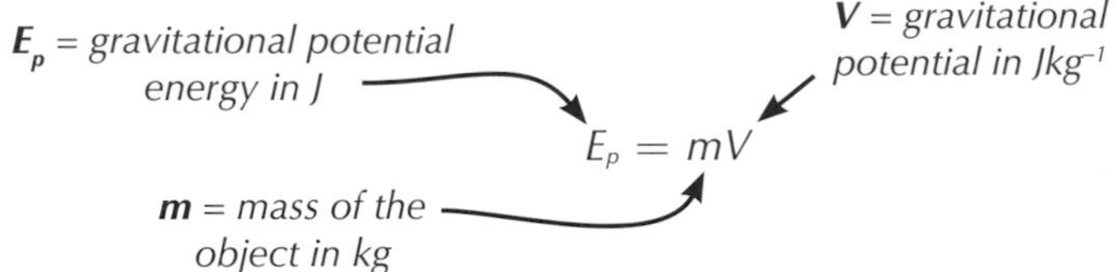

So the gravitational potential energy of an object at a distance of r from the centre of a black hole is:

$$E_p = -\frac{GMm}{r}$$

Tip: You don't need to know this derivation, but being able to follow it will help you to understand what the Schwarzschild radius actually is, and you need to be able to use the equation at the end.

To escape the black hole, the object needs to gain enough gravitational potential energy so that $E_p = 0$. This means it needs to gain a gravitational potential energy of $\frac{GMm}{r}$.

As it travels away from the centre of the black hole, its kinetic energy is transferred into gravitational potential energy, so it just needs enough kinetic energy to escape. If the object has a velocity v at a distance of r from the centre of the black hole, then it has kinetic energy of $E_k = \frac{1}{2}mv^2$ (see page 6).

The kinetic energy needed to escape is just equal to gravitational potential energy that it needs to gain:

$$\frac{1}{2}mv^2 = \frac{GMm}{r}$$

Dividing through by m and making r the subject gives:

$$r = \frac{2GM}{v^2}$$

The Schwarzschild radius is the distance at which the escape velocity is equal to the speed of light. By replacing v with the speed of light, c, you get the Schwarzschild radius, R_S:

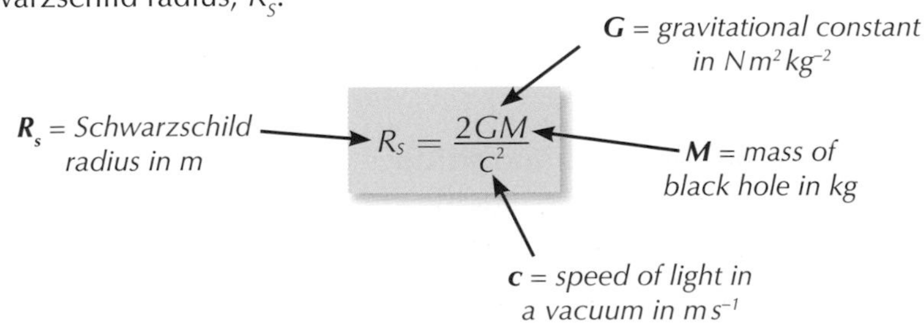

Figure 5: *Karl Schwarzschild, the German astronomer who derived the Schwarzschild radius.*

Examples

a) Calculate the Schwarzschild radius for a black hole that has a mass of 6.00 × 10³⁰ kg.

Use the formula above:

$$R_S = \frac{2GM}{c^2} = \frac{2(6.67 \times 10^{-11})(6.00 \times 10^{30})}{(3.00 \times 10^8)^2} = 8893.33...$$
$$= 8890 \text{ m (to 3 s.f.)}$$

b) Calculate the average density of the matter within the event horizon of the black hole.

The radius of the event horizon is 8893.33... m, and the volume of a sphere is $\frac{4}{3}\pi r^3$. So the volume of the black hole is:

$$V = \frac{4}{3}\pi r^3 = \frac{4}{3}\pi(8893.33...)^3 = 2.946... \times 10^{12} \text{ m}^3$$

So density $\rho = \frac{m}{V} = \frac{6 \times 10^{30}}{2.946... \times 10^{12}}$

$= 2.036... \times 10^{18}$

$= 2.04 \times 10^{18} \text{ kg m}^{-3}$ (to 3 s.f.)

Tip: Make sure you give your answer to the appropriate number of significant figures. You should give your answer to the lowest number of s.f. given in the question or one more.

Tip: Remember... density is just mass divided by volume. You can assume the black hole is spherical and use the formula for the volume of a sphere to help work out the density.

Tip: That's a factor of 5 denser than your average neutron star.

Practice Questions — Application

Q1 A black hole has a Schwarzschild radius of 1.2 km. A photon is emitted from a source 950 m from the centre of the black hole. Will the photon be able to escape the black hole? Explain your answer.

Q2 There is thought to be a supermassive black hole 4.31 million times as massive as the Sun at the centre of the Milky Way.

a) Calculate the mass of this black hole.

b) What is its Schwarzschild radius?

c) How many times larger is the volume of the black hole than the volume of the Sun?

Tip: The mass and radius of the Sun can be found in the Data and Formulae booklet in the exam.
$m_{Sun} = 1.99 \times 10^{30}$ kg
$r_{Sun} = 6.96 \times 10^8$ m

Practice Questions — Fact Recall

Q1 Why can stars with a core mass greater than 1.4 solar masses not form white dwarfs?

Q2 Describe how a contracting core of a star creates a supernova. What change in absolute magnitude occurs when a star explodes as a supernova?

Q3 Describe how neutron stars are formed.

Q4 Explain what is meant by the escape velocity of an object.

Q5 What is a black hole? How is one formed?

Q6 What is meant by an event horizon?

Q7 What is meant by the Schwarzschild radius of a black hole?

Q8 What is thought to be at the centre of the every galaxy?

Q9 Write down the formula for the Schwarzschild radius of a black hole.

12. Doppler Effect and Red Shift

Learning Objectives:

- Understand the Doppler effect.
- Understand and be able to apply the formulas for red shift:

$$z = \frac{\Delta f}{f} = \frac{v}{c}$$

$$\frac{\Delta \lambda}{\lambda} = -\frac{v}{c}$$

for $v \ll c$.

Specification Reference A.1.4

When a light source is moving, the wavelength of the light it gives out gets shifted. Depending on where you are standing in relation to its motion, it may look redder or bluer than it should.

The Doppler Effect

You'll have experienced the **Doppler effect** loads of times with sound waves. Imagine a police car driving past you. As it moves towards you its siren sounds higher-pitched, but as it moves away, its pitch is lower. This change in frequency and wavelength is called the Doppler effect.

The frequency and the wavelength change because the waves bunch together in front of the source and stretch out behind it. The amount of stretching or bunching together depends on the velocity of the source.

Tip: The distance between wavefronts is equal to λ, the wavelength.

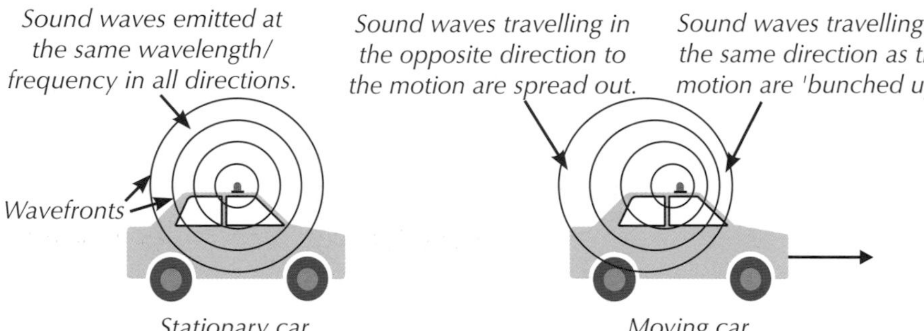

Sound waves emitted at the same wavelength/ frequency in all directions.
Sound waves travelling in the opposite direction to the motion are spread out.
Sound waves travelling in the same direction as the motion are 'bunched up'.
Wavefronts
Stationary car
Moving car

Figure 2: *Doppler shift of sound waves from a moving police car siren.*

Figure 1: *The Doppler effect is used in weather radars to detect the movement of precipitation. A microwave signal is directed at the precipitation, which reflects it. The reflected signal is measured to see how the motion of the precipitation has affected the signal.*

Red shift

The Doppler effect happens with all waves, including electromagnetic radiation. When a light source moves away from us, the wavelength of the light reaching us becomes longer and the frequencies become lower. This shifts the light that we receive towards the red end of the electromagnetic spectrum and is called a **red shift**. The light that we receive from a star moving away from us is redder than the actual light emitted by the star.

Tip: Remember, red light is the lowest frequency of light in the visible spectrum.

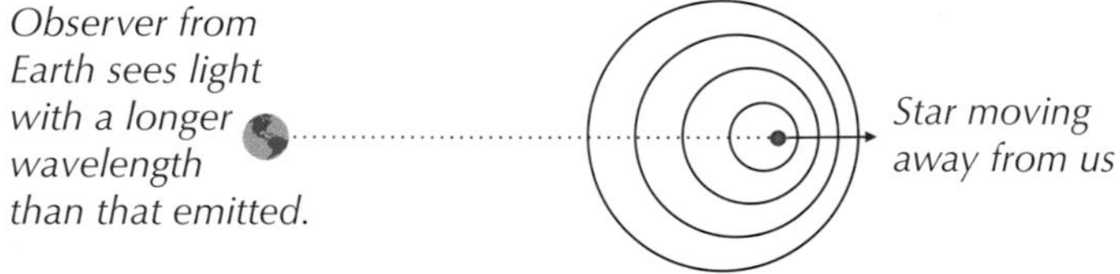

Observer from Earth sees light with a longer wavelength than that emitted.
Star moving away from us

Figure 3: *The red shift of light emitted by a star moving away from us.*

Tip: It's important to realise that the frequency of the source doesn't change, just the frequency of the radiation reaching us.

When a light source moves towards us, the opposite happens and the light undergoes a **blue shift**. The light from the star looks bluer than it actually is.

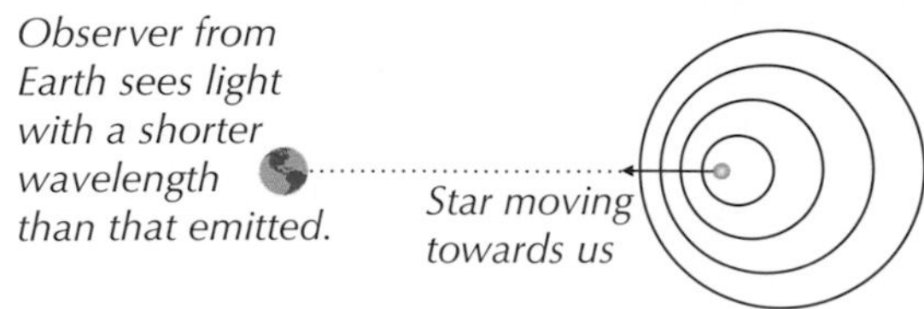

Observer from Earth sees light with a shorter wavelength than that emitted.
Star moving towards us

Figure 4: *The blue shift of light emitted by a star moving towards us.*

Tip: Blue light has the highest frequency of the visible light spectrum. In blue shift, light gets shunted towards (or beyond) the blue end of the visible spectrum.

The amount of red (or blue) shift depends on how fast the star is moving away from (or towards) us. The higher the velocity, the more the waves are shifted

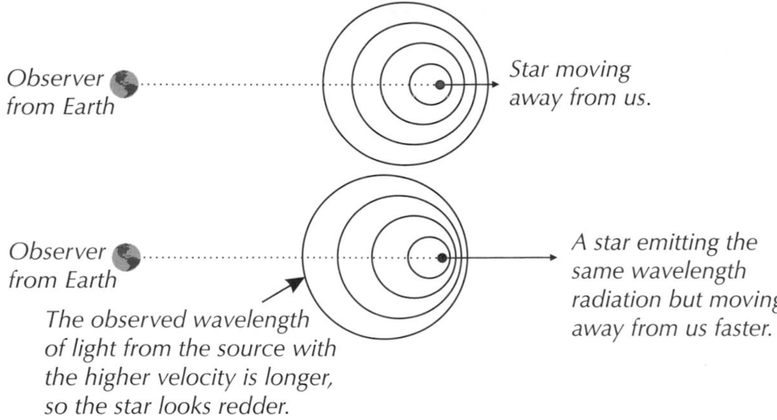

Observer from Earth
Star moving away from us.
Observer from Earth
A star emitting the same wavelength radiation but moving away from us faster.
The observed wavelength of light from the source with the higher velocity is longer, so the star looks redder.

Figure 5: *Red (or blue) shift increases with the velocity of the source.*

The amount of red shift, z, is linked to the velocity that the object is moving away from us at, the **recessional velocity**, by the following formula:

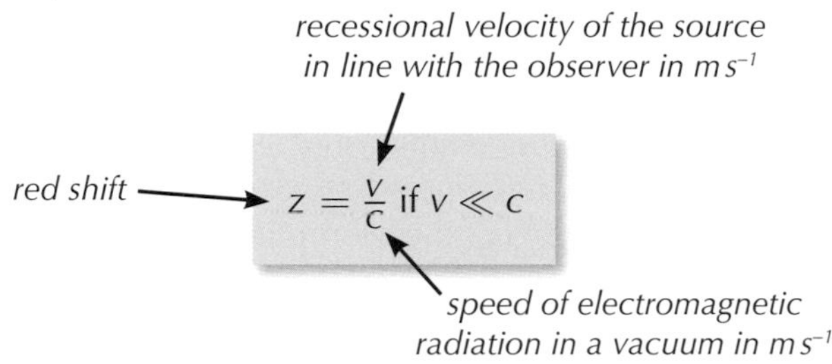

recessional velocity of the source in line with the observer in m s⁻¹
red shift
$z = \frac{v}{c}$ if $v \ll c$
speed of electromagnetic radiation in a vacuum in m s⁻¹

Tip: $v \ll c$ means that v is much less than c. For velocities close to c, this doesn't work.

Tip: You can use any units for v and c in this equation, as long as they are the same.

If the source is moving away, $v > 0$ and so the red shift is positive. If the source is moving towards the observer, $v < 0$ and the red shift is negative — the radiation is blue-shifted.

This equation works for all electromagnetic radiation, but you'll only need to use it to calculate red and blue shifts of optical and radio frequencies.

An increase in wavelength is always referred to as a red shift, even if it's a shift of wavelength taking place at a wavelength higher than that of red visible light, e.g. a shift from infrared to radio wavelengths. A decrease in wavelength is always referred to as a blue shift.

Example

A star is receding from the Earth at a velocity of 525 km s^{-1}. Calculate the red shift of the star.

The recessional velocity is in km s^{-1}, so convert it into m s^{-1} to match the speed of light units.

$$z = \frac{v}{c} = \frac{525\,000}{3.00 \times 10^8} = 1.75 \times 10^{-3}$$

Tip: The speed of light, $c = 3.00 \times 10^8$ m s^{-1}.

Tip: Remember that red shift has no units.

Figure 6: The Andromeda galaxy is closest to the Milky Way and is actually moving towards us, unlike most galaxies (see page 184). In several billion years, it will collide with the Milky Way.

Example

The red shift of the Andromeda galaxy is -3.70×10^{-4}. How fast is the Andromeda galaxy moving? Is it receding from or approaching the Milky Way?

- Rearranging the equation $z = \frac{v}{c}$ gives $v = zc$

$$v = zc = (-3.70 \times 10^{-4}) \times (3.00 \times 10^{8})$$
$$= -111\ 000$$
$$= -1.11 \times 10^{5}\ \text{ms}^{-1}$$

- The velocity is negative, so the Andromeda galaxy is approaching us.

Observing red shift

The entire radiation spectrum of a moving source will be shifted, depending on its motion — including any absorption lines in the spectrum.

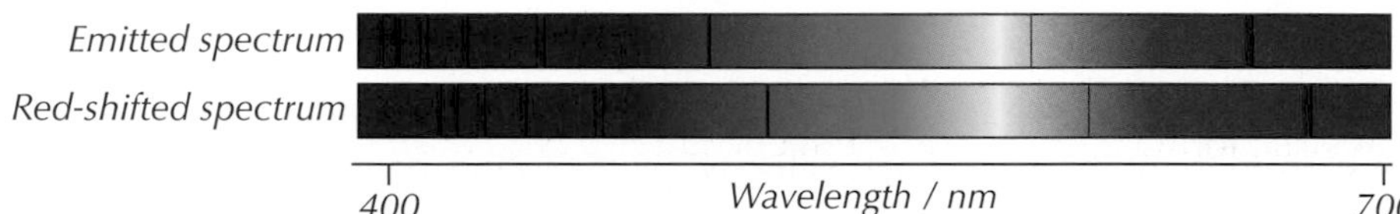

Figure 7: The absorption lines on the line absorption spectrum of a red-shifted star will all be shifted closer to (or beyond) the red end of the spectrum.

Tip: Measuring a laboratory source will give the actual positions of the absorption lines of an atom or molecule without red shift.

Different atoms and molecules only absorb particular wavelengths of light that correspond to the differences between their energy levels. You can identify the actual wavelengths of the absorption lines for a particular atom or molecule in the lab.

You can work out the red shift of a star by looking at the wavelength or frequency of known absorption lines (like the Balmer series — page 167) in the observed spectrum and comparing them to the wavelengths or frequencies they should be. You can calculate the red shift from the change in frequency and the frequency emitted by the source:

Tip: The units don't matter — Δf and f (or $\Delta\lambda$ and λ) just need to be in the same units.

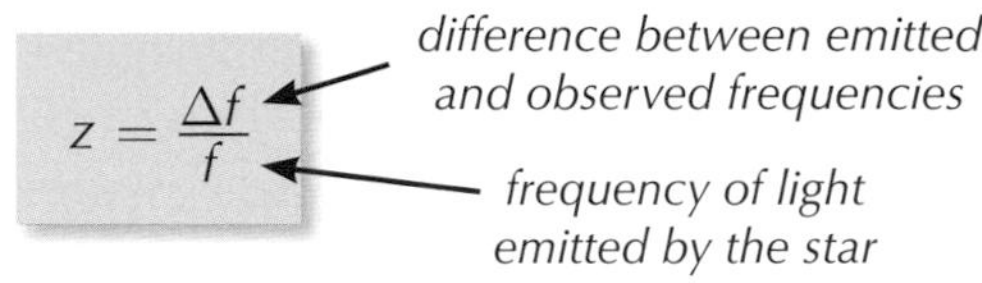

Δf is the difference between the emitted frequency (f) and the observed frequency (f_{obs}), $f - f_{obs}$.

- If the star is red-shifted, $f > f_{obs}$, so Δf and z will be positive.
- If the star is blue-shifted, $f < f_{obs}$, so Δf and z will be negative.

Tip: $\Delta\lambda$ is the difference between the emitted wavelength (λ) and the observed wavelength (λ_{obs}), $\lambda - \lambda_{obs}$.

You can also find red shift by observing the change in wavelength of light from a source:

Tip: Notice the negative sign in this equation. You'll get this formula and the one above in the Data and Formulae booklet in the exam.

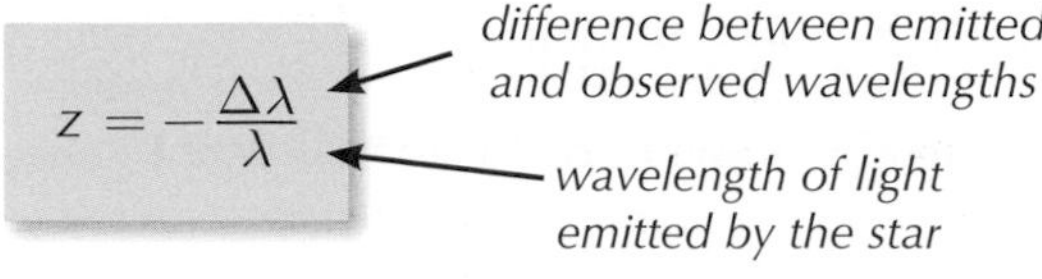

Example

A star is receding from Earth at an unknown velocity. The wavelength of a hydrogen absorption line in the spectrum of this star is 661 nm. The wavelength of the same absorption line observed in a laboratory source is 656 nm. Calculate the velocity at which the star is receding from Earth.

- Combining $z = -\frac{\Delta\lambda}{\lambda}$ and $z = \frac{v}{c}$, we get $\frac{v}{c} = -\frac{\Delta\lambda}{\lambda}$ so $v = -\frac{\Delta\lambda}{\lambda} \times c$
- So $v = -\frac{656 - 661}{656} \times (3.00 \times 10^8) = 2.286... \times 10^6$ m s^{-1}.
- So the star is receding at 2.29×10^6 m s^{-1} (to 3 s.f.).

Tip: Remember, the wavelength of the absorption line found from a laboratory source isn't red-shifted and is the actual wavelength of the absorption line.

Cosmological red shift

All distant galaxies show red shift, and are moving away from us. The way astronomers tend to look at this stuff, the galaxies aren't actually moving through space away from us. Instead, space itself is expanding and the light waves are being stretched along with it. This is called cosmological red shift to distinguish it from red shift produced by sources that are moving through space.

The same formula works for both types of red shift as long as v is much less than c. If v is close to the speed of light, you need to use a nasty, relativistic formula instead (you don't need to know that one).

Tip: There's more on expanding space later — see pages 184-186.

Practice Questions — Application

Q1 A hydrogen absorption line is measured in the spectra of two stars. The line is at a frequency of 4.37×10^{14} Hz in the spectrum of star A and 5.2×10^{14} Hz in the spectrum of star B. The frequency of the hydrogen absorption line is measured in a laboratory to be 4.57×10^{14} Hz.

a) Which star is moving away from us? Explain how you know.

b) Calculate the red shift of this star.

c) How fast is this star travelling?

Q2 The Whirlpool galaxy is receding from us at a velocity of 463 km s^{-1}.

a) Will its red shift be positive or negative? Explain how you know.

b) Calculate its red shift.

c) A lab source of atomic hydrogen shows a strong absorption line at a wavelength of 0.21121 m. Calculate the wavelength this absorption line would be observed at if emitted from this galaxy.

Tip: Remember, $\Delta\lambda = \lambda - \lambda_{obs}$.

Practice Questions — Fact Recall

Q1 Explain how the Doppler effect makes police car sirens sound higher pitched as they travel towards us.

Q2 What is red shift? What is blue shift?

Q3 Write down a formula for red shift, z, in terms of the velocity of the radiation source. What assumption does this formula make?

Q4 Explain how you can tell that a star is moving away from or towards us by looking at its spectrum.

Q5 Write down two formulas for calculating red shift, from frequency and wavelength measurements.

Q6 What is meant by cosmological red shift?

13. The Big Bang Theory

As you've seen by now, astrophysics is full of loads of weird and wonderful objects and ideas. We can't explain them all, but astronomers are trying to use all the evidence we've got to discover more about the origin, evolution and fate of the universe. And right now, the best idea they've got is the Big Bang theory.

Learning Objectives:

- Know that Hubble's law is $v = Hd$, and that it provides a simple interpretation of the expansion of the universe.
- Be able to estimate the age of the universe, assuming H is constant.
- Understand the Big Bang theory as the current consensus for the origin of the universe.
- Understand the evidence for the Big Bang theory, including the red shift of distant galaxies, cosmological microwave background radiation and the relative abundance of H and He.

Specification Reference A.1.4

The cosmological principle

When you read that nearly all the galaxies in the universe are moving away from the Earth (see p.183 and below), it's easy to imagine that the Earth is at the centre of the universe, or that there's something really special about it. Earth is special to us because we live here — but on a universal scale, it's just like any other lump of rock.

The idea that no part of the universe is any more special than any other is summarised by the **cosmological principle**:

On a large scale the universe is:

- **homogeneous** (every part is the same as every other part) and
- **isotropic** (everything looks the same in every direction) — so it doesn't have a centre.

Until the 1930s, astronomers believed that the universe was infinite in both space and time (that is, it had always existed), and static. This seemed the only way that it could be stable using Newton's law of gravitation (page 35). Even Einstein modified his theory of general relativity to make it consistent with this Steady-State Universe.

***Figure 1:** This image shows the relative brightness and distribution of over 1.6 million galaxies across the entire sky. On a large scale, the universe is approximately homogeneous and isotropic.*

Hubble's law

Edwin Hubble was the first scientist to realise that the universe is expanding. He used type 1a supernovae as standard candles (see page 161) to calculate the distances to galaxies, as well as measuring their red shift. The spectra from galaxies all show red shift (apart from a few very close ones). The amount of red shift gives the recessional velocity — how fast the galaxy is moving away (see page 181). Hubble realised that the speed that galaxies moved away from us depended on how far they were away.

A plot of recessional velocity against distance showed that they were proportional, which suggests that the universe is expanding. The further away a galaxy is, the faster it's travelling away from us. This gives rise to **Hubble's law**:

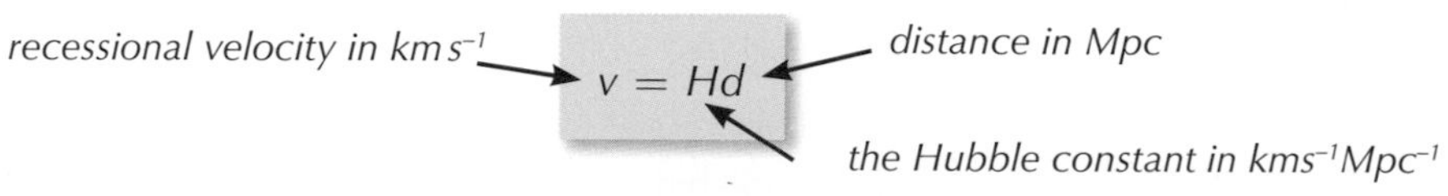

Tip: The SI unit (p.292) for H is s^{-1}. To get H in SI units, you need v in $m\,s^{-1}$ and d in m (1 Mpc = 3.08×10^{22} m).

Tip: You can use Hubble's law to calculate the distance to a distant source if you know its red shift, by using $z = \frac{v}{c}$ to work out its recessional velocity.

Since distance is very difficult to measure, astronomers used to disagree greatly on the value of H, with measurements ranging from 50 to 100 $km\,s^{-1}\,Mpc^{-1}$. It's now generally accepted that H lies between 65 and 80 $km\,s^{-1}\,Mpc^{-1}$ and most agree it's in the mid to low 70s. You'll be given a value to use in the exam, either in the Data and Formulae booklet or in a question where you need it.

Example

A galaxy is receding from us at 950 kms^{-1}. Assuming the Hubble constant is 65 kms^{-1} Mpc^{-1}, how far away is the galaxy in Mpc?

$v = Hd$ so $d = \frac{v}{H} = \frac{950}{65} = 14.61... = 14.6$ Mpc (to 3 s.f.)

Tip: If $v = Hd$ then $H = \frac{v}{d}$. So a graph of recessional velocity (v) against distance from Earth (d) can be used to estimate H. The gradient of the line of best fit is an estimate of H.

The Big Bang theory

The universe is expanding and cooling down (because it's a closed system). So further back in time it must have been denser and hotter. If you trace time back far enough, you get a hot Big Bang:

Tip: A closed system just means that energy and momentum are conserved (see page 5). If there's only so much energy in the universe, as it expands, it must also be cooling.

The Big Bang theory:

The universe started off very hot and very dense (perhaps as an infinitely hot, infinitely dense point) and has been expanding ever since.

The spectra from all galaxies (apart from a few very close ones that are moving towards us) show red shift. This shows they're all moving apart (see page 183). The red shift of distant galaxies is one piece of evidence for the Big Bang theory (see the next page for more).

Since the universe is expanding uniformly away from us it seems as though we're at the centre of the universe, but this is an illusion. You would observe the same thing at any point in the universe.

A good way to visualise this is to think of the universe as the surface of a balloon with lots of dots on it, representing galaxies. As you blow up the balloon, the space between all the galaxies (dots) gets bigger. Each galaxy sees all the other galaxies moving away from it, even though it's not at the centre of the motion.

Age and size

If the universe has been expanding at the same rate for its whole life, the age of the universe can be estimated by:

$$t = \frac{distance}{velocity} = \frac{1}{H}$$

(This is only an estimate though — see dark energy below.)

Tip: Hubble's law says $v = Hd$ so $\frac{1}{H} = \frac{d}{v}$.

Example

If H = 75 kms^{-1}Mpc^{-1}, calculate the age of the universe.

The Hubble constant is in km s^{-1}Mpc^{-1}, but you need it in s^{-1} to get the time in s.

Multiplying by 10^3 gives it in m s^{-1}Mpc^{-1} and dividing by 1 Mpc = 3.08×10^{22} m gives it in m $s^{-1}m^{-1}$, which is just s^{-1}.

75 km s^{-1}Mpc^{-1} = $(75 \times 10^3) \div (3.08 \times 10^{22})$ s^{-1} = $2.4... \times 10^{-18}$ s^{-1}

So $t = \frac{1}{H} \approx \frac{1}{2.4... \times 10^{-18} s^{-1}} = 4.11 \times 10^{17}$ s = 13 billion years (to 2 s.f.).

Tip: The universe is actually thought to be 13.75 billion years old to within 1%.

Tip: The universe is bigger than this sphere, but it isn't observable to us, because we can only see light that has had time to travel to us.

The absolute size of the universe is unknown, but there is a limit on the size of the observable universe. This is simply a sphere (with the Earth at its centre) with a radius equal to the maximum distance that light can travel during its age, taking into account the expansion of space itself. So if $H = 75$ km s^{-1} Mpc^{-1}, then this sphere would have a radius of about 13 billion light years, but taking into account the expansion of the universe, it is thought to be more like 46-47 billion light years.

Dark energy

Tip: There has been a lot of controversy surrounding dark energy in the astrophysics community, but it is now generally accepted that it does exist.

Even though we can estimate the age and observable size of the universe, it is just that — an estimate. This is because the rate of expansion of the universe hasn't been constant.

All the mass in the universe is attracted together by gravity. This attraction tends to slow down the rate of expansion of the universe. It's thought that the expansion was decelerating until about 5 billion years ago.

But in the late 90s, astronomers found evidence that the expansion is now accelerating. Astronomers are trying to explain this acceleration using **dark energy** — a type of energy that fills the whole of space. There are various theories of what this dark energy is, but it's really hard to test them.

Cosmic Microwave Background Radiation

The Big Bang model predicts that loads of electromagnetic radiation was produced in the very early universe. This radiation should still be observed today (it hasn't had anywhere else to go).

Because the universe has expanded, the wavelengths of this cosmic background radiation have been stretched and are now in the microwave region — so it's known as **cosmic microwave background radiation** (**CMBR**). This was picked up accidentally by the astronomers Penzias and Wilson in the 1960s.

Figure 2: *A WMAP image of the CMBR. You can see that, except for the red horizontal band which shows Milky Way emissions, the CMBR is mostly homogeneous and isotropic, but shows small variations.*

The Cosmic Background Explorer (COBE) and Wilkinson Microwave Anisotropy Probe (WMAP) satellites have been sent into space to have a detailed look at the radiation. They found the CMBR has a perfect black body spectrum corresponding to a temperature of 2.73 K (see page 164).

The CMBR is largely isotropic and homogeneous, which agrees with the cosmological principle (see page 184). There are very tiny fluctuations in temperature due to tiny energy-density variations in the early universe, which were needed for the initial 'seeding' of galaxy formation.

The background radiation also shows the Doppler effect, indicating the Earth's motion through space. It turns out that the Milky Way is rushing towards an unknown mass (the Great Attractor) at over a million miles an hour.

Relative abundance of H and He

The Big Bang model also explained the large abundance of helium in the universe (which had puzzled astrophysicists for a while). The early universe had been very hot, so at some point it must have been hot enough for hydrogen fusion to happen. This means that, together with the theory of the synthesis of the heavier elements in stars, the relative abundances of all of the elements can be accounted for.

Practice Questions — Application

Q1 The Antennae galaxies are a pair of colliding galaxies at a distance of 1.4×10^7 pc. Calculate the maximum and minimum recessional velocities of the Antennae galaxies using $H = 70 \pm 5$ km s^{-1} Mpc^{-1}.

Q2 Assuming that H has been constant since the universe began, the universe is approximately 13.7 billion years old.

a) Why is this figure only an estimate?

b) A student claims that this means he can calculate the absolute size of the universe. Why is he wrong?

Tip: 1 Mpc = 1×10^6 pc.

Practice Questions — Fact Recall

Q1 State the cosmological principle.

Q2 What link did Hubble find between red shift and distance?

Q3 Write down Hubble's law, including the units of each quantity.

Q4 What is the Big Bang theory?

Q5 How can we estimate the age of the universe from the Hubble constant?

Q6 Why can't we measure the absolute size of the universe?

Q7 What might dark energy explain?

Q8 Explain what CMBR is and how it supports the Big Bang theory.

Q9 How does the relative abundance of H and He in the universe support the Big Bang theory?

Learning Objectives:

- Apply the concept of red shift to spectroscopic binary systems.
- Know that quasars are bright radio sources and are the most distant objects that we can measure.
- Understand that quasars show large red shifts, indicating that they are very far away.

Specification Reference A.1.4

14. Applications of Red Shift

Since astronomers discovered red shift, it has helped to explain and observe quite a few strange things going on in space...

Spectroscopic binary stars

About half of the stars we observe are actually two stars that orbit each other. Many of them are too far away from us to be resolved with telescopes (see page 148 for more on resolving power), but the lines in their spectra show a binary star system. These are called spectroscopic binary stars. An eclipsing binary system is one whose orbital plane lies almost in our line of sight, so the stars eclipse each other as they orbit.

By observing how the absorption lines in the spectrum change with time the orbital period can be calculated. For simplicity, think about only one absorption line from the spectrum of an eclipsing binary system — see Figure 1.

Tip: Astronomers have used a similar method to find extrasolar planets (planets beyond the Solar System).

Position of binary star system:

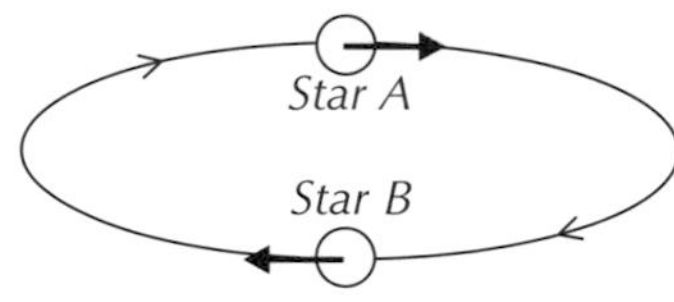

•*Observer*

Both stars are moving at right angles to our line of sight, so there's no red shift (other than that of the binary system as a whole, as a result of its recessional velocity — which will be the same for both stars).

Absorption line spectrum:

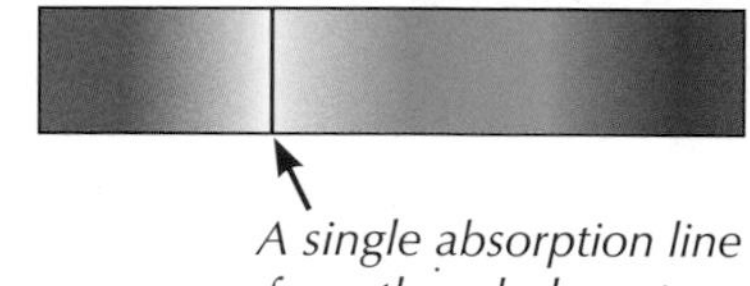

A single absorption line from the whole system

Tip: Two stars that look like one star are called optical doubles. Some optical doubles may not actually be binary systems. They might just be in the same line of sight but nowhere near each other.

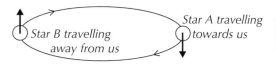

Star B travelling away from us

Star A travelling towards us

•*Observer*

Both stars are moving along our line of sight. Star A shows maximum blue shift. Star B shows maximum red shift.

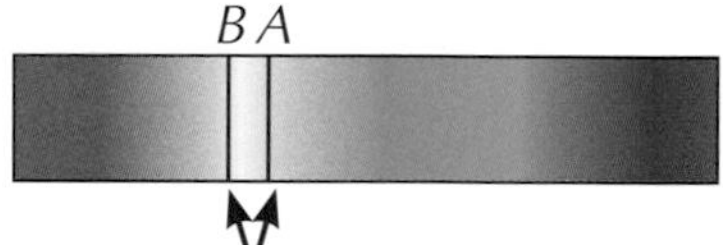

Two separate absorption lines (one red-shifted and one blue-shifted) — one from each star.

Figure 1: *How the absorption lines in the spectrum of a spectroscopic binary star system change as the stars orbit each other.*

Tip: The orbital period of a spectroscopic binary system can be anywhere from a few minutes to hundreds of thousands of years.

As you can see in Figure 1, as the stars orbit each other, the separation between the lines goes from zero up to the maximum separation and back to zero again in half a period. So the orbital period is double the time between the two positions in Figure 1.

Apparent magnitude of an eclipsing binary system

If you plot a graph of apparent magnitude against time for an eclipsing binary system, you'll get a graph like the one in Figure 3. As the stars eclipse each other, the apparent magnitude drops because some of the light is blocked out. It drops more as the dimmer star passes in front of the brighter star.

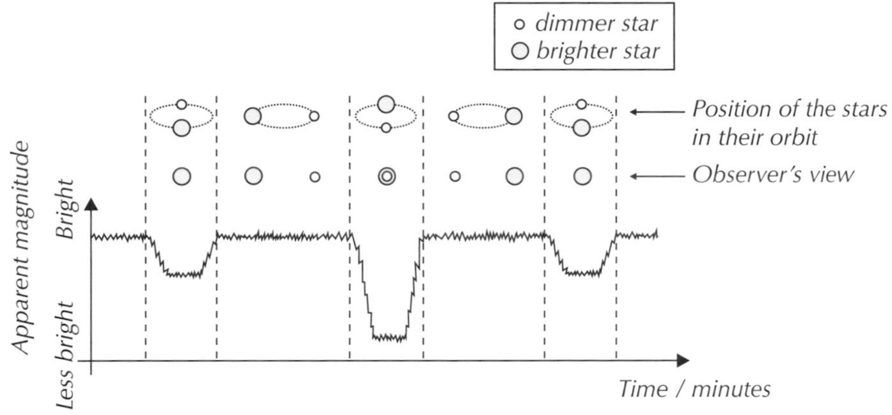

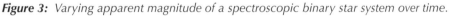

Figure 3: *Varying apparent magnitude of a spectroscopic binary star system over time.*

Figure 2: *The binary system Alpha Centauri is the third brightest star system in the sky. Alpha Centauri A and B orbit each other once every 80 years. Their companion Proxima Centauri (out of the frame of this image) is thought to orbit the pair with a period of millions of years.*

Quasars

Quasars (quasi-stellar objects) were discovered in the late 1950s and were first thought to be stars in our galaxy. The puzzling thing was that their spectra were nothing like normal stars. They sometimes shot out jets of material, and many of them were very active radio sources.

The 'stars' produced a continuous spectrum that was nothing like a black body radiation curve, and instead of absorption lines there were emission lines of elements that astronomers had not seen before.

Tip: Remember from AS physics — emission lines are bright lines corresponding to particular wavelengths of light emitted by a source.

However, these lines looked strangely familiar and in 1963 Maarten Schmidt realised that they were simply the Balmer series of hydrogen (see p.167) but red-shifted enormously.

This huge red shift suggests they're a huge distance away (see page 184) — in fact, the most distant objects seen. The measured red shifts give us distances of billions of light years. Using the inverse square law for intensity (see p.165) gives an idea of just how bright quasars are:

Example

A quasar has the same intensity as a star 20 000 ly away with the same power output as the Sun (4×10^{26} W). Its red shift gives a distance of 1×10^{10} ly. Calculate its power output.

$$P \propto Id^2 \Rightarrow \frac{P_{quasar}}{P_{star}} = \left(\frac{d_{quasar}}{d_{star}}\right)^2$$ ($I_{quasar} = I_{star}$ so they cancel out of the equation).

$$\Rightarrow P_{quasar} = P_{star} \times \left(\frac{d_{quasar}}{d_{star}}\right)^2 = 4 \times 10^{26} \times \left(\frac{1 \times 10^{10}}{20000}\right)^2 = 1 \times 10^{38}\text{ W}$$

That's bright — about 10 times the power output of the entire Milky Way galaxy.

Tip: This is just the inverse square law. $I = \frac{P}{4\pi d^2}$ so $P = 4\pi Id^2$.

There's also very good evidence to suggest that quasars are only about the size of the Solar System. Let me run that past you again. That's the power of a trillion Suns from something the size of the Solar System.

Figure 4: The active galaxy M87 — 50 million light years from Earth. The supermassive black hole at the centre is emitting a 5000-light-year-long jet of matter.

These numbers caused a lot of controversy in the astrophysics community — they seemed crazy. Many astrophysicists thought there must be a more reasonable explanation. But then evidence for the distance of quasars came when sensitive CCD equipment detected the fuzzy cloud of a galaxy around a quasar.

The current consensus is that a quasar is a very powerful galactic nucleus centred around a huge black hole more than 10^6 times the mass of the Sun. Almost all galaxies are thought to have these 'supermassive' black holes at their centres (see page 177), but only some eject huge amounts of material from their nuclei. Those that do are known as **active galactic nuclei** and a galaxy containing one is known as an active galaxy.

The black hole in an active galactic nucleus is surrounded by a doughnut shaped mass of whirling gas falling into it, which emits matter and radiation. In the same way as a pulsar (see p.177), magnetic fields produce jets of matter and radiation streaming out from the poles. The black hole must consume the mass of about 10 Suns per year to produce the energy observed.

Practice Questions — Application

Q1 Algol is an eclipsing binary system in the constellation Perseus. The graph below shows how its apparent magnitude varies over a period of time.

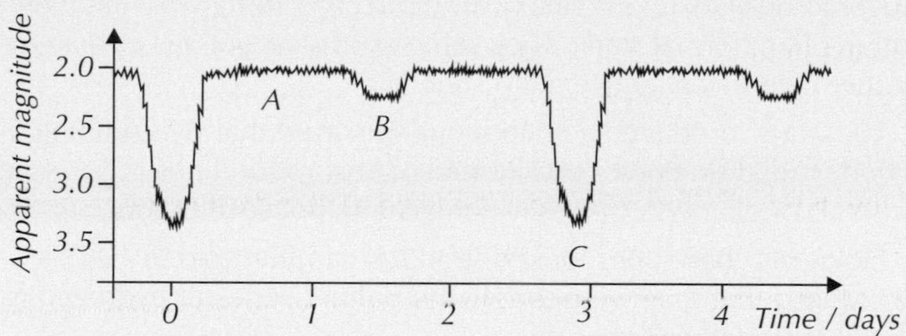

a) Do both the stars have the same apparent magnitude?

b) Describe the positions of the two stars at points A, B and C, as viewed by an observer in the plane of their orbit.

c) Write down the approximate period of the system in days.

Q2 Calculate the distance to a quasar with a red shift of 0.12.

Tip: You can use Hubble's law for this question (page 184) and $H = 65$ km s^{-1} Mpc^{-1}.

Practice Questions — Fact Recall

Q1 Explain how spectroscopic binary stars can be identified by observing how their spectral lines change.

Q2 How would you find the orbital period of a spectroscopic binary star?

Q3 Why does the apparent magnitude of an eclipsing binary star change with time?

Q4 What were quasars first thought to be?

Q5 How do we know that quasars are very far away?

Q6 Describe what a quasar is and what is thought to cause them to emit such large amounts of radiation.

Section Summary

Make sure you know...

- What the principal focus, focal point and focal plane are for a converging lens.
- How to draw ray diagrams to show an image being formed by a converging lens.
- That images can be real or virtual.
- The lens equation $\frac{1}{f} = \frac{1}{u} + \frac{1}{v}$ and how to use it.
- How to draw a ray diagram of an astronomical refracting telescope in normal adjustment.
- How to calculate angular magnification.
- What the focal point of a concave mirror is.
- How to draw a ray diagram for the Cassegrain arrangement for a reflecting telescope showing the path of rays through the telescope as far as the eyepiece.
- The structure and operation of a CCD.
- That a diffraction pattern is caused by light passing through a circular aperture.
- What is meant by resolving power, and how to calculate it using the Rayleigh criterion $\theta \approx \frac{\lambda}{D}$.
- The relative merits of using reflecting and refracting optical telescopes, including the problems of spherical and chromatic aberration.
- The similarities and differences between optical telescopes and single-dish radio telescopes, I-R, U-V and X-ray telescopes (including their positioning, use, resolving power and collecting power).
- That a parsec (pc) is the distance to an object with an angle of parallax of 1 arcsecond.
- That a light year (ly) is the distance light will travel in a year in a vacuum.
- What is meant by apparent magnitude, *m*, and how it is related to intensity.
- What is meant by absolute magnitude, M, and that $m - M = 5 \log\left(\frac{d}{10}\right)$.
- How type 1a supernovae can be used as standard candles to measure the distance to galaxies.
- The general shape of black body curves and how they vary with temperature.
- How stars can be assumed to be black bodies and classified according to their black-body temperature.
- Wien's displacement law for black bodies: $\lambda_{max}T = 0.0029$ m K, and Stefan's law: $P = \sigma AT^4$
- The inverse square law $I = \frac{P}{4\pi d^2}$ and the assumptions needed to use it.
- That Balmer absorption lines are due to electron transitions in atomic hydrogen from the n = 2 state.
- The colour, temperature and prominent absorption lines of each spectral class of OBAFGKM.
- The features and axes scales of the Hertzsprung-Russell (H-R) diagram.
- The movement of a Sun-like star on the H-R diagram as it evolves into a white dwarf.
- What a supernova is and that it has a rapid increase in absolute magnitude.
- That a neutron star is a very small and dense remnant of a high-mass star and is made of neutrons.
- That a black hole is produced by the collapse of the core of a very high-mass star to an infinitely dense point, and that it has an escape velocity $v > c$.
- That the Schwarzschild radius (R_s) is the event horizon of a black hole and $R_s = \frac{2GM}{c^2}$.
- What is meant by the Doppler effect and red shift, *z*, and that $z = \frac{\Delta f}{f} = \frac{v}{c}$ and $\frac{\Delta\lambda}{\lambda} = -\frac{v}{c}$ for $v \ll c$.
- Hubble's law: $v = Hd$ and how to use it to estimate the age of the universe.
- How to calculate the red shift of distant galaxies.
- The Big Bang theory and how CMBR and the relative H and He abundances are evidence for it.
- That dark energy might explain the accelerating expansion of the universe.
- How to calculate the red shift of objects and what the red shift tells you about their motion, e.g. quasars and spectroscopic binary stars.

Exam-style Questions

1 The Hubble Space Telescope (HST) is a Cassegrain telescope in orbit around the Earth.

1 (a) Draw a ray diagram to show two axial rays travelling through a typical Cassegrain arrangement as far as the eye lens.

(2 marks)

1 (b) When the HST was launched, it suffered from a problem called spherical aberration which had to be corrected in the first servicing mission of 1993.

1 (b) (i) Explain the problem of spherical aberration.

(1 mark)

1 (b) (ii) Describe how spherical aberration can be avoided.

(1 mark)

1 (c) The HST can observe light with wavelengths in the infrared, ultraviolet and visible regions of the electromagnetic spectrum. Explain why HST would be unable to observe the same radiation if it was based on Earth.

(1 mark)

1 (d) The HST records images using a charge-coupled device (CCD).
Describe the structure and operation of a CCD.
The quality of your written communication will be assessed in this question.

(6 marks)

2 Mu Cephei is a red giant star in the constellation Cepheus. Analysis of the radiation emitted by Mu Cephei gives the value of its peak wavelength as λ_{max} = 828.6 nm. The intensity of the radiation detected was 5.1×10^{-9} W m^{-2}.

2 (a) (i) Explain what is meant by a black body.

(1 mark)

2 (a) (ii) Estimate the surface temperature of Mu Cephei in kelvin, stating any assumptions made.

(3 marks)

2 (b) Mu Cephei is estimated to have a radius of around 1500 solar radii.
The radius of the Sun is 6.96×10^{8} m.

2 (b) (i) Calculate the power output of Mu Cephei in watts.

(3 marks)

2 (b) (ii) Calculate the distance to Mu Cephei in light years.

(2 marks)

2 (b) (iii) Suggest one reason why this value may be inaccurate.

(1 mark)

3 The properties of some stars in the constellation Canis Major are given in the table.

Name	Apparent magnitude	Absolute magnitude	Spectral class
Adhara	1.50	–4.11	B
Aludra	2.45	–7.51	B
Omicron[1]	3.89	–5.02	K
Sirius A	–1.44	1.45	A
Wezen	1.83	–6.87	F

3 (a) Which of these stars appears dimmest?

(1 mark)

3 (b) (i) Define the term absolute magnitude.

(1 mark)

3 (b) (ii) Which of these stars is closer than 10 parsecs to Earth? Explain your answer.

(2 marks)

3 (c) (i) Calculate the distance to Wezen in parsecs.

(2 marks)

3 (c) (ii) Describe the composition and colour of Wezen, and the main absorption lines that you would expect to see in its line spectrum.

(3 marks)

4 The VLA (Very Large Array) is an array of radio telescopes in New Mexico.

4 (a) The array combines the power of 27 radio telescopes, each with a 25 m diameter dish. Its maximum resolving power is equivalent to that of a giant radio telescope with a diameter of 36 km.

4 (a) (i) Calculate the resolving power of a single 25 m radio telescope when observing point sources of electromagnetic radiation of wavelength 8.5×10^{-3} m.

(2 marks)

4 (a) (ii) How many times better is the maximum resolving power of the VLA than a single 25 m dish when observing point radio waves with a wavelength of 8.5×10^{-3} m.

(2 marks)

4 (b) In 2011, the VLA detected object A, a strong radio source with a red shift of 5.95.

4 (b) (i) Explain why the formula for red shift cannot be used to calculate the recessional velocity of this object.

(2 marks)

4 (b) (ii) Suggest what type of object could have been observed and explain your answer.

(2 marks)

5 Menkalinan is a spectroscopic eclipsing binary system 82 light years away. It consists of two almost identical stars of spectral class A and its orbital plane is close to our line of sight.

5 (a) Astronomers calculated the distance to Menkalinan by measuring its angle of parallax.

5 (a) (i) Explain what is meant by the angle of parallax.

(1 mark)

5 (a) (ii) Explain why parallax can't be used to measure the distance to all stars.

(1 mark)

5 (b) A graph of apparent magnitude against time for Menkalinan is shown in Figure 1.

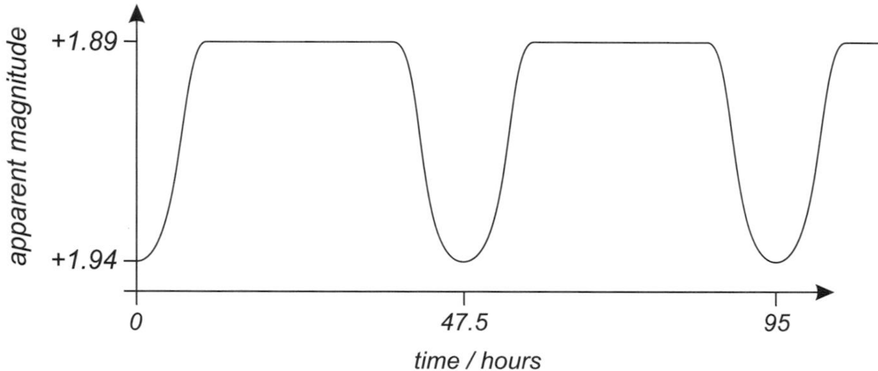

Figure 1: *Light curve for Menkalinan.*

5 (b) (i) What can you say about the relative brightness of the two stars?

(1 mark)

5 (b) (ii) Write down the orbital period of Menkalinan.

(1 mark)

5 (c) The spectrum from one of the stars is studied and an absorption line is seen to fluctuate between 434.026 nm and 434.076 nm.

5 (c) (i) Explain why the wavelength of the light from the star is observed to fluctuate.

(1 mark)

5 (c) (ii) Show that the orbital velocity of the star is approximately 18 km s^{-1}.

(3 marks)

5 (d) The two stars in Menkalinan are classified as subgiants. Subgiants are thought to be stars that have stopped fusing hydrogen in their cores and are contracting, heating up, and beginning to fuse hydrogen in a shell surrounding the core. Describe the next stage in the stars' evolution, describing any reactions in the stars that would take place as part of this evolution.

(2 marks)

6 (a) Copy and complete the Hertzsprung-Russell (H-R) diagram on the axes below, marking on your diagram the main sequence stars, white dwarfs, red giants and any missing axis labels.

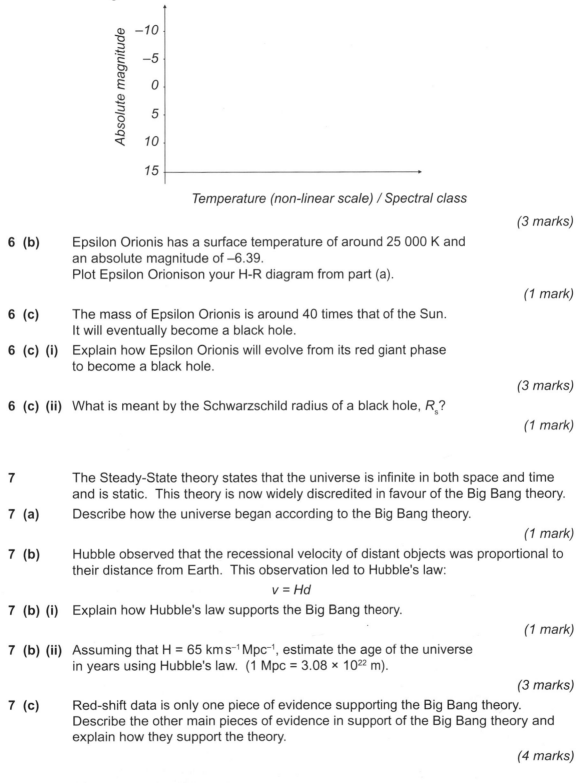

(3 marks)

6 (b) Epsilon Orionis has a surface temperature of around 25 000 K and an absolute magnitude of –6.39.
Plot Epsilon Orionison your H-R diagram from part (a).

(1 mark)

6 (c) The mass of Epsilon Orionis is around 40 times that of the Sun. It will eventually become a black hole.

6 (c) (i) Explain how Epsilon Orionis will evolve from its red giant phase to become a black hole.

(3 marks)

6 (c) (ii) What is meant by the Schwarzschild radius of a black hole, R_s?

(1 mark)

7 The Steady-State theory states that the universe is infinite in both space and time and is static. This theory is now widely discredited in favour of the Big Bang theory.

7 (a) Describe how the universe began according to the Big Bang theory.

(1 mark)

7 (b) Hubble observed that the recessional velocity of distant objects was proportional to their distance from Earth. This observation led to Hubble's law:

$$v = Hd$$

7 (b) (i) Explain how Hubble's law supports the Big Bang theory.

(1 mark)

7 (b) (ii) Assuming that H = 65 $\text{km s}^{-1}\,\text{Mpc}^{-1}$, estimate the age of the universe in years using Hubble's law. (1 Mpc = 3.08×10^{22} m).

(3 marks)

7 (c) Red-shift data is only one piece of evidence supporting the Big Bang theory. Describe the other main pieces of evidence in support of the Big Bang theory and explain how they support the theory.

(4 marks)

1. Lenses

There are two types of lenses that you need to know about — converging and diverging lenses. They have different shapes and different properties.

Learning Objectives:
- Know the properties of converging and diverging lenses.
- Understand what is meant by the principal focus and focal length of a lens.
- Know how to draw a ray diagram for an image formed by a converging or diverging lens.
- Be able to use the lens equation: $\frac{1}{u} + \frac{1}{v} = \frac{1}{f}$.
- Know how to calculate linear magnification.
- Understand what is meant by the power of a lens and be able to calculate it using: power = $\frac{1}{f}$.

Specification Reference B.2.1

Types of lenses

Lenses change the direction of light rays by refraction — the change in direction of light as it enters a different medium. There are two main types of lens — converging and diverging. Both have different effects on light...

Converging lenses

Converging lenses are convex in shape — they bulge outwards. Converging lenses bring parallel light rays together (see Figure 1).

The **principal axis** of a lens is a straight line that passes through the centre of the lens, perpendicular to its surface on both sides. Rays parallel to the principal axis of the lens converge onto a point in front of the lens on the axis called the **principal focus**. Rays that are parallel to each other but not to the principal axis converge somewhere else on the **focal plane** — the plane perpendicular to the principal axis of the lens on which the principal focus lies. The **focal length**, f, is the distance between the lens axis and the focal plane — f is positive for a converging lens because the focal point is in front of the lens.

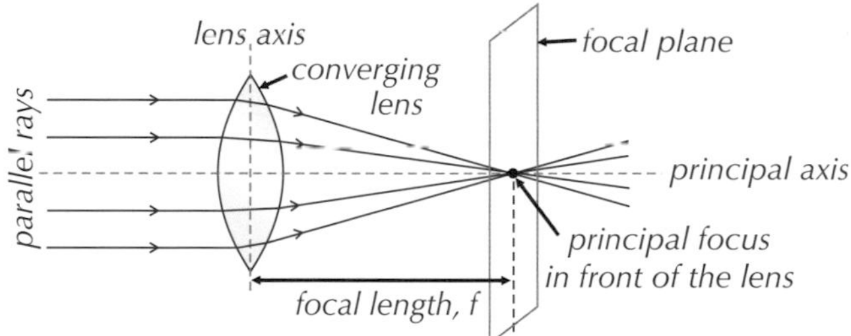

Figure 1: Parallel rays of light are brought together by a converging lens at its principal focus.

Tip: A light ray travelling along the principal axis won't be refracted — it will just carry on in a straight line.

Diverging lenses

Diverging lenses are concave in shape — they cave inwards. They cause parallel rays of light to diverge (spread out). The principal focus of a diverging lens is at a point behind the lens. The principal focus is the point that rays from a distant object appear to have come from. The focal length, f, is the distance between the lens axis and the principal focus. f is a negative value for a diverging lens because it is behind the lens.

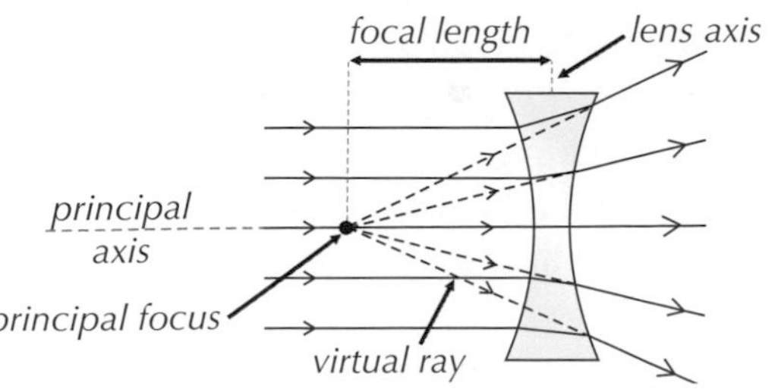

Figure 3: Parallel rays of light are spread out by a diverging lens.

Tip: You should remember refraction from AS physics.

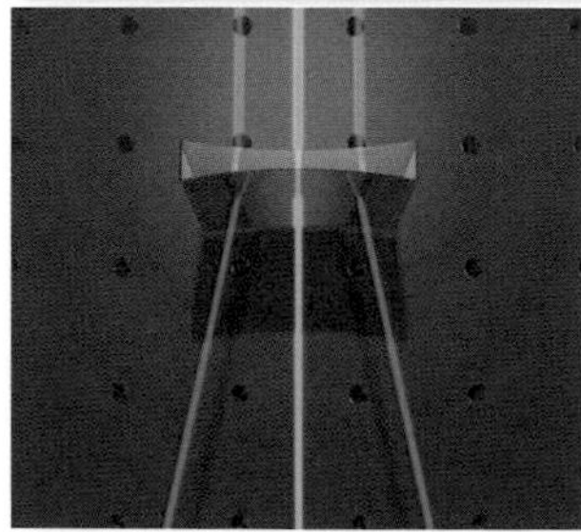

Figure 2: A diverging lens causes parallel rays of light to diverge.

Ray diagrams

When light rays from an object pass through a lens, an **image** is formed where the rays meet. To work out where an image will appear, you can draw a **ray diagram**. A ray diagram shows how light rays travel from the object through a lens. Two rays coming from one point on an object will meet where that part of the image is formed.

For objects sitting on the principal axis, you only need to draw two rays to work out where the image will be: one passing through the centre of the lens that doesn't get refracted at all, and one initially parallel to the principal axis that passes through the principal focus (see previous page). The principal focus for a converging lens is on the other side of the lens to the object, but the principal focus for a diverging lens is on the same side as the object (see Figures 1 and 3), so the methods of drawing the ray diagrams are slightly different.

Tip: All rays parallel to the principal axis pass through, or appear to have come from, a principal focus — see Figures 1 and 3.

Converging lenses

When drawing light being refracted by a converging lens, there are two things to remember:

- An incident ray parallel to the principal axis refracts through the lens and passes through the principal focus on the other side.
- An incident ray passing through the centre of the lens carries on in the same direction.

Tip: Remember — the principal focus is one focal length away from the lens axis.

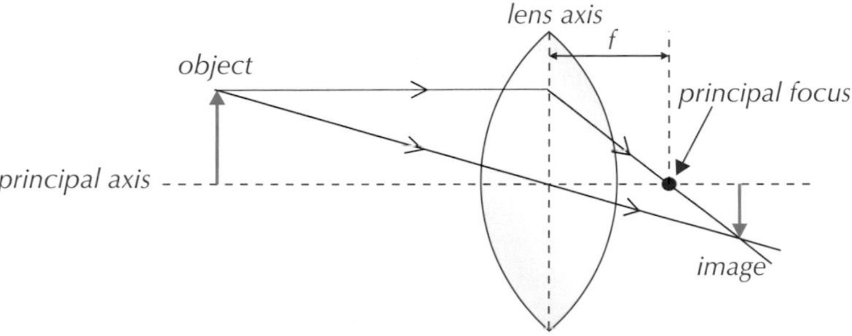

Figure 4: *Ray diagram to show image formation by a converging lens.*

Tip: In reality the ray through the lens centre will refract twice, as it enters and leaves the lens — but in ray diagrams you can just draw it as one refraction at the lens axis.

Diverging lenses

When drawing light being refracted by a diverging lens, remember:

- An incident ray parallel to the principal axis refracts through the lens and appears to have come from the principal focus.
- An incident ray passing through the centre of the lens carries on in the same direction.

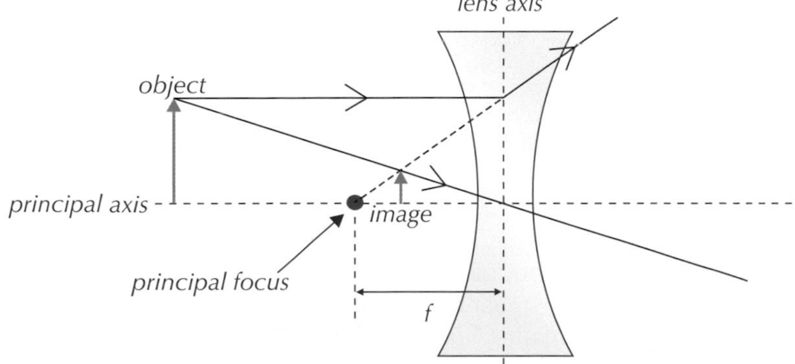

Figure 5: *Ray diagram to show image formation by a diverging lens — the image is formed where the virtual ray and the central ray cross.*

Tip: In Figure 5, the dashed red ray coming from the image is a virtual ray — it appears to be coming from that point, but isn't really.

Real and virtual images

Lenses can produce real or virtual images. A **real image** is formed when light rays from an object are made to pass through another point in space. The light rays are actually there, and the image can be captured on a screen.

A **virtual image** is formed when light rays from an object appear to have come from another point in space. The light rays aren't really where the image appears to be, so the image can't be captured on a screen.

You can tell if an image is real or virtual by drawing a ray diagram (see previous page). If the image is formed on the other side of the lens to the object — the image is real. If the image is formed on the same side of the lens as the object — the image is virtual. Again, there are different rules for converging and diverging lenses.

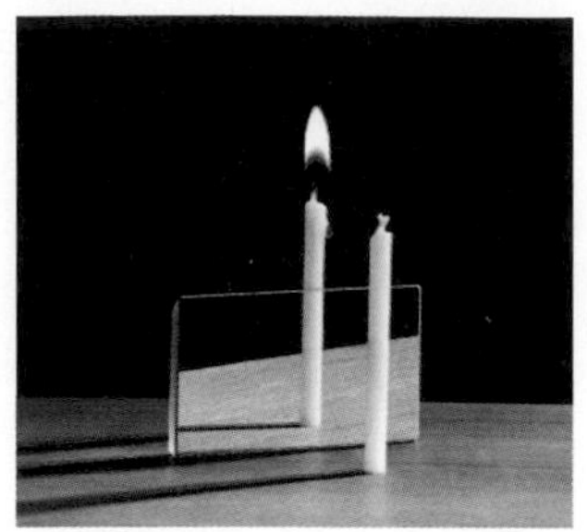

Figure 6: *Plane mirrors also produce virtual images — here the image of the unlit candle appears to come from behind the mirror.*

Converging lenses

Converging lenses can form both real and virtual images, depending on where the object is.

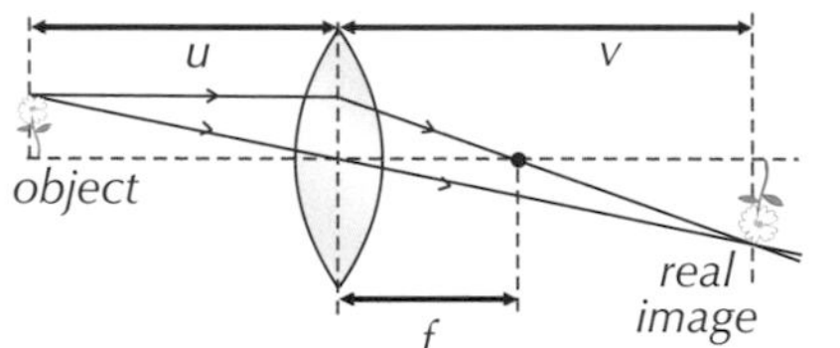

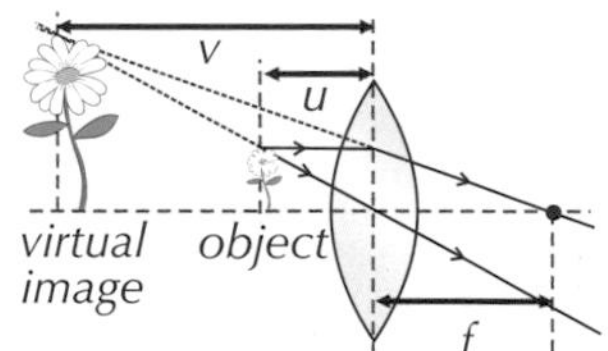

Figure 7: *A ray diagram showing a converging lens forming a real image (left) and a virtual image (right).*

Tip: An image that's formed on the same side of the lens as the object will have a negative *v*. Diverging lenses always have a negative focal length, *f*, because the rays appear to go through the focal point of the lens on the same side as the object.

In Figure 7, *u* = distance between object and lens axis (always positive), *v* = distance between image and lens axis (positive if image is real, negative if image is virtual) and *f* = focal length. The focal length of a converging lens is always positive and a diverging lens always has a negative focal length. The values *u*, *v* and *f* are related (see next page).

The distance of the object from the lens axis, *u*, in relation to the focal length, *f*, of the lens affects the image formed — whether it is real or virtual, its orientation, its size and its position (see Figures 8 and 9).

u	*Image type*	*Image orientation*	*Image size*	*v*
beyond 2f	*real*	*inverted*	*smaller than object*	*between f and 2f*
At 2f	*real*	*inverted*	*same as object*	*2f*
between 2f and f	*real*	*inverted*	*bigger than object*	*bigger than 2f*
between f and 0 (the lens axis)	*virtual*	*right way up*	*bigger than object*	*negative*

Figure 8: *Table showing the properties of an image formed by a converging lens when the object is at various positions.*

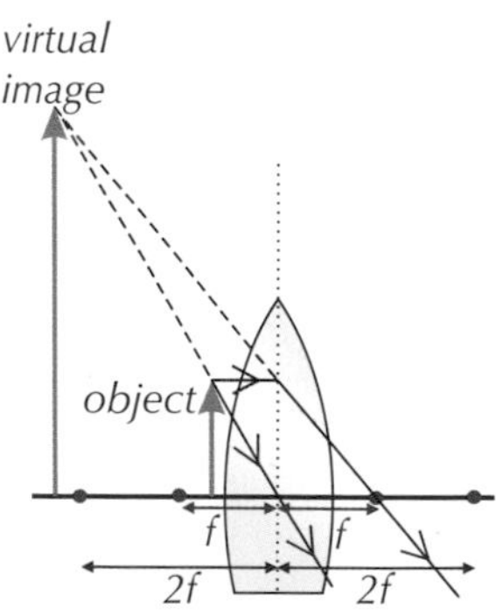

Figure 9: *An object nearer to a converging lens than the focal length will produce a virtual image, the right way up, bigger than the object and on the same side of the lens.*

Diverging lenses

A diverging lens always produces a virtual image, so *v* is always negative. The image is the right way up, smaller than the object and on the same side of the lens as the object — no matter where the object is.

Objects off the principal axis

When the bottom of an object is on the principal axis, the bottom of the image is also on the axis. But if the bottom of the object isn't on the principal axis, you need to find where the bottom of the image is too. You just need to repeat the process you followed on page 197 of drawing two rays from the top of the object to find the position of the top of the image. Only this time, you draw the rays from the bottom of the object to find the bottom of the image.

Tip: You can do this with any part of an object — if you draw two rays coming from one part of the object, they'll converge at the same point on the image... but it's usually most useful to find the top and bottom so that you can see the image's size.

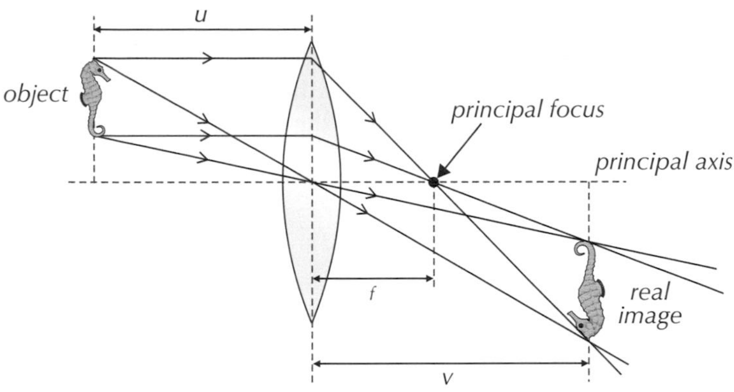

Figure 10: *A ray diagram showing where the image of an object positioned off the principal axis will be formed.*

Lens equation

The focal length of a lens, f, the distance between the object and the lens axis, u, and the distance between the image and the lens axis, v, are linked by the lens equation:

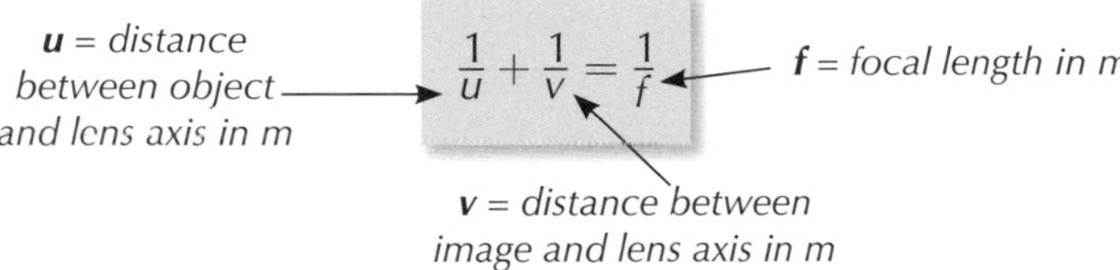

Tip: Remember... v is positive if the image is real and negative if the image is virtual. f is positive if the lens is converging and negative if the lens is diverging.

Tip: You don't have to have u, v and f in metres to use this equation, but they do all need to be in the same distance units.

Example

An object is placed 0.25 m from a diverging lens with a focal length of –0.40 m. Calculate the distance from the lens the image is formed.

To find the image's distance from the lens, v, use the lens equation:

$$\frac{1}{u} + \frac{1}{v} = \frac{1}{f}$$

$f = -0.40$ m and $u = 0.25$ m, so:

$$\frac{1}{0.25} + \frac{1}{v} = \frac{1}{-0.40}$$

$$4 + \frac{1}{v} = -2.5$$

$$\frac{1}{v} = -6.5$$

$$v = \frac{1}{-6.5} = -0.15\text{ m (to 2 s.f.)}$$

Tip: Diverging lenses always produce images between the lens and the object, so v is always a smaller number than u (see previous page).

Tip: Don't forget that diverging lenses always produce virtual images, behind the lens — that's why v here is negative (see previous page).

Magnification and Power

Tip: Linear magnification is just a number — it has no units. If the image is smaller than the object, the magnification will be less than 1. If the image is on the same side as the object (virtual) the magnification will be negative.

Linear magnification

A lens can be used to magnify an image — this could be an increase or a decrease in the size of an image compared to the object. The **linear magnification** produced by a lens can be calculated using the equation:

$$m = \frac{v}{u}$$

m *= linear magnification*

v *= size of image in m*

u *= size of object in m*

Example

An object is placed 1.20 m from a lens. The lens produces an image at a distance of 1.75 m on the other side of the lens. Find the magnification.

$u = 1.20$ and $v = 1.75$ so $m = \frac{1.75}{1.20} = 1.46$ (to 3 s.f.)

Power

The more powerful a lens is, the shorter its focal length. The power of a lens is the reciprocal of its focal length. So it can be calculated using:

Tip: Reciprocal just means "1 over". Which is nothing to do with cricket.

$$P = \frac{1}{f}$$

P *= lens power in dioptres, D*

f *= focal length in m*

A more powerful (thicker) lens converges the rays more strongly and will have a shorter focal length. Diverging lenses have a negative power because they have a negative focal length.

Example

A lens has a focal length of 2.5 cm. Find the power of the lens.

First, convert the focal length from cm to m: 2.5 cm = 0.025 m.

So: $P = \frac{1}{f} = \frac{1}{0.025} = 40\,\text{D}$

Practice Questions — Application

Tip: Use something simple as the object in Q3 — like a vertical arrow.

Tip: Remember *f* = focal length for Q4.

Q1 A lens is used to magnify an object of height 0.20 m. The height of the image is 0.36 m. Find the linear magnification produced.

Q2 The power of a lens is 2.4 D. Find the focal length of the lens.

Q3 An object is placed 3 m from a diverging lens on its principal axis. The lens has a focal length of –1.5 m. Draw a ray diagram to show the image formed.

Q4 An object is placed 65 cm from a lens. An image is formed 105 cm from the lens on the opposite side to the object. Find *f* for the lens.

Practice Questions — Fact Recall

Q1 Describe the different properties of converging and diverging lenses.

Q2 What is the principal focus of a lens?

Q3 Explain how to use a ray diagram to find where an image is formed by a converging lens.

Q4 Describe the main properties of real and virtual images.

Q5 What equation links object distance, image distance and focal length?

Q6 What is the equation that links the power of a lens and its focal length?

2. Physics of the Eye

Our eyes contain converging lenses which are used to focus light onto the retina at the back of the eye. There are, however, many different parts of the eye that all play an important role in helping us to see...

Learning Objectives:

- Know the basic structure of the eye.
- Know that the eye is an optical refracting system.
- Describe what is meant by the near and far points of the eye.
- Describe the roles of the rods and cones in the sensitivity of the eye.
- Be able to explain spatial resolution in terms of rods and cones.
- Be able to explain what is meant by the persistence of vision.

Specification Reference B.2.1

The structure of the eye

Our eyes focus light to form images that can be detected and allow us to see. There are many different parts that make up the eye which enable us to do this (see Figure 1).

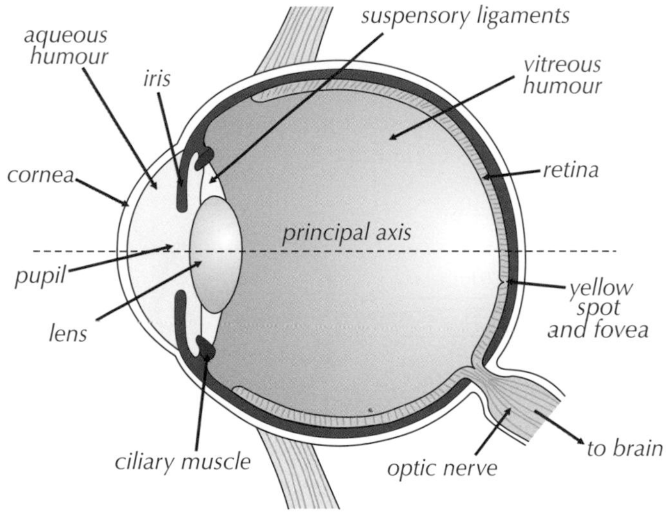

Figure 1: *The basic structure of an eye.*

The **cornea** is a transparent 'window' with a convex shape, and a high refractive index. The cornea does most of the eye's focusing. The **aqueous humour** is a watery substance that lets light pass through the pupil to the lens.

The **iris** is the coloured part of the eye. It consists of radial and circular muscles that control the size of the pupil — the hole in the middle of the iris. This regulates the intensity of light entering the eye.

The lens acts as a fine focus and is controlled by the **ciliary muscles**. When the ciliary muscles contract, tension is released and the lens takes on a fat, more spherical shape. When they relax, the suspensory ligaments pull the lens into a thin, flatter shape. The eye is said to be 'accommodated' when ciliary muscles are not fully relaxed, and 'unaccommodated' when they are.

The **vitreous humour** is a jelly-like substance that keeps the eye's shape. Images are formed on the **retina**, which contains light-sensitive cells called rods and cones (see page 202). The **yellow spot** is a particularly sensitive region of the retina. In the centre of the yellow spot is the **fovea**. This is the part of the retina with the highest concentration of cones. The **optic nerve** carries signals from the rods and cones to the brain.

Tip: The cornea has a high refractive index compared to air, which causes light entering the eye to be highly refracted.

Tip: Remember, the shape of a lens affects its focusing power (see page 200).

Tip: The image formed on the retina is upside down but it's interpreted by the brain to seem the right way up.

The far point and near point

The eye is an optical refracting system — it can focus light from a range of distances. The **far point** is the furthest distance that the eye can focus comfortably — for normally sighted people that's infinity. When your eyes are focusing at the far point, they're unaccommodated. The **near point** is the closest distance that the eye can focus on. For young people it's about 9 cm.

Tip: See page 200 for a recap on power.

Tip: Don't worry about learning all these numbers, but make sure you know how the power of a lens changes depending on the position of the object, in order to focus.

Tip: Don't get confused by all the extra eye bits — this is just a ray diagram for a lens. Remember... if an object does not sit on the principal axis, you need to draw two sets of rays to find the top and bottom of the image — see page 199 for more on ray diagrams like this.

Tip: If the eye is focused, the image is formed on the retina — if not it will appear blurry since the image is formed somewhere else (see vision defects — pages 205-207).

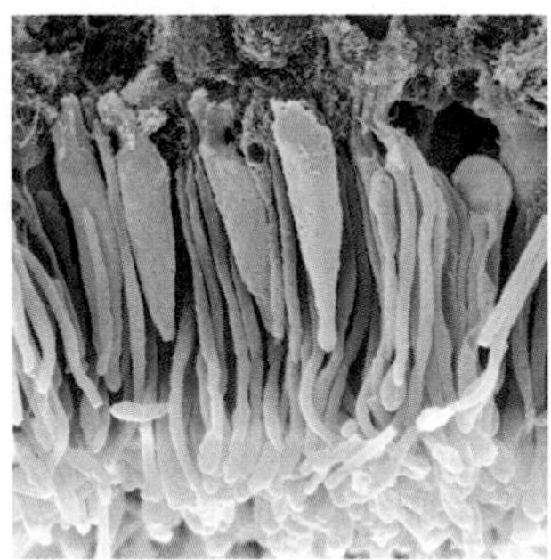

Figure 3: A coloured image of retina rods and cones taken with a scanning electron microscope. The rod cells are shown in white and the cone cells in green.

The cornea and aqueous humour act as a fixed converging lens with a power of about 41 D. The power of the eye's lens itself is about 18 D when unaccommodated. By changing shape, it can increase to about 29 D in young people to view objects at the near point.

You can add together the powers of the cornea, aqueous humour and lens. That means you can think of the eye as a single converging lens of power 59 D at the far point. This gives a focal length of 1.7 cm.

When looking at nearer objects, the eye's power increases, as the lens changes shape and the focal length decreases — but the distance between the lens and the image, v, stays the same, at 1.7 cm (see Figure 2 below).

Example

This ray diagram shows the eye focusing on an object. Rays from the top and bottom of the object show where the top and bottom of the image is formed. The focal length tells you the distance the object is at — you can calculate it using the lens equation (see page 199).

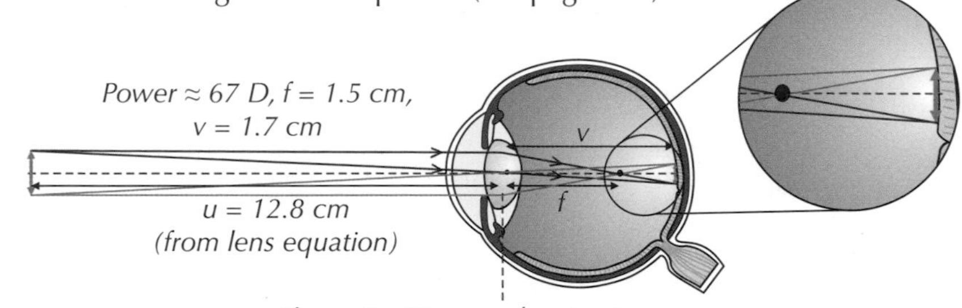

***Figure 2:** Diagram showing image formation of a nearby object by the eye.*

Rods and cones

Sensitivity of the eye

Rods and cones are cells at the back of the retina that respond to light. They're called **photodetectors** as they detect light and convert it to an electrical signal.

Light travels through the retina to the rods and cones at the back. Rods and cones all contain chemical pigments that bleach when light falls on them. This bleaching stimulates the cell to send signals to the brain via the optic nerve. The cells are reset (i.e. unbleached) by enzymes using vitamin A from the blood. Rods are more sensitive to light, but don't detect colour — we rely on rods to see in darker conditions. There's only one type of rod but there are three types of cone, which are sensitive to red, green and blue light.

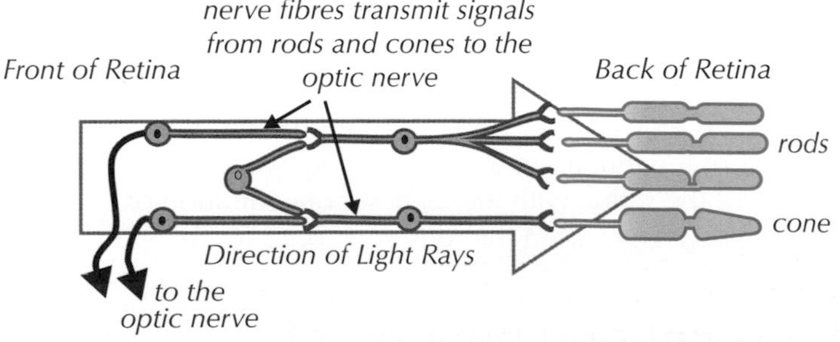

***Figure 4:** Light travels to the rods and cones at the back of the retina, which then send electrical signals to the brain via the optic nerve.*

The red, green and blue cones each absorb a range of wavelengths (see Figure 5). The eye is less responsive to blue light than to red or green, so blues often look dimmer. The brain receives signals from the three types of cone and interprets their weighted relative strengths as colour — see Figure 5.

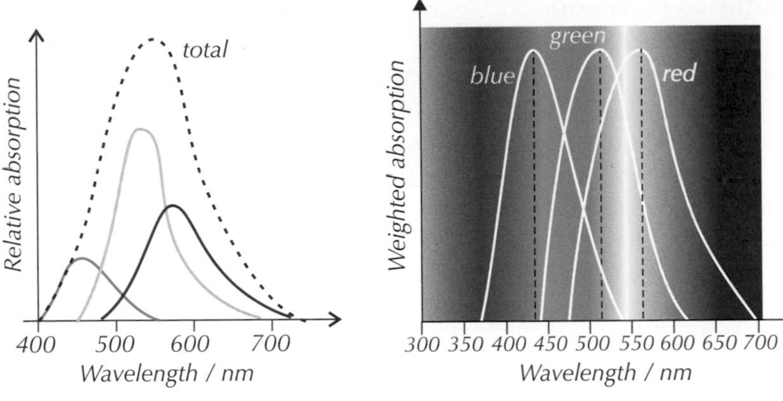

Figure 5: *Graph to show relative absorption of different wavelengths of light by the cones (left) and the weighted absorption of light against wavelength (right).*

Exam Tip
If you're asked to sketch three curves to show how the response of each type of cone varies with wavelength — it's the graph on the left you're being asked to draw.

Any colour can be produced by combining different intensities of red, green and blue light.

Example

Yellow light produces almost equal responses from the red and green cones. Yellow light can therefore be 'faked' by combining red and green light of almost equal intensity — the electrical signal from the retina will be the same and the brain interprets it as 'yellow'.

Spatial resolution

In order to see something in detail, you need good **spatial resolution** — this is a measure of the ability to form separate images of objects that are close together.

Two objects can only be distinguished from each other if there's at least one rod or cone between the light from each of them. Otherwise the brain can't resolve the two objects and it 'sees' them as one — see Figure 6.

Tip: You may have heard resolution talked about in terms of image resolution, e.g. of an image taken with a digital camera. The greater the resolution, the greater the detail in the image.

Example

In Figure 6, each square represents a cone and each blue square represents a cone detecting light.

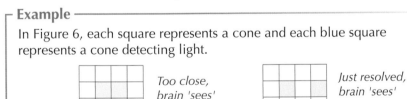

Too close, brain 'sees'

Just resolved, brain 'sees'

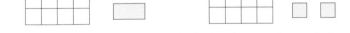

Figure 6: *Diagram to represent the limits of our spatial resolution.*

Spatial resolution is best at the yellow spot (see p. 201) — the cones are very densely packed here and each cone always has its own nerve fibre, which means that the signals sent are more detailed. There are no rods in the yellow spot, though. This means that in dim light, when cones don't work, resolution is best slightly off the direct line of sight, where the rods are more densely packed.

Away from the yellow spot, resolution is much worse. The light-sensitive cells are not as densely packed and the rods share nerve fibres, meaning that the signals from them are much less detailed — there are up to 600 rods per fibre at the edges of the retina.

Tip: The fovea, within the yellow spot, is the part of the retina which gives the very best spatial resolution. It is responsible for our central sharpest vision that we use for reading, watching TV and driving.

Persistence of vision

Tip: Persistence of vision is what causes you to still see the flash of a camera after a picture is taken.

Persistence of vision is where an afterimage remains for a short amount of time on the retina after a bright image is removed.

Nerve impulses from the eye take about a fifth of a second to decay. So a very dim light flashing faster than five times per second (5 Hz) seems to be on continuously. This is called flicker fusion. This has some practical uses — a flickering image can be used to create a continuous image. At higher light intensities, more nerve cells are 'firing' so a higher frequency is needed for flicker fusion to occur.

Figure 7: *Energy-saving light bulbs (a type of fluorescent light) don't give out light constantly — they flicker on and off (usually at twice the frequency of the electricity supply).*

Examples

- Cinema and TV rely on persistence of vision to give the illusion of a smooth moving picture rather than jerky movements. The picture is actually formed by a sequence of still frames, but as long as there are enough frames per second (fps) you don't see the rapid flickering.
- Fluorescent lights also work using persistence of vision — they flicker on and off repeatedly but so fast that you don't see it.

Practice Questions — Fact Recall

Q1 What is the role of the following parts of the eye:
a) cornea,
b) iris,
b) ciliary muscles?

Q2 Name the part of the eye where images are formed.

Q3 Describe how images are focused by the eye.

Q4 a) What is meant by the far point of the eye?
b) What is meant by the near point of the eye?

Q5 a) Where are rods and cones found in the eye?
b) How many types of rods and cones are there?

Q6 a) What is meant by spatial resolution?
b) What is required for an eye to detect two objects as being separate?

Q7 What is persistence of vision?

Q8 Give two practical uses of persistence of vision.

Tip: There's more about near points and far points on pages 205-206.

3. Defects of Vision

Converging lenses and diverging lenses can both be used to help correct problems people have with their vision. Whether a converging or a diverging lens is used depends on the condition the person has...

Myopia

Short-sighted (myopic) people are unable to focus on distant objects — this happens if their far point is closer than infinity (see page 201).

Myopia occurs when the cornea and lens are too powerful or the eyeball is too long. The focusing system is too powerful and images of distant objects are brought into focus in front of the retina. A lens of negative power is needed to correct this defect, to reduce the overall power of the system — so a diverging lens is placed in front of the eye (see Figure 1).

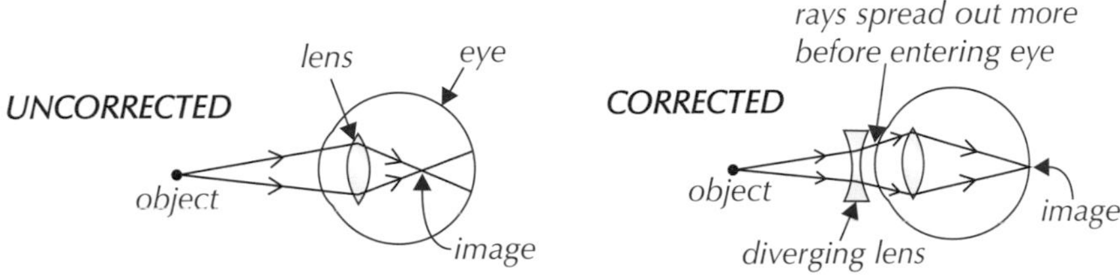

Figure 1: *Ray diagrams to show where an image is formed for a person with uncorrected myopia (left) and for corrected myopia (right).*

Choosing a lens to correct for short sight (myopia) depends on the far point. To correct for short sight, a diverging lens is chosen which has its principal focus at the eye's faulty far point. The principal focus is the point that rays from a distant object appear to have come from (see page 196).

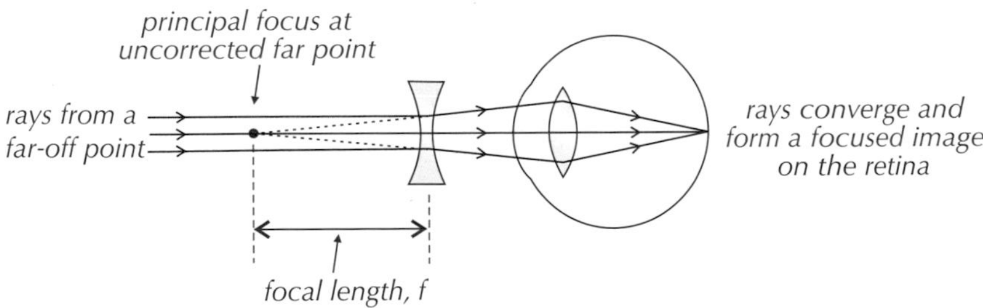

Figure 2: *A ray diagram to show how a diverging lens can be used to correct short sight — the lens has its principal focus at the eye's faulty far point.*

The lens must have a negative focal length which is the same as the distance to the eye's far point. This means that objects at infinity, which were out of focus, now seem to be in focus at the far point.

Example

A short-sighted person has a far point of 5 m.
Calculate the power of lens needed to correct their vision.

Focal length, f = far point = –5 m

Power needed $= \frac{1}{f} = \frac{1}{-5} = -0.2$ D

Learning Objectives:

- Know what is meant by the vision defects myopia and hypermetropia and be able to draw ray diagrams to show how correction lenses work.
- Know how to calculate the power of a corrective lens.
- Know what is meant by the vision defect astigmatism and know the format of a lens prescription for astigmatism.

Specification Reference B.2.1

Tip: Light is actually refracted in stages by the cornea, aqueous humour and the lens, but for simplicity we just show the total refraction at the lens. You might be asked to assume it all refracts at the cornea instead.

Tip: As well as correcting the far point, the diverging lens also makes the near point a little further away than it was. This isn't usually a problem — short-sighted people usually have a near point that is closer than normal anyway.

Tip: Diverging lenses always have a negative focal length (p. 196).

Tip: The power of a lens to correct for short sight is always negative.

> **Tip:** Long-sightedness is common among young children whose lenses have grown quicker than their eyeballs.

Figure 3: Image to show how a long-sighted person would see this scene. They would be unable to focus on the statue, but able to focus on things further away.

Hypermetropia

Long-sighted (hypermetropic) people are unable to focus clearly on near objects. This happens if their near point is further away than normal (25 cm or more).

Hypermetropia occurs because the cornea and lens are too weak or the eyeball is too short. The focusing system is too weak and images of near objects are brought into focus behind the retina. A lens of positive power is needed to correct the defect, to increase the overall power of the system — so a converging lens is placed in front of the eye (see Figure 4).

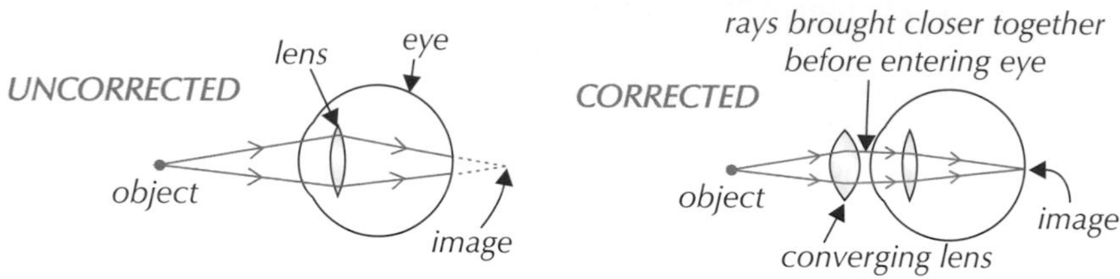

Figure 4: Ray diagrams to show where an image is formed for a person with uncorrected hypermetropia (left) and for corrected hypermetropia (right).

> **Exam Tip**
> You might see lenses drawn as a single straight line, instead of a lens shape, in the exam.

People with hypermetropia have a near point which is too far away. An 'acceptable' near point is 25 cm. A converging lens is used to produce a virtual image of objects that are 0.25 m away at the eye's (uncorrected) near point (see Figure 5). This means that close objects, which were out of focus, now seem to be in focus at the near point.

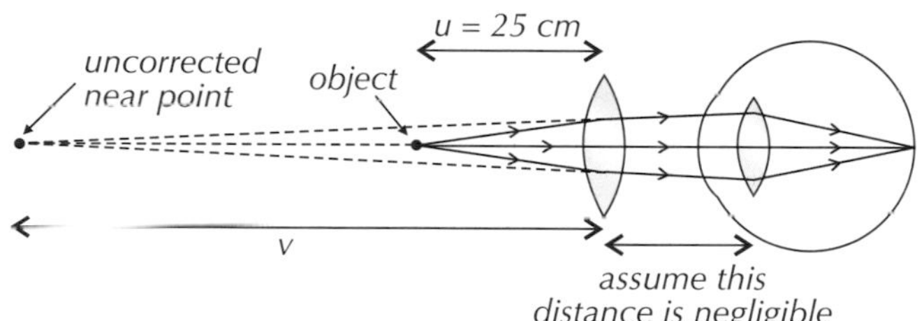

Figure 5: A ray diagram to show how a converging lens can be used to correct long sight — the lens produces a virtual image of objects 25 cm away at the patient's uncorrected near point.

Figure 6: People with hypermetropia may need to wear glasses for reading.

You can work out the focal length, and hence the power of lens needed, using the lens equation $\frac{1}{u} + \frac{1}{v} = \frac{1}{f}$ (see p. 199). The space between the eye lens and the correcting lens does affect the overall power of the system, but the effect is just a fraction of a dioptre if the lens is close to your eye and is unnoticeable to most patients.

> **Tip:** The power of a lens used to correct for long sight is always positive.

Example

A long-sighted person has a near point of 5 m. What power of lens is needed to correct this?

$u = 0.25$ m, $v = -5$ m (v is negative because the image is on the same side of the lens as the object — i.e. virtual)

$$\frac{1}{f} = \frac{1}{0.25} - \frac{1}{5} = 3.8$$

So the lens power needed = +3.8 D

Astigmatism

Astigmatism is caused by an irregularly shaped cornea or lens which has different focal lengths for different planes. For instance, when vertical lines are in focus, horizontal lines might not be.

The condition is corrected with a cylindrical lens. The prescription for the cylindrical lens should state both a power (see page 200) and an axis angle for correction — see Figure 7.

Example

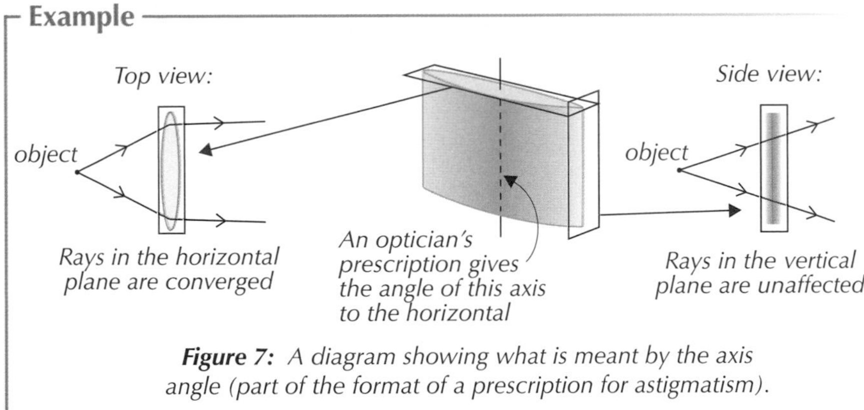

Figure 7: *A diagram showing what is meant by the axis angle (part of the format of a prescription for astigmatism).*

Tip: "Format of a prescription" sounds a bit posh, but it just means what an optician would prescribe for you if you needed some correction for your eyesight, e.g. glasses.

Practice Questions — Application

Q1 a) Copy and complete the ray diagram below to show where an image of an object 25 m away is formed in the eye of a person with a far point of 15 m.

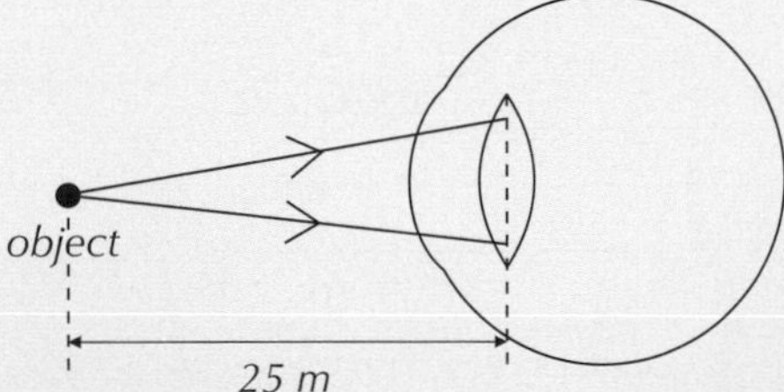

b) What defect of vision does this person suffer from?

c) Explain how an external lens could be used to correct this defect.

Q2 A woman is short-sighted and has a far point of 4.2 m. Calculate the power of lens needed to correct her far point.

Q3 A lens prescription for hypermetropia uses a converging lens with a focal length of 0.27 m. Calculate the patient's uncorrected near point.

Tip: It might not seem clear at first how to answer Q2. First think about what equation you'll need to use to calculate the power.

Practice Questions — Fact Recall

Q1 What is meant by myopia?

Q2 a) What is meant by hypermetropia?

b) What type of lens can be used to correct it?

Q3 a) What does it mean if someone suffers from astigmatism?

b) What is the format of a prescription used to correct the sight of someone who suffers from astigmatism?

Learning Objectives:

- Know what is meant by intensity of sound.
- Know the basic structure of the ear.
- Be able to describe how sound is transmitted in the ear.

Specification Reference B.2.2

4. Physics of the Ear

Our ears are used to transfer sound energy into electrical signals that are sent to the brain. The clever brain then interprets these signals as sound. The ear is made up of lots of different parts — you need to know how it all works...

Intensity of sound

The **intensity** of a sound wave is defined as the amount of sound energy that passes per second per unit area (perpendicular to the direction of the wave). That's power per unit area. If the sound energy arriving at the ear per second is P, then the intensity of the sound is:

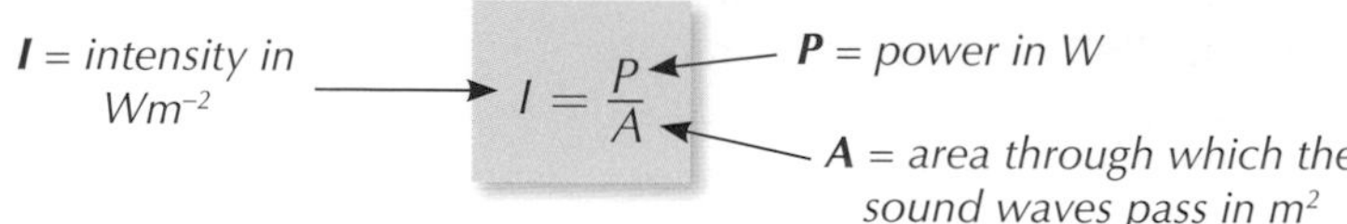

$$I = \frac{P}{A}$$

The SI unit of intensity is Wm^{-2}, but you'll often see decibels used instead (see page 211). For any wave, intensity $\propto$ amplitude^2 — so doubling the amplitude will result in four times the intensity. Intensity is related to the loudness of sound (see page 210).

Tip: The amplitude of a wave is its maximum displacement from its rest position:

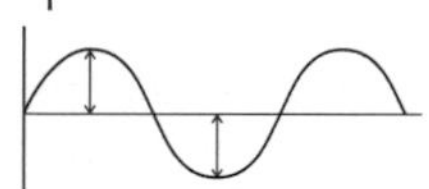

The structure of the ear

The ear consists of three sections:

- the outer ear (pinna and auditory canal)
- the middle ear (**ossicles** and **Eustachian tube**)
- the inner ear (semicircular canals, **cochlea** and **auditory nerve**)

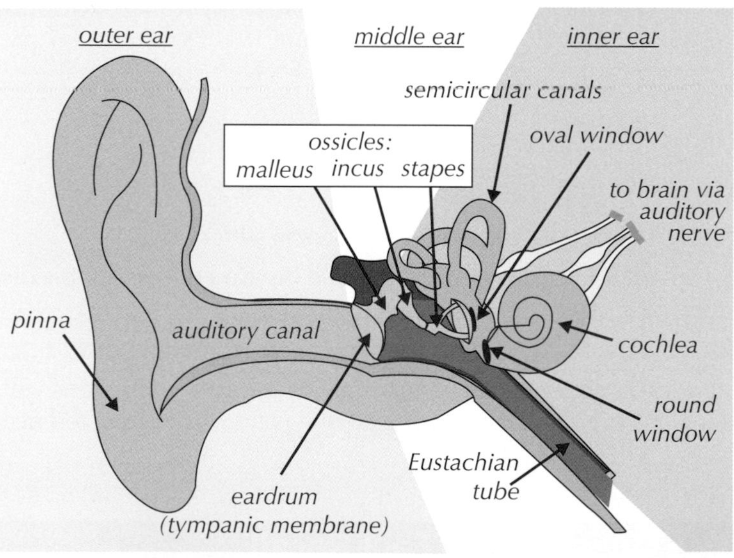

Figure 1: *The basic structure of the ear.*

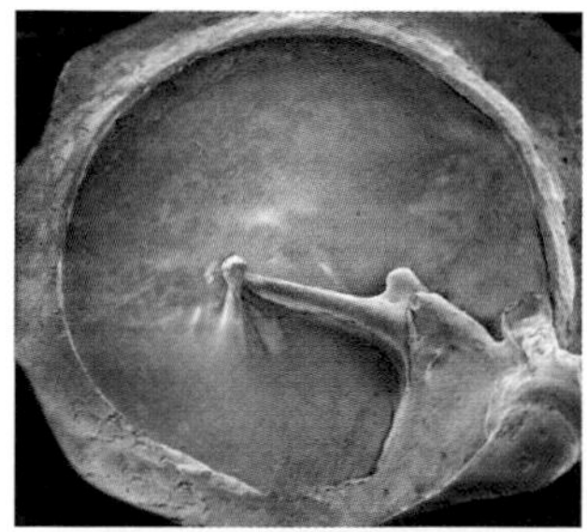

Figure 2: *A coloured scanning electron micrograph of an eardrum, shown in red.*

The **tympanic membrane** (eardrum) separates the outer and middle ears. Although separated, the outer and middle ears both contain air at atmospheric pressure, apart from slight pressure variations due to sound waves. This pressure is maintained by yawning and swallowing — the middle ear is opened up to the outside via the Eustachian tube (which is connected to the throat).

The oval and round windows separate the middle and inner ears. The inner ear is filled with fluid called perilymph (or endolymph in the cochlear duct). This fluid allows vibrations to pass to the basilar membrane in the cochlea. The semicircular canals are involved with maintaining balance.

The transmission process

The pinna (external ear) acts like a funnel, channelling the longitudinal sound waves into the auditory canal — this concentrates the energy onto a smaller area, which increases the intensity. The sound waves consist of variations in air pressure, which force the tympanic membrane (eardrum) to vibrate.

The tympanic membrane is connected to the malleus — one of the three tiny bones (ossicles) in the middle ear. The three bones act as a lever system. The malleus passes the vibrations of the eardrum on to the incus and the stapes (which is connected to the oval window).

As well as transmitting vibrations, the ossicles have other functions, such as amplifying the force of the vibrations and reducing the energy reflected back from the inner ear. The ossicles amplify the force of the vibrations by around 50% — so the force of the vibrations is multiplied by about 1.5. The oval window has a much smaller area than the tympanic membrane. Together with the increased force produced by the ossicles, this results in greater pressure variations at the oval window — the pressure variations at the oval window are about 20 times greater than those at the eardrum. The oval window transmits vibrations to the fluid in the inner ear (see Figure 3).

Pressure waves in the fluid of the cochlea make the **basilar membrane** vibrate. Different regions of this membrane have different natural frequencies, from 20 000 Hz near the middle ear to 20 Hz at the other end. When a sound wave of a particular frequency enters the inner ear, one part of the basilar membrane resonates and so vibrates with a large amplitude. Hair cells attached to the basilar membrane trigger nerve impulses at this point of greatest vibration. These electrical impulses are sent, via the auditory nerve, to the brain, where they are interpreted as sounds.

Tip: Remember, $I = \frac{P}{A}$.

Tip: You might see these vibrations referred to as mechanical vibrations — it just means the same thing.

Tip: Malleus, incus and stapes are the Latin words for hammer, anvil and stirrup — this might help you to remember which one is which.

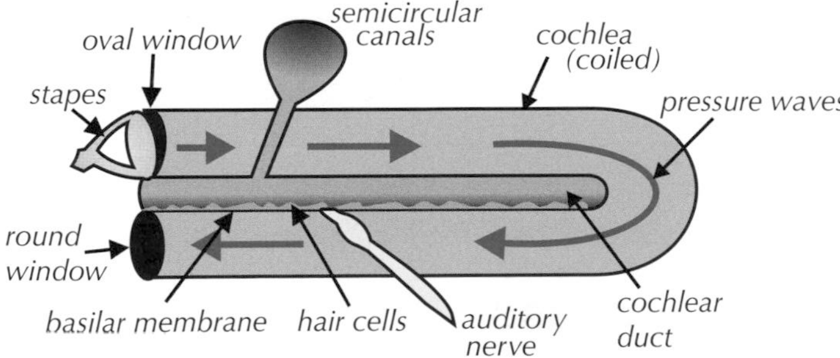

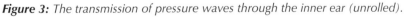

Figure 3: *The transmission of pressure waves through the inner ear (unrolled).*

Practice Questions — Fact Recall

Q1 What is meant by the intensity of sound?

Q2 Name the main parts of the outer ear, middle ear and inner ear.

Q3 Describe the main roles of the ossicles in the ear.

Q4 How are the pressure variations at the oval window different to those at the eardrum?

Q5 Describe how sound travels through and is detected by the ear.

5. Intensity and Loudness

How loud we perceive a sound to be depends on the intensity of the sound and its frequency. Our ears can be damaged if they're exposed to an excessive amount of noise. They also naturally deteriorate as we get older.

Learning Objectives:

- Understand how humans perceive loudness and why a logarithmic scale is used.
- Know what is meant by the threshold of hearing.
- Be able to calculate the intensity level of sound using: intensity level = $10\log\left(\frac{I}{I_0}\right)$.
- Be able to explain the use of the dB and dBA scales.
- Know how to produce and interpret equal loudness curves.
- Be able to describe the effects of hearing loss and represent this on equal loudness curves.

Specification Reference B.2.2

Range of hearing

Humans can hear a limited range of frequencies. Young people can hear frequencies ranging from about 20 Hz (low pitch) up to 20 000 Hz (high pitch). As you get older, the upper limit decreases.

Our ability to discriminate between frequencies depends on how high that frequency is. For example, between 60 and 1000 Hz, you can hear frequencies 3 Hz apart as different pitches. At higher frequencies, a greater difference is needed for frequencies to be distinguished. Above 10 000 Hz, pitch can hardly be discriminated at all.

The loudness of sound you hear depends on the intensity (see p. 208) and frequency of the sound waves. The weakest intensity you can hear depends on the frequency of the sound wave. The ear is most sensitive at around 3000 Hz. For any given intensity, sounds of this frequency will be loudest.

Tip: See next page for more on the threshold of hearing.

Humans can hear sounds at intensities ranging from about 10^{-12} Wm^{-2} to 100 Wm^{-2}. Sounds over a level called the threshold of feeling, equal to about 1 Wm^{-2}, can be felt.

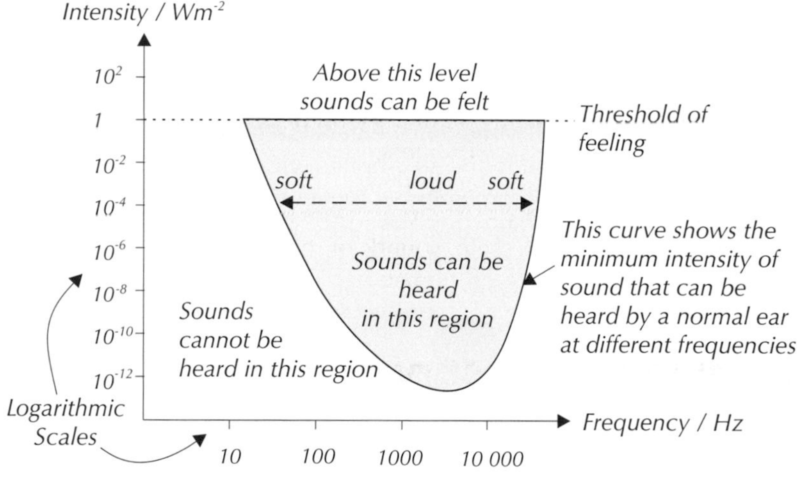

Figure 1: *A graph to show range of human hearing.*

Tip: A logarithmic scale is different to a linear scale, e.g. 1, 2, 3. It lets you show values of something that increases logarithmically — see pages 283-284 for more on logs.

Perceived loudness

The perceived loudness of a sound depends on its intensity (and its frequency — see above). However, the relationship between perceived loudness and the intensity is not linear, but logarithmic:

$$\Delta L \propto \log\left(\frac{I_2}{I_1}\right)$$

ΔL = increase in decibels, dB
I_2 = new intensity in Wm^{-2}
I_1 = original intensity in Wm^{-2}

This means that loudness, L, goes up in equal intervals if intensity, I, increases by a constant factor (provided the frequency of the sound doesn't change). E.g. if you double the intensity, double it again and so on, the loudness keeps going up in equal steps. The ear is logarithmic in its response to changes in sound intensity.

Decibels

Threshold of hearing

Since the ear's response is logarithmic (see previous page), we use a logarithmic scale called the **decibel scale** to measure it in.

Tip: Loudness can also be measured in phons — see below.

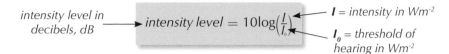

You can often measure loudness using a decibel meter. The decibel scale is a logarithmic scale which actually measures intensity level. The intensity level of a sound of intensity I is defined as:

$$\text{intensity level} = 10\log\left(\frac{I}{I_0}\right)$$

intensity level in decibels, dB; *I = intensity in Wm^{-2}*; *I_0 = threshold of hearing in Wm^{-2}*

Tip: See pages 283-284 for more on logs.

I_0 is the **threshold of hearing** — the minimum intensity of sound that can be heard by a normal ear at a frequency of 1000 Hz (1 kHz). The value of I_0 is 1×10^{-12} Wm^{-2}. The units of the intensity level are decibels (dB). Intensity level can be given in bels — one decibel is a tenth of a bel — but decibels are usually a more convenient size.

Example

A siren emits sound waves. The intensity of the sound 5.0 m from the siren is 0.94 Wm^{-2}. Calculate the intensity level at this distance.

Intensity level $= 10\log\left(\frac{I}{I_0}\right) = 10\log\left(\frac{0.94}{1 \times 10^{-12}}\right)$

$= 119.73... = 120$ dB (to 2 s.f.)

Adjusted decibel scale

The perceived loudness of a sound depends on its frequency as well as its intensity. Two different frequencies with the same loudness will have different intensity levels on the dB scale. The **dBA scale** is an adjusted decibel scale which is designed to take into account the ear's response to different frequencies. On the dBA scale, sounds of the same intensity level have the same loudness for the average human ear.

Equal loudness curves

Figure 2 shows **equal loudness curves** for a normal ear.

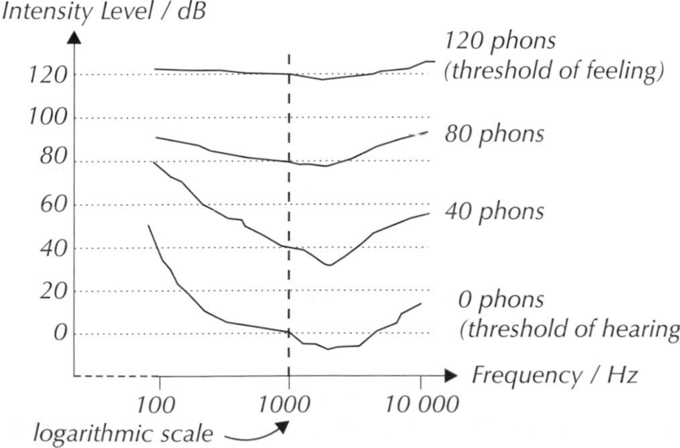

Figure 2: *Equal loudness curves.*

Tip: At 1000 Hz, the loudness in phons is the same value as the intensity level in decibels (shown by the dotted line in Figure 2).

Exam Tip
You might be asked in the exam how to generate an equal loudness curve, so learn this method.

To generate equal loudness curves, start by generating a control frequency of 1000 Hz using a signal generator set at a particular intensity level. Then take a second signal generator and set the signal to a different frequency. Play alternating sounds from each generator, altering the intensity of (only) the second generator each time, until the sounds appear to have the same loudness. Make note of the intensity level at this volume.

Repeat this for several different frequencies in the second generator, and plot the resulting curve on a graph. Change the intensity level of the control frequency and repeat the experiment again. If you measure intensity level in decibels, then the loudness of the sound is given in phons.

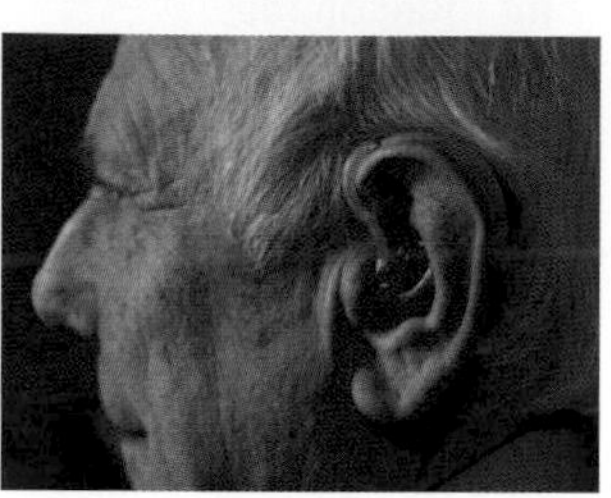

Figure 3: A hearing aid can be used to amplify the range of frequencies most needed by a person with a hearing problem.

Tip: These curves show the general shapes for normal hearing and hearing defects, but the actual curves are a bit more wiggly. So don't panic if the curve you see in an exam is a little less smooth.

Defects of hearing

As you get older, your hearing deteriorates generally, but higher frequencies are affected most. Your ears can be damaged by excessive noise. This results in general hearing loss, but frequencies around 4000 Hz are usually worst affected. People who've worked with very noisy machinery have most hearing loss at the particular frequencies of the noise causing the damage. Equal loudness curves can show hearing loss (see Figure 4).

For a person with hearing loss, higher intensity levels are needed for the same loudness, when compared to a normal ear. A peak in the curve shows damage at a particular range of frequencies.

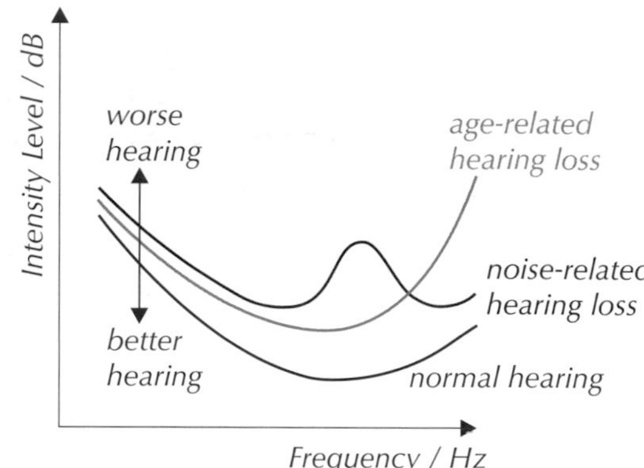

Figure 4: Equal loudness curves at 0 phons.

Practice Questions — Application

Q1 In some cities, high-frequency alarm systems have been used to deter young people from gathering in certain areas by emitting an annoying sound. Explain why the system only deters young people.

Q2 A smoke detector emits sound waves at a frequency of 3000 Hz. At a distance of 15 m, the intensity level is 40 dB. Calculate the intensity at a distance of 15 m in Wm^{-2}.

Practice Questions — Fact Recall

Q1 What two things does the perceived loudness of a sound depend on?

Q2 Explain why a logarithmic scale is needed to reflect the response of the human ear.

Q3 What unit is used to measured sound intensity?

Q4 What is the dBA scale used for?

Q5 What is meant by the threshold of hearing? Give the value of the threshold of hearing for a normal ear.

Q6 Give two reasons why your hearing might deteriorate. Draw equal loudness curves for normal hearing and for hearing which has deteriorated due to each of the two reasons given.

Tip: Don't get the dB and dBA scales confused.

6. Physics of the Heart

The heart's a pretty important organ, and it's beating constantly without us even noticing (most of the time). It's controlled by electrical impulses in nerve cells, which we can measure with detectors on the skin surface.

Learning Objectives:

- Know the basic structure of the heart.
- Be able to explain why the heart is a double pump.
- Be able to describe how electrical signals are generated and conducted in nerve cells.
- Be able to sketch the action potential of a nerve cell.
- Be able to describe the heart's response to the action potential originating at the sino-atrial node.
- Be able to sketch the action potential of heart muscle.
- Be able to describe how to obtain an ECG waveform and explain the shape of a normal ECG waveform.

Specification Reference B.2.1

The structure of the heart

The heart is a large muscle. It acts as a double pump, with the left-hand side pumping blood from the lungs to the rest of the body and the right-hand side pumping blood from the body back to the lungs.

Traditionally, a diagram of the heart is drawn as though you're looking at it from the front, so the right-hand side of the heart is drawn on the left-hand side of the diagram and vice versa (just to confuse you).

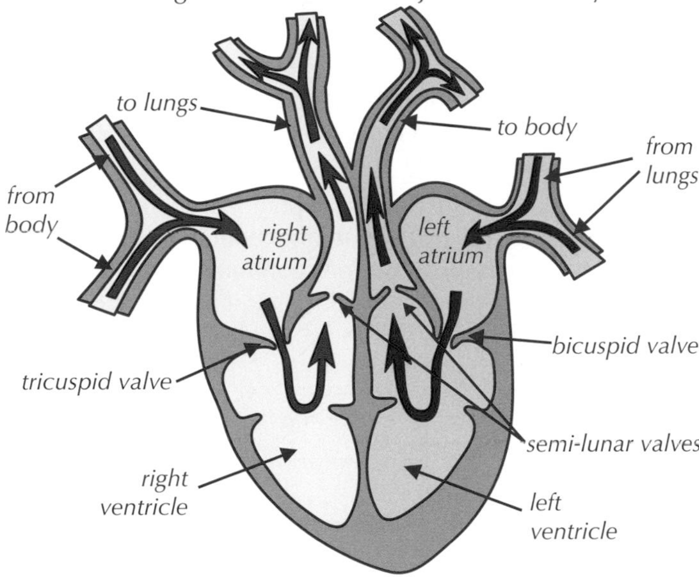

Figure 1: *Simple structure of the heart.*

Each side of the heart has two chambers — an atrium and a ventricle — separated by a valve. Blood enters the atria from the veins, then the atria contract, squeezing blood into the ventricles. The ventricles then contract, squeezing the blood out of the heart into the arteries. The valves are there so that the blood doesn't go back into the atria when the ventricles contract.

Electrical signals in the body

Nerve cells

Electrical signals are sent around the body via nerve cells — these signals are interpreted and a sensation is felt or an action carried out, e.g. the contraction of a muscle. These signals may originate in the brain, other types of cells or, for the heart, in the sino-atrial node (see page 216). When an electrical signal reaches part of a nerve cell, that part of the nerve cell is said to be stimulated.

Figure 2 shows the typical structure of a nerve cell which sends electrical signals to muscle fibres. The main part of the nerve cell is the cell body, which contains a nucleus. **Dendrites** carry signals from other nerve cells to the cell body. The nerve fibre (**axon**) extends from the cell body. It's made up of a long, thin core insulated by a myelin sheath. If a nerve cell is stimulated enough by an electrical signal, the signal passes down the nerve fibre to the muscle fibre to make it contract.

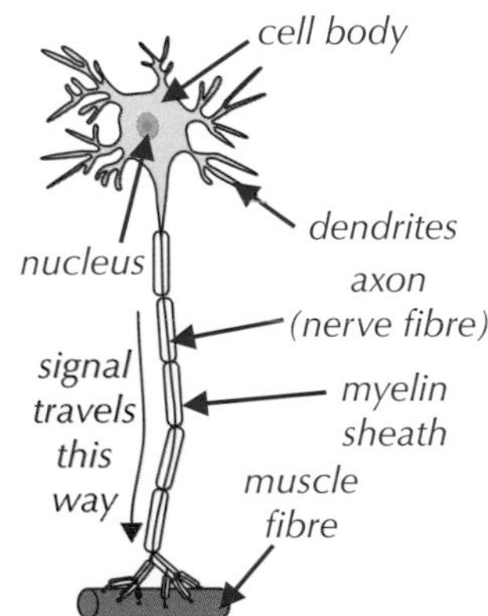

Figure 2: *Typical structure of a nerve cell which sends signals to muscle fibre.*

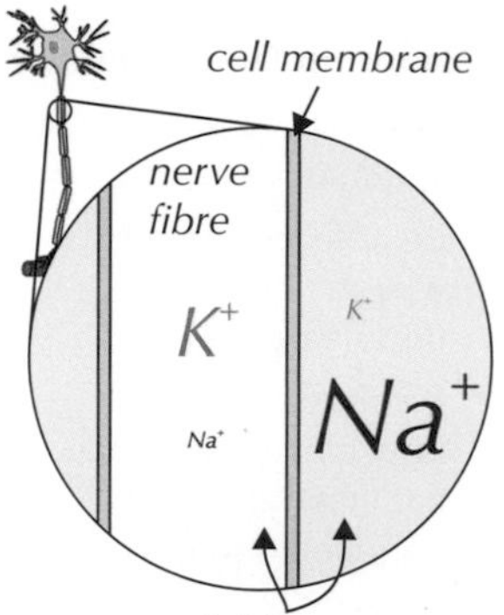

potential difference across the membrane is –70 mV

Figure 3: *Concentrations of K⁺ and Na⁺ in and around part of the nerve fibre (axon) of an unstimulated nerve cell.*

Tip: A concentration gradient just means the concentration of a substance in one place is higher than in another. If that substance can flow between the two places, it will flow from the higher to the lower concentration area to even out the concentrations.

Tip: If something is permeable it means things can pass through it. And if something is impermeable things can't pass through it.

Tip: You might also see electrical signals called electrical impulses — they're the same thing.

Resting potential

In a nerve cell's resting state (when it's not being stimulated), there's a high concentration of potassium ions (K^+) inside the cell compared to outside it and an even higher concentration of sodium ions (Na^+) outside the cell compared to inside it (see Figure 3). The cell membrane is impermeable to both types of ion. As there's a greater concentration of positive ions on the outside than on the inside of the cell, there is a potential difference across the cell membrane. This is called the **resting potential** — it's about –70 mV. (The minus sign shows the inside of the cell has a negative charge relative to the outside of the cell.)

Action potential

An **action potential** is what happens when a nerve cell is stimulated enough by an electrical signal. It is just a series of changes in potential difference across parts of the cell membrane that get passed along the nerve fibre.

When a region of the nerve cell is stimulated, the cell membrane at that point becomes excited, making it permeable to Na^+ ions, which begin to enter the cell (due to the concentration gradient and the potential difference). When enough Na^+ ions enter the cell, a threshold potential (around –55 mV) is reached and the flow of Na^+ ions speeds up.

This flow of Na^+ ions increases the potential of the cell and the potential difference across the cell membrane reduces from –70 mV to 0 V. This is called **depolarisation**. The Na^+ ions continue to flow into the cell and the potential difference across the membrane increases to about +30 mV (i.e. 30 mV in the opposite direction) — this is called reverse polarisation.

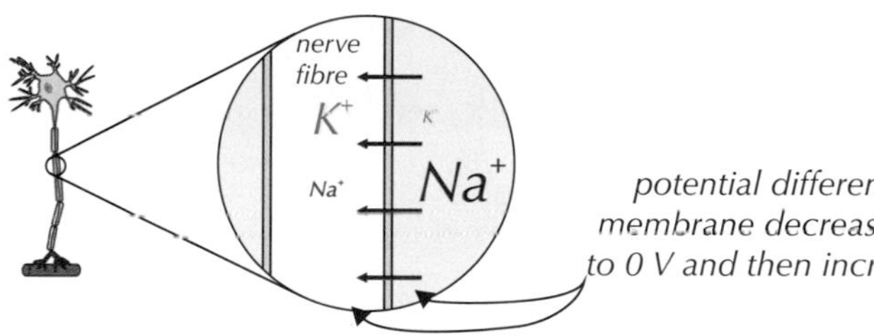

Figure 4: *The flow of Na⁺ ions across the cell membrane of a nerve cell that has been stimulated — it undergoes depolarisation, then reverse polarisation.*

At +30 mV, the membrane becomes impermeable to Na^+ ions but permeable to K^+ ions. K^+ ions flow out of the cell until the potential difference across the membrane is reduced to –70 mV again — this is called repolarisation.

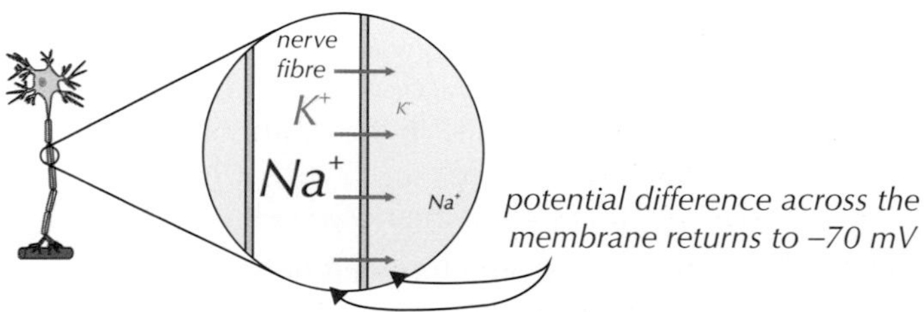

Figure 5: *The flow of K⁺ ions across the cell membrane of a nerve cell that has been depolarised — this is known as repolarisation.*

Figure 6 shows the action potential of a stimulated nerve cell.

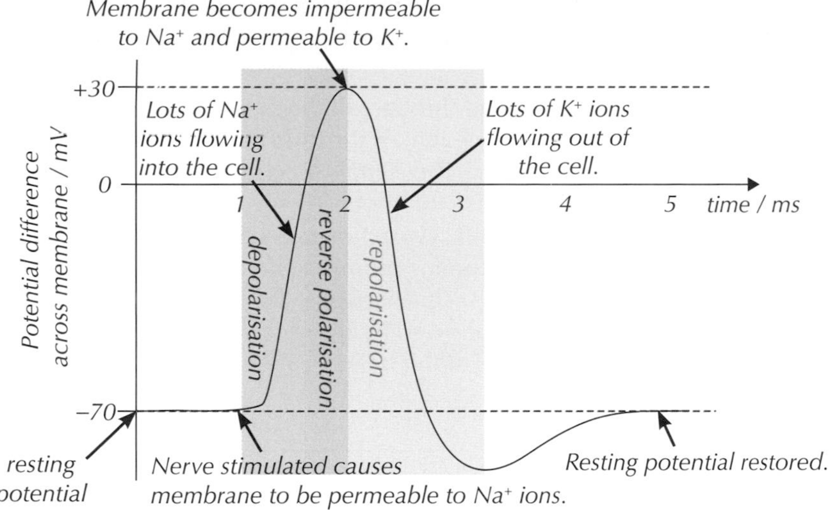

Figure 6: *The action potential of a nerve cell.*

In Figure 6, the potential difference across the membrane actually drops lower than –70 mV before levelling off. This is known as an overshoot — repolarisation carries on for a short time after it reaches the resting potential. Eventually, the membrane becomes impermeable to K^+ ions and repolarisation stops, at which point the cell pumps ions across the cell membrane to get back to the resting potential.

Directly after the action potential the potential difference across the membrane has returned back to its resting potential, but the concentrations aren't the same as they were at the beginning — the concentration of Na^+ inside the cell is too high and the concentration of K^+ outside the cell is too high. The cell gradually restores the original concentrations of Na^+ and K^+ over tens of milliseconds by pumping ions across the membrane. The nerve cell is then at rest again and ready for when it is stimulated next.

When an action potential happens in one part of a membrane, it triggers the next part of the membrane to become permeable to Na^+ ions, so the action potential is passed on. This is how electrical signals travel along the nerve fibre.

Tip: This all happens in just a few milliseconds — no more than 5 ms.

Tip: The signal cannot travel backwards along the nerve fibre, because an action potential can't happen again until the concentrations of Na^+ and K^+ ions are back to normal, which takes up to 50 ms.

Action potential of heart muscle

The heart is a muscle. When it is stimulated by an electrical signal it contracts and then relaxes, enabling the heart to pump blood around the body (see page 213).

The heart muscle is made up of millions of muscle and nerve cells. The resting potential of a heart nerve cell is about –80 mV. When part of a heart nerve cell is stimulated by an electrical signal, it starts to depolarise (just like normal nerve cells — see previous page). When the potential difference across the membrane of a heart nerve cell reaches a threshold value, the depolarisation speeds up (charges can pass across the membrane quicker). This causes neighbouring cells to depolarise and the signal spreads throughout the heart.

After a cell has depolarised, there is reverse polarisation until the potential difference across the cell membrane reaches around +40 mV, and then repolarisation back to resting potential — just like with normal nerve cells.

Tip: If the potential difference never reaches the threshold value, the action potential fails to start.

Tip: Heart nerve cells have something called gap junctions that allow charge to pass between them — you don't need to know about them, but it's how the electrical signal spreads.

Tip: You might see the sino-atrial node called the pacemaker. Artificial pacemakers can be fitted in someone to regulate their heartbeat.

The electrical signals that cause the heart to contract are produced by a group of cells in the heart in the **sino-atrial** (S-A) **node** in the right atrium (see Figure 7). These cells produce electrical signals that pulse about 70 times a minute.

These signals first spread through all the nerve cells of the atria, causing an action potential which makes the atria contract (see Figure 8), forcing blood into the ventricles. The signals then pass to the **atrioventricular** (AV) **node**, which delays the pulse for about 0.1 seconds before passing it on to the nerve cells of the ventricles. An action potential in these cells causes the ventricles to contract and blood is pumped through two valves to the lungs and body (see Figure 1). As this happens, the nerve cells of the atria repolarise and relax, which is followed by the repolarisation and relaxation of the ventricles — this is one beat of the heart.

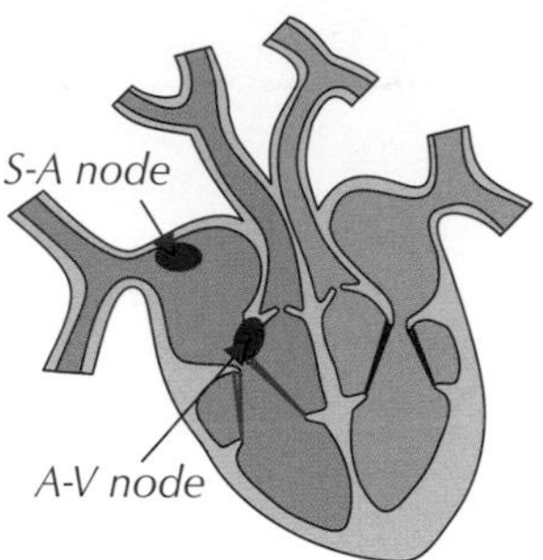

Figure 7: *The positions of the sino-atrial (S-A) and atrioventricular(AV) nodes of the heart.*

Tip: The action potential of a heart nerve cell has what's called a plateau between depolarisation and repolarisation, where the heart muscle cells contract. It's caused by other ions flowing across the membrane.

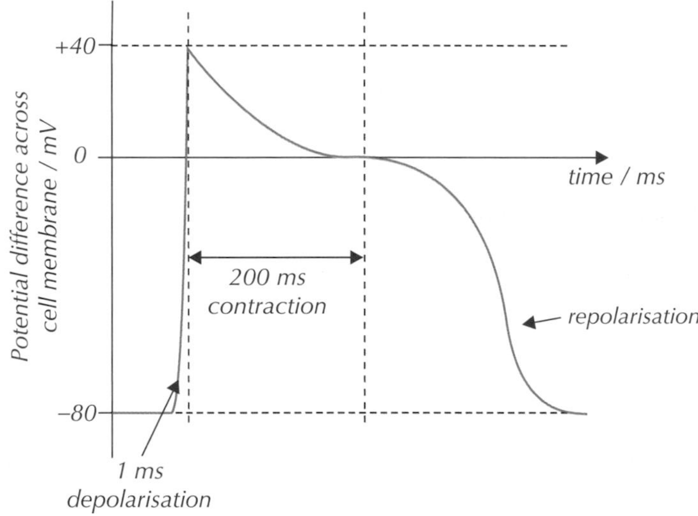

Figure 8: *The action potential of a nerve cell in the heart, showing the variation of potential difference during one heartbeat.*

Electrocardiograms

ECG waveforms

The potential difference between the polarised and depolarised heart cells produces a weak electrical signal at the surface of the body. This is plotted against time to give an **electrocardiogram** (**ECG**), which can provide useful information about the condition of the heart.

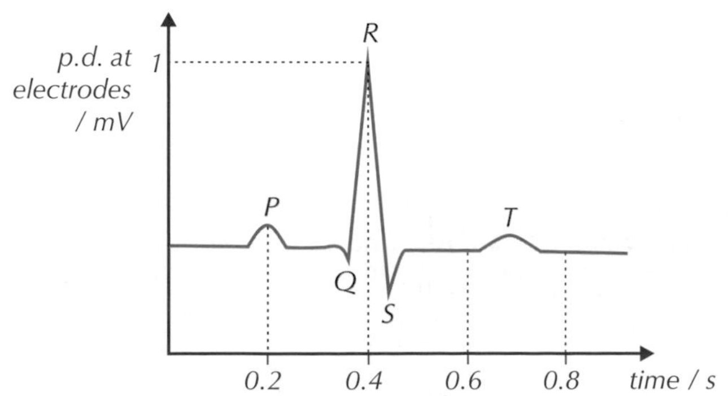

Figure 9: *A typical electrocardiogram (ECG).*

A normal ECG, covering a single heartbeat, has three separate parts: a P wave, a QRS wave and a T wave:

- The P wave corresponds to the depolarisation and contraction of the atria.
- The QRS wave (about 0.2 seconds later) corresponds to the depolarisation and contraction of the ventricles. This completely swamps the trace produced by the repolarisation and relaxation of the atria.
- Finally, the T wave (another 0.2 seconds later) corresponds to the repolarisation and relaxation of the ventricles.

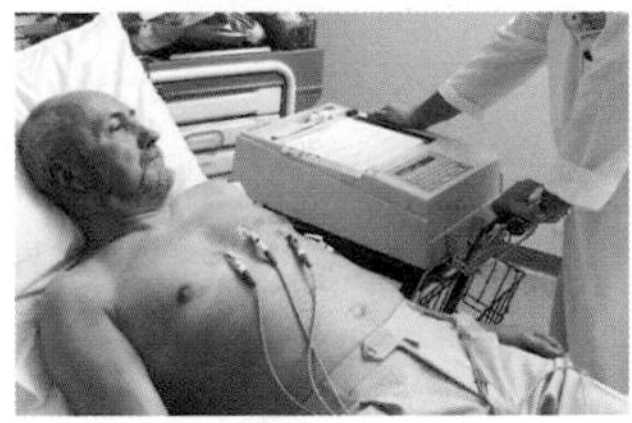

Figure 10: *A patient undergoing a procedure to obtain an ECG — electrodes are attached to his chest to measure the electrical activity of this heart.*

Obtaining an ECG trace

When obtaining an ECG, electrodes are placed on the body in pairs and the difference in potential difference between the two sites is measured. There are 12 standard ways of placing the pairs of electrodes on the body to obtain an ECG — each producing a slightly different waveform. In all cases the signal is heavily attenuated (absorbed and weakened) by the body and needs to be amplified by a high impedance amplifier.

Electrodes are placed on the chest and the limbs where the arteries are close to the surface. The right leg is never used since it is too far away from the heart. In order to reduce the electrical resistance at the point of contact, hairs and dead skin cells are removed (e.g. using sandpaper), a conductive gel is used and the electrodes are securely attached. To reduce unwanted signals, the patient should also remain relaxed and still during the procedure, and the leads used should be shielded from any possible interference from a.c. sources in the area.

Tip: Typical connections for a pair of electrodes are the right and left arm, the right arm and left leg, and the left arm and left leg.

Practice Question — Application

Q1 Shown to the right is an ECG for a person with a healthy heart. Explain the shape of the graph in terms of what is happening to the atria and ventricles in the heart.

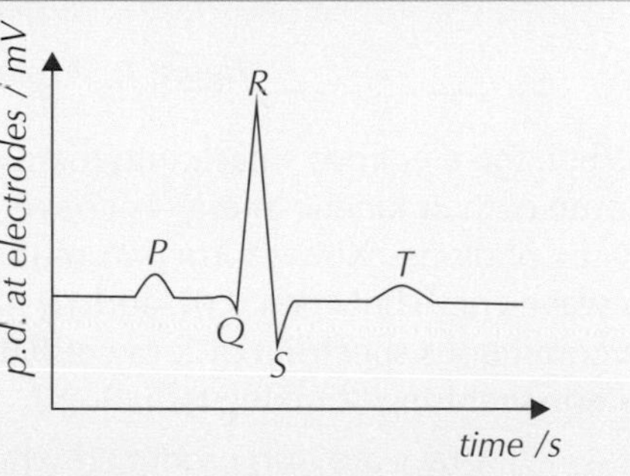

Practice Questions — Fact Recall

Q1 Explain why the heart is called a "double pump".

Q2 What is the role of valves in the heart?

Q3 Describe the structure of a typical nerve cell which sends electrical signals to muscle fibre.

Q4 What two types of ions are involved in the movement of electrical signals along a nerve cell?

Q5 What is the value of the resting potential of a typical nerve cell membrane? What is it for a heart nerve cell?

Q6 Sketch a graph to show the action potential for a nerve cell in heart muscle. Include labels on your graph to show what is happening at each point.

Q7 Suggest two things that could be done to help get a good trace when obtaining an ECG.

7. X-ray Production

Learning Objectives:
- Know the basic structure of a rotating-anode X-ray tube.
- Be able to explain the shape of an X-ray spectrum for an X-ray tube.
- Understand what factors affect the photon energy of X-rays produced in a rotating-anode X-ray tube.
- Understand how the beam intensity of X-ray photons in a rotating-anode X-ray tube can be controlled.

Specification Reference B.2.5

Tip: 'Evacuated' means all (or most of) the air has been removed.

X-rays are really important in medical imaging. Before you can use them though, you need to be able to produce them — the next few pages will show you how that's done.

X-ray tubes

The X-rays used for diagnostic imaging are produced in an evacuated **X-ray tube**. In an X-ray tube, electrons are emitted from a filament when it is heated by a current. The electrons are accelerated through a high potential difference (the tube voltage) towards a rotating tungsten anode.

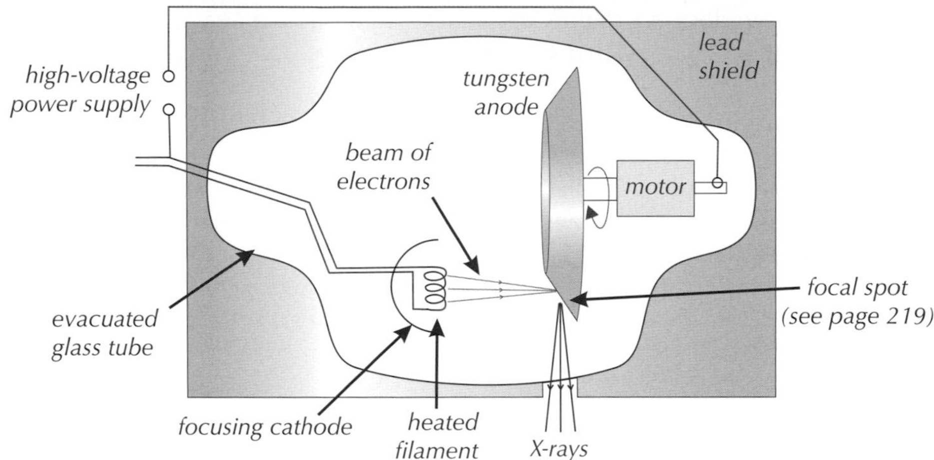

Figure 1: *A rotating-anode X-ray tube.*

When the electrons smash into the tungsten anode, they decelerate and some of their kinetic energy is converted into electromagnetic energy, as X-ray photons. X-rays form part of the electromagnetic spectrum and have a wavelength between 0.01 and 10 nanometres. The tungsten anode emits a continuous spectrum of X-ray radiation (see Figure 4) — this is called bremsstrahlung ('braking radiation').

X-rays are also produced when beam electrons knock out electrons from the inner shells of the tungsten atoms. This is known as ionisation (or excitation). Electrons in the atoms' outer shells fall into the vacancies in the inner energy levels, and release energy in the form of X-ray photons.

Figure 2: *William David Coolidge, American physicist, holding an early version of the X-ray tube he invented.*

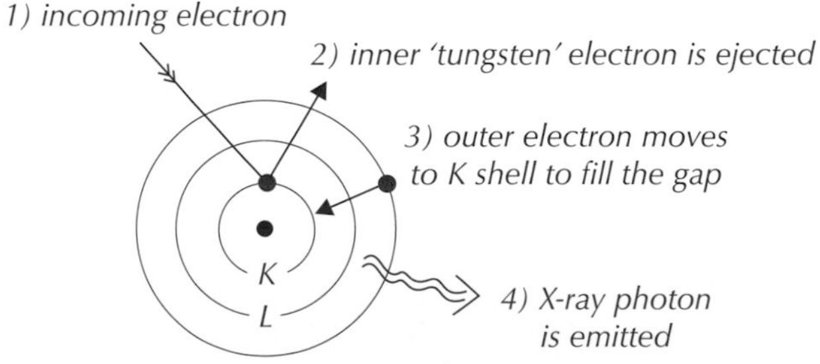

Figure 3: *X-rays are emitted when outer electrons move to inner energy shells to fill vacancies in tungsten atoms.*

Tip: The X-ray photon is released when the outer electron moves into a lower energy level, not when the inner electron is ejected.

This process results in line spectra superimposed on a continuous spectrum. Because there are fixed energy gaps between the electrons in an atom, photons are released at certain fixed energies. So spikes of radiation at these particular energies are formed — see Figure 4.

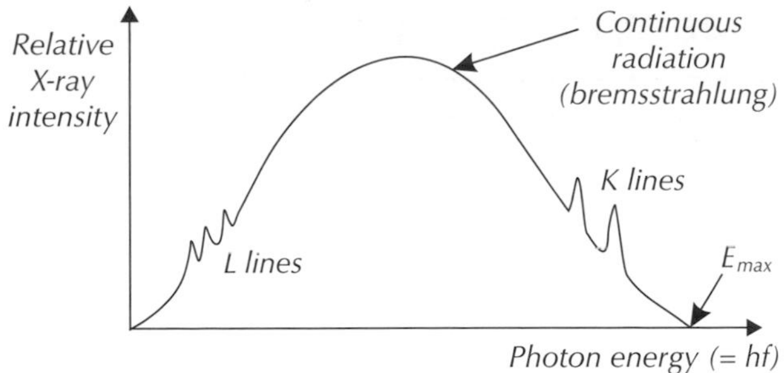

Figure 4: *An X-ray spectrum for a tungsten anode.*

Only about 1% of the electrons' kinetic energy is converted into X-rays. The rest is converted into heat, so, to avoid overheating, the tungsten anode is rotated at about 3000 rpm. It's also mounted on copper — this conducts the heat away effectively.

Example

An electron tube operates with a peak voltage of 25 kV and an electron beam current of 35 mA. Find the number of electrons arriving at the tungsten anode every second and the maximum kinetic energy of the X-ray photons released.

Current is the rate of flow of charge, i.e. $I = \frac{\Delta Q}{\Delta t}$.

So the number of electrons per second can be found by dividing the current by the charge on an electron:

$$\text{Electrons per second} = \frac{35 \times 10^{-3}}{1.6 \times 10^{-19}} = 2.2 \times 10^{17} \text{ (to 2 s.f.)}$$

The maximum kinetic energy the photons can have is the energy of the electrons. $E_{max} = e \times V$, so:

$$E_{max} = (1.6 \times 10^{-19}) \times (25 \times 10^{3}) = 4 \times 10^{-15} \text{ J}$$

Tip: The K and L lines show which shell the electrons are filling vacancies in to cause the release of energy.

Tip: The maximum energy E_{max} of the X-rays depends on the energy of the electrons (see below).

Tip: The focal spot also needs to be kept above a certain size to avoid overheating (see below).

Exam Tip
The magnitude of the charge on an electron (1.6×10^{-19} C) is given in the exam Data and Formulae booklet.

Tip: Remember, an eV (1.6×10^{-19} J) is the energy an electron would have if it was accelerated through 1 V. So the energy in J is just voltage $\times$ (1.6×10^{-19}).

Improving image sharpness

The X-rays produced from the anode are emitted from a focal spot. The X-rays form a shadow (umbra) behind the object (see Figure 5). This results in a dark shadow between B and C, where none of the X-rays reach, and a partial shadow between A and B and between C and D. An image is therefore formed with fuzzy or unclear edges, and low sharpness. There are two ways of improving the image sharpness:

- Increasing the distance between the anode and the object, and decreasing the distance between the object and the screen.
- Reducing the width of the focal spot. This can be done by decreasing the slope of the anode. A value for θ of 17° is usually used for diagnostic X-rays, with a focal spot width of around 1 mm.

However, too small a focal spot can lead to the anode overheating. The minimum size you can feasibly use depends on the potential difference between the filament and the target, the tube current and the exposure time — these factors all affect the heating of the anode.

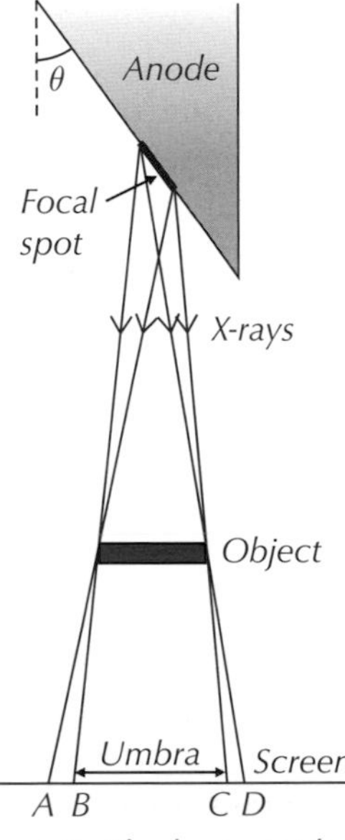

Figure 5: *Shadows cast by X-rays have a 'fuzzy' region around the edges.*

Tip: In diagnostic X-rays, the distance between the anode and the object is usually around 1 m. The distance between the object and the screen varies but is kept as low as possible (e.g. the screen is pressed against the patient).

Varying beam intensity and photon energy

The intensity of the X-ray beam is the energy per second per unit area passing through a surface (at right angles). There are two ways to increase the intensity of the X-ray beam:

- Increase the tube voltage. This gives the electrons more kinetic energy. Higher energy electrons can knock out electrons from shells deeper within the tungsten atoms — giving more 'spikes' on the graphs. Individual X-ray photons also have higher maximum energies. Intensity is approximately proportional to voltage squared.

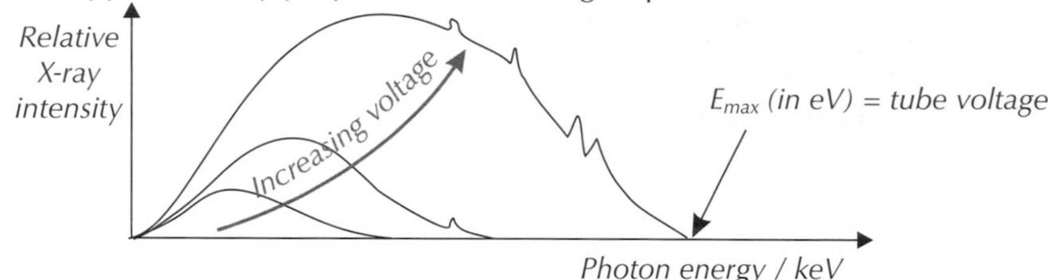

Figure 6: *Increasing the tube voltage increases the intensity of the photons as well as their maximum kinetic energy.*

- Increase the current supplied to the filament. This liberates more electrons per second, which then produce more X-ray photons per second. Individual photons have the same energy as before. Intensity is approximately proportional to current.

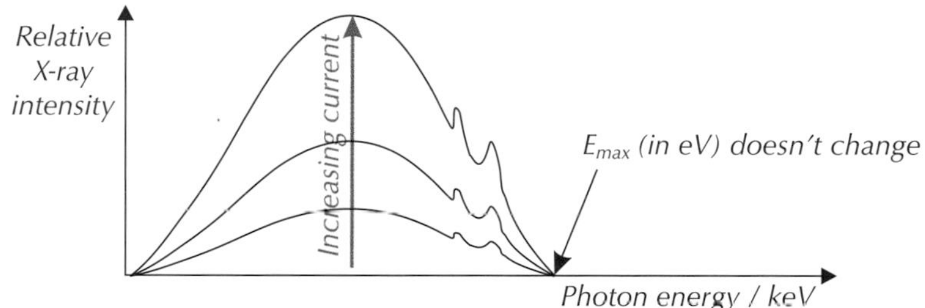

Figure 7: *Increasing the tube current increases the intensity of the photons but not their maximum kinetic energy.*

Tip: Because X-rays are harmful to the patient, the intensity needs to be carefully controlled — you need the lowest possible intensity that will give a clear image.

Tip: The intensity of the X-ray beam is related to the area under the graph.

Tip: Current is a measure of the number of electrons passing a point, not of their energy. This is why the maximum photon energy stays the same.

Practice Question — Application

Q1 In an X-ray tube, the electrons are accelerated through a potential difference of 85.0 kV towards the anode. What's the maximum energy an emitted X-ray photon could have in joules?

Practice Questions — Fact Recall

Q1 a) Draw and label a diagram of a rotating-anode X-ray tube.

b) Explain why the anode in the X-ray tube rotates.

c) Give one way of improving sharpness for a diagnostic X-ray image produced with a rotating-anode X-ray tube.

Q2 What causes the continuous spectrum of photon energies and the spikes at certain photon energies in a graph of relative X-ray intensity against photon energy for a rotating-anode X-ray tube?

Q3 a) What effect does increasing the X-ray tube voltage have on the relative intensity and maximum photon energy of emitted X-rays?

b) What effect does increasing the X-ray tube current have on the relative intensity and maximum photon energy of emitted X-rays?

8. X-ray Imaging

Now you've seen how X-rays are produced, here are some ways in which they're used in medicine. There are various types of X-ray imaging used today, from the basic X-ray tube and film set-up to advanced CT scans.

Learning Objectives:

- Know how sharp X-ray images are produced whilst keeping the patient's dose as low as possible.
- Know what intensifying screens are used for and how they work.
- Understand what X-ray attenuation is.
- Be able to perform calculations involving the attenuation coefficient μ, the mass attenuation coefficient μ_m and the half-value thickness $x_{\frac{1}{2}}$ of a material.
- Understand that different materials absorb X-rays by different amounts.
- Be able to describe why the barium meal technique is used.
- Understand how a CT scanner works.

Specification Reference B.2.5

Producing X-ray images

To produce basic X-ray images, the patient is placed between an X-ray tube (p. 218) and a detector plate. Traditionally this detector plate is some kind of photographic film, which is then processed to produce an image.

Nowadays in some places these are being replaced by digital sensors that require a lower exposure to produce clear images. X-rays are absorbed by certain parts of the body (e.g. bones) and pass through others (e.g. skin, muscle), so a 'shadow' is cast on the detector plate around harder tissues (see the next page for more on X-ray absorption). The differences in exposure across the plate can be processed to form a black and white photograph.

Medical X-rays are a compromise between producing really sharp, clear images (see page 219), whilst keeping the amount of radiation the patient is exposed to as low as possible. To do this, radiographers need to:

- Put the detection plate close to the patient and the X-ray tube far away from the patient.
- Make sure the patient keeps still — if they move around, the image will be blurred.
- Put a lead collimator grid between the patient and film to stop scattered radiation 'fogging' the image and reducing contrast.
- Use intensifying screens (see Figure 2) next to the film surface. These contain crystals that fluoresce — they absorb X-rays and re-emit the energy as visible light, which helps to develop the photograph image quickly. Because the intensifying screen is close to the film, the photons of visible light hit the film in the correct place and little to no image quality is lost. Intensifying screens mean a shorter exposure time is needed, keeping the patient's radiation dose lower.

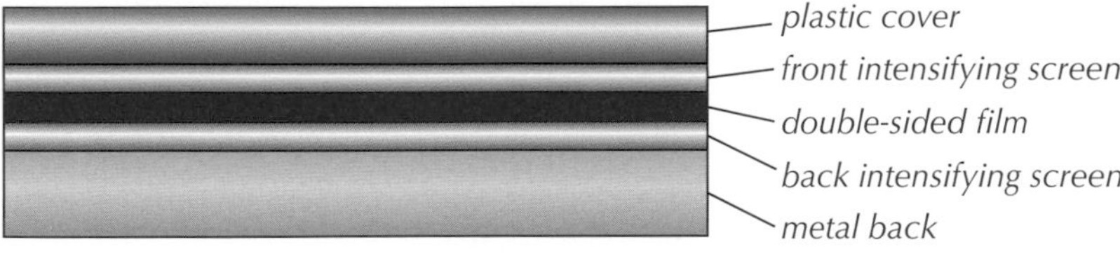

Figure 2: *An X-ray film cassette made up of a cover, a metal back, photographic film and two intensifying screens.*

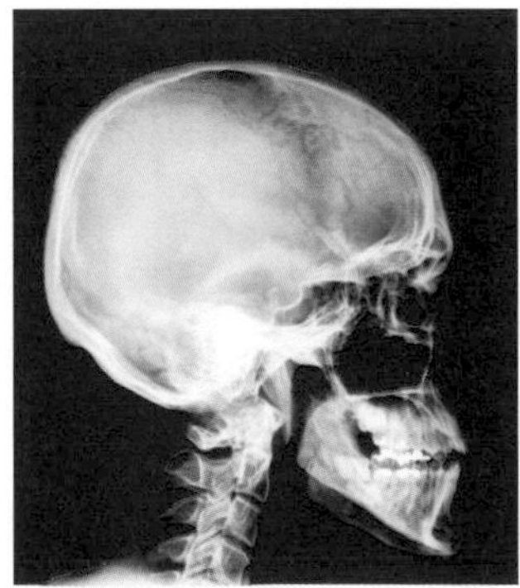

Figure 1: *An X-ray image of a human skull. X-ray photographs are negative images — the 'white' parts of the image are where the film has remained clear as it has not been exposed to radiation (which would cause it to develop and turn black).*

X-ray attenuation

When X-rays pass through matter (e.g. a patient's body), they are absorbed and scattered. The intensity of the X-ray beam decreases (attenuates) exponentially with the distance from the surface, according to the material's **linear attenuation coefficient**:

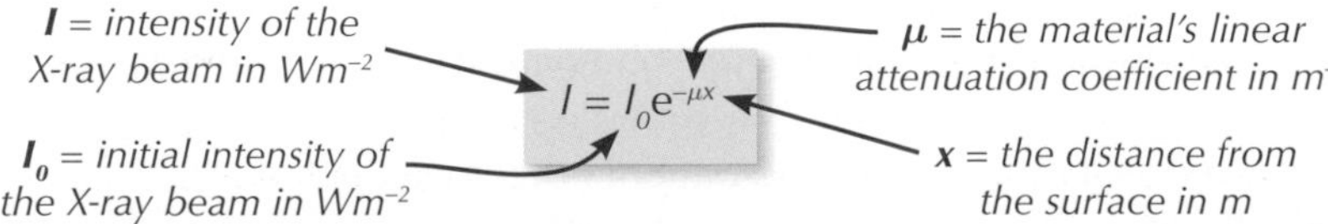

Tip: 'ln' is the natural logarithm and you can use it to get rid of exponentials because ln e = 1. You might see it written as '$\log_e$'. There's more on this on page 283.

Example

The linear attenuation coefficient of a tissue is 20 m⁻¹. How far will an X-ray travel inside the tissue before its intensity is 40% of the original intensity?

You know that the intensity is 40% of the original intensity, i.e. $\frac{I}{I_0} = 0.4$. This gives:

$$I = I_0 e^{-\mu x} \Rightarrow e^{-\mu x} = \frac{I}{I_0} = 0.4$$

Take the natural logarithm of both sides and rearrange to make x the subject:

$$-\mu x = \ln 0.4 \quad \Rightarrow \quad x = -\frac{\ln 0.4}{\mu} = -\frac{\ln 0.4}{20}$$

$$= 4.6 \times 10^{-2}\,\text{m (to 2 s.f.)}$$

Half-value thickness

Half-value thickness, $x_{\frac{1}{2}}$, is the thickness of material required to reduce the intensity to half its original value. This depends on the linear attenuation coefficient of the material, and is given by:

$$x_{\frac{1}{2}} = \frac{\ln 2}{\mu}$$

$x_{\frac{1}{2}}$ = *half-value thickness in m*

μ = *linear attenuation coefficient in m⁻¹*

Tip: The half-value thickness and linear attenuation coefficient of a material are different for different wavelengths of radiation (i.e. different energies).

Example

What's the half-value thickness for a bone with a linear attenuation coefficient of 48 m⁻¹?

$$x_{\frac{1}{2}} = \frac{\ln 2}{\mu} = \frac{\ln 2}{48} = 1.4 \times 10^{-2}\,\text{m (to 2 s.f.)}$$

The mass attenuation coefficient

Tip: ρ is the Greek letter 'rho' and it's used for density.

The **mass attenuation coefficient**, μ_m, is a measure of how much radiation is absorbed per unit mass. For a material of density ρ, it's given by:

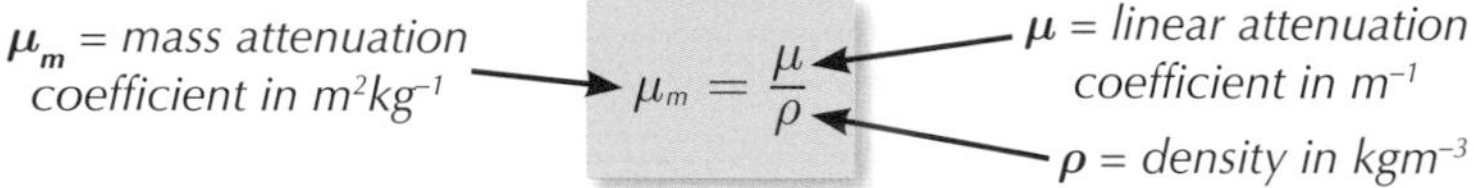

X-ray absorption

X-rays are attenuated by absorption and scattering. How much energy is absorbed by a material depends on its atomic number. So tissues containing atoms with different atomic numbers (e.g. soft tissue and bone) will contrast in the X-ray image. X-rays are absorbed more by bone than soft tissue, so bones show up brightly in X-rays.

If the tissues in the region of interest have similar attenuation coefficients then artificial contrast media can be used — e.g. a barium meal. Barium has a high atomic number, so it shows up clearly in X-ray images and can be followed as it moves along the patient's digestive tract.

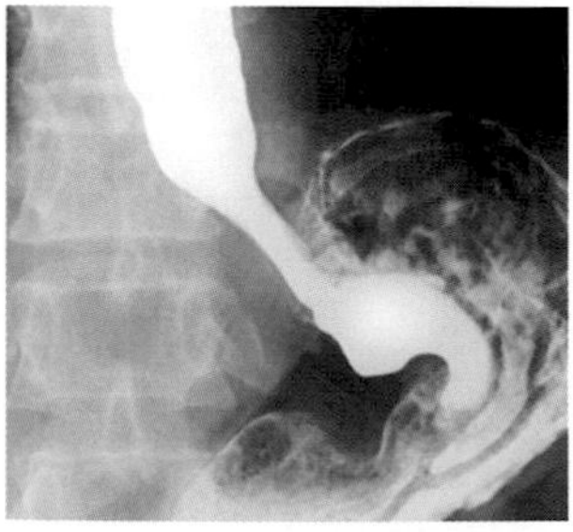

Figure 3: *An X-ray image of a stomach after a barium meal has been swallowed.*

CT scanning

Computed tomography (CT) scans produce an image of a two-dimensional slice through the body. A narrow X-ray beam consisting of a single wavelength (monochromatic) rotates around the body and is picked up by thousands of detectors. The detectors feed the signal to a computer.

The computer works out how much attenuation has been caused by each part of the body and produces a very high quality image. However, the machines are expensive and the scans involve a high radiation dose for the patient.

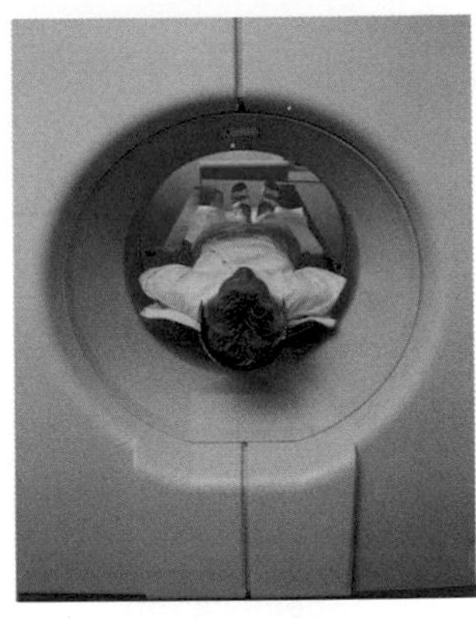

Figure 4: *A female patient undergoing an upper-body CT scan.*

Fluoroscopy

Moving images can be created using a fluorescent screen and an image intensifier. This is useful for imaging organs as they work. X-rays pass through the patient and hit the fluorescent screen, which emits light.

The light causes electrons to be emitted from the photocathode (see Figure 5). The electrons travel through the glass tube towards the fluorescent viewing screen. Electrons in the glass are focused onto the viewing screen and gain kinetic energy as they are accelerated by a potential difference between the photocathode and the viewing screen. Both of these things mean the image on the viewing screen is about 5000 times brighter than on the first screen.

Imaging can last several minutes, so image intensifiers are particularly important — they reduce the patient's dose of radiation by around a thousand times.

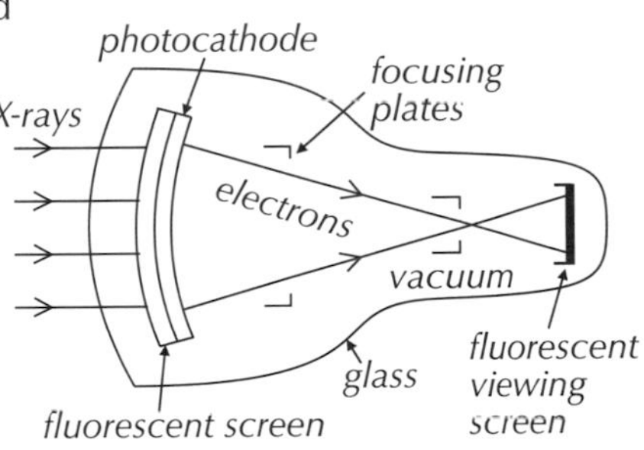

Figure 5: *An image intensifier.*

Practice Question — Application

Q1 X-rays with initial intensity 30.0 Wm^{-2} are used to image bone with $\rho = 1900\ kgm^{-3}$ and $\mu_m = 0.133\ m^2kg^{-1}$.

a) Find the linear attenuation coefficient μ of the bone.

b) Find the intensity of the X-rays after they pass through 0.690 cm of bone.

Practice Questions — Fact Recall

Q1 Give three things a radiographer can do to make sure a clear X-ray image is formed while minimising a patient's exposure.

Q2 What's the half-value thickness of a material, in terms of X-rays?

Q3 Why can X-rays be used to form images of bones and other hard tissues but not skin, muscles and other soft tissues?

Q4 Explain what a barium meal is used for.

Q5 Describe how a CT scanner works.

Q6 a) Explain how an intensifying screen works.

b) Give one advantage of using intensifying screens in X-ray imaging.

9. Magnetic Resonance Imaging

Magnetic resonance imaging is another way of looking inside the body without needing to undertake any kind of surgery. It's generally considered much safer than X-rays but, as with anything, it has its downsides.

Learning Objectives:

- Understand how an image is formed in a magnetic resonance scanner and how its quality can be controlled.
- Be able to compare the advantages and disadvantages of magnetic resonance imaging to CT scanning and ultrasound.

Specification References B.2.4, B.2.5

Producing images

In **magnetic resonance (MR) imaging**, the patient lies in the centre of a huge superconducting magnet that produces a uniform magnetic field. Hydrogen nuclei in the patient's body align themselves with the field. The magnet needs to be cooled by liquid helium — this is partly why the scanner is so expensive.

Radio frequency coils are used to transmit radio waves, which excite the hydrogen nuclei. When the radio waves are switched off, the hydrogen nuclei de-excite and emit radio frequency (RF) signals — this is the MR signal. The radio frequency coils receive the RF signals and send them to a computer. The computer measures various quantities of the MR signal — amplitude, frequency, phase — and analyses them to generate an image of a cross-section through the body.

Controlling the contrast

Radio waves are applied in pulses. Each short pulse excites the hydrogen nuclei and then allows them to relax and emit a signal. The response of different tissue types (and therefore the contrast of the image) can be enhanced by varying the time between pulses.

Tissues consisting of large molecules such as fat are best imaged using rapidly repeated pulses. This technique is used to image the internal structure of the body. Allowing more time between pulses enhances the response of watery substances. This is used for diseased areas.

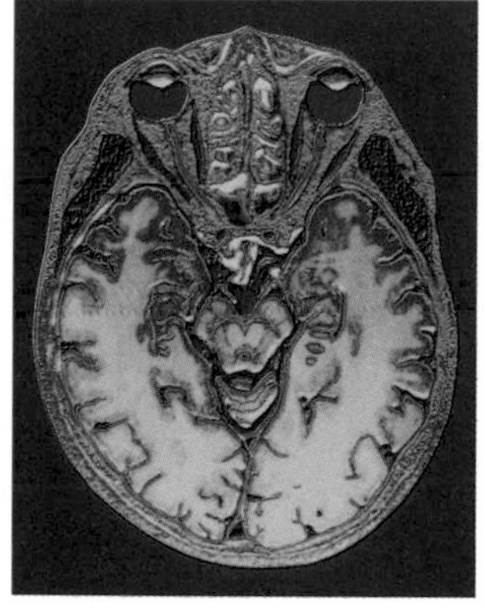

Figure 1: An MR scan of a healthy brain.

Advantages and disadvantages

MR scanning has advantages and disadvantages compared to CT scans and ultrasound (see page 226) that need to be taken into account when considering whether it would be appropriate for a particular type of procedure.

Advantages of MR scanning

- There are no known side effects.
- MR produces non-ionising radiation unlike the X-rays used in CT scans, so it won't damage living cells in the same way as CT scans.
- An image can be made for any slice in any orientation of the body, and multi-plane images can be made from the same scan. CT needs a new scan for each image.
- MR gives higher quality images for soft tissue types, such as the brain, and better resolution between tissue types for an overall better resolution final picture.
- Contrast between different tissue types can be weighted (see above) to investigate different situations.
- MR gives real-time images, whereas a CT scanner needs to be rotated and then the image needs to be processed and put together.

Tip: Ionising radiation knocks electrons off atoms and molecules, which can damage body cells — this can lead to cancer developing.

Tip: See page 229 for more on the advantages and disadvantages of ultrasound.

Disadvantages of MR scanning

- The imaging of bones is very poor compared to CT scans.
- Scans can be noisy and take a long time.
- Scanners are fairly narrow, so some people suffer from claustrophobia inside them.
- MR scanners can't be used on people with pacemakers or some metal implants — the strong magnetic fields would be very harmful.
- Scanners cost millions of pounds, and much more than CT or ultrasound scanners.

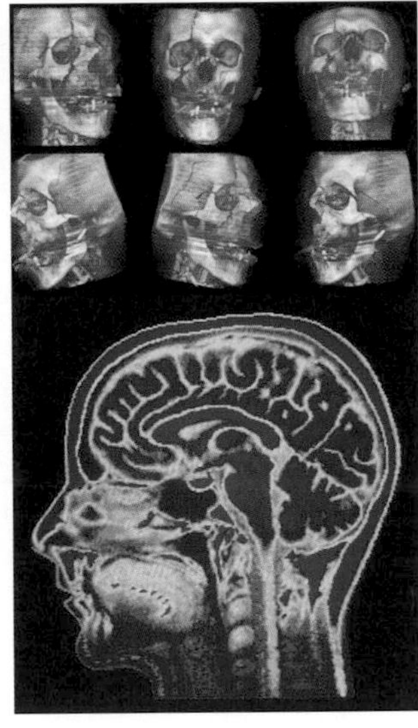

Figure 2: *CT scans (top) can show clear detail of bone damage, in this case to the skull. MR scans (bottom), on the other hand, are best suited to building a clear image of the brain and other soft tissue.*

Practice Question — Application

Q1 For each of the following, say whether an MR scan would be appropriate for diagnosis and explain your answer.

a) A possible abscess in an otherwise healthy patient's kidney.
b) A possible tumour deep within a patient's brain.
c) A possible heart defect in a patient fitted with a pacemaker.
d) A possible fracture to the radius (arm bone).
e) A possible case of deep vein thrombosis (blood clot).

Practice Questions — Fact Recall

Q1 Briefly outline how an MR scanner is used to create an image.

Q2 How can radiographers control the contrast of an MR image?

Q3 Which of these statements is a true disadvantage of MR imaging?

a) The resolution is not as high as CT scanning.
b) The radiation used is ionising.
c) It's difficult to differentiate between different types of tissue.
d) Scanners cost millions of pounds.

Q4 Give two reasons why an MR scan might be preferred to a CT scan to obtain a medical image.

Q5 Give two reasons why an MR scan might not be a feasible way of obtaining a medical image.

10. Ultrasound

You'll have heard of ultrasound from its wide usage in prenatal scans. The main reason for its use is that it's the safest and cheapest form of non-invasive imaging we have — but, naturally, that does mean it comes with its downsides.

Learning Objectives:

- Understand what ultrasound is.
- Understand that ultrasound waves are reflected at material boundaries by an amount that depends on the acoustic impedance of the materials.
- Understand that ultrasound waves are attenuated as they travel through materials.
- Understand what piezoelectric devices are and how they're used in ultrasound.
- Know what an A-scan is and what a B-scan is, and know the applications of each.
- Know the advantages and disadvantages of ultrasound imaging compared to other forms of non-invasive imaging.

Specification Reference B.2.4

What is ultrasound?

Ultrasound waves are sound waves with higher frequencies than humans can hear (>20 000 Hz). For medical purposes, pulses of ultrasound waves are produced by an ultrasound scanner, usually with frequencies from 1 to 15 MHz. The scanner is placed on the surface of the patient's skin. When an ultrasound wave meets a boundary between two different materials, some of it is reflected and some of it is transmitted (undergoing refraction if the angle of incidence is not 90°). The reflected waves are detected by the ultrasound scanner and are used to generate an image — see page 228.

Acoustic impedance

The amount of reflection an ultrasound wave experiences at a boundary depends on the difference in **acoustic impedance**, Z, between the materials. The acoustic impedance of a material is defined as:

$$Z = \rho c$$

Z *= acoustic impedance in kgm^{-2}s^{-1}*
ρ *= density in kgm^{-3}*
c *= speed of sound in the medium in ms^{-1}*

Tip: The acoustic impedance of bone varies between 1.5×10^6 and 8×10^6 kgm^{-2}s^{-1}. Skin is around 1.7×10^6 kgm^{-2}s^{-1} and air is much lower — only 4.1×10^2 kgm^{-2}s^{-1}.

Example

At 20 °C the density of air is approximately 1.2 kgm^{-3} and the speed of sound in air is 340 ms^{-1}. Find the acoustic impedance of air.

$$Z = \rho c = 1.2 \times 340 = 408\ \text{kgm}^{-2}\text{s}^{-1}$$

Say an ultrasound wave travels through a material with an impedance Z_1. It hits the boundary between this material and another material with an impedance Z_2. The incident wave has an intensity of I_i. If the two materials have a large difference in impedance, then most of the energy is reflected (the intensity of the reflected wave I_r will be high). If the impedance of the two materials is the same then there is no reflection. The fraction of wave intensity that is reflected is called the intensity reflection coefficient, R.

$$R = \frac{I_r}{I_i} = \left(\frac{Z_2 - Z_1}{Z_2 + Z_1}\right)^2$$

R *= intensity reflection coefficient*
I_r *= intensity of reflected wave in Wm^{-2}*
I_i *= intensity of incident wave in Wm^{-2}*
Z_1 *= acoustic impedance of first material in kgm^{-2}s^{-1}*
Z_2 *= acoustic impedance of second material in kgm^{-2}s^{-1}*

Exam Tip
This equation might seem daunting, but don't worry — you don't need to learn it for the exam, just practise using it.

Example

An ultrasound wave with an intensity of 7.1×10^{-3} Wm^{-2} hits a boundary, and a wave with an intensity of 4.9×10^{-4} Wm^{-2} is reflected back. What's the intensity reflection coefficient for the boundary?

$$R = \frac{I_r}{I_i} = \frac{4.9 \times 10^{-4}}{7.1 \times 10^{-3}} = 0.069 \text{ (to 2 s.f.)}$$

Tip: The intensity reflection coefficient has no units — it's just a ratio.

Like X-rays, ultrasound waves also undergo attenuation when they travel through a material. This means the intensity of the reflected wave will always be lower the further the boundary is from the transducer (see below). Higher-frequency waves give better resolution, but the higher the frequency of the wave, the more it is attenuated. This means lower-frequency waves have to be used to image tissue deeper within the body.

The acoustic impedance also affects the attenuation — the larger the impedance, the greater the attenuation of the ultrasound moving through it.

The piezoelectric effect

Ultrasound is produced and detected in ultrasound imaging using a transducer:

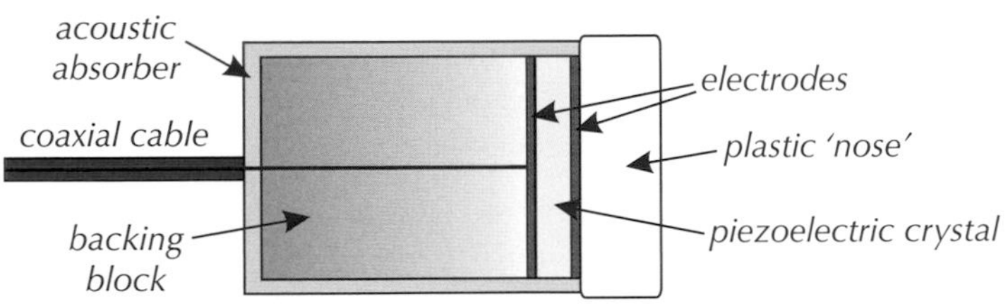

Figure 1: *An ultrasound transducer.*

Tip: A transducer is a device which converts one form of energy into another — here electrical energy is converted into sound.

Tip: The plastic nose is what's in contact with the patient's skin.

The transducer contains **piezoelectric crystals**, which produce a potential difference (p.d.) when they are deformed (squashed or stretched) — the rearrangement in structure displaces the centres of symmetry of their electric charges. This is called the piezoelectric effect.

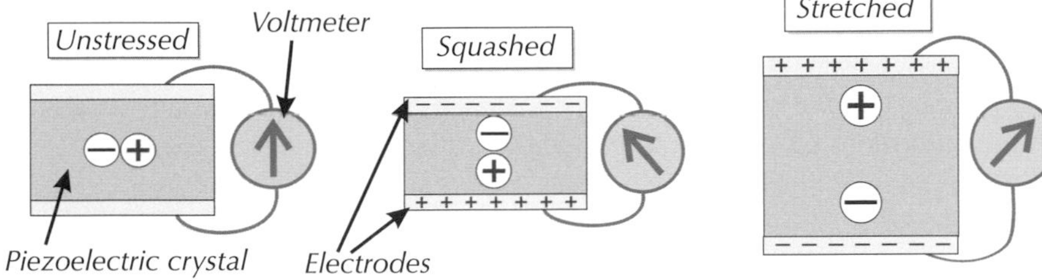

Figure 2: *A p.d. is produced when piezoelectric crystals are deformed.*

When you apply a p.d. across a piezoelectric crystal, the crystal deforms. If the p.d. is alternating, then the crystal vibrates at the same frequency. A piezoelectric crystal can act as a receiver of ultrasound, converting sound waves into alternating voltages, and also as a transmitter, converting alternating voltages into sound waves.

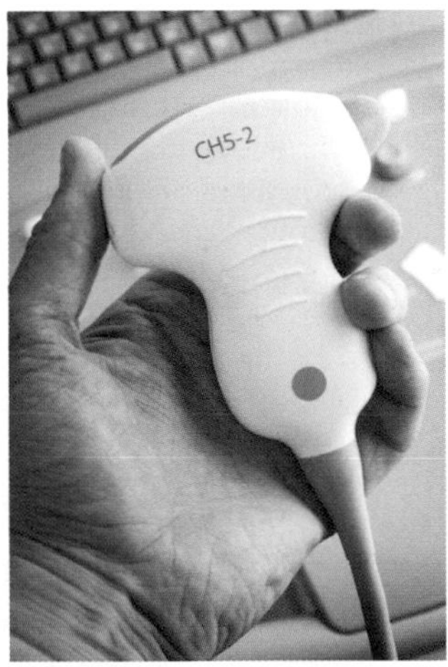

Figure 3: *An ultrasound transducer.*

Ultrasound devices use lead zirconate titanate (PZT) crystals. The thickness of the crystal is half the wavelength of the ultrasound that it produces. Ultrasound of this frequency will make the crystal resonate (like air in an open pipe — see pages 27-28) and produce a large signal. The PZT crystal is heavily damped using the backing material, to produce short pulses and increase the resolution of the device.

Tip: The vibrations of the crystal are greatest when the frequency of the potential difference equals the natural frequency of the crystals (see page 27).

Coupling mediums

Soft tissue has a very different acoustic impedance from air, so almost all the ultrasound energy is reflected from the surface of the body if there is air between the transducer and the body. To avoid this, you need a **coupling medium** between the transducer and the body — this displaces the air and has an impedance much closer to that of body tissue. The use of coupling media is an example of impedance matching. The coupling medium is usually an oil or gel that is smeared onto the skin.

Types of ultrasound scan

There are two types of ultrasound scan you need to know about. A-scans are mostly used for measuring distances, while B-scans are used to form images.

The A-scan

The amplitude scan (A-scan) sends a short pulse of ultrasound into the body simultaneously with an electron beam sweeping across a cathode ray oscilloscope (CRO) screen. The scanner receives reflected ultrasound pulses that appear as vertical deflections on the CRO screen.

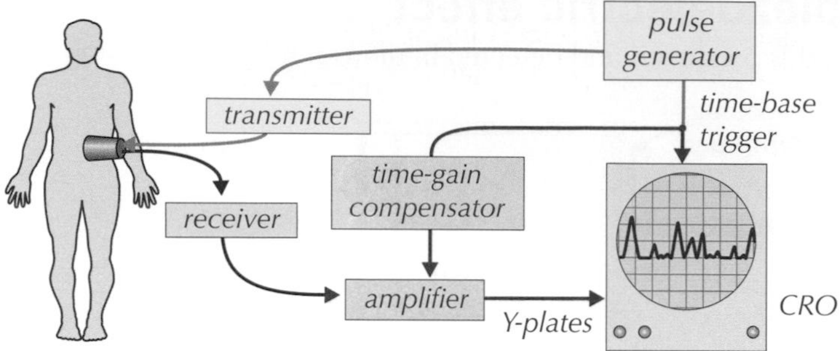

Figure 4: *The set-up of an amplitude scan.*

Weaker pulses (that have travelled further in the body and arrive later) are amplified more to avoid the loss of valuable data — this process is called time-gain compensation (TGC). The horizontal positions of the reflected pulses indicate the time the 'echo' took to return, and are used to work out distances between structures in the body (e.g. the diameter of a baby's head in the uterus, or the depth of an eyeball). A stream of pulses can produce a steady image on the screen (due to persistence of vision — see page 204), although modern CROs can store a digital image after just one exposure.

Tip: A-scans can be used to monitor a baby's growth in the uterus by measuring the diameter of the head at different stages of pregnancy.

The B-scan

In a brightness scan (B-scan), the electron beam sweeps down the screen rather than across. The amplitude of the reflected pulses is displayed as the brightness of the spot.

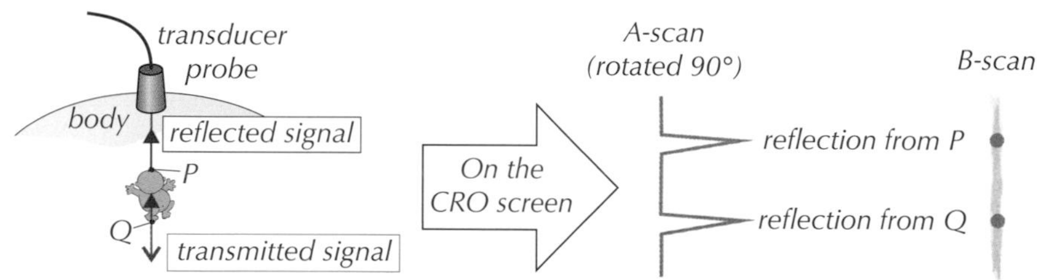

Figure 5: *The CRO output of a B-scan compared to an A-scan.*

You can use a linear array of transducers to produce a two-dimensional image, such as in the prenatal scanning of a fetus. Because of this, B-scanners are much more common than A-scanners.

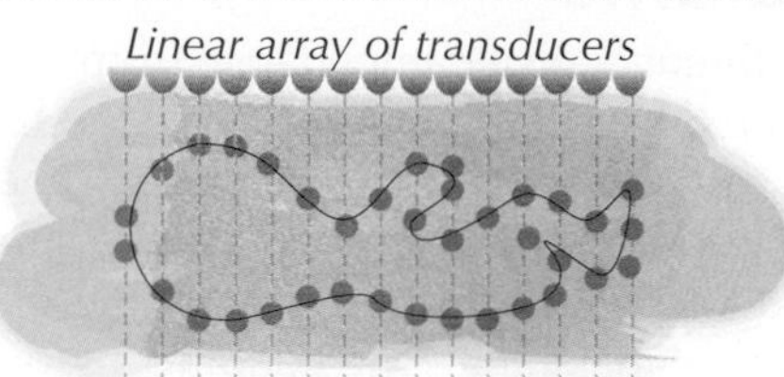

Figure 7: *A linear array of (B-scan) transducers can form a 2D image.*

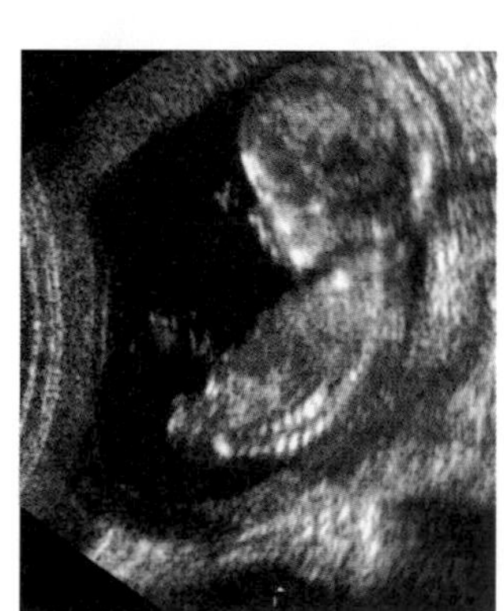

Figure 6: *An ultrasound scan of a fetus at 13 weeks.*

Advantages and disadvantages

As with X-rays (pages 221-223) and MR imaging (pages 224-225), there are advantages and disadvantages to ultrasound.

Advantages

- There are no known hazards — in particular, no exposure to ionising radiation, unlike X-ray imaging.
- It's good for imaging soft tissues, since you can obtain real-time images — X-ray fluoroscopy can achieve this, but involves a huge dose of radiation.
- Ultrasound devices are relatively cheap and portable, unlike MR scanners which cost millions of pounds (and X-ray machines aren't cheap either).

Tip: Because the images are obtained in real time and the scan isn't harmful, the patient can watch the images as they are formed.

Disadvantages

- Ultrasound doesn't penetrate bone — so it can't be used to detect fractures or examine the brain.
- Ultrasound cannot pass through air spaces in the body (due to mismatch in impedance) — so it can't produce images from behind the lungs.
- The resolution is poor (about 10 times worse than X-rays), so you can't see fine detail.

Tip: Remember, nearly all of the sound wave is reflected back at boundaries with air (see page 227).

Practice Questions — Application

Q1 a) The density of water at 20 °C is 1000 kgm^{-3} and the acoustic impedance is 1.5 × 10^{6} kgm^{-2}s^{-1}. What's the speed of sound, c?

b) A sound wave travels from bone (Z = 8.0 × 10^{6} kgm^{-2}s^{-1}) to water. What will the intensity of the reflected wave be as a percentage of the intensity of the incident wave?

Q2 Give two reasons why ultrasound scanning is a preferred option for imaging an unborn fetus to each of the following:

a) CT scanning

b) MR imaging

Practice Questions — Fact Recall

Q1 What is ultrasound?

Q2 What's the acoustic impedance of a material?

Q3 What's the piezoelectric effect?

Q4 Explain how an ultrasound wave is generated and detected.

Q5 Why is a coupling medium needed to obtain a clear ultrasound image?

Q6 a) Briefly describe what an A-scan is.

b) Briefly describe what a B-scan is.

c) Give an example of a use for both A-scans and B-scans.

Q7 a) Give two advantages of ultrasound imaging compared to other forms of non-invasive imaging (CT scans, MR scans).

b) Give two disadvantages of ultrasound imaging compared to other forms of non-invasive imaging (CT scans, MR scans).

11. Endoscopy

Learning Objectives:

- Know the properties of an optical fibre.
- Understand what total internal reflection is and how it applies to optical fibres.
- Know the difference between coherent and non-coherent optical fibre, and know what each is used for.
- Know what an endoscope is.
- Understand the advantages of endoscopy and keyhole surgery compared to traditional methods.

Specification Reference B.2.4

Sometimes the imaging methods covered in the last few chapters don't quite fit the bill, and you need something that gets a clearer view. Endoscopes let you see deep inside a patient while causing minimal amounts of damage.

Optical Fibres

Optical fibres are a bit like electric wires — but instead of carrying current they transmit light. A typical optical fibre consists of a glass core (about 5 μm to 50 μm in diameter) surrounded by a cladding, which has a slightly lower refractive index. The difference in refractive index means that light travelling along the fibre will be reflected at the cladding-core interface.

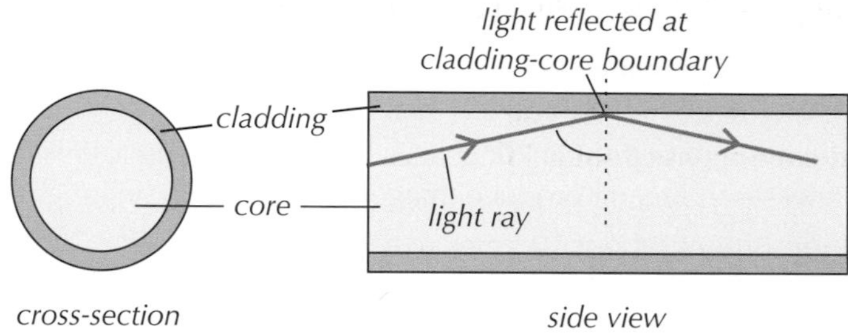

Figure 1: *A cross-section and side view of an optical fibre.*

Tip: You covered refractive index, angle of incidence, critical angle and total internal reflection in AS physics.

If the light ray's angle of incidence is less than or equal to a critical angle, some light will be lost out of the fibre. But if the angle of incidence is larger than the critical angle, the light ray will be completely reflected inside the fibre. This phenomenon is called **total internal reflection** and means that the ray zigzags its way along the fibre — so long as the fibre isn't too curved.

Tip: Total internal reflection can only happen when light is travelling from a more optically dense to a less optically dense medium.

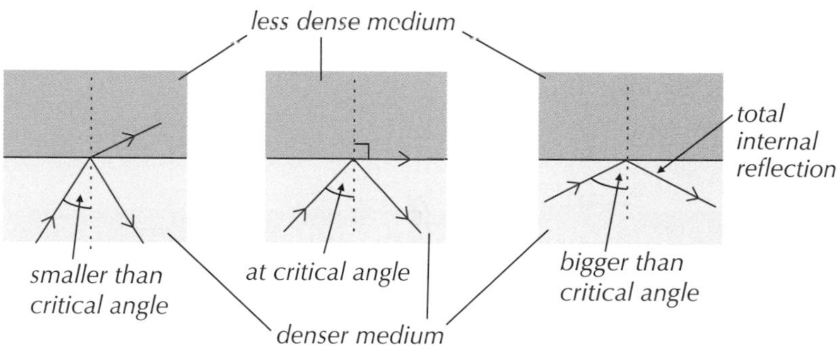

Figure 2: *Light rays hitting the core-cladding boundary at various angles.*

Figure 3: *Total internal reflection of a laser beam inside an optical fibre.*

Calculating the critical angle

The **critical angle**, θ_c, depends on the refractive index of the core, n_1, and cladding, n_2, in an optical fibre.

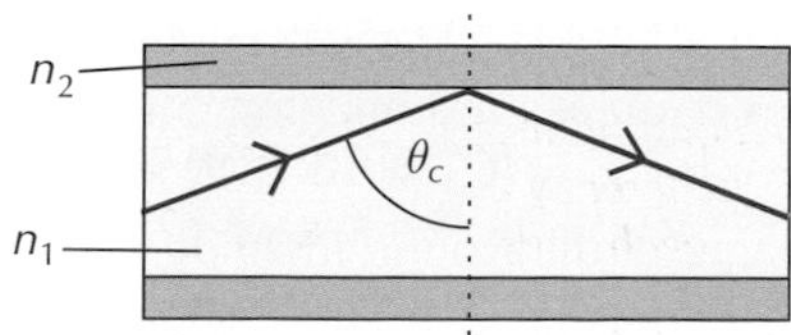

Figure 4: *The critical angle of an optical fibre.*

You can work out the critical angle using this formula:

$$\sin\theta_c = \frac{n_2}{n_1}$$

θ_c = the critical angle in °

n_2 = the refractive index of the cladding

n_1 = the refractive index of the core

Tip: The equation for the critical angle is derived from Snell's law — you covered that at AS. $n_1 \sin i = n_2 \sin r$, but at the critical angle $r = 90°$ (see Figure 2). $\sin 90° = 1$, so $\sin i = \frac{n_2}{n_1}$, where $i = \theta_c$.

Examples

An optical fibre consists of a core with a refractive index of 1.5 and cladding with a refractive index of 1.4.

a) What is the critical angle of the core-cladding boundary?

You need to find the critical angle θ_c, so make that the subject by taking the inverse sin ($\sin^{-1}$) of both sides:

$$\sin\theta_c = \frac{n_2}{n_1} \Rightarrow \theta_c = \sin^{-1}\left(\frac{n_2}{n_1}\right) = \sin^{-1}\left(\frac{1.4}{1.5}\right)$$

$$= 69° \text{ (to 2 s.f.)}$$

b) Would total internal reflection occur if the incident angle of light is 70°?

$70° > \theta_c$, so total internal reflection would occur.

Optical fibre bundles

An image can be transmitted along a bundle of optical fibres. This can only happen if the relative positions of fibres in a bundle are the same at each end (otherwise the image would be jumbled up) — a fibre-optic bundle in this arrangement is said to be coherent.

The resolution (i.e. how much detail can be seen) depends on the thickness of the fibres. The thinner the fibres, the more detail that can be resolved — but thin fibres are more expensive to make. Images can be magnified by making the diameters of the fibres get gradually larger along the length of the bundle.

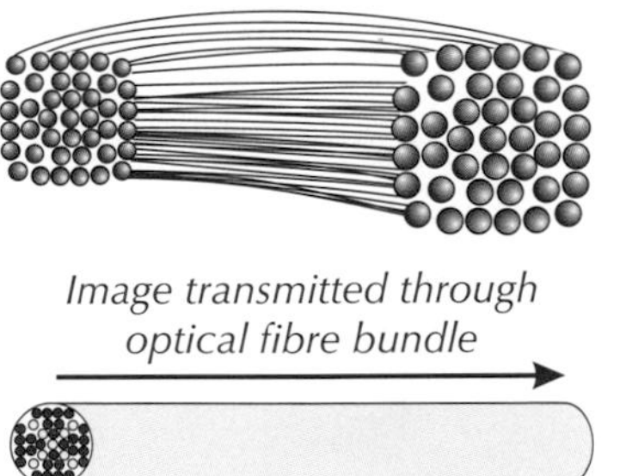

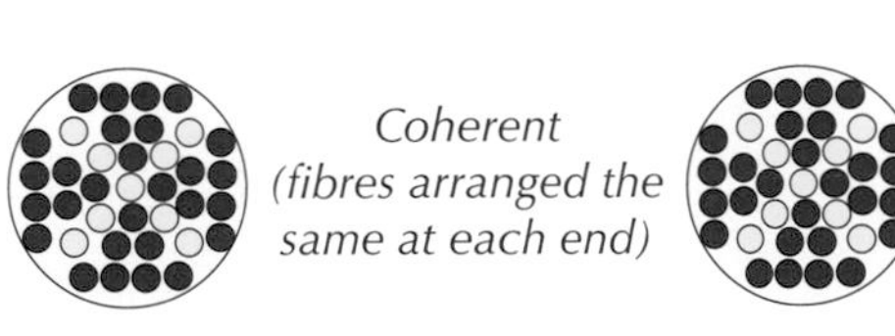

Figure 5: Coherent optical fibre bundles are used to transmit images.

Figure 6: An optical fibre bundle, spread out.

If the relative position of the fibres does not remain the same between each end the bundle of fibres is said to be non-coherent. Non-coherent bundles are much easier and cheaper to make. They can't transmit an image but they can be used to get light to hard-to-reach places — kind of like a flexible torch.

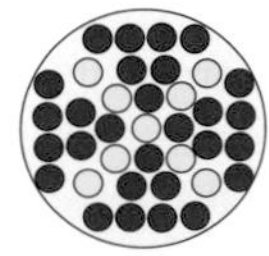

Non-coherent (fibres arranged differently at each end)

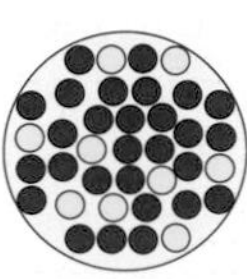

Figure 7: Non-coherent optical fibre bundles have fibres in different relative positions at each end.

Endoscopes

Endoscopes use optical fibres to create an image. An endoscope consists of a long tube containing two bundles of fibres — a non-coherent bundle to carry light to the area of interest and a coherent bundle to carry an image back to the eyepiece. Endoscopes are widely used by surgeons to examine inside the body.

An objective lens is placed at the distal end (furthest from the eye) of the coherent bundle to form an image, which is then transmitted by the fibres to the proximal end (closest to the eye) where it can be viewed through an eyepiece.

Figure 8: A medical endoscope.

Endoscopes are flexible to give them more reach inside the body. The more an endoscope bends, the more likely light is to escape because bending reduces the angle of incidence — the radius of curvature needs to be kept above a certain level (usually around 20 times the fibre diameter).

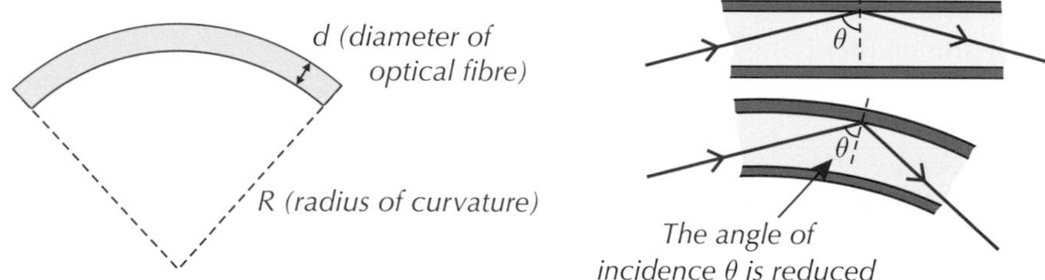

Figure 9: Decreasing the radius of curvature decreases the angle of incidence for an incident beam of light on the core-cladding boundary.

The endoscope tube can also contain a water channel for cleaning the objective lens, a tool aperture to perform keyhole surgery (see below) and a CO_2 channel. This allows CO_2 to be pumped into the area in front of the endoscope, making more room in the body.

Tip: Often the image is displayed on a screen rather than through an eyepiece. This makes it easier for more than one person to see what is happening during an operation.

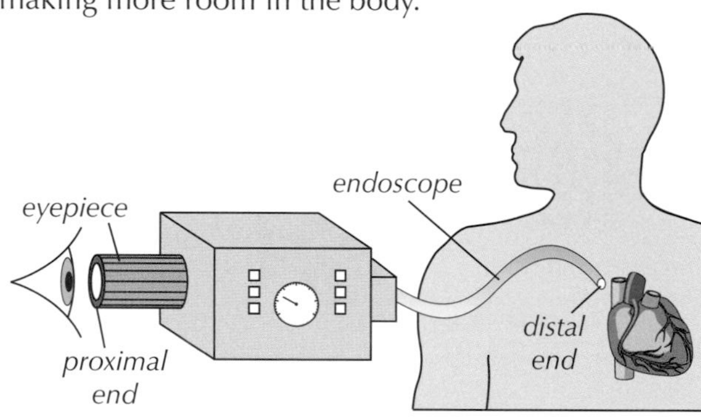

Figure 10: An endoscope can be used to see inside the body.

Keyhole surgery

Traditional surgery needs a large cut to be made in the body so that there's room for the surgeons to get in and perform an operation. This means that there's a large risk of infection to the exposed tissues and that permanent damage could be done to the patient's body.

New techniques in minimally invasive surgery (MIS or keyhole surgery) mean that only a few small holes need to be cut in the body. An endoscope can be used in keyhole surgery to show the surgeon an image of the area of interest. Surgical instruments are passed through the endoscope tube, or through additional small holes in the body, so that the operation can be carried out.

Common procedures include the removal of the gall bladder, investigation of the middle ear, and removal of abnormal polyps in the colon so that they can be investigated for cancer. Recovery times tend to be quicker for keyhole surgery, so the patient can usually return home on the same day — which makes it much cheaper for the hospital and nicer for the patient.

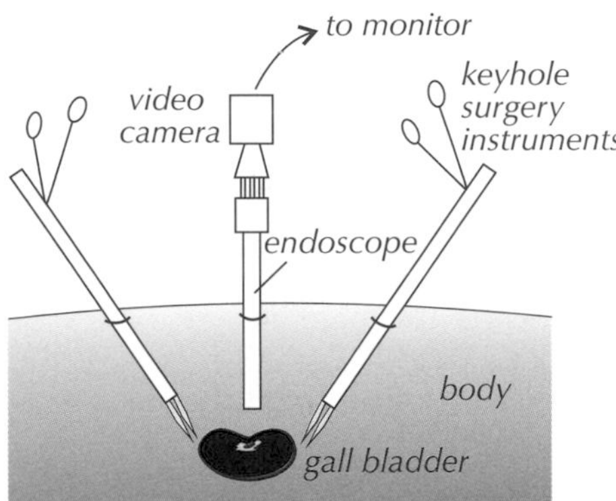

Figure 12: *Endoscopes are used in keyhole surgery*

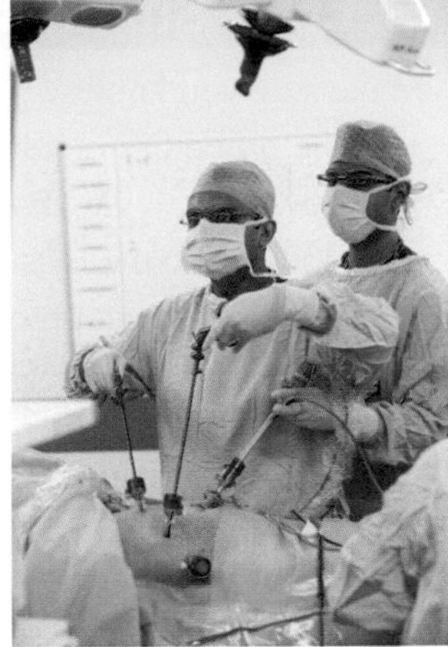

Figure 11: *Endoscopes being used in an operation to remove the gall bladder.*

Practice Questions — Application

Q1 a) Calculate the critical angle for an optical fibre if the core has $n = 1.61$ and the cladding has $n = 1.54$.

b) Say whether a beam of light with the following angles of incidence would be totally internally reflected along the fibre:

(i) 70.0°
(ii) 75.6°
(iii) 80.1°

Q2 An endoscope is being designed so that it can carry light signals that strike the core-cladding boundary at an angle greater than 65°. If the refractive index of the core is 1.70, what should the refractive index of the cladding be?

Q3 In a gastroscopy, an endoscope is sent down the patient's throat to see inside their digestive tract. Say what role each of the following would play in a gastroscopy:

a) Non-coherent optical fibre bundles.

b) Coherent optical fibre bundles.

Exam Tip
The formula for finding the critical angle is given on the AS formulae booklet. Remember, n_1 refers to the material light is travelling <u>from</u> (i.e. the core) and n_2 refers to the material light is travelling <u>to</u> (i.e. the cladding).

Practice Questions — Fact Recall

Q1 Draw and label a cross-section of an optical fibre strand.

Q2 What's the name of the process where a beam of light bounces off the core-cladding interface of an optical fibre without leaving the core?

Q3 a) What's the difference between a coherent and a non-coherent optical fibre bundle?

b) Which type of optical fibre bundle is needed to transmit images?

Q4 What's an endoscope?

Q5 Give two examples of uses for endoscopes in medicine.

Q6 Give two advantages of keyhole surgery compared to traditional methods of surgery for the patient.

Section Summary

Make sure you know...

- The properties of lenses and what is meant by the principal focus and focal length.
- How to draw ray diagrams for an image formed by a converging or diverging lens.
- How to use the lens equation, and how to calculate the power of a lens and linear magnification.
- The basic structure of the eye, and that the eye is an optical refracting system with a near point and a far point.
- The role of rods and cones in the sensitivity of the eye and in its spectral response as a photodetector.
- How to explain the spatial resolution of the eye in terms of rods and cones.
- What is meant by persistence of vision, and examples of where this effect is useful.
- What is meant by the vision defects myopia, hypermetropia and astigmatism, and how to correct them.
- How to draw ray diagrams and calculate powers for lenses used to correct defects of vision.
- What is meant by intensity of sound.
- The basic structure of the ear, and how sound is transmitted in it.
- The range of human hearing, and how it varies with frequency.
- How humans perceive loudness and why a logarithmic scale is needed to reflect this.
- How to calculate the intensity level of sound and what is meant by the threshold of hearing.
- What the dB and dBA scales are and why they're used.
- How to produce and interpret equal loudness curves.
- That hearing deteriorates with age and can be damaged by excessive noise, and the effect of hearing loss on equal loudness curves.
- The basic structure of the heart, and why it is a double pump and the function of the valves within it.
- How electric signals are generated and conducted in nerve cells.
- How to sketch the action potential of a nerve cell and of heart muscle.
- How to describe the heart's response to the action potential originating at the sino-atrial node.
- How to obtain an ECG waveform and be able to explain the shape of a normal ECG waveform.
- Know what X-rays are and how they are produced in a rotating-anode X-ray tube.
- How the beam intensity and photon energy of X-rays produced in an X-ray tube can be controlled.
- How X-ray images are produced and how the radiographer can improve the sharpness and contrast while keeping the patient's exposure to a minimum, including the use of intensifying screens.
- That X-rays undergo exponential attenuation that depends on a material's attenuation coefficient, μ.
- That the half-value thickness is the thickness required to reduce the intensity to half its original value.
- That different tissues absorb X-rays by different amounts.
- How a CT scanner works and how it produces an image.
- How a barium meal and fluoroscopy can be used to produce real-time images with X-rays.
- How an MR scanner works and how it produces an image.
- That ultrasound waves are attenuated by materials, and reflected at tissue boundaries by an amount that depends on the difference in acoustic impedance between the two tissues.
- That piezoelectric devices can be used to produce and detect ultrasound waves.
- What an A-scan and a B-scan are, and the applications of each.
- The advantages and disadvantages of CT, MR and ultrasound scans.
- What optical fibres are and their uses in medicine.
- The difference between coherent and non-coherent optical fibre bundles and the uses of each.

Exam-style Questions

1 Below is a diagram of the eye.

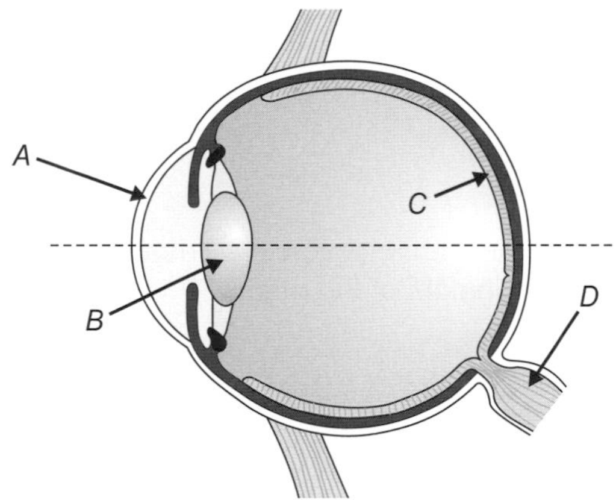

1 (a) State what the letters *A*-*D* represent.

(2 marks)

1 (b) (i) State what is meant by persistence of vision.

(1 mark)

1 (b) (ii) Give two practical situations where persistence of vision is important.

(2 marks)

1 (c) Explain which part of the retina gives the best spatial resolution, and why.

(3 marks)

1 (d) Explain how an A-scan can be used to measure the depth of an eyeball.

(3 marks)

2 (a) Name the part of the ear which acts like a funnel for sound waves.

(1 mark)

2 (b) Explain why there are greater pressure variations at the oval window of the ear than at the eardrum.

(2 marks)

2 (c) State what is meant by the threshold of hearing, I_0.

(2 marks)

2 (d) (i) When a machine is in operation, the intensity level of sound it produces 5 m away is measured as 81 dB. Calculate the intensity of the sound at this point in Wm^{-2}.

(2 marks)

2 (d) (ii) Explain why a dBA scale might be used instead of a dB scale when considering whether people working near the machine should be issued with ear protectors.

(2 marks)

3 (a) Copy and complete the ray diagram below to show the image formed by a converging lens of the object shown.

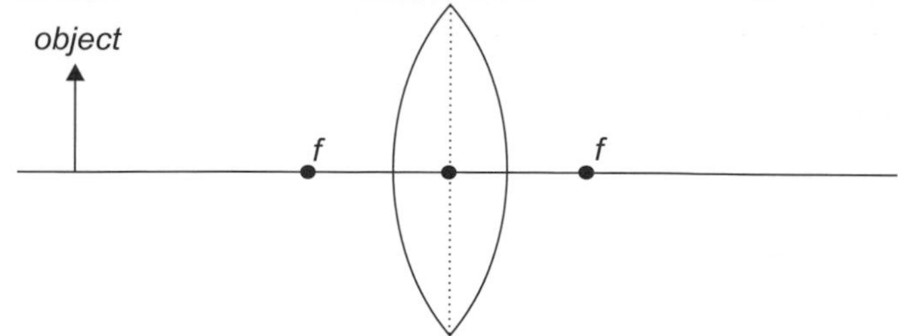

(2 marks)

3 (b) A converging lens is used to produce an image with a linear magnification of 1.61 and a height of 29.3 cm. Find the height of the object.

(2 marks)

3 (c) A hypermetropic person has a near point of 4.9 m.

(c) (i) Explain what kind of image a corrective lens for this condition will produce, and where it will produce it.

(2 marks)

3 (c) (ii) The person needs to be able to read a book 25 cm away from their eyes. What power of lens is needed for this to be possible?

(2 marks)

3 (d) State which type of vision defect can be corrected with a cylindrical lens.

(1 mark)

4 (a) In a rotating-anode X-ray tube, X-rays are produced in a continuous spectrum of intensity and in spikes of intensity at certain photon energies.

4 (a) (i) Explain why the anode is rotated.

(2 marks)

4 (a) (ii) Explain what causes the continuous spectrum of photon energies.

(1 mark)

4 (a) (iii) Explain what causes the spikes of intensity at certain photon energies.

(2 marks)

4 (b) (i) What is the half-value thickness, $x_{\frac{1}{2}}$, of a material?

(1 mark)

4 (b) (ii) Calculate how far an X-ray beam will travel through a tissue with $\mu = 9.64 \text{ m}^{-1}$ before its intensity becomes a fifth of its initial intensity.

(3 marks)

4 (c) Give two advantages of using a CT scan compared to MR or ultrasound.

(2 marks)

5 (a) Describe where the valves in the heart are found and what their role is.

(2 marks)

5 (b) The graph below shows the action potential of a nerve cell.

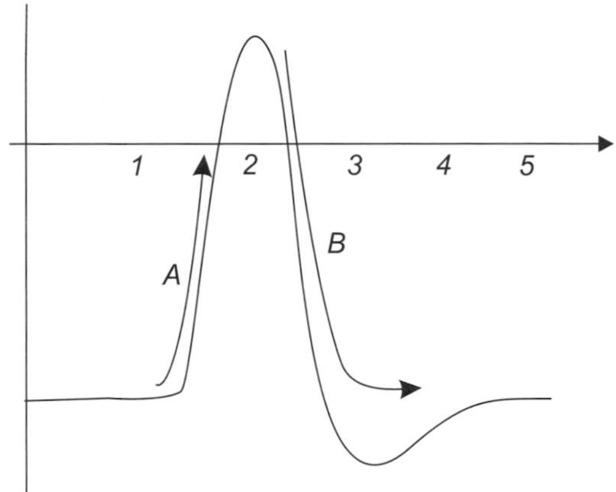

5 (b) (i) Add labels to both axes and a scale to the *y*-axis of the graph.

(2 marks)

5 (b) (ii) State what is happening during A and B on the graph.

(2 marks)

5 (c) Explain the role of the sino-atrial nodes in the heart.

(2 marks)

5 (d) (i) Describe what an ECG trace shows.

(1 mark)

5 (d) (ii) State two methods which can ensure a good ECG waveform is obtained from a patient.

(2 marks)

6 (a) (i) State what is meant by the critical angle of total internal reflection.

(1 mark)

6 (a) (ii) The refractive index of medium *A* is 1.25 and the refractive index of medium *B* is 1.15. Calculate the critical angle for a beam of light travelling from medium *A* to medium *B*.

(2 marks)

6 (b) (i) Explain what is meant by a coherent optical fibre bundle.

(1 mark)

6 (b) (ii) Give one use for coherent optical fibre bundles.

(1 mark)

6 (c) State and explain two advantages of the use of endoscopes and keyhole surgery compared to traditional surgery methods, including safety and cost factors in your answer.

(4 marks)

Learning Objectives:
- Understand what a cathode ray is and how they are produced in a discharge tube.
- Understand the principle of thermionic emission of electrons.
- Know that the work done accelerating an electron through a p.d. is equal to the kinetic energy it has gained when it reaches the anode.
- Understand the equation $\frac{1}{2}mv^2 = eV$, where e is the charge on an electron.
- Understand and be able to use the equation $F = \frac{eV}{d}$.

Specification Reference D.4.1

1. Discovering Electrons

This section is a bit different to the ones that you've seen so far. It covers a few topics that you've already seen at some point at AS and A2 in much more historical detail. You'll see how three important ideas in physics developed through a series of important discoveries and experiments. The first one is electrons...

Discovery of cathode rays

During the 1800s, scientists thought that the atom was the smallest particle that existed. In the late 1800s a series of experiments changed their minds.

The phrase '**cathode ray**' was first used in 1876, to describe what causes the glow that appears on the wall of a discharge tube like the one in Figure 1, when a high potential difference is applied across the terminals. The **cathode** is connected to the negative terminal of the battery and becomes negatively charged as electrons flow from the battery to the cathode. The **anode** is connected to the positive battery terminal and becomes positively charged.

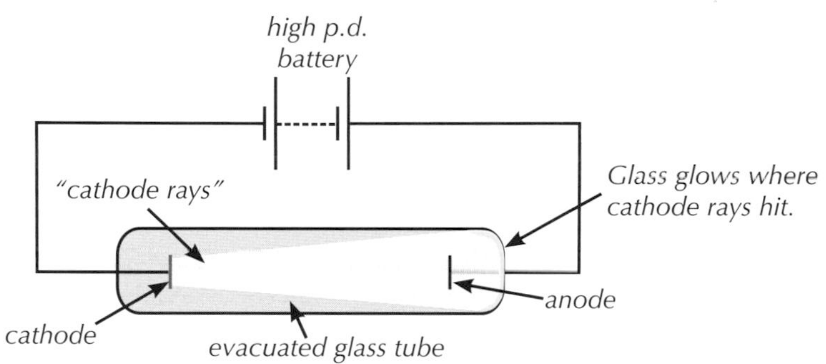

Figure 1: *A cathode ray discharge tube.*

Tip: The cathode rays don't actually glow. They ionise atoms in the glass when they collide with them at high speeds, causing electrons to excite and de-excite — which releases photons.

The rays seemed to come from the cathode (hence their name) and there was a lot of argument about what the rays were made of. J. J. Thomson ended the debate in 1897, when he demonstrated (see pages 242-244) that cathode rays:

a) have energy, momentum and mass,

b) have a negative charge,

c) have the same properties, no matter what gas is in the tube and what the cathode is made of,

d) have a charge-to-mass ratio much bigger than that of hydrogen ions. So they either have a tiny mass, or a much higher charge — Thomson assumed they had the same size charge as hydrogen ions and a tiny mass.

Thomson concluded that all atoms contain these 'cathode ray particles', that were later called electrons. Cathode rays are just beams of electrons.

Thermionic emission

When you heat a metal, its free electrons gain a load of thermal energy. Give them enough energy and they'll break free from the surface of the metal — this is called **thermionic emission**. Once they've been emitted, the electrons can be accelerated by an electric field in an **electron gun** — see Figure 2.

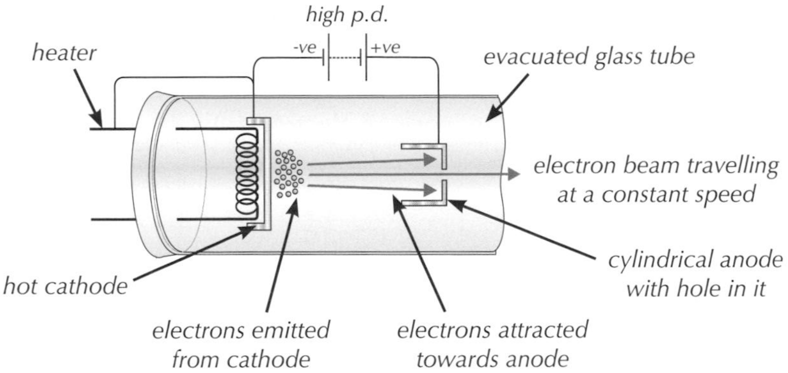

Figure 2: *An electron gun.*

A heating coil heats the metal cathode. The electrons that are emitted are accelerated towards the cylindrical anode by the electric field set up by the high voltage (see next page).

Electrons are tiny compared to the smallest atom, so they are easily stopped or deflected by atoms. So the glass tube in an electron gun has to be evacuated of air so that the electrons can travel freely in the electric field.

Some electrons pass through a little hole in the anode, making a narrow electron beam. The electrons in the beam move at a constant velocity because there's no field beyond the anode — i.e., there's no force.

Electron guns are combined with fluorescent screens in modern cathode ray tubes (CRTs). The electron beam is directed at the screen, causing it to emit light and produce a picture on the screen. CRTs are used in old-fashioned TV screens and computer monitors.

Tip: Try breaking the word down to remember what it means — think of it as 'therm' (to do with heat) + 'ionic' (to do with charge) + 'emission' (giving off) — so it's 'giving off charged particles when you heat something'.

Tip: If you increase the potential difference between the anode and cathode, the electrons will move faster (they'll have more kinetic energy — see page 243). If you increase the current through the heater, more electrons will be emitted per second by the cathode.

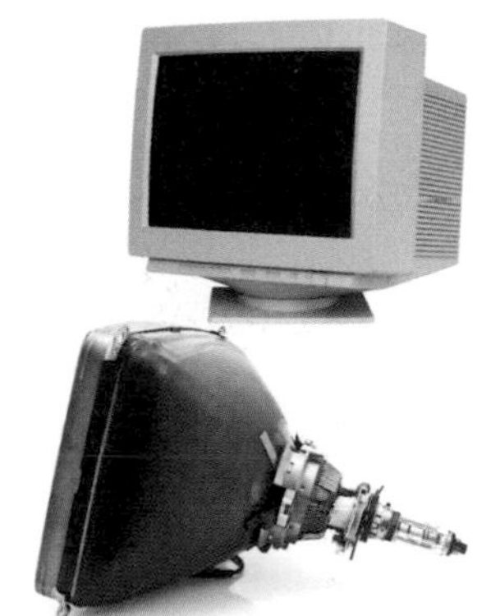

Figure 3: *Old-fashioned computer monitors (top) and TV screens contain CRTs. They are made up of an electron gun and a vacuum tube with a fluorescent screen at the end (bottom).*

Work done and electronvolts

You've met the equation for the work done to move a charge through a potential difference on page 50. It's just:

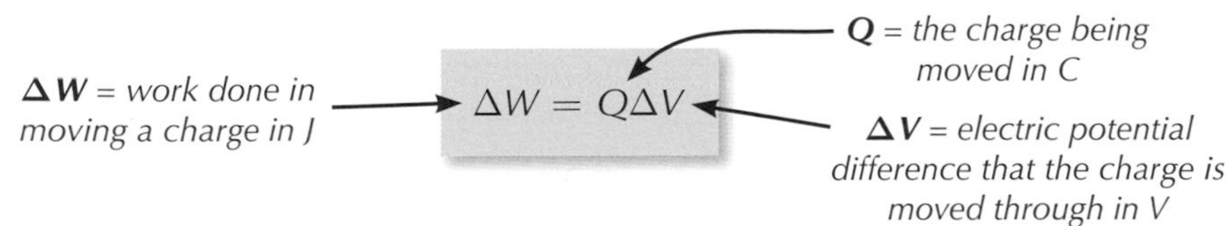

ΔW = work done in moving a charge in J
ΔW = QΔV
Q = the charge being moved in C
ΔV = electric potential difference that the charge is moved through in V

Here, Q is the charge of a single electron, e, and ΔV is just the potential difference between the cathode and anode, V. So you get that the work done in accelerating an electron through a p.d. V is $\Delta W = eV$.

Tip: This is just one derivation of this formula, but it can be applied when d is the distance over which the p.d. is applied (instead of the distance travelled). This can be shown by knowing that electric field strength, $E = \frac{V}{d}$ (p. 48) and that force $F = EQ$ (p. 46).

From AS physics, work done (ΔW) = force (F) × distance moved (d), so from this, we get that $Fd = eV$ and so:

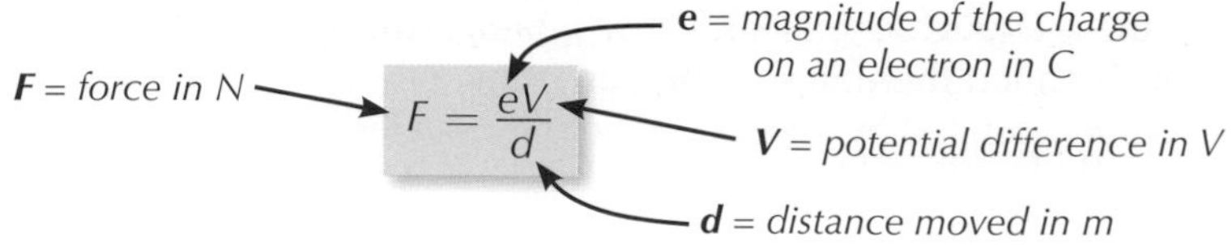

F = force in N
$F = \frac{eV}{d}$
e = magnitude of the charge on an electron in C
V = potential difference in V
d = distance moved in m

Tip: The magnitude of the charge on an electron, $e = 1.60 \times 10^{-19}$ C.

Example

Calculate the force needed to move an electron 1.0×10^{-6} m through a potential difference of 2 kV.

Use the equation: $F = \frac{eV}{d} = \frac{(1.60 \times 10^{-19})(2000)}{(1.0 \times 10^{-6})} = 3.2 \times 10^{-10}$ N

The kinetic energy that the electron will have as it leaves the anode (through the hole) is equal to the work done in accelerating it through the potential difference between the cathode and anode, and is given by $\frac{1}{2}mv^2$:

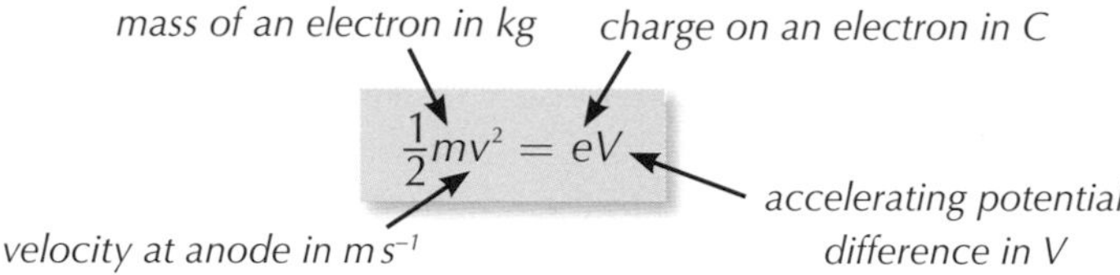

Tip: This equation was used by Thomson to work out the charge-to-mass ratio (e/m) of an electron (see next topic).

Example

Calculate the velocity of an electron that has been accelerated through a potential difference of 150 V.

Rearranging $\frac{1}{2}mv^2 = eV$ we get that:

$$v = \sqrt{\frac{2eV}{m}}$$

$$= \sqrt{\frac{2(1.60 \times 10^{-19})(150)}{(9.11 \times 10^{-31})}}$$

$= 7.26 \times 10^6$ m s^{-1} (to 3 s.f.)

Tip: The mass and charge of an electron are given as constants in the Data and Formulae booklet in the exam.

From this formula you can define a new unit of energy called the **electronvolt** (eV):

1 electronvolt is the kinetic energy carried by an electron after it has been accelerated from rest through a potential difference of 1 volt.

Tip: 1 eV = 1.60×10^{-19} J

So, the work done in eV on an electron accelerated by a potential difference is:

energy gained by electron (in eV) = accelerating voltage (in V)

Tip: The unit MeV is the mega-electronvolt (equal to 1.60×10^{-13} J) and GeV is the giga-electronvolt (1.60×10^{-10} J).

Example

Calculate the kinetic energy of an electron, in eV and joules, that has been accelerated by a CRT through a potential difference of 5 kV.

- Using the definition of electronvolts, kinetic energy = 5×10^3 eV.
- To find the energy in joules, multiply the p.d. by the charge of an electron. Kinetic energy = $eV = (1.6 \times 10^{-19}) \times (5 \times 10^3) = 8 \times 10^{-16}$ J.

Tip: When the first CRTs were made, we didn't know the value for the charge on an electron — that was worked out much later on.

Practice Question — Application

Q1 An electron gun uses thermionic emission to produce electrons which are accelerated by a high potential difference.

a) With reference to a suitable equation, explain what would happen to the beam of electrons if you increased the potential difference at the anode.

b) Calculate the kinetic energy, in J, of an electron that has been accelerated through a potential difference of 12 kV.

c) Calculate the force needed to accelerate the electron in part b) if the distance over which it is accelerated is 1.25 nm.

Tip: The charge on an electron is 1.60×10^{-19} C and is given in the Data and Formulae booklet in the exam.

Practice Questions — Fact Recall

Q1 What did scientists in the late 1800s mean by cathode rays?

Q2 Describe what is meant by thermionic emission.

Q3 Sketch a labelled diagram of an electron gun.

Q4 Write down the equation for the force on an electron in terms of the distance moved and the potential difference the electron is moved through.

Q5 Explain where the formula $\frac{1}{2}mv^2 = eV$ comes from.

2. Specific Charge of an Electron

So scientists thought that subatomic particles existed, but they had yet to prove it. It was the measurement of the ratio of charge to mass for an electron that convinced them that they were probably much smaller than the atom...

Learning Objectives:

- Know one method of determining the specific charge, e/m, of an electron.
- Understand and be able to use the equations $F = Bev$ and $r = \frac{mv}{Be}$.
- Understand the significance of J. J. Thomson's determination of e/m and its comparison with the specific charge of the hydrogen ion.

Specification Reference D.4.1

Finding the specific charge of the electron

The **specific charge** or charge-to-mass ratio of a charged particle is just its charge per unit mass measured in $C\,kg^{-1}$. For an electron, the specific charge is denoted e/m. In 1897, Thomson measured e/m and showed that subatomic particles exist. There are a few different ways of measuring it, and you need to know one method inside out for your exam — it doesn't matter which one though (see the Tip at the top of the next page).

Tip: You studied specific charge way back in Unit 1: Section 1 of AS physics — just remember you need to have the mass in kg and the charge in C and it should be easy.

Experiment to find the specific charge of an electron (e/m):

Electrons are charged particles, so they can be deflected by an electric or a magnetic field. This method uses a magnetic field in a piece of apparatus called a fine-beam tube (see Figure 1).

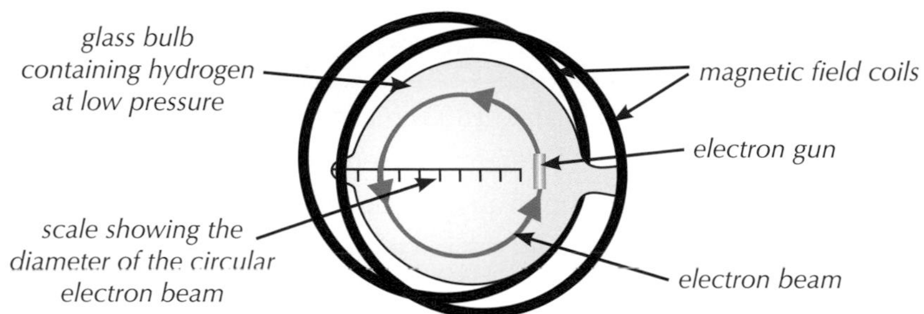

Figure 1: *A fine-beam tube.*

Tip: It's important that the hydrogen gas is at a low pressure so that the hydrogen atoms aren't already excited and there are as few hydrogen atoms as possible to inhibit the electron beam. You want just enough hydrogen atoms for the beam to be visible, but not enough to stop the beam.

A beam of electrons from an electron gun (see page 239) is passed through low-pressure hydrogen gas. The electrons in the beam collide with the hydrogen atoms along its path and transfer some of their energy, causing electrons in the atoms to move into higher energy levels. This is known as excitation. As the electrons in these excited hydrogen atoms fall back to the ground state, they emit light. The electron beam is seen as a glowing trace through the gas.

Two circular magnetic field coils either side of the tube generate a uniform magnetic field inside the tube. The electron beam is fired at right angles to the magnetic field, so the beam curves round in a circle.

Tip: Check out Unit 4: Section 4 — Magnetic Fields (p. 71) if you're having trouble with the experiment.

The circular motion of the electron beam means that the magnetic force on the electron (see p. 75 is acting as a centripetal force (see p. 15). Magnetic force is given by $F = Bev$ and centripetal force is given by $F = \frac{mv^2}{r}$. So equating these gives:

$$\frac{mv^2}{r} = Bev$$

Tip: These formulas are found on:
p. 75 for magnetic force
p.15 for centripetal force

So the radius of the circular path of the electrons is given by:

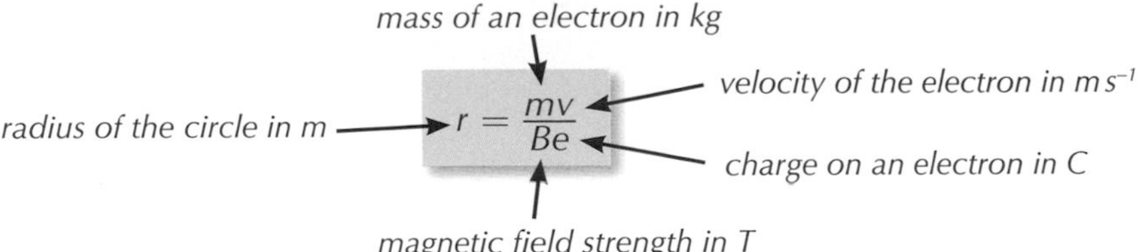

Tip: Your teacher might have shown you a different method for calculating *e/m*. That's fine... just choose the one you understand the best and learn it.

You can rearrange the equation for the kinetic energy of the electron to find the velocity, in terms of the accelerating potential of the electron gun.

$$\frac{1}{2}mv^2 = eV \Rightarrow v = \sqrt{\frac{2eV}{m}}$$

Tip: Remember, $\frac{1}{2}mv^2 = eV$ comes from $F = \frac{eV}{d}$ (see page 240).

If you substitute this into the equation for the radius of the path above (and tidy it all up a bit) you get:

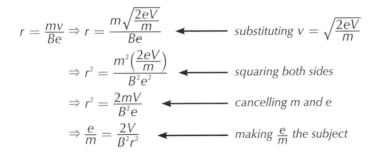

$$r = \frac{mv}{Be} \Rightarrow r = \frac{m\sqrt{\frac{2eV}{m}}}{Be} \quad \longleftarrow \text{substituting } v = \sqrt{\frac{2eV}{m}}$$

$$\Rightarrow r^2 = \frac{m^2\left(\frac{2eV}{m}\right)}{B^2e^2} \quad \longleftarrow \text{squaring both sides}$$

$$\Rightarrow r^2 = \frac{2mV}{B^2e} \quad \longleftarrow \text{cancelling } m \text{ and } e$$

$$\Rightarrow \frac{e}{m} = \frac{2V}{B^2r^2} \quad \longleftarrow \text{making } \frac{e}{m} \text{ the subject}$$

Figure 2: J. J. Thomson won the 1906 Nobel Prize in Physics for discovering the electron. He balanced a beam of electrons between a magnetic and an electric field to find the specific charge of an electron (it was a little bit like Millikan's experiment in the next topic).

So the specific charge of an electron can be found using the equation:

$$\frac{e}{m} = \frac{2V}{B^2r^2}$$

specific charge of an electron → $\frac{e}{m}$; *accelerating potential* → V; *radius of the circle* → r; *magnetic field strength* → B

You can measure all the quantities on the right-hand side of the equation using the fine-beam tube, leaving you with the specific charge, $\frac{e}{m}$.

Tip: You don't need to know how to measure these quantities using the fine-beam tube — just make sure you can use them to calculate *e/m*.

Example

A beam of electrons is accelerated through a potential difference of 200 kV by an electron gun in a fine-beam tube. The magnetic field strength in the tube is 0.0754 T and the radius of the circular beam is measured to be 2.00 cm. Calculate the specific charge of an electron.

Use the equation for specific charge: $\frac{e}{m} = \frac{2V}{B^2r^2}$

$$= \frac{2(200\,000)}{(0.0754)^2(2.00 \times 10^{-2})^2}$$

$$= 1.76 \times 10^{11}\ \text{C kg}^{-1} \text{ (to 3 s.f.)}$$

Tip: You can check that this value is right in the Data and Formulae booklet.

The significance of Thomson's findings

HOW SCIENCE WORKS

The largest specific charge that had ever been measured before was the specific charge of an H^+ ion. Using his own method, Thomson found in 1897 that $\frac{e}{m}$ is much greater than the specific charge of the H^+ ion, meaning that it either has a much greater charge, or is much lighter. He assumed that electrons had the same charge and that they were very light.

It turns out that $\frac{e}{m}$ (1.76×10^{11} C kg^{-1}) is about 1800 times greater than the specific charge of a hydrogen ion or proton (9.58×10^{7} C kg^{-1}). And the mass of a proton is about 1800 times greater than the mass of an electron — Thomson was right, electrons and protons do have the same size charge.

Practice Question — Application

Q1 An experiment to determine the specific charge of an electron uses the apparatus below.

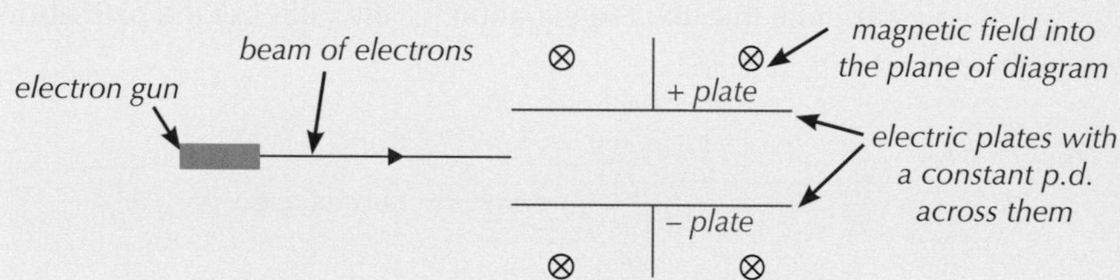

A beam of electrons is passed between two deflecting plates with a potential difference applied across them. A magnetic field is applied perpendicular to the electric field and the electron beam using an electromagnet. The whole apparatus is contained within a vacuum.

a) Before the electromagnet is turned on, what would you expect to happen to the beam of electrons as it travels between the plates?

b) The electromagnet is turned on and provides a magnetic field such that the electron beam travels in a straight line (i.e. it isn't deflected). Show that the magnetic field strength, B, is related to the potential difference applied across the plates, V, by the equation: $B = \frac{V}{vd}$, where v is the velocity of the electron beam, and d is the distance between the plates.

c) The kinetic energy of an electron upon entering the field is 4.2 keV and these measurements were taken: $V = 5000$ V, $d = 50$ mm, $B = 2.6$ mT. Calculate e/m of an electron.

Tip: For Q1 b), you need to think about the two forces that are acting on the electron. Remember, the electric force on an electron is given by $F = \frac{eV}{d}$. The apparatus is in a vacuum so you can ignore the effect of gravity.

Tip: For Q1 c) use the equation $\frac{1}{2}mv^2 = eV$ and remember that 1 eV = e J.

Practice Questions — Fact Recall

Q1 Describe an experimental set-up that could be used to determine the specific charge of an electron, including the quantities that you would need to measure.

Q2 Derive an equation for the radius of a beam of electrons travelling at a velocity v in a magnetic field of strength B.

Q3 Explain the significance of the discovery that the specific charge of an electron is much greater than that of the hydrogen ion.

Tip: You only need to be able to describe one experiment for finding the specific charge of an electron — it doesn't matter which one.

3. Millikan's Oil-Drop Experiment

So in 1897, J. J. Thomson had discovered that electrons exist and after measuring their charge-to-mass ratio he thought that they must be very, very light. But evidence didn't come until 1909, when Robert Millikan estimated the charge of an electron, meaning the mass could also be estimated.

Learning Objectives:

- Know Stokes' law for the viscous force on a spherical object and use it to calculate the radius of an oil drop.
- Understand the principle of Millikan's experiment to determine the charge of an electron.
- Be able to explain the motion of a falling charged oil droplet without an electric field, including the terminal velocity.
- Be able to explain the motion of a falling charged oil droplet with an electric field, and how it can be held stationary.
- Know that the condition for holding a charged oil droplet of charge Q stationary between two oppositely charged plates is $\frac{QV}{d} = mg$.
- Know the significance of Millikan's findings of the quantisation of charge.

Specification Reference D.4.1

Stokes' law

Before you start thinking about Millikan's experiment, you need a bit of extra theory.

When you drop an object into a fluid, like air, it experiences a **viscous drag force**. This force acts in the opposite direction to the velocity of the object, and is due to the **viscosity** of the fluid. Viscosity, in simple terms, is just how thick the fluid is. Water is more viscous than air, honey is more viscous than water. Viscosity is measured in pascal seconds (Pa s = kg m^{-1} s^{-1}). You can calculate this viscous force on a spherical object using Stokes' law:

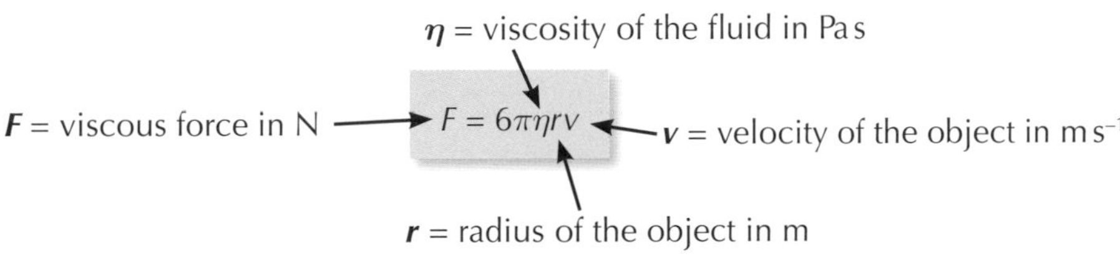

Example

Find the viscous drag force acting on a spherical drop of honey with a radius of 0.25 cm falling through air with a viscosity of 1.8 × 10^{-5} Pa s at 4.5 m s^{-1}.

Radius = 0.25 cm = 2.5 × 10^{-3} m. Substitute into $F = 6\pi\eta rv$:

$F = 6 \times \pi \times (1.8 \times 10^{-5}) \times (2.5 \times 10^{-3}) \times 4.5 = 3.82 \times 10^{-6}$ N (to 3 s.f.).

Millikan's experimental set-up

This is the apparatus that Millikan used to calculate the charge on an electron:

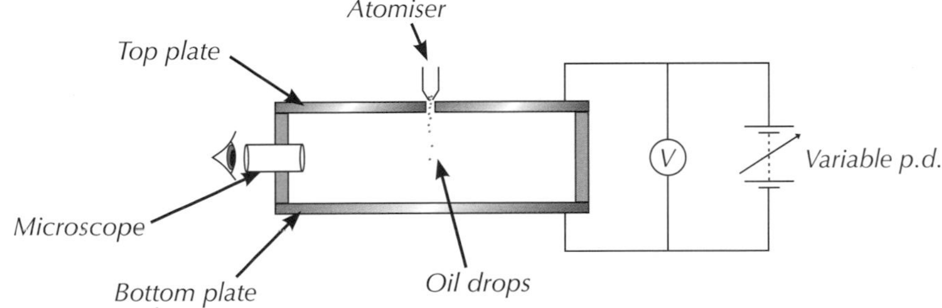

***Figure 1:** The basic apparatus for Millikan's oil-drop experiment.*

Tip: To give you a feel for the size of the apparatus, Millikan's plates were circular, with a diameter of about the width of this page. They were separated by about 1.5 cm.

The atomiser created a fine mist of oil drops that were charged by friction as they left the atomiser (positively if they lost electrons, negatively if they gained electrons). Some of the drops fell through a hole in the top plate and could be viewed through the microscope.

When he was ready, Millikan could apply a potential difference between the two plates, producing a field that exerted a force on the charged drops. By adjusting the p.d., he could vary the strength of the field.

Tip: The eyepiece carried a scale to measure distances (and so velocities) accurately.

> **Tip:** Millikan had to take account of things like upthrust as well, but you don't have to worry about that — keep it simple.

> **Tip:** $g = 9.81\ \text{m s}^{-2}$, the acceleration due to gravity.

> **Tip:** You learnt about terminal velocity in AS physics — it's just the velocity of an object when the driving forces equal the frictional forces.

> **Tip:** η is the Greek letter 'eta'.

> **Exam Tip**
> You won't be given this one in the Data and Formulae booklet, so you need to remember how to derive it.

Forces on an oil drop with no electric field between the plates

With the electric field turned off, the forces acting on each oil drop are:

- the weight of the drop, $F = mg$ — acting downwards
- the viscous force from the air, $F = 6\pi\eta rv$ (Stokes' law — see previous page) — acting upwards

The drop will reach **terminal velocity** (i.e. it will stop accelerating) when these two forces are equal. So:

$$mg = 6\pi\eta rv$$

Since the mass of the drop is the volume of the drop multiplied by the density, ρ, of the oil, and the drop is spherical, this can be rewritten as:

$$\frac{4}{3}\pi r^3 \rho g = 6\pi\eta rv$$

So the radius of the oil drop (or any sphere moving through a fluid) is:

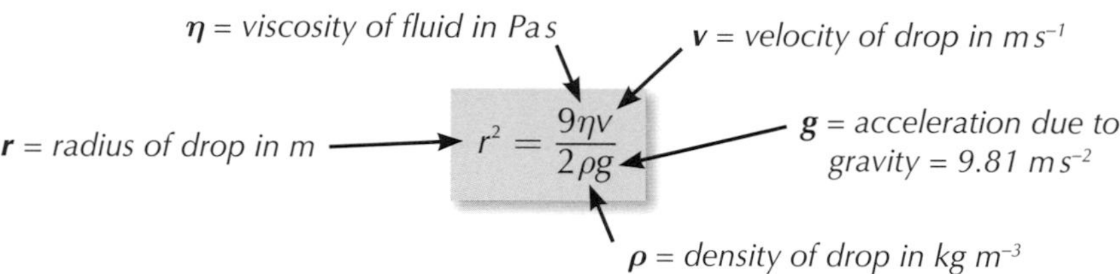

Millikan measured η and ρ in separate experiments, and v could be measured using the microscope, so he could now calculate r — ready to be used when he switched on the electric field (see below).

Example

A drop of water, with radius 4.7×10^{-7} m, is falling vertically through air at a steady speed of $2.7 \times 10^{-5}\ \text{m s}^{-1}$. The viscosity of air is 1.8×10^{-5} Pa s. Calculate the density of the water drop.

$r^2 = \frac{9\eta v}{2\rho g}$ rearranged gives $\rho = \frac{9\eta v}{2r^2 g}$

$$= \frac{9 \times (1.8 \times 10^{-5}) \times (2.7 \times 10^{-5})}{2 \times (4.7 \times 10^{-7})^2 \times 9.81}$$

$= 1009.21.... = 1000\ \text{kg m}^{-3}$ (to 2 s.f.)

Forces on an oil drop with an electric field between the plates

> **Tip:** The applied p.d. had to be adjusted so that the force due to the electric field was acting upwards. This means that if the droplet was negatively charged, the top plate would need to be positively charged, and vice versa.

Millikan's next step was to apply a p.d. across the plates, creating an electric field. The field introduced a third major factor — an electric force on the drop.

He adjusted the applied p.d. until the drop was stationary. Since the viscous force is proportional to the velocity of the object, once the drop stopped moving, the viscous force disappeared.

Now the only two forces acting on the oil drop were:

- the weight of the drop — acting downwards
- the force due to the uniform electric field — acting upwards

The weight of the drop is just $F = mg$ as before, and the electric force is given by:

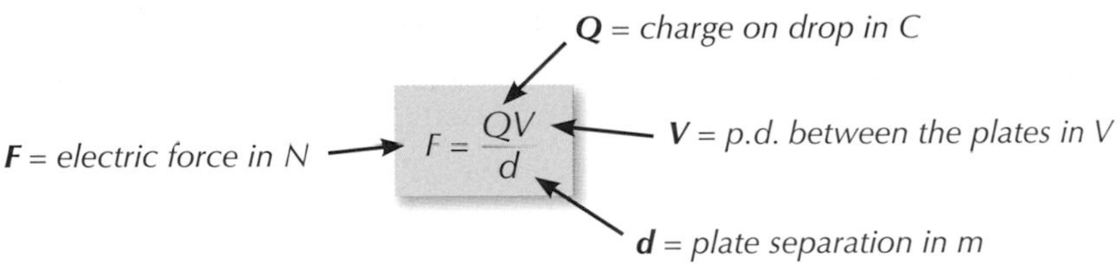

Since the drop is stationary, this electric force must be equal to the weight, so:

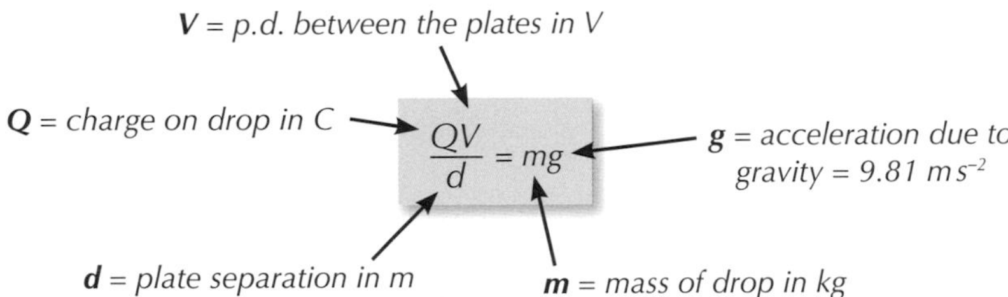

Which gives the following equation:

$$\frac{QV}{d} = \frac{4}{3}\pi r^3 \rho g$$

The first part of the experiment gave a value for r, so the only unknown in this equation is Q. This meant that Millikan could find the charge on the drop. He repeated the experiment for hundreds of drops. The charge on any drop was always a whole number multiple of -1.6×10^{-19} C.

Example

An oil drop of mass 1.63×10^{-14} kg is held stationary in the space between two charged plates. The plates are 3.00 cm apart and have a 5000 V potential difference across them. The density of the oil used is 880 kg m^{-3}. Find the charge on the oil drop in terms of e, the charge on an electron.

$$\frac{QV}{d} = mg, \text{ so } Q = \frac{mgd}{V}$$

$$= \frac{(1.63 \times 10^{-14}) \times 9.81 \times (3.00 \times 10^{-2})}{5000}$$

$$= 9.59... \times 10^{-19} \text{ C}$$

$$= 9.60 \times 10^{-19} \text{ C (to 3 s.f.)}$$

Divide this by the charge on an electron to find the charge in terms of e.

$$Q = \frac{9.60 \times 10^{-19}}{1.60 \times 10^{-19}} e$$

$$= 6e$$

Tip: If you're struggling to understand the electric fields in this experiment, go to pages 45-51.

Tip: You'll get this equation in the Data and Formulae booklet, but you need to remember and understand when and how to use it.

Tip: All that's happened here is that mass has been substituted for volume × density (ρ). The drop is spherical, so volume = $\frac{4}{3} \times \pi \times$ radius^3.

Tip: Remember, the magnitude of the charge on an electron, $e = 1.6 \times 10^{-19}$ C.

Figure 2: Robert Andrews Millikan won the 1923 Nobel Prize for Physics for determining the charge on an electron and for his work on the photoelectric effect (see page 256-261).

Quantisation of electric charge

HOW SCIENCE WORKS

The results of the oil-drop experiment were really significant. Millikan concluded that charge can never exist in smaller quantities than 1.6×10^{-19} C. He assumed that this was the charge carried by an electron. Later experiments confirmed that both these things are true.

> Charge is "quantised". It exists in "packets" of size 1.60×10^{-19} C — the **fundamental unit of charge**.
> This is the size of the charge carried by one electron.

This discovery meant that the mass of an electron could be calculated exactly, proving that it was the lightest particle ever discovered.

Practice Question — Application

Q1 A scientist repeated Millikan's oil-drop experiment and observed an oil drop's motion between two horizontal plates. The plates were 4.0 mm apart and were oppositely charged by applying a p.d. across them. The density of the oil used was 980 kg m^{-3}.
The viscosity of air was 1.8×10^{-5} Pa s.

a) The scientist observed that an oil drop fell at a steady speed of 2.5×10^{-5} m s^{-1} when no p.d. was applied across the plates. Calculate the radius of the oil drop.

b) The scientist then applied a p.d. across the plates and adjusted it until an oil drop identical to the one in part a) was stationary. The applied p.d. was 98 V. Find the charge on the oil droplet.

c) The scientist kept everything in the experiment the same except the plate separation, which he doubled. He then adjusted the applied p.d. again, so that another oil droplet with an identical radius was stationary. The applied p.d. was half the applied p.d. in part b). Find the charge on the oil droplet.

Practice Questions — Fact Recall

Q1 Write down Stokes' law, defining any variables.

Q2 Sketch the basic set-up for Millikan's oil-drop experiment.

Q3 What is the name and formula for the force that causes an oil drop's velocity to change when there is an electric field between the plates in Millikan's oil-drop experiment?

Q4 Name all the forces acting on a charged oil drop in Millikan's experiment when:

a) the electric field is turned off

b) the electric field is turned on and the drop is in motion

c) the electric field is turned on and the drop is stationary

Q5 Derive an equation linking charge, applied p.d., plate separation and oil-drop radius for an oil drop held stationary in an electric field.

Q6 Describe the result that led Millikan to believe that the charge on an electron was 1.6×10^{-19} C.

Q7 Explain the significance of Millikan's discovery of the quantisation of charge in determining properties of the electron.

4. Light — Newton vs Huygens

The next four topics are all about how physicists developed the theory of light. The big question is — what is light... a wave or a particle? Scientists have disagreed over this question time and time again. The answer they've settled on for now — it's a bit of both...

Learning Objectives:

- Understand Newton's corpuscular theory of light.
- Understand Huygens' wave theory of light.
- Be able to compare Newton and Huygens' theories of light and explain why Newton's was preferred.
- Understand the significance of Young's double-slit experiment.
- Be able to explain the production of fringes by Young's double-slit experiment.
- Know that Huygens' theory of light was eventually widely accepted.

Specification Reference D.4.2

Newton's corpuscular theory

In 1672, Newton published his *New Theory about Light and Colors*. In it he suggested that light was made up of a stream of tiny particles that he called '**corpuscles**'.

One of his major arguments for light being a particle was that light was known to travel in straight lines, yet waves were known to bend in the shadow of an obstacle (diffraction). Experiments weren't accurate enough then to detect the diffraction of light. Light was known to reflect and refract, but that was it. His theory was based on the principles of his laws of motion — that all particles, including his 'corpuscles', will 'naturally' travel in straight lines.

Newton believed that reflection was due to a force that pushed the particles away from the surface — just like a ball bouncing back off a wall. Refraction worked if the corpuscles travelled faster in a denser medium.

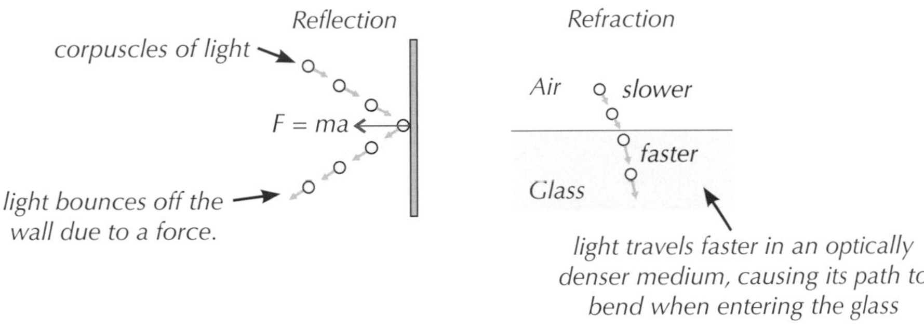

***Figure 1:** Reflection and refraction of light explained by Newton's corpuscular theory.*

***Figure 2:** Newton (top) and Huygens (bottom) disagreed on the nature of light.*

Huygens' wave theory

HOW SCIENCE WORKS

The idea that light might be a wave had existed for some time before it was formalised by Huygens in 1678. At the time, nobody took much notice of him because his theory was different from Newton's.

Huygens developed a general model of the propagation of waves in what is now known as **Huygens' principle**:

> Every point on a wavefront may be considered to be a point source of secondary **wavelets** that spread out in the forward direction at the speed of the wave. The new wavefront is the surface that is tangential to all of these secondary wavelets.

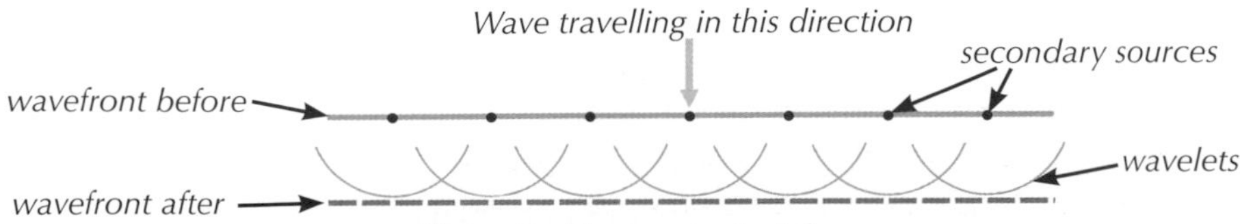

***Figure 3:** Huygens' principle.*

In other words... if you consider a snapshot in time of a wavefront, each point along it is considered as a point wave source that then spreads out in front in a hemispherical 'wavelet' to form the new wavefront in front. The wavelets spread out at the speed of the wave. See Figure 3 for a diagram of Huygens' principle.

By applying his theory to light, Huygens found that he could explain reflection and refraction easily. He predicted that light should slow down when it entered a denser medium, rather than speed up. He also predicted that light should diffract around tiny objects and that two coherent light sources should interfere with each other (see below).

Tip: If you can't remember refraction, reflection, diffraction and interference, it'll really help to go back and look at your AS physics notes before tackling this stuff.

Tip: A key difference between Newton's theory and Huygens' theory is that Huygens predicted that light would slow down in an optically denser medium, whereas Newton predicted that light would speed up.

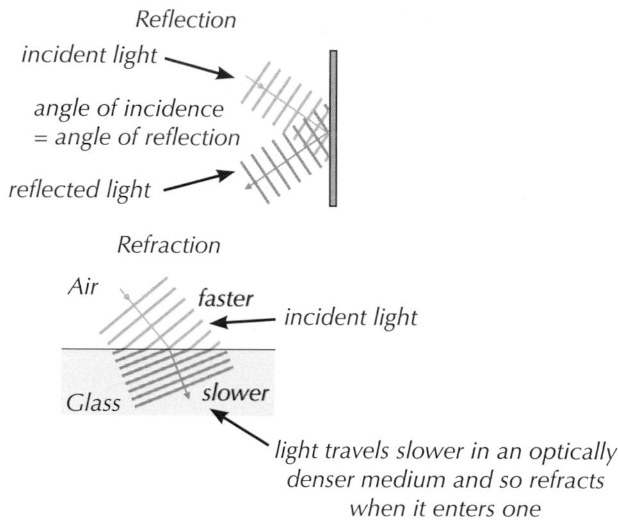

Figure 4: *Reflection and refraction of light explained by Huygens' wave theory.*

Up until the end of the 18th century, most scientists sided with Newton. He'd been right about so many things before, so it was generally assumed that he must be right about light being corpuscular. The debate raged for over 100 years until Thomas Young carried out experiments on the interference of light in Cambridge in around the year 1800...

Tip: If you need a recap on Young's double-slit experiment, it was covered in full detail at AS level in Unit 2: Section 3.

Young's double-slit experiment

HOW SCIENCE WORKS

Diffraction and interference are both uniquely wave properties. If it could be shown that light showed interference patterns, that would help decide once and for all between corpuscular theory and wave theory.

In order to get clear interference patterns, you need two coherent sources. The problem with showing light interfering was getting two coherent light sources, as light is emitted from most sources in random bursts.

Tip: You may remember from AS physics that coherent means that they have the same wavelength and frequency and a fixed phase difference between them.

Young solved this problem by using only one point source of light (a light source passed through a narrow slit). In front of this was a slide with two narrow slits in it — a double slit. Light spreading out by diffraction from the slits was equivalent to two coherent point sources.

Light from the double slit was projected onto a screen and bright and dark 'fringes' were formed where light from the two slits overlapped (see Figure 5).

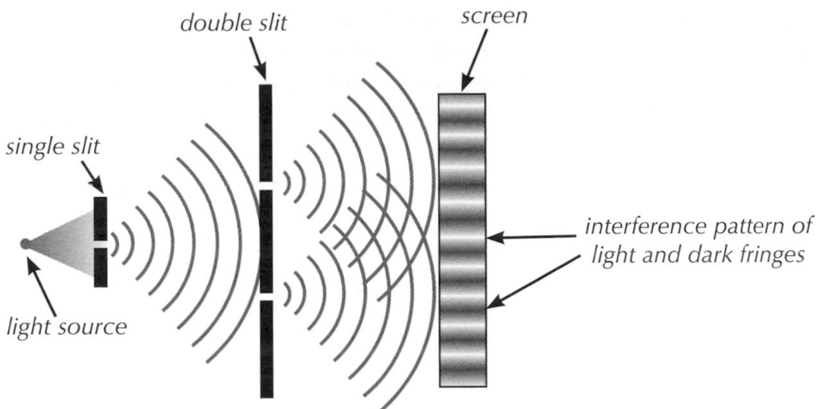

Figure 5: *Young's double-slit system producing an interference pattern.*

Figure 6: *Young used light from a window and a piece of card with a slit to create the monochromatic source. Nowadays this experiment is reproduced with laser light because it is monochromatic (all the same wavelength) and coherent.*

The dark and bright fringes are produced by **constructive** and **destructive interference**. When the waves from the two slits are in phase (meaning that they are both at the same point in their wave cycle) the waves will reinforce each other. This is called constructive interference and produces a bright fringe on the screen. Bright fringes are formed when the path difference between the waves at the screen is zero, or any multiple of the wavelength.

When the waves from the two slits are exactly out of phase (meaning their phase difference is 180°, where the full wavelength is represented by 360°) the waves will cancel each other out. This is called destructive interference and produces a dark fringe on the screen.

Tip: Path difference and phase difference are different things. The two waves below are in phase — they have 0 phase difference, but their path difference is λ.

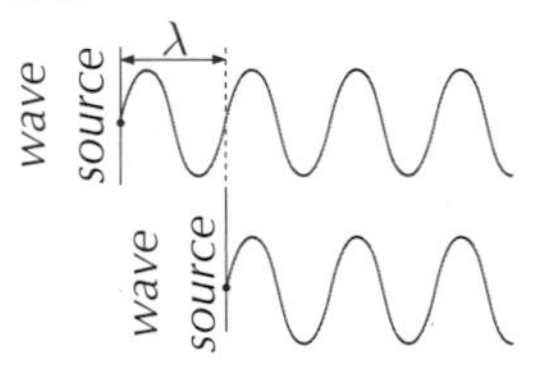

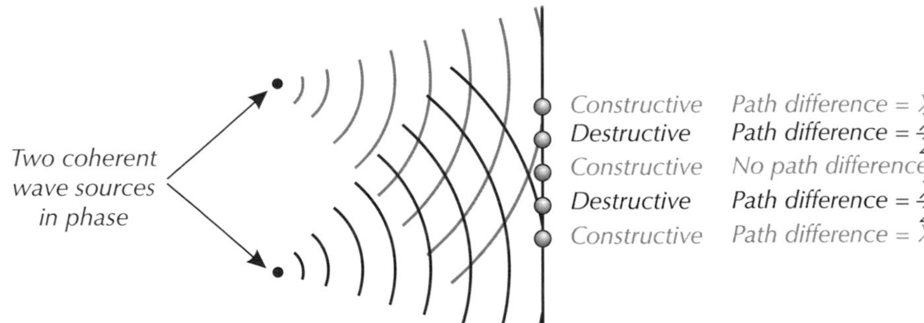

Figure 7: *Two coherent wave sources creating an interference pattern of constructive and destructive interference, depending on the path difference.*

Young's experiment was proof that light could both diffract (through the narrow slits) and interfere (to form the interference pattern on the screen). Newton's corpuscular theory predicted that there would be only two fringes, corresponding to the two slits that the corpuscles could pass through. Young's experiment showed that this clearly wasn't happening, and Huygens' theory could explain everything.

Tip: You only need to know about Young's double-slit experiment and how it was evidence for light being a wave. You don't need to do any of the nasty calculations that you had to do in AS physics. Phew.

Why Huygens' theory was not accepted

But Newton was... well... Newton, so Huygens' theory still wasn't accepted, even after the double-slit evidence supported it so strongly. Newton's other theories had been successful and he was so respected that his theory was still accepted.

Tip: A polarised wave is just a wave in which all the vibrations are in one plane. Have a look at your AS physics notes if you're still not sure.

There were also problems with Huygens' wave theory. It used longitudinal waves, but light was known to be able to be polarised — a property of transverse waves only. Also, Huygens' theory failed to explain why sharp shadows were formed by light.

It wasn't until the speed of light in water (which is more optically dense than air) was measured to be less than its speed in air that many people started to believe Huygens.

Practice Question — Application

Q1 In the 18th century, most scientists believed that light was made up of small particles called corpuscles. An experiment in which light was shone through a pinhole onto a screen is shown below. According to the corpuscular theory, the light beam reaching the screen should have got thinner as the pinhole width was decreased, but instead it was observed to get bigger.

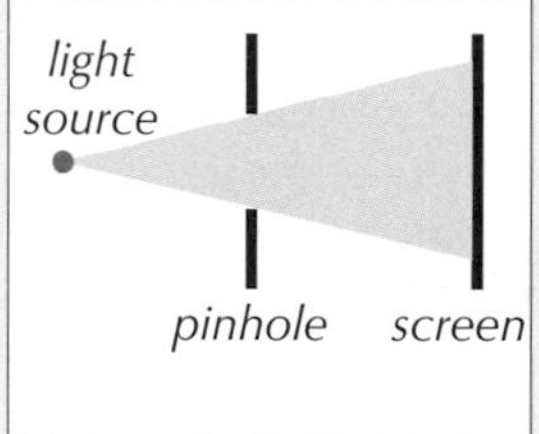

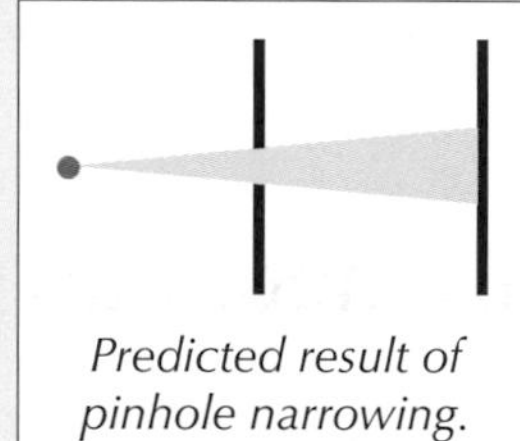

Predicted result of pinhole narrowing.

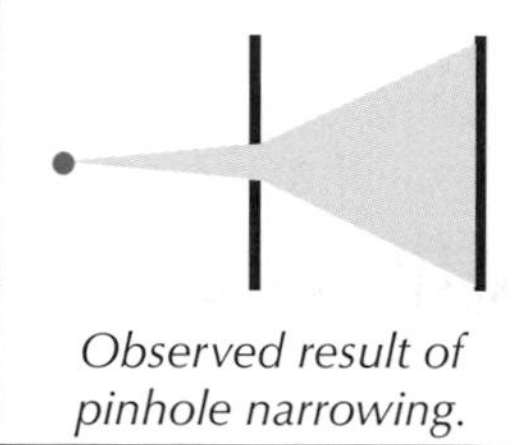

Observed result of pinhole narrowing.

a) Explain why the width of the beam was predicted to decrease.

b) Explain why the width of the beam actually increased.

Practice Questions — Fact Recall

Q1 Briefly describe Newton's corpuscular theory of light.

Q2 Explain the main argument in support of Newton's corpuscular theory of light.

Q3 Explain briefly the concept of Huygens' principle.

Q4 Give a reason why Newton's theory was preferred to Huygens' theory.

Q5 What difficulty did scientists face when trying to observe the interference and diffraction of light?

Q6 Explain Young's double-slit experiment and how he got around the problem described in Q5.

Q7 Explain the significance Young's double-slit experiment.

Q8 What discovery finally convinced many scientists of Huygens' wave theory of light?

5. Electromagnetic Waves

Once Huygens' wave theory had mostly been accepted, scientists began to research the wave nature of light. Several developments in the 19th century led them to discover that light was in fact a transverse, electromagnetic wave...

Transverse waves

HOW SCIENCE WORKS

In 1808, Etienne-Louis Malus discovered that light could be partially polarised by reflection. A polarised wave is a wave in which all the vibrations are in the same plane, and polarisation is a property of transverse waves only (have a look back at AS physics if this doesn't sound too familiar). Huygens' wave theory predicted that light spread like sound, as a longitudinal wave, which led scientists to struggle to explain polarisation.

In 1817, Young suggested that light was a transverse wave consisting of vibrating electric and magnetic fields at right angles to each other and the direction of travel. We now know this is true, and can explain why light could be polarised.

Light as an electromagnetic wave

HOW SCIENCE WORKS

James Clerk Maxwell predicted the existence of electromagnetic waves before they were even discovered. In the 1860s, he showed theoretically that all electromagnetic waves should travel at the same speed in a vacuum, c. He calculated the speed of an electromagnetic wave in a vacuum using:

$$c = \frac{1}{\sqrt{\mu_0 \varepsilon_0}}$$

c = *the speed of the wave in* ms^{-1}

ε_0 = *the permittivity of free space* $= 8.85 \times 10^{-12}\ Fm^{-1}$

μ_0 = *the permeability of free space* $= 4\pi \times 10^{-7}\ Hm^{-1}$

μ_0 relates to the magnetic flux density due to a current-carrying wire in free space, while ε_0 relates to the electric field strength due to a charged object in free space.

Example

The speed of an electromagnetic wave in a vacuum is:

$$c = \frac{1}{\sqrt{\mu_0 \varepsilon_0}} = \frac{1}{\sqrt{(4\pi \times 10^{-7}) \times (8.85 \times 10^{-12})}} = 3.00 \times 10^{8}\ ms^{-1} \text{(to 3 s.f.)}$$

By the time Maxwell did this calculation, the velocity of light could be measured quite accurately, and it was found to be very close to Maxwell's value of c. This suggested that light is an electromagnetic wave.

Learning Objectives:

- Understand the nature of electromagnetic waves.
- Know Maxwell's formula for the speed of electromagnetic waves in a vacuum: $c = \frac{1}{\sqrt{\mu_0 \varepsilon_0}}$ where μ_0 is the permeability of free space and ε_0 is the permittivity of free space.
- Know that Maxwell's formula showed that the speed of light was the same as the speed of an electromagnetic wave in a vacuum.
- Know that Hertz's discovery of radio waves was further evidence for light as an electromagnetic wave.

Specification Reference D.4.2

Tip: μ_0 and ε_0 are both constants given in the exam Data and Formulae booklet. The unit H stands for 'henry'. It's the standard unit for inductance.

Figure 1: *James Clerk Maxwell was a Scottish physicist who made great contributions to the theory of electromagnetism.*

Radio waves

In the late 1880s, Heinrich Hertz produced and detected radio waves using electric sparks. He used an induction coil and a capacitor to produce a high voltage, and showed that radio waves were produced when high voltage sparks jumped across a gap of air. He detected these radio waves using a loop of wire with a gap in it in which sparks were induced by the radio waves (see Figure 2).

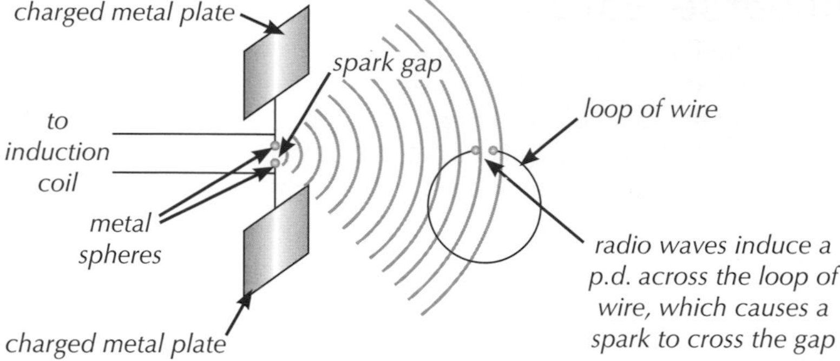

Figure 2: *Hertz's experimental set-up used to discover radio waves.*

Tip: An induction coil is like a transformer — whenever the current is interrupted a high voltage is induced in the secondary coil.

Tip: Induction is covered earlier in the book, on page 79.

Figure 3: *Heinrich Hertz discovered radio waves using a set-up similar to the one in Figure 2.*

In later experiments, Hertz used a flat metal sheet to create stationary radio waves, showing that they could both be reflected and show interference. He also went on to show that radio waves can be refracted, diffracted and polarised.

As well as showing that radio waves show all the properties of electromagnetic waves, he measured their velocity using stationary radio waves.

Stationary radio waves

A **stationary wave** is the superposition of two progressive waves with the same frequency (or wavelength) and amplitude, moving in opposite directions. They can be created by reflecting a progressive wave back on itself. They can be demonstrated by oscillating a piece of string — see Figure 4.

The wave generated by the oscillator is reflected back and forth. For most frequencies the resultant pattern is a jumble. However, if the oscillator happens to produce an exact number of waves in the time it takes for a wave to get to the end and back again, then the original and reflected waves reinforce each other.

The frequencies at which this happens are called **resonant frequencies** and it causes a stationary wave where the overall pattern doesn't move along — it just vibrates up and down, so the string forms oscillating 'loops'. The points on the wave with zero amplitude are known as nodes, and the bits of the wave with maximum amplitude are called antinodes.

Tip: A progressive wave is a wave that carries energy from one place to another.

Tip: You've met stationary waves before in AS physics, so hopefully this will all sound familiar. If not, have a look back at your AS notes.

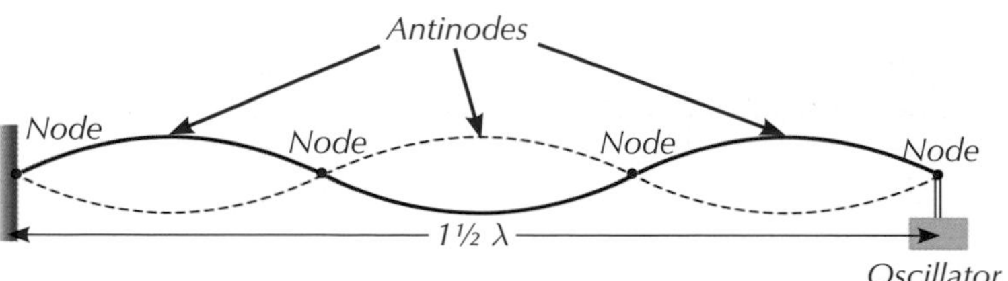

Figure 4: *A stationary wave with four nodes and three antinodes.*

Using the set-up in Figure 5, Hertz produced stationary radio waves at a fixed resonant frequency. He moved the radio wave detector between the transmitter and the reflecting sheet and measured the distance between nodes. Since the distance between nodes is half a wavelength, he could work out the wavelength of the waves and use $c = f\lambda$ to calculate the wave speed.

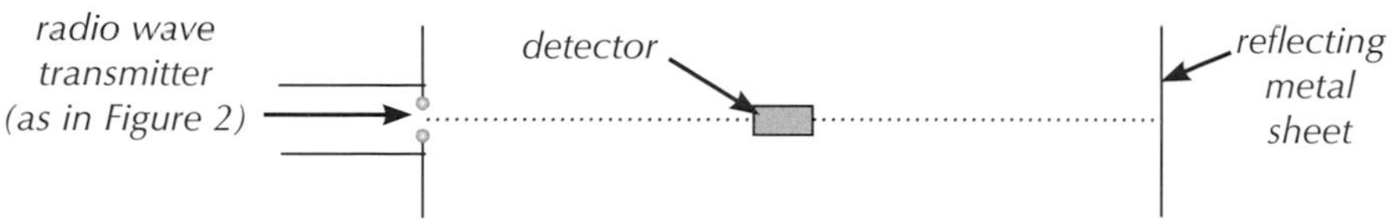

Figure 5: *Experiment to measure the velocity of radio waves.*

He measured the speed of radio waves to be the same in a vacuum as the rest of the electromagnetic spectrum. This helped to confirm that radio waves, like light, are electromagnetic waves.

The wave theory of light was the accepted theory up until the very end of the 19th century, when the photoelectric effect was discovered. Then the particle theory had to be resurrected, and it was all up in the air again...

Tip: You've seen the equation for the speed of a wave in AS physics:

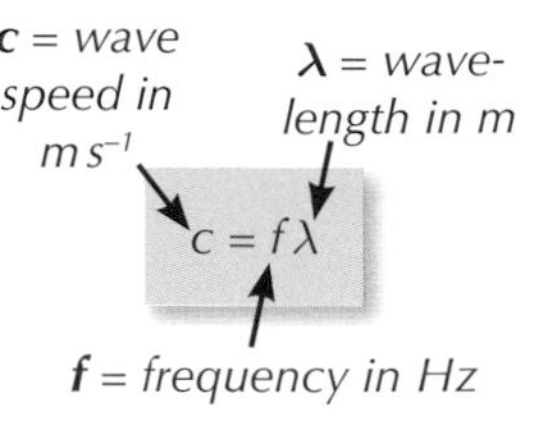

Practice Question — Application

Q1 An experimental set-up to determine the wave speed of microwave radiation is shown in Figure 6 below.

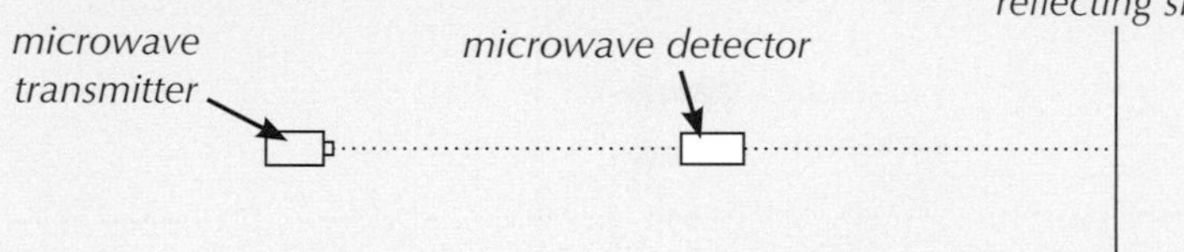

Figure 6: *An experiment to determine the speed of microwave radiation.*

The frequency of the microwaves is adjusted until the detector can detect nodes and antinodes as it is moved between the transmitter and reflector. The frequency is 1.5×10^{10} Hz.

a) The distance between two adjacent nodes is measured to be 0.01 m. Calculate the wavelength of the microwaves.

b) Calculate the speed of the microwaves.

Tip: Have a look at your AS level notes if you don't remember how to work out the wavelength from nodes and antinodes.

Practice Questions — Fact Recall

Q1 What discovery led scientists to believe that light was a transverse wave, not a longitudinal one?

Q2 Write down the equation derived by Maxwell for the speed of an electromagnetic wave, labelling any constants.

Q3 What discovery of Heinrich Hertz supported the idea that light is an electromagnetic wave?

Q4 What properties of radio waves did Heinrich Hertz discover?

6. The Photoelectric Effect

In 1705, light was a particle. In 1805, light was a wave. You should remember from AS physics that observations of photoelectricity presented a few problems that wave theory just couldn't explain. By 1905, Einstein's photon theory of light had been published — and light was a particle again. I wish they'd make their minds up...

Learning Objectives:

- Know how classical wave theory failed to explain observations of photoelectricity, such as the existence of a threshold frequency for incident light and variation of the stopping potential with frequency for different metals.
- Know that the photoelectric effect is instantaneous.
- Know that the maximum kinetic energy of the emitted photoelectrons is independent of the intensity of the incident light.
- Understand Einstein's photon theory of light and its significance for the nature of electromagnetic radiation.
- Know that the stopping potential of a metal can be measured using a potential divider and a vacuum photocell.

Specification Reference D.4.2

What is the photoelectric effect?

If you shine electromagnetic radiation of a high enough frequency onto the surface of a metal, it will instantly emit electrons (see Figure 1). For most metals, this frequency falls in the ultraviolet range.

Because of the way atoms are bonded together in metals, metals contain 'free electrons' that are able to move about the metal. The free electrons on or near the surface of the metal absorb energy from the radiation, making them vibrate.

If an electron absorbs enough energy, the bonds holding it to the metal break and the electron is released. This is called the **photoelectric effect** and the electrons emitted are called photoelectrons.

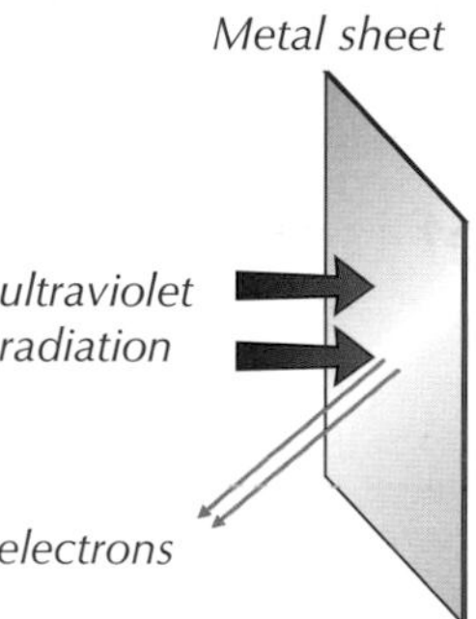

Figure 1: *The photoelectric effect.*

Tip: Remember — photoelectrons are just the electrons released from a metal's surface.

You don't need to know the details of any experiments on this, you just need to learn the main conclusions:

Conclusion 1 For a given metal, no photoelectrons are emitted if the radiation has a frequency below a certain value — called the **threshold frequency**.

Conclusion 2 The photoelectrons are emitted with a variety of kinetic energies ranging from zero to some maximum value. This value of maximum kinetic energy increases with the frequency of the radiation.

Conclusion 3 The intensity of radiation is the amount of energy per second hitting an area of the metal. The maximum kinetic energy of the photoelectrons is unaffected by varying the intensity of the radiation.

Conclusion 4 The number of photoelectrons emitted per second is proportional to the intensity of the radiation.

Conclusion 5 The emission of photoelectrons is instantaneous as soon as the frequency is above the threshold frequency.

Tip: Don't get the photoelectric effect confused with thermionic emission (page 239). The difference is that the photoelectric effect is the result of incident electromagnetic radiation on a metal, whereas thermionic emission is due to heating.

The photoelectric effect and wave theory

You can't explain all the observations and conclusions of the photoelectric effect experiment if EM radiation only acts as a wave...

Threshold frequency

Wave theory says that for a particular frequency of EM wave, the energy carried should be proportional to the intensity of the beam. The energy carried by the EM wave would also be spread evenly over the wavefront.

This means that if EM radiation were shone on a metal, each free electron on the surface of the metal would gain a bit of energy from each incoming wave. Gradually, each electron would gain enough energy to leave the metal. If the EM waves had a lower frequency (i.e. were carrying less energy) it would take longer for the electrons to gain enough energy, but it would happen eventually. However, electrons are never emitted unless the waves are above a threshold frequency — so wave theory can't explain the threshold frequency.

Tip: The key thing about the photoelectric effect is that it shows that light can't just act as a wave. Certain observations of the photoelectric effect can't be explained by classical wave theory.

Kinetic energy of photoelectrons

The higher the intensity of the waves, the more energy they should transfer to each electron — the kinetic energy should increase with intensity.

Wave theory can't explain the fact that the kinetic energy depends only on the frequency in the photoelectric effect.

Exam Tip
You might have to explain how changing the intensity and frequency of the light affects the photoelectrons emitted — so make sure you learn it.

The photon model of light

Max Planck's wave packets

Max Planck was the first to suggest that EM waves can only be released in discrete packets, or quanta. The energy, E, carried by one of these wave packets is:

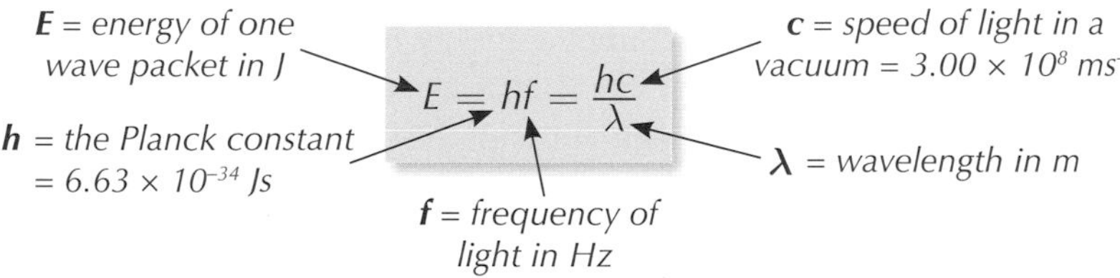

Tip: One quanta is called a 'quantum'.

Tip: Remember, $c = f\lambda$, so $f = \frac{c}{\lambda}$.

Example

Calculate the wavelength of a wave packet with an energy of 4.12×10^{-19} J.

Rearrange $E = \frac{hc}{\lambda}$ into $\lambda = \frac{hc}{E}$ and substitute in the values for E, h and c to calculate the wavelength.

$$\lambda = \frac{hc}{E} = \frac{(6.63 \times 10^{-34}) \times (3.00 \times 10^{8})}{4.12 \times 10^{-19}} = 4.83 \times 10^{-7}\text{m (to 3 s.f.)}$$

Exam Tip
Remember that for calculations like this you'll be given Planck's constant, h, and the speed of light, c — hurrah.

Einstein's photons

Einstein went further by suggesting that EM waves (and the energy they carry) can only exist in discrete packets. He called these wave packets **photons**.

He saw these photons of light as having a one-on-one, particle-like interaction with an electron in a metal surface. Each photon would transfer all its energy to one specific electron. The photon model could be used to explain the photoelectric effect.

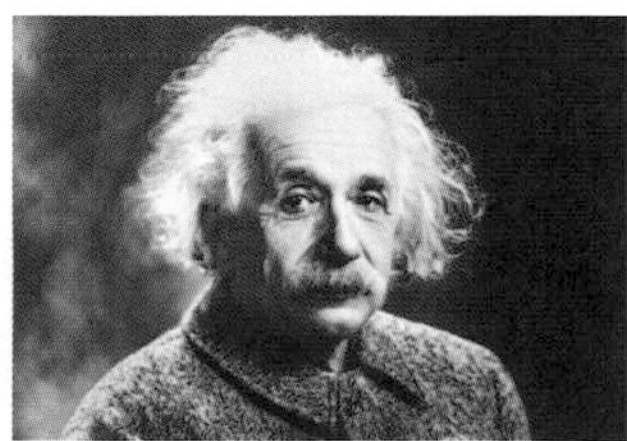

Figure 2: Albert Einstein, the physicist who explained the photoelectric effect using photons.

Exam Tip
Asking you to explain why there's a threshold frequency and how this shows light acts as a particle is an exam favourite — make sure you know it.

Figure 3: Solar cells use the photoelectric effect to convert light energy into electricity.

Exam Tip
You won't get this equation in the exam Data and Formulae booklet, but you will get $E = hf$. As long as you remember that the work function is the energy of a photon with the threshold frequency, you don't have to learn this equation — just replace E for ϕ and f for f_o then rearrange.

Tip: There are loads of ways electrons leaving the metal can lose energy, e.g. they might have to do work to get to the surface of the metal.

Exam Tip
You'll be given the equations $hf = \phi + E_k$ and $E_k = \frac{1}{2}mv_{max}^2$ in the exam Data and Formulae booklet, so you don't need to learn them as long as you know what each part shows and how to use them.

Explaining the photoelectric effect

The photon model of light can explain the observations and conclusions for the photoelectric effect that the wave model of light can't...

Work function and threshold frequency

When EM radiation hits a metal, the metal's surface is bombarded by photons. If one of these photons collides with a free electron, the electron will gain energy equal to hf (as $E = hf$).

Before an electron can leave the surface of the metal, it needs enough energy to break the bonds holding it there. This energy is called the **work function** energy (symbol ϕ) and its value depends on the metal.

If the energy gained from the photon is greater than the work function energy, the electron is emitted. If it isn't, the electron will just shake about a bit, then release the energy as another photon. The metal will heat up, but no electrons will be emitted. Since, for electrons to be released $hf \geq \phi$, the threshold frequency, f_o, must be:

$$f_o = \frac{\phi}{h}$$

Example

For a metal with a work function of 8.4×10^{-19} J, the minimum frequency of EM radiation needed for a photoelectron to be released would be:

$$f_o = \frac{\phi}{h} = \frac{8.4 \times 10^{-19}}{6.63 \times 10^{-34}} = 1.3 \times 10^{15}\,\text{Hz (to 2 s.f.)}$$

Maximum kinetic energy

The energy transferred from EM radiation to an electron is the energy it absorbs from one photon, hf. The kinetic energy it will be carrying when it leaves the metal is hf minus any other energy losses. These energy losses are the reason the electrons emitted from a metal have a range of kinetic energies.

The minimum amount of energy an electron can lose is the work function energy, so the maximum kinetic energy, E_k, is given by the equation $E_k = hf - \phi$. Rearranging this equation gives you the photoelectric equation:

$$hf = \phi + E_k$$

Kinetic energy = ½ mass × velocity², so the maximum kinetic energy a photoelectron can have is:

$$E_k = \frac{1}{2}mv_{max}^2$$

E_k = maximum kinetic energy of a photoelectron

v_{max} = maximum velocity of an emitted electron

m = mass of an electron = 9.11×10^{-31} kg

You can use this to write the photoelectric equation as:

$$hf = \phi + \frac{1}{2}mv_{max}^2$$

The kinetic energy of the electrons is independent of the intensity, because they can only absorb one photon at a time.

Example

The threshold frequency of light needed to cause the photoelectric effect in aluminium is 1.03×10^{15} Hz. Light with a frequency of 3.45×10^{15} Hz is shone on an aluminium sheet. Calculate the maximum kinetic energy of a photoelectron emitted from the surface of this sheet.

To work out the maximum kinetic energy you need to rearrange and use the photoelectric equation.

First, use the threshold frequency to calculate the work function, ϕ.

$\phi = hf_o = (6.63 \times 10^{-34}) \times (1.03 \times 10^{15}) = 6.83 \times 10^{-19}$ J (to 3 s.f.)

Then substitute this, Planck's constant and the frequency of the light being shone on the metal into the photoelectric equation. $hf = \phi + E_k$, so

$$E_k = hf - \phi = (6.63 \times 10^{-34} \times 3.45 \times 10^{15}) - 6.83 \times 10^{-19}$$
$$= 1.60 \times 10^{-18} \text{ J (to 3 s.f.)}$$

Stopping potential

The maximum kinetic energy can be measured using the idea of **stopping potential**. The circuit diagram in Figure 4 shows the experimental set-up for measuring stopping potential using a potential divider and a vacuum photocell. For a fixed frequency, f, of incident light, the stopping potential can be determined.

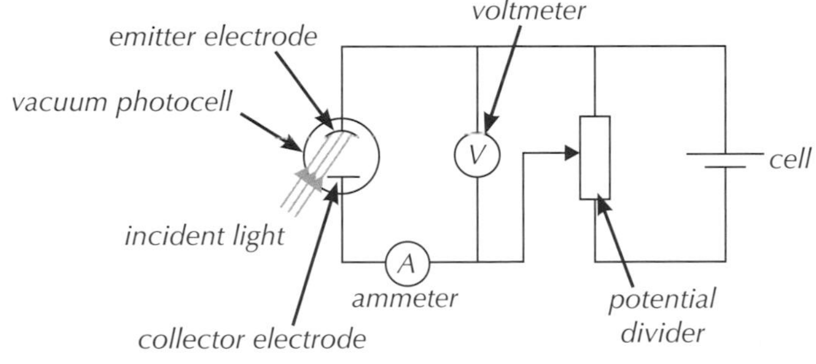

Figure 4: The experimental set-up for determining the stopping potential for a given frequency of incident light.

A vacuum photocell is basically two plates within a vacuum. When connected in a circuit, a potential difference can be applied across them. Light incident on the emitter electrode causes photoelectrons to be released. If the photoelectrons reach the collector electrode, they cause a current to flow in the circuit.

At the start of the experiment, the potential divider is set so that the p.d. across the photocell is zero. The ammeter records the current through the circuit caused by photoelectric emission from the photocell.

The potential divider is then adjusted so that the potential difference gets higher and higher (with the emitter electrode becoming more and more positive in relation to the collector electrode). The photoelectrons have to do work against the potential difference, and so lose kinetic energy. The maximum kinetic energy is reduced by eV, where V is the potential difference and e the magnitude of the charge on an electron.

Figure 5: A photocell.

Tip: The number of photoelectrons reaching the collector electrode per second decreases as the applied potential difference between the electrode is increased.

Exam Tip
There are other ways of measuring the stopping potential, but this is the one you need to know for the exam.

As the potential difference across the photocell gets higher, fewer photoelectrons reach the collector electrode, so the current through the ammeter gets lower.

When the potential difference gets high enough, all photoelectrons are stopped (because even the electrons with the maximum kinetic energy are stopped by the p.d.). This is known as the stopping potential, V_s. No photoelectrons reach the collector electrode and the current falls to zero. Different frequencies of light can be used, and the stopping potential for each frequency can be found.

The work done by the p.d. in stopping the fastest electrons is equal to the energy they were carrying:

$$\frac{1}{2}mv_{max}^2 = eV_s$$

e = *charge on the electron* = *1.60 × 10⁻¹⁹ C*

V_s = *stopping potential in V*

Tip: $\frac{1}{2}mv_{max}^2 = eV_s$, so $\frac{\left(\frac{1}{2}mv_{max}^2\right)}{e} = V_s$ and so the kinetic energy in eV is equal to the stopping potential, V_s.

Example

Light of frequency 6.1 × 10¹⁴ Hz is directed onto a metal plate with work function of 3.3 × 10⁻¹⁹ J. Find the stopping potential of the metal plate for this frequency of light.

First, find the maximum kinetic energy of a photoelectron,

$\frac{1}{2}mv^2 = hf - \phi = (6.63 \times 10^{-34})(6.1 \times 10^{14}) - (3.3 \times 10^{-19})$
$= 7.443 \times 10^{-20}$ J

So -7.443×10^{-20} J $= eV_s$ and $V_s = 7.443 \times 10^{-20} \div (1.60 \times 10^{-19})$
$= 0.4651...$ V $= 0.465$ V (to 3 s.f.)

Equating the two equations for maximum kinetic energy of a photoelectron gives $hf - \phi = eV_s$, which rearranges to:

$$V_s = \frac{hf}{e} - \frac{\phi}{e}$$

This is of the form $y = mx + c$, where $y = V_s$, $x = f$, $m = \frac{h}{e}$ and $c = -\frac{\phi}{e}$.

The graph in Figure 6 shows how stopping potential and frequency are related.

Tip: You saw graphs like this at AS level. If you plot one and want to work out the work function, you need to extend your line back to the y-intercept, as shown by the dotted line in Figure 6.

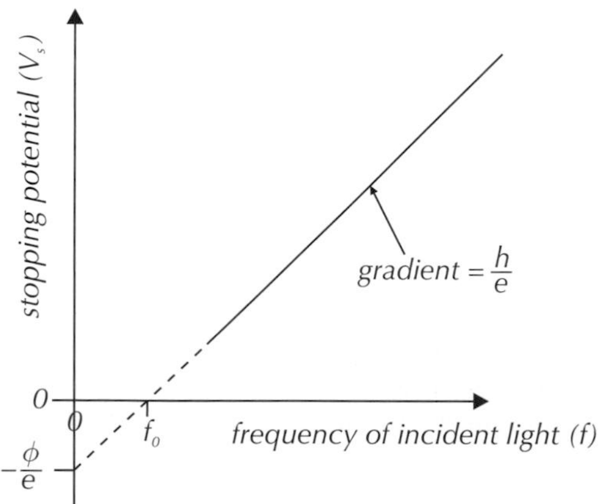

Figure 6: *A graph of stopping potential against frequency of light for the photoelectric effect.*

The first experiments that produced this graph confirmed Einstein's photon theory of light. So light was a particle again... but what about all the evidence of light being a wave — it diffracts and interferes, whereas particles do not...

Practice Question — Application

Q1 Light of wavelength 550 nm is shone on a vacuum photocell with no potential difference across it. The emitter electrode of the photocell has a work function of 2.1 eV.

a) Find the energy of a photon of the incident light.

b) Find the maximum kinetic energy of a photoelectron emitted from the emitter electrode.

c) Find the stopping potential of the metal emitter electrode surface for this wavelength of light.

d) A potential difference is applied to the photocell so that the emitter electrode is at +0.14 V relative to the collector electrode. Find the maximum kinetic energy of the photoelectrons reaching the collector electrode now.

Tip: Remember, the magnitude of the charge on an electron is $e = 1.60 \times 10^{-19}$ C and the speed of light in a vacuum is $c = 3.00 \times 10^{8}$ m s^{-1}. They are both given in the Data and Formulae booklet in the exam.

Practice Questions — Fact Recall

Q1 What were the five main conclusions drawn from detailed experimentation on the photoelectric effect?

Q2 Describe Einstein's photon theory of light.

Q3 When low-frequency light is shone on a piece of metal, no photoelectrons are emitted at all. Explain how wave theory fails to explain this result, and how photon theory explains it.

Q4 What is the work function of a metal?

Q5 Write down an equation for the threshold frequency of a metal.

Q6 What does wave theory predict should happen to the kinetic energy of photoelectrons as the intensity of the light is increased? What actually happens? Explain why photoelectrons have a maximum kinetic energy according to Einstein's photon theory.

Q7 Write down an equation for the maximum kinetic energy of a photoelectron emitted from a metal with work function ϕ when light of frequency f is incident on it.

Q8 What is the stopping potential of a metal? Write down an equation for the maximum kinetic energy of a photoelectron in terms of the stopping potential.

Q9 Light is shone on a vacuum photocell connected to a circuit with a constant p.d. (V) applied across it. The ammeter in the circuit measures that no current is flowing through the circuit. The frequency of the light is increased and a current starts to flow. Explain why this happens.

Learning Objectives:

- Understand de Broglie's wave-particle duality hypothesis.
- Know that the equation $p = \frac{h}{\lambda}$ links a particle property with a wave property and can be used to calculate the de Broglie wavelength of a particle.
- Know that the accelerating voltage of an electron is linked to its de Broglie wavelength by $\lambda = \frac{h}{\sqrt{2meV}}$.

Specification Reference D.4.2

7. Wave-Particle Duality

Is it a wave? Is it a particle? You're probably a bit tired of this debate... that's understandable. Don't worry, scientists have basically agreed to disagree... there's evidence for both arguments, so in the end they just decided it could be either a wave or a particle... and so can everything else. Hopefully some of this will be familiar from AS physics...

Is light a particle or a wave?

As you saw on page 251, diffraction and interference of light can only be explained using waves. If the light was acting as a particle, the light particles in the beam would either not get through the gap (if they were too big), or just pass straight through and the beam would be unchanged.

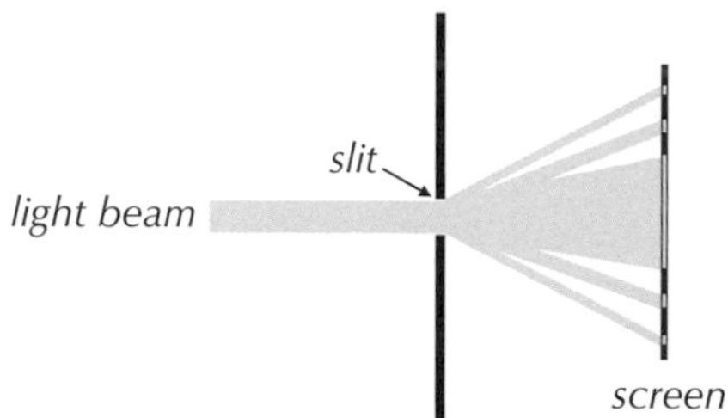

Figure 1: *Diffraction of light waves as they pass through a narrow slit.*

But the results of photoelectric effect experiments (see p.256) can only be explained by thinking of light as a series of particle-like photons. If a photon of light is a discrete bundle of energy, then it can interact with an electron in a one-to-one way. All the energy in the photon is given to one electron.

The photoelectric effect and diffraction show that light behaves as both a particle and a wave — this is known as **wave-particle duality**.

Exam Tip
Make sure you know these two examples that show light acts as both a wave and a particle — they might just come up in the exam.

Wave-particle duality theory

Louis de Broglie made a bold suggestion in his PhD thesis. He said if 'wave-like' light showed particle properties (photons), 'particles' like electrons should be expected to show wave-like properties.

The de Broglie equation relates a wave property (wavelength, λ) to a moving particle property (momentum, $p = mv$).

$$p = \frac{h}{\lambda}$$

***p** = momentum in kg m s^{-1}*

h = the Planck constant = 6.63×10^{-34} Js.

***λ** = de Broglie wavelength in m*

It comes from assuming that a photon of energy $E = hf$ has a mass, m, given by $mc^2 = hf$. Then momentum is given by $mc = \frac{hf}{c}$ and rearranging $c = f\lambda$ gives $\frac{f}{c} = \frac{1}{\lambda}$. So $p = mc = \frac{h}{\lambda}$.

The de Broglie wave of a particle can be interpreted as a 'probability wave'. Many physicists at the time weren't very impressed — his ideas were just speculation. But later experiments confirmed the wave nature of electrons and other particles.

Tip: Energy and mass are linked by the equation $E = mc^2$ — you might have come across this in AS physics.

Electron diffraction

Diffraction patterns are observed when accelerated electrons in a vacuum tube interact with the spaces in a graphite crystal. As they pass through the spaces, they diffract just like waves passing through a narrow slit and produce a pattern of rings. This provides evidence that electrons have wave properties.

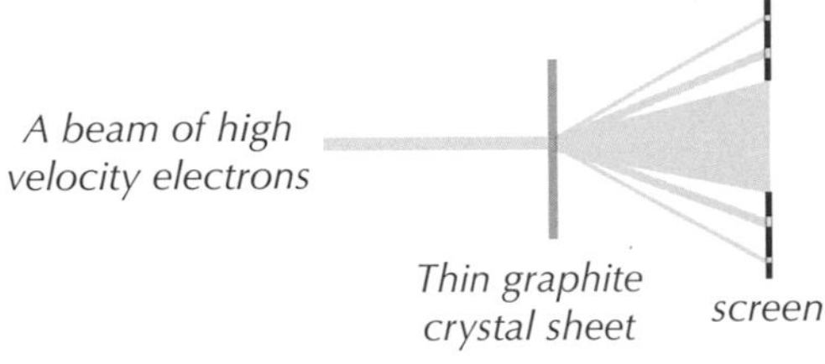

Figure 2: *Electron diffraction — an experiment that shows electrons have wave properties.*

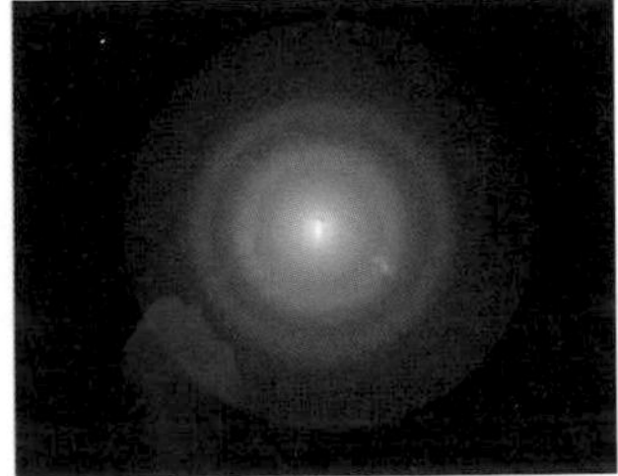

Figure 3: *An electron diffraction pattern.*

According to wave theory, the spread of the lines in the diffraction pattern increases if the wavelength of the wave is greater. In electron diffraction experiments, a smaller accelerating voltage, i.e. slower electrons, gives widely spaced rings. Increase the electron speed and the diffraction pattern circles squash together towards the middle. This fits in with the de Broglie equation — if the velocity is higher, the wavelength is shorter and the spread of lines is smaller.

In general, λ for electrons accelerated in a vacuum tube is about the same size as electromagnetic waves in the X-ray part of the spectrum. The de Broglie wavelength of an electron is related to the accelerating voltage by:

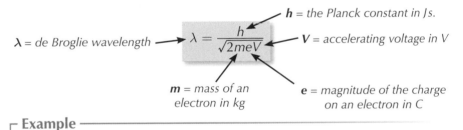

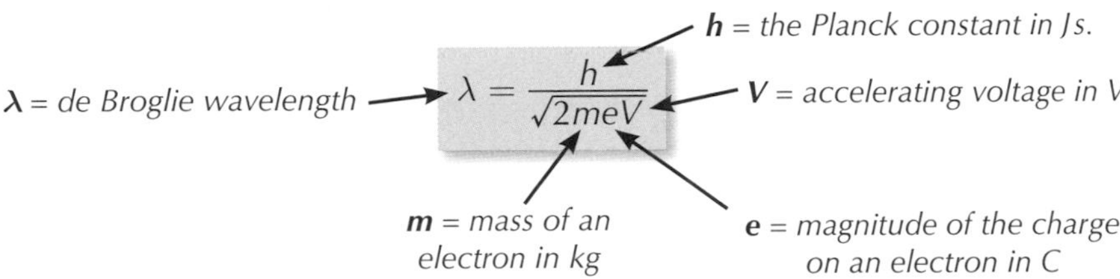

Exam Tip
You don't need to know all the detail of this experiment for the exam — just make sure you know electron diffraction supports de Broglie's hypothesis.

Tip: $e = 1.60 \times 10^{-19}$ C, m (of an electron) $= 9.11 \times 10^{-31}$ kg and $h = 6.63 \times 10^{-34}$ Js.

Example

An electron of mass 9.11 × 10^{-31} kg is fired from an electron gun with a de Broglie wavelength of 1.07 × 10^{-10} m. What anode voltage is needed to produce this velocity?

Rearranging $\lambda = \frac{h}{\sqrt{2meV}}$ gives $V = \frac{h^2}{2me\lambda^2}$.

$$\text{So } V = \frac{(6.63 \times 10^{-34})^2}{2(9.11 \times 10^{-31})(1.60 \times 10^{-19})(1.07 \times 10^{-10})^2}$$

$= 131.70...$ V $= 132$ V (to 3 s.f.)

Tip: For more on electron guns, pop back to page 239.

You only get diffraction if a particle interacts with an object of about the same size as its de Broglie wavelength.

Example

A tennis ball with a mass of 0.058 kg and speed 100 ms^{-1} has a de Broglie wavelength of 10^{-34} m. That's 10^{19} times smaller than the nucleus of an atom. There's nothing that small for it to interact with, and so it only acts as a particle.

Tip: Electrons can be used to investigate the spacing between atoms in a crystal — an electron beam will diffract when the de Broglie wavelength of the electrons is roughly the same size as the spaces between the atoms (see pages 265-266).

Tip: Be careful when you're dealing with numbers in standard form — make sure you punch everything into your calculator correctly. Always check that the magnitude of your answer seems about right.

Example

An electron of mass 9.11×10^{-31} kg is fired from an electron gun at 5.4×10^{6} ms^{-1}. Roughly what size of object will give the most noticeable electron diffraction?

An electron will diffract when the size of the object is roughly the same size as its de Broglie wavelength, so you need to find λ.

Momentum of electron $= mv = 9.11 \times 10^{-31} \times 5.4 \times 10^{6}$
$= 4.9194 \times 10^{-24}$ kg ms^{-1}

Substitute this into de Broglie's equation:

$$\lambda = \frac{h}{mv} = \frac{6.63 \times 10^{-34}}{4.9194 \times 10^{-24}} = 1.3 \times 10^{-10} \text{ m (to 2 s.f.)}$$

So, only crystals with atom layer spacing around this size are likely to cause the diffraction of this electron.

Example

Electrons with a wavelength of 2.13×10^{-10} m are diffracted as they pass between atoms in a crystal lattice. Estimate the velocity of the electrons.

Rearranging the de Broglie equation, $\lambda = \frac{h}{mv}$, gives $v = \frac{h}{m\lambda}$.

Substitute in $\lambda = 2.13 \times 10^{-10}$ m, $h = 6.63 \times 10^{-34}$ Js and $m = 9.11 \times 10^{-31}$ kg to get:

$$v = \frac{6.63 \times 10^{-34}}{9.11 \times 10^{-31} \times 2.13 \times 10^{-10}} = 3\,400\,000 \text{ ms}^{-1} \text{ (to 2 s.f.)}$$

Tip: You could write the answer to this calculation in standard form as 3.4×10^{6} ms^{-1}.

Tip: For these questions you will need to know that the mass of an electron is 9.11×10^{-31} kg and the magnitude of the charge on an electron is 1.60×10^{-19} C.

Practice Questions — Application

Q1 Electrons fired from an electron gun have a de Broglie wavelength of 0.9×10^{-10} m. How will increasing the velocity of the electrons affect their de Broglie wavelength?

Q2 Calculate the de Broglie wavelength of an electron accelerated through a potential difference of 4200 V.

Q3 An electron has a de Broglie wavelength of 1.71×10^{-10} m.

a) Calculate the momentum of the electron.

b) Calculate the kinetic energy of the electron.

Q4 An alpha particle has a mass of 6.64×10^{-27} kg and travels at a velocity of 75 ms^{-1}. Calculate the speed of an electron that has the same de Broglie wavelength as this alpha particle.

Practice Questions — Fact Recall

Q1 Describe what is meant by wave-particle duality.

Q2 Name two effects that show electromagnetic waves have both wave and particle properties.

Q3 Name the phenomenon that shows that electrons have wave-like properties.

8. Electron Microscopes

Electron microscopes take advantage of the wave-particle duality of electrons to produce high-resolution images of very small things — like atoms.

Basic operation

Electron microscopes work by firing electrons at a sample and seeing how they interact with it (see below).

Electron microscopes get much better resolution than normal optical microscopes because they can interact with (i.e. be diffracted by) much smaller objects. This is because their de Broglie wavelength is so small.

The de Broglie wavelength depends on the anode potential used to accelerate the electrons. To resolve detail around the size of an atom, the electron wavelength needs to be similar to the diameter of an atom — around 0.1 nm. Using $\lambda = \frac{h}{\sqrt{2meV}}$ from page 263, this means an anode voltage of about 150 V.

Learning Objectives:

- Know that the anode potential needed to produce electrons with de Broglie wavelengths similar to the size of an atom is around 150 V.
- Understand the principle of operation of transmission electron microscopes (T.E.M.).
- Understand the principle of operation of scanning tunnelling microscopes (S.T.M.).

Specification Reference D.4.2

Transmission electron microscopes (T.E.M.)

A **transmission electron microscope (T.E.M.)** works a bit like a slide projector, but uses electrons instead of light. The electrons are accelerated towards the sample under test using a positive electric potential (e.g. an electron gun). The beam is focused onto the sample using magnetic fields. Any interactions of the electrons with the sample are transformed into an image which is projected onto a screen. A very thin specimen must be used for a T.E.M. to work.

Tip: Electromagnetic coils are used as 'magnetic lenses' which focus the beam of electrons.

Tip: The tube that the electrons travel in must be evacuated so that they don't interact with anything else other than the sample.

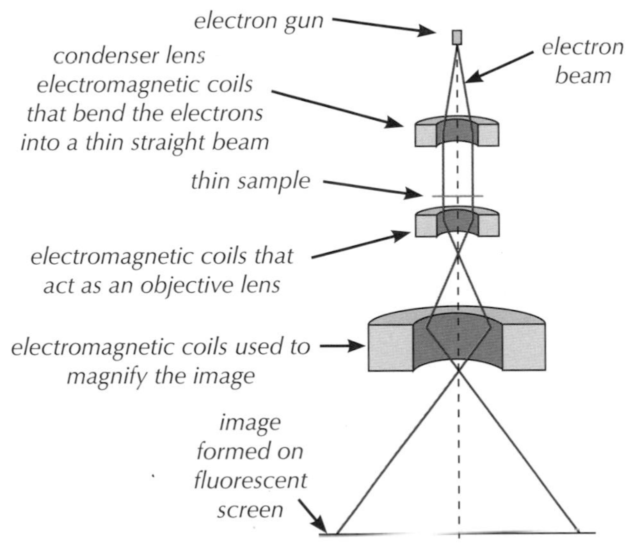

Figure 1: *The set-up of a transmission electron microscope (T.E.M.), showing an electron beam passing from an electron gun through a sample to form a magnified image on a screen.*

Figure 2: *A T.E.M. image of the atomic surface of silicon.*

The magnetic field of the condenser lens focuses the electrons into a thin, straight beam which passes through the thin sample. The structure of the sample causes some of the electrons to diffract.

The magnetic fields of the coils that act as objective and magnifier lenses deflect the electrons so that they eventually form a magnified image on a fluorescent screen.

Tip: The electrons are produced by thermionic emission in the electron gun (page 239).

Tip: Smaller de Broglie wavelengths mean the electrons can interact with smaller things, so you can see more detail.

The smaller the de Broglie wavelength, the better the resolution. A higher anode potential means that the electrons travel at a higher velocity, and so their de Broglie wavelength is smaller. So increasing the anode potential, or the speed of the electrons, gives a better resolution.

Scanning tunnelling microscope (S.T.M.)

A scanning tunnelling microscope (S.T.M.) is a different kind of microscope that uses principles of quantum mechanics. A very fine probe is positioned very close (around 1 nm away) to the surface of a sample. A high voltage is applied between the probe and the surface, making the probe negatively charged in relation to the sample.

Tip: If the probe is too high, there will be no detectable current. If it is too close, it may hit the sample surface and be damaged.

Electrons "tunnel" from the probe to the surface, resulting in a weak electrical current. The smaller the distance between the probe and the surface, the greater the current. By scanning the probe over the surface and measuring the current, you produce a 3D image of the surface of the sample.

There are two ways you can image a sample surface:

- Fix the distance — keep the distance of the probe from the sample surface the same and measure the changes in current.
- Fix the current — keep the current the same by adjusting the probe height and measure the changes in probe height.

Tip: If the distance of the probe from the sample is fixed and the probe reaches a raised bit of the surface, the gap will decrease and the current will increase. If the current is fixed and the probe reaches a raised bit, the distance will increase in order to keep the current constant.

The position of the probe is controlled by three piezoelectric transducers made from materials which experience a tiny change in length when a potential difference is applied to them. This tiny change in length allows the probe to be moved by tiny distances when scanning the sample surface and altering the distance of the probe from the sample.

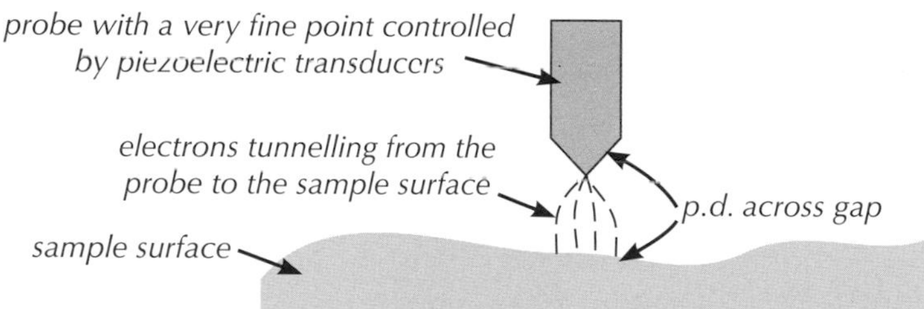

Figure 3: *A scanning tunnelling microscope (S.T.M.) scanning a surface.*

Tip: The likelihood of an electron tunnelling across the gap is small, but finite. Fortunately, you don't need to know anything else about tunnelling — it's a complicated business.

Figure 4: *An S.T.M. image of gold atoms (red, yellow and brown) on a graphite substrate (green).*

Practice Questions — Fact Recall

Q1 What anode potential is needed to produce electrons with de Broglie wavelengths similar to the size of an atom (around 0.1 nm)?

Q2 Describe how a transmission electron microscope (T.E.M.) produces an image of a very thin sample.

Q3 Describe how a scanning tunnelling microscope (S.T.M.) produces a 3D image of the surface of a sample.

Q4 Describe how the position of an S.T.M. probe is made to move by tiny distances.

9. Michelson-Morley Experiment

The final fascinating development in this section covers Einstein's theory of special relativity. Maxwell's theory of EM waves (p.253) led scientists to believe all EM waves were vibrations in an invisible 'ether'. The Michelson-Morley experiment tried to measure the speed of the Earth through the ether, with surprising results...

Learning Objectives:

- Understand the principle of the Michelson-Morley interferometer.
- Be able to outline the Michelson-Morley experiment that was designed to detect absolute motion.
- Understand the significance of the failure of the Michelson-Morley experiment to detect absolute motion.
- Appreciate the invariance of the speed of light.

Specification Reference D.4.3

Absolute motion

During the 19th century, most physicists believed in the idea of **absolute motion**. They thought everything, including light, moved relative to a fixed background — something called the ether.

Michelson and Morley tried to measure the absolute speed of the Earth through the ether using a piece of apparatus called an interferometer. They expected the motion of the Earth to affect the speed of light they measured in certain directions. According to Newton, the speed of light measured in a lab moving parallel to the light would be $(c + v)$ or $(c - v)$, where v is the speed of the lab.

By measuring the variance in the speed of light parallel and perpendicular to the motion of the Earth, Michelson and Morley hoped to find v, the absolute speed of the Earth.

The Michelson-Morley interferometer

The interferometer was basically two mirrors and a semi-silvered glass block which acts as a partial reflector. When you shine light at a partial reflector, some of the light is transmitted and the rest is reflected, making two separate beams. The mirrors were at right angles to each other, and an equal distance from the partial reflector.

Tip: This experiment is a simplified version of the one actually used — Michelson and Morley used more mirrors to increase the path length of the light.

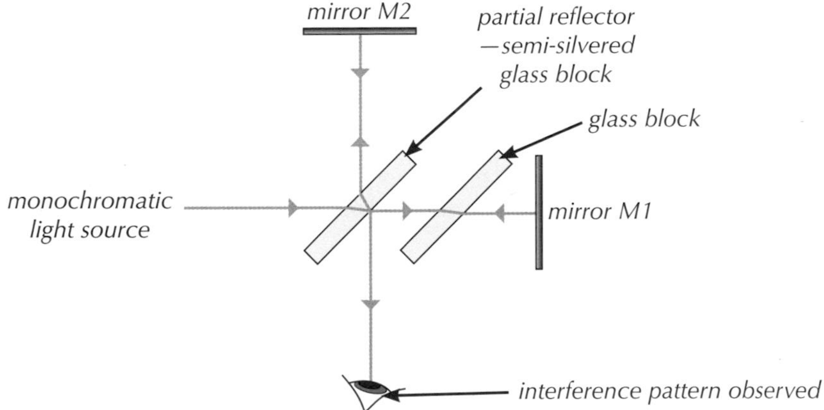

Figure 1: *The set up of the Michelson-Morley interferometer*

Tip: Remember, monochromatic light is light that is all of the same wavelength and frequency — it's used here because different wavelengths of light are refracted by different amounts.

Monochromatic light is sent towards the partial reflector. Some light is reflected, and some transmitted, so the light is split into two beams travelling at right angles to each other. The other glass block is needed so that both light beams travel through the same amount of glass and air.

The beams are reflected at mirrors M1 and M2. When the reflected beams meet back at the beam-splitter, they have a phase difference that depends on the difference in their path lengths. They form an interference pattern (see page 251). This interference pattern is recorded by the observer.

Then the whole interferometer is rotated through 90° and the experiment repeated.

Tip: Both beams must travel through the same amount of glass and air, so that they are both slowed down by the glass for the same amount of time, and so they both take the same amount of time to get to the observer.

Expected outcome

According to Newton's laws, light moving parallel to the motion of the Earth should take longer to travel to the mirror and back than light travelling at right angles to the Earth's motion. So rotating the apparatus should have changed the travel time for the two beams. This would cause a tiny shift in the interference pattern.

Observed outcome

HOW SCIENCE WORKS

They repeated the experiment over and over again — at different times of day and at different points in the year. Taking into account the expected range of the experimental error, they could detect absolutely no shift in the interference pattern. The time taken by each beam to travel to each mirror was unaffected by rotating the apparatus.

So, Newton's laws didn't work in this situation. Most scientists were really puzzled by this "null result". Eventually, the following conclusions were drawn:

- It's impossible to detect absolute motion — the ether doesn't exist.
- The speed of light has the same value for all observers (it is invariant).

Tip: Einstein used this result to come up with his theory of special relativity — see next topic.

Practice Questions — Fact Recall

Q1 Describe the idea of absolute motion.

Q2 How was it hoped that the Michelson-Morley experiment would provide evidence for absolute motion?

Q3 In the Michelson-Morley experimental set-up, explain what the following objects were used for:

a) semi-silvered glass block

b) plane mirrors

c) unsilvered glass block

Q4 What results were expected from the Michelson-Morley experiment?

Q5 The Michelson-Morley experiment failed to detect absolute motion. Explain why this is significant and what conclusions can be drawn from it.

10. Special Relativity

The invariance of the speed of light, as demonstrated by the Michelson-Morley experiment, is one of the cornerstones of special relativity. The other key concept is that of an inertial frame of reference.

Frames of reference

A **frame of reference** is just a space or system of coordinates that we decide to use to describe the position of an object — you can think of a frame of reference as a set of coordinates.

> An **inertial frame** of reference is one in which Newton's first law is obeyed. (Newton's first law says that objects won't accelerate unless they're acted on by an external force.)

Imagine sitting in a carriage of a train waiting at a station. You put a marble on the table. The marble doesn't move, since there aren't any horizontal forces acting on it. Newton's first law applies, so it's an inertial frame. You'll get the same result if the carriage moves at a steady speed (as long as the track is smooth, straight and level) — another inertial frame.

As the train accelerates out of the station, the marble moves without any force being applied. Newton's 1st law doesn't apply. The accelerating carriage isn't an inertial frame.

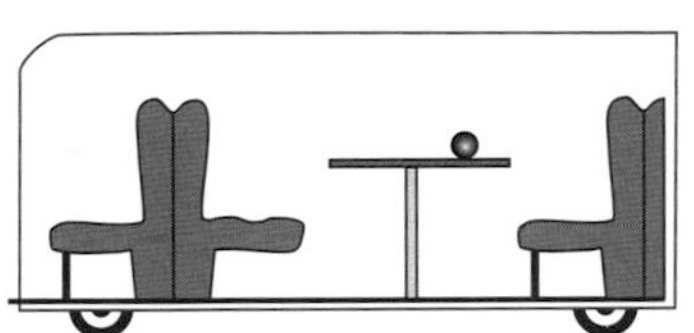

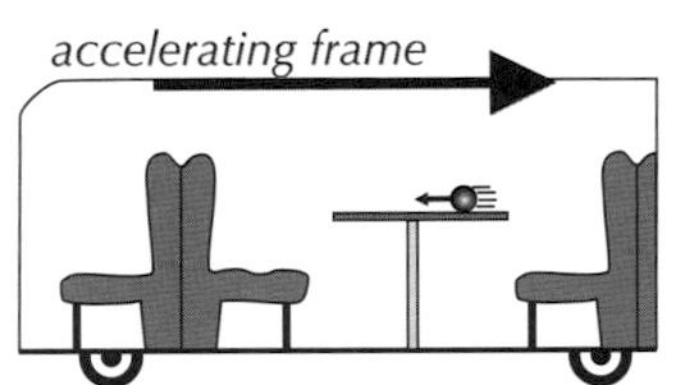

Figure 1: *A stationary train carriage, or a train carriage moving at a constant speed (left), is an inertial frame. An accelerating train carriage (right) is not an inertial frame.*

Rotating or accelerating reference frames aren't inertial. In most cases, though, you can think of the Earth as an inertial frame — it's near enough.

Special relativity

Einstein's theory of special relativity only works in inertial frames and is based on two postulates (assumptions):

- Physical laws have the same form in all inertial frames.
- The speed of light in free space is invariant.

The first postulate says that if we do any physics experiment in any inertial frame we'll always get the same result. That means it's impossible to use the result of any experiment to work out if you're in a stationary reference frame or one moving at a constant velocity.

The second postulate says that the speed of light (in a vacuum) always has the same value. It isn't affected by the movement of the person measuring it or by the movement of the light source.

Learning Objectives:

- Understand the concept of an inertial frame of reference.
- Know the two postulates of Einstein's theory of special relativity.
- Understand what proper time is and that time dilation is a consequence of special relativity.
- Be able to use the equation for time dilation: $t = t_0\left(1 - \frac{v^2}{c^2}\right)^{-\frac{1}{2}}$
- Be able to explain how muon decay gives evidence of time dilation.
- Understand length contraction as a consequence of special relativity and be able to use the equation: $l = l_0\left(1 - \frac{v^2}{c^2}\right)^{\frac{1}{2}}$.
- Understand the equivalence of mass and energy and be able to use the formulas $E = mc^2$ and $E = \frac{m_0c^2}{\left(1 - \frac{v^2}{c^2}\right)^{\frac{1}{2}}}$.

Specification Reference D.4.3

Tip: Einstein proposed special relativity in the same year that he put forward his photon theory of light (p.257) — 1905.

Tip: Special relativity <u>only works in inertial frames</u>.

Time dilation

Einstein's theory of special relativity has a few consequences — one of which is that 'a moving clock runs slower than a stationary clock'. Hopefully this will soon make sense...

The **proper time** between two events, t_0, is the time interval between the events as measured by an observer that is stationary in relation to the events. Special relativity says that an observer of the two events that is moving at a constant velocity in relation to the events will measure a longer time interval, t, between the two events. This is known as **time dilation**, and so a clock that is moving in relation to an observer will appear to run slow.

Imagine again a train carriage moving at a constant velocity. Set up an experiment in which an observer on the train reflects a beam of light vertically between two mirrors so that it bounces from one mirror to the other and back again (see Figure 2).

Tip: Anti-aging tip: If you were to go travelling in space at close to the speed of light for several years, you'd come back and everyone on Earth would have aged more than you.

To the stationary observer:

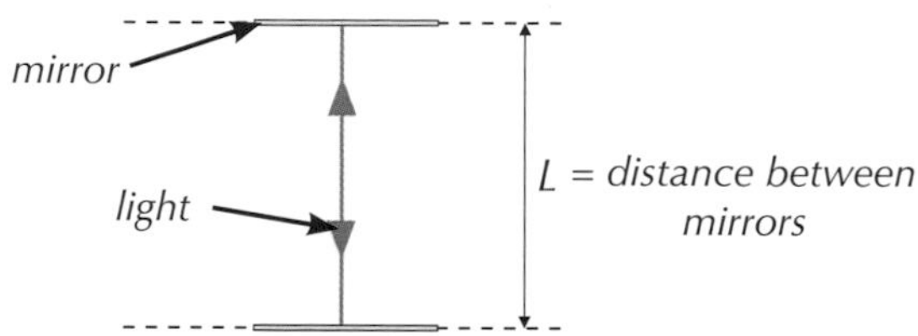

Figure 2: *View of an observer on the train.*

Tip: The mirrors are stationary relative to the train carriage.

The stationary observer relative to this event is the person on the train. The stationary observer sees that the light has travelled $2L$.

Time = distance ÷ speed, so the proper time taken for this event is: $t_0 = \frac{2L}{c}$

To the moving observer:

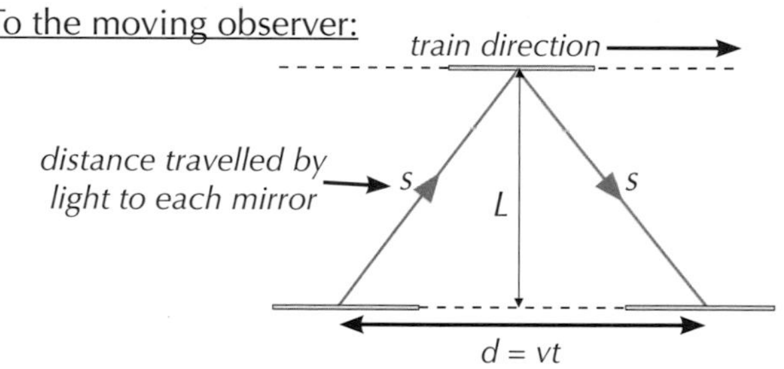

Figure 3: *View of an observer on the platform.*

Tip: $d = vt$ is the distance the mirrors have moved in the time measured by the moving observer for the light to bounce back to the first mirror.

Tip: The train must be moving at a velocity $-v$, i.e. the same speed but in the opposite direction.

The moving observer in relation to this event is the observer on the platform. They are moving in relation to the event (and the train) at velocity v.

The light has travelled $2s = 2\sqrt{L^2 + \left(\frac{vt}{2}\right)^2}$ and time = distance ÷ speed, so the time taken for this event, t, is:

$$t = 2s \div c = \frac{2\sqrt{L^2 + \left(\frac{vt}{2}\right)^2}}{c}$$ using Pythagoras' theorem.

Multiplying by c, squaring both sides and solving for t gives: $t = \frac{2L}{c\sqrt{\left(1 - \frac{v^2}{c^2}\right)}}$.

Using $t_0 = \frac{2L}{c}$ (see above) you can substitute in for L to get:

Tip: Don't get confused here — the person on the platform may seem stationary to you, but they are moving in relation to the event.

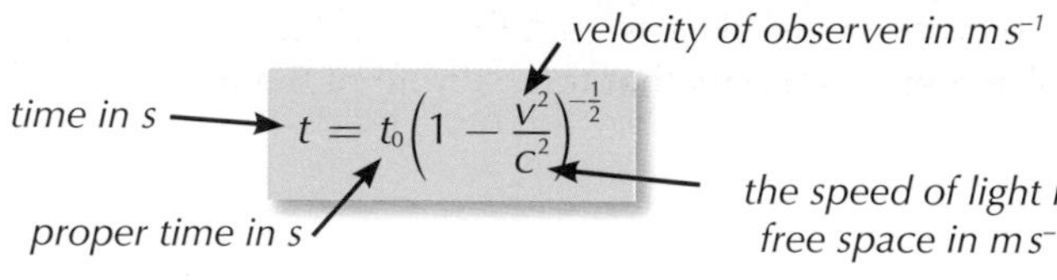

$$t = t_0\left(1 - \frac{v^2}{c^2}\right)^{-\frac{1}{2}}$$

This is the formula for time dilation. The $\left(1 - \frac{v^2}{c^2}\right)^{-\frac{1}{2}}$ bit is known as the relativity factor.

Example

Anne is on a high-speed train travelling at 0.90*c*. She switches on a torch for exactly 2 seconds. Claire is standing on the platform and sees the same event, but records a longer time. It appears to Claire that Anne's clock is running slow.

In this experiment, Anne is the stationary observer, so she measures the proper time, t_0. Claire is moving at 0.9*c* relative to the event, and so measures a time *t* given by:

$$t = \frac{t_0}{\sqrt{1 - \frac{v^2}{c^2}}} = \frac{2}{\sqrt{1 - \frac{(0.90c)^2}{c^2}}} = \frac{2}{\sqrt{1 - 0.90^2}} = 4.6 \text{ s (to 2 s.f.)}$$

To the external observer (e.g. Claire) moving clocks appears to run slowly. Likewise, if Anne observed Claire, it would appear that Claire's clock was running slowly.

Tip: This is a really fast train... the moving observer has to be going really fast for time dilation to have much of an effect.

Tip: It's really important that you get the "stationary observer" right.

Muon decay

Muons are particles created in the upper atmosphere that move towards the ground at speeds close to c. In the laboratory (at rest) they have a half-life of less than 2 μs. From this half-life, you would expect most muons to decay between the top of the atmosphere and the Earth's surface, but that doesn't happen.

Scientists can measure the decay of muons (see Figure 4). First the average speed, *v*, of the muons is determined (it's about 0.99*c*). Two detectors are used to measure the muon count rate at high altitude (MR1) and at ground level (MR2). The two count rates are then compared. By knowing the half-life of the muons, you can predict the change in count rate between the two detectors.

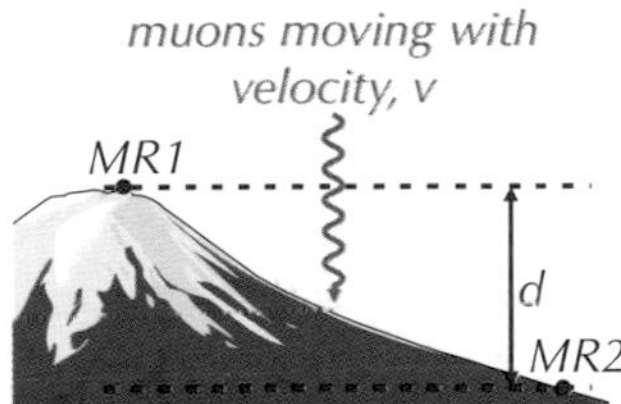

Figure 4: An experiment to measure the decay of muons as they travel from the upper atmosphere towards the ground at velocity v.

Example

Here are some typical results from the muon decay experiment in Figure 4:

- Count at MR1 = 500 per minute
- Count at MR2 = 325 per minute
- Distance between detectors (d) = 2000 m
- Time as determined by a stationary observer = $d \div v$ = 6.73 μs
- Half-life of muons at rest = 1.53 μs

We can do some calculations using the data above. In the reference frame of the observer the muons seemed to have travelled for 4.4 half-lives between the two detectors. You would expect the count rate at the second detector to be only about 25 counts per minute.

However, in a muon's reference frame, travelling at 0.99*c*, the time taken for the journey is just t_0 = 0.95 μs. From the point of view of the muons, the time elapsed is less than their half-life. From the point of view of the observer, it appears that the half-life of the muons has been extended.

> **Tip:** Remember — a stationary observer would be travelling at the same velocity as the object, so they're stationary relative to the object.

Length contraction

Another consequence of Einstein's theory of special relativity is that an object moving in the same direction as its length looks shorter to an external observer. It's known as **length contraction** and is very similar to time dilation.

A stationary observer measures the length of an object as l_0. An observer moving at a constant velocity, v, will measure a shorter length, l. l is given by the equation:

> **Tip:** The length contraction equation is in the Data and Formulae booklet in the exam.

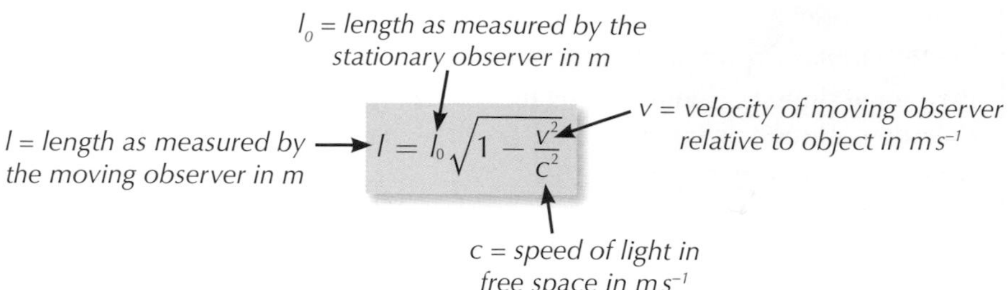

> **Tip:** Length contraction effects all lengths measured by a stationary and a moving observer — including distances travelled.

This equation comes from the equation for time dilation on page 270. It is the formula for length contraction.

Example

Anne (still in the train moving at 0.90c from the previous page) measures the length of her carriage as 3.0 m. Claire, on the platform, measures the length of the carriage as it moves past her.

Claire measures a length:

$$l = l_0\sqrt{1 - \frac{v^2}{c^2}} = 3.0\sqrt{1 - \frac{(0.90c)^2}{c^2}} = 3.0\sqrt{1 - 0.90^2} = 1.3\,\text{m (to 2 s.f.)}$$

> **Tip:** It's only the length in the direction of travel that appears to shrink. The height of the carriage will appear the same to both observers.

Relativistic mass and energy

The last consequence of special relativity you need to know about is that the faster an object moves, the more massive it gets. An object with rest mass m_0 moving at a velocity v has a **relativistic mass**, m, given by the equation:

> **Tip:** So increasing an object's kinetic energy increases its mass — but it's only noticeable near the speed of light.

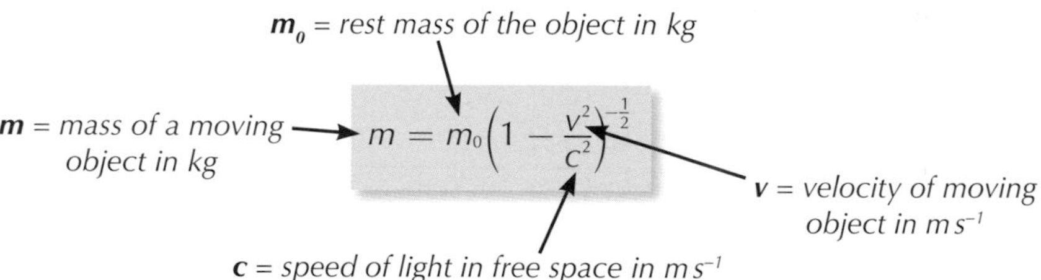

m_0 = rest mass of the object in kg
m = mass of a moving object in kg
$m = m_0\left(1 - \frac{v^2}{c^2}\right)^{-\frac{1}{2}}$
v = velocity of moving object in m s^{-1}
c = speed of light in free space in m s^{-1}

As the relative speed of an object approaches c, the mass approaches infinity. So, in practice, no massive object can move at a speed greater than or equal to the speed of light.

> **Tip:** Shortly after Einstein published his theory, electron beam experiments gave evidence of relativistic mass.

Einstein extended his idea of relativistic mass to write down the most famous equation in physics:

$$E = mc^2$$

m = mass in kg

E = energy in J

c = speed of light in free space in ms^{-1}

> **Tip:** This equation is in the exam Data and Formulae booklet.

This equation says that mass can be converted into energy and vice versa. Or, alternatively, any energy you supply to an object increases its mass — it's just that the increase is usually too small to measure.

The total energy of a relativistic object is given by the equation:

$$E = \frac{m_0 c^2}{\left(1 - \frac{v^2}{c^2}\right)^{\frac{1}{2}}}$$

Tip: This formula just comes from substituting the formula for the relativistic mass into $E = mc^2$ — it's in the Data and Formulae booklet too.

Example

A beam of protons is accelerated to a speed of 1.69 × 10⁸ m s⁻¹. Calculate the relativistic mass and the total energy of one of the protons. Rest mass of a proton = 1.67 × 10⁻²⁷ kg

$$m = m_0\left(1 - \frac{v^2}{c^2}\right)^{-\frac{1}{2}} = (1.67 \times 10^{-27})\left(1 - \frac{(1.69 \times 10^8)^2}{(3 \times 10^8)^2}\right)^{-\frac{1}{2}}$$

$$= 2.021... \times 10^{-27} = 2.02 \times 10^{-27}\,\text{kg (to 3 s.f.)}$$

Total energy $= E = mc^2 = (2.021... \times 10^{-27})(3 \times 10^8)^2$

$= 1.819... \times 10^{-10} = 1.82 \times 10^{-10}$ J (to 3 s.f.)

Practice Questions — Application

Q1 A ball with a diameter of 6.7×10^{-2} m travels at $0.98c$ past a stationary observer. What diameter would the ball appear to have to the observer if measured in line with the direction of travel?

Q2 A beam of electrons with a constant speed of 2.8×10^8 m s^{-1} is fired past two detectors a fixed distance d apart. A stationary observer (relative to the detectors) measured the time taken for the beam to travel between the two detectors as 77 ns.

a) Calculate the distance d in the frame of reference of:

(i) the detectors (ii) the electrons

b) The rest mass of an electron is 9.11×10^{-31} kg. Calculate the relativistic mass of the electrons in the beam.

c) Calculate the total energy of the electrons.

Q3 Unstable particles with a half-life of 11.0 ns are accelerated to $0.95c$ and fired in a thin beam past two detectors spaced 20 m apart.

Approximate the ratio: $\frac{\text{intensity of the beam at second detector}}{\text{intensity of the beam at first detector}}$.

Tip: Q1 hint — the observer isn't stationary relative to the ball...

Tip: The difference in distance can be calculated using length contraction.

Tip: If you're struggling with Q3, start off working out the time taken for the particles to travel from one detector to the other.

Practice Questions — Fact Recall

Q1 What is meant by a frame of reference?

Q2 What is meant by an inertial frame of reference?

Q3 Write down the two postulates of special relativity.

Q4 Describe what is meant by time dilation. Write down a formula for it.

Q5 Explain how muon decay provides evidence for time dilation.

Q6 Write down the formula that you would use to calculate the observed length of a fast-moving object.

Q7 What is meant by relativistic mass?

Q8 Write down two formulas for the equivalence of mass and energy.

Section Summary

Make sure you know...

- How cathode rays are produced in a discharge tube.
- How electrons are released from the surface of a metal by thermionic emission.
- That the work done in accelerating an electron (from rest) through a potential difference is equal to the kinetic energy it has at the anode, and be able to use the formulae $\frac{1}{2}mv^2 = eV$ and $F = \frac{eV}{d}$.
- Any one method of determining the specific charge of an electron e/m, and be able to calculate the specific charge of an electron, given experimental values.
- How to use the equations for centripetal force $F = \frac{mv^2}{r}$ and magnetic force $F = Bev$.
- Why the measurement of the specific charge of an electron was significant.
- How to use Stokes' law for the viscous force on a spherical object $F = 6\pi\eta rv$ to calculate the radius of an oil drop.
- Millikan's experimental set-up for measuring the charge of an oil drop.
- How a charged oil drop moves without an electric field, including its terminal velocity.
- How a charged oil drop moves within an electric field, including how it can be held stationary.
- That a stationary oil drop in an electric field must obey the equation $\frac{QV}{d} = mg$.
- What is meant by the quantisation of charge and why it was significant.
- Newton's corpuscular theory and Huygens' wave theory of light, including the differences between them, and why Newton's theory was preferred.
- The principle of Young's double-slit experiment and its significance at the time.
- How bright and dark fringes are produced in Young's double-slit experiment.
- The nature of EM waves and be able to use the formula for the vacuum speed of an EM wave $c = \frac{1}{\sqrt{\mu_0 \varepsilon_0}}$.
- How Hertz discovered radio waves and showed that they had all the properties of EM waves.
- The concept of the photoelectric effect, including that the emission of photoelectrons is instantaneous above a threshold frequency and that the maximum kinetic energy of the emitted photoelectrons is independent of the intensity of the incident light.
- How classical wave theory failed to explain observations of photoelectricity.
- Einstein's photon theory of light.
- What the stopping potential of a metal is and be able to describe an experiment to measure it.
- The wave-duality theory and the evidence for particles acting as waves and waves acting as particles.
- How to use the de Broglie equation $p = \frac{h}{\lambda}$, and that it links a wave property to a particle property.
- That an electron's de Broglie wavelength is linked to the accelerating voltage by $\lambda = \frac{h}{\sqrt{2meV}}$.
- The structure and operation of T.E.M. and S.T.M. microscopes, and how to increase the resolution.
- The structure of the interferometer used to detect absolute motion, and how the Michelson-Morley experiment intended to detect absolute motion, but failed.
- What an inertial frame of reference is.
- The concepts of proper time and time dilation and be able to use the equation $t = t_0\left(1 - \frac{v^2}{c^2}\right)^{-\frac{1}{2}}$.
- How muon decay provides evidence for time dilation.
- The concept of length contraction and be able to use the equation $l = l_0\left(1 - \frac{v^2}{c^2}\right)^{\frac{1}{2}}$.
- The concept of relativistic mass and the equivalence of mass and energy by $E = mc^2$ and $E = \frac{m_0c^2}{\left(1 - \frac{v^2}{c^2}\right)^{\frac{1}{2}}}$.

Exam-style Questions

1 A transmission electron microscope uses thermionic emission to release electrons, which are then accelerated through a potential difference to a speed *v*, to form a beam. The beam is focused onto a thin sample of silicon. The diameter of a silicon atom is 2.20×10^{-10} m.

1 (a) (i) Describe what is meant by thermionic emission.

(2 marks)

1 (a) (ii) Explain why a transmission electron microscope tube must be evacuated of air.

(1 mark)

1 (b) Explain why electrons must behave as a wave in order for a transmission electron microscope to work.

(2 marks)

1 (c) (i) Show that the anode potential of the electron gun is related to the de Broglie wavelength of an electron in the beam by the equation:

$$V = \frac{1.51 \times 10^{-18}}{\lambda^2}.$$

(3 marks)

1 (c) (ii) Suggest a suitable anode potential to view the silicon atoms in the sample.

(2 marks)

1 (d) Explain why increasing the speed of the electrons would improve the resolution of the microscope.

(2 marks)

2 (a) (i) Write down the two postulates of Einstein's theory of special relativity.

(2 marks)

2 (a) (ii) Einstein's theory of special relativity only works in inertial reference frames. What is meant by an inertial reference frame?

(1 mark)

2 (b) In an experiment, a beam of electrons is accelerated to a velocity of 2.9×10^8 ms^{-1}. The rest mass of an electron is 9.11×10^{-31} kg.

Show that the relativistic mass of an electron at this velocity is approximately four times greater than its rest mass.

(2 marks)

2 (c) An electron travels 10 km. A stationary observer measures the time taken for the electron to travel this distance. In the electron's reference frame, the time taken to travel this distance is different to the time measured by the observer. Describe how this time would compare to the time measured by the observer. Name this effect.

(2 marks)

3 In the 17th and 18th centuries, there was a great debate over the nature of light. The two main theories were Newton's corpuscular theory of light and Huygens' wave theory of light.

In the early 19th century, Young's double-slit experiment produced two coherent light sources by passing light from one source through a double-slit system, as shown below.

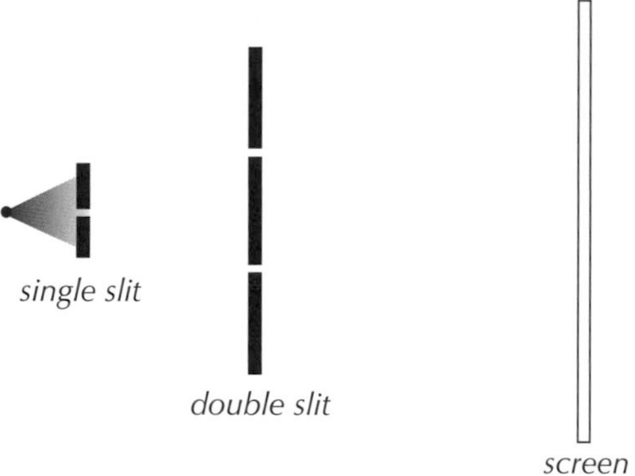

3 (a) (i) Explain what pattern you would expect to be formed on the screen according to Newton's corpuscular theory of light, giving a reason for your answer.

(2 marks)

3 (a) (ii) Describe the pattern that will actually be seen on the screen and explain how it supports Huygens' wave theory.

(3 marks)

3 (a) (iii) Give one reason why Huygens' theory was not widely accepted, despite the results of Young's double-slit experiment.

(1 mark)

3 (b) Light actually exhibits both wave and particle properties. State one example of a phenomenon that can only be explained by the particle theory of light.

(1 mark)

4 The diagram below shows a cathode ray discharge tube.

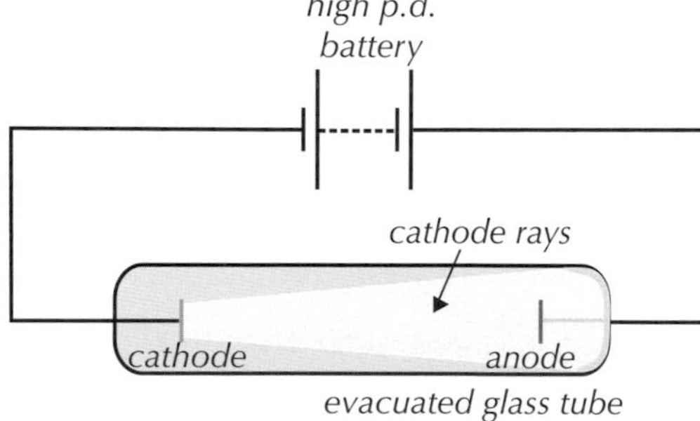

Describe how cathode rays are produced in a discharge tube and outline the key discoveries of their properties that led scientists to predict the existence of subatomic particles.
The quality of your written communication will be assessed in this question.

(6 marks)

5 The apparatus in the diagram below is used to determine the specific charge of an electron. The beam of electrons is accelerated to a velocity, *v*, of 8.44×10^6 ms^{-1} by the electron gun. The magnetic field strength, *B*, is 1.20×10^{-3} T and the radius, *r*, of the beam is determined to be 4.00 cm.

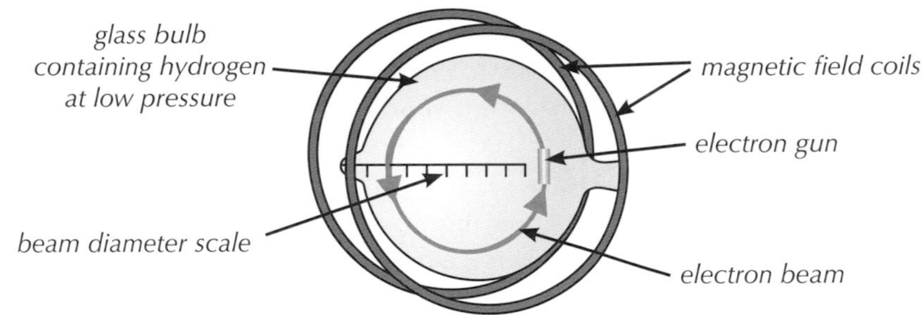

5 (a) Show that the specific charge of an electron in the beam is given by:

$$\frac{e}{m} = \frac{v}{Br}$$

(2 marks)

5 (b) Calculate the specific charge of an electron in the beam from the measurements of this experiment. Give your answer to an appropriate number of significant figures.

(3 marks)

5 (c) J. J. Thomson calculated the value of the specific charge of an electron in 1897. Explain the significance of his findings.

(2 marks)

6 Heinrich Hertz used a radio wave transmitter with a fixed frequency, *f*, and a flat metal sheet to create stationary radio waves. He measured the distance between the antinodes of the stationary wave using a radio wave detector.

6 (a) Describe how you could calculate the wave speed of a radio wave using this experiment.

(2 marks)

6 (b) The experiment is carried out with a radio wave frequency of 400 kHz. The distance between two antinodes is 375 m. Calculate the wave speed.

(1 mark)

6 (c) Calculate the speed of an electromagnetic wave using only the constants:
permittivity of free space, $\varepsilon_0 = 8.85 \times 10^{-12}$ F m^{-1}
permeability of free space, $\mu_0 = 4\pi \times 10^{-7}$ H m^{-1}

(2 marks)

6 (d) What did the results of Hertz's stationary waves experiment provide evidence for?

(1 mark)

Investigative and Practical Skills

1. Variables and Data

When you're planning an experiment you need to think carefully about what things you're going to change, what things you're going to measure and how you're going to record your results.

Variables

You probably know this all off by heart but it's easy to get mixed up sometimes. So here's a quick recap. A **variable** is a quantity that has the potential to change, e.g. mass. There are two types of variable commonly referred to in experiments:

Independent variable — the thing that you change in an experiment.

Dependent variable — the thing that you measure in an experiment.

Tip: When drawing graphs, the dependent variable should go on the *y*-axis and the independent variable on the *x*-axis.

Example

You could investigate the effect of varying the temperature on the volume of some gas in a gas syringe at a fixed pressure.

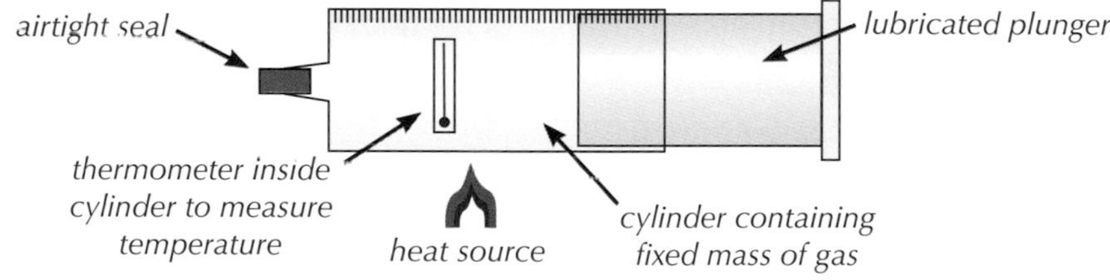

Figure 1: *Experimental set-up for investigating the effect of temperature on the volume of a gas.*

- The independent variable will be the temperature inside the cylinder.
- The dependent variable will be the volume of the gas cylinder.
- All the other variables must be kept the same. These include the pressure inside the cylinder (done by making sure the plunger is well lubricated) and the type of gas used.

Tip: For more on gases, see pages 124-136.

Types of data

Experiments always involve some sort of measurement to provide data. There are different types of data — and you need to know what they are.

1. Discrete data

You get discrete data by counting. E.g. the number of weights used to damp a harmonic oscillator would be discrete. You can't have 1.25 weights. That'd be daft. Shoe size is another good example of a discrete variable.

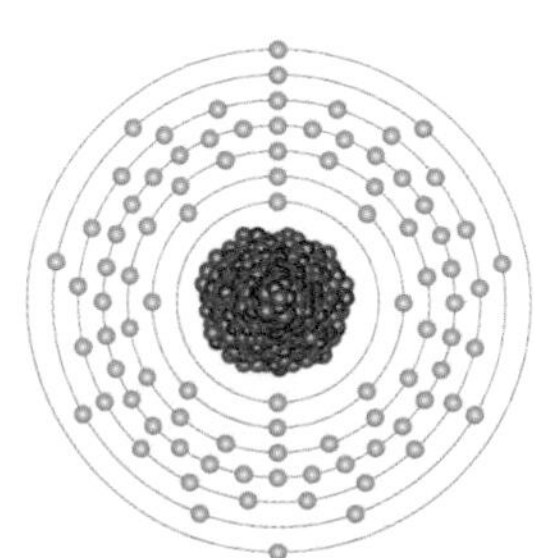

Figure 2: *The number of nucleons in a uranium nucleus is an example of discrete data.*

2. Continuous data

A continuous variable can have any value on a scale. For example, the extension of a spring or the current through a circuit. You can never measure the exact value of a continuous variable.

3. Categoric data

A categoric variable has values that can be sorted into categories. For example, types of material might be brass, wood, glass, steel.

Figure 3: Different types of materials. Material is a type of categoric data.

4. Ordered (ordinal) data

Ordered data is similar to categoric, but the categories can be put in order. For example, if you classify frequencies of light as 'low', 'fairly high' and 'very high' you'd have ordered data.

Tables of data

Before you start your experiment, make a table to write your results in. You'll need to repeat each test at least three times to check your results are reliable (see page 288 for more on reliable results). Figure 4 (below) is the sort of table you might end up with when you investigate the effect of temperature on the volume of a gas.

Temp (°C)	Volume (cm^3) Run 1	Volume (cm^3) Run 2	Volume (cm^3) Run 3	Average (mean) volume (cm^3) (to 3 s.f.)
30.0	52.1	52.1	52.1	**52.1**
40.0	53.8	53.8	53.6	**53.8**
50.0	55.6	55.4	55.6	**55.6**
60.0	57.4	57.2	57.3	**57.3**
70.0	59.3	59.5	59.5	**59.5**
80.0	61.2	61.1	60.3	**61.2**

***Figure 4:** Table of results showing the effect of temperature on the volume of a gas.*

Tip: To find the average of each set of repeated measurements you need to add them all up and divide by how many there are (see page 286 for more on averaging).

For example, the average volume at 60.0 °C is:

$$\frac{(57.4 + 57.2 + 57.3)}{3}$$

$= 57.3\ cm^3$

Watch out for **anomalous results**. These are ones that don't fit in with the other values and are likely to be wrong. They're usually due to experimental errors, such as making a mistake when measuring. You should ignore anomalous results when you calculate averages.

Tip: Just because you ignore anomalous results in your calculations, you shouldn't ignore them in your write-up. Try to find an explanation for what went wrong so that it can be avoided in future experiments.

Example

Look at the table in Figure 4 again — the volume at 80.0 °C in Run 3 looks like it might be an anomalous result. It's much lower than the values in the other two runs. It could have been caused by the plunger stiffening up by the end of Run 3.

The anomalous result has been ignored when the average was calculated — that's why the average volume at 80.0 °C is 61.2 cm^3 ((61.2 + 61.1) ÷ 2 = 61.2 (to 3 s.f.)), rather than 60.9 cm^3 ((61.2 + 61.1 + 60.3) ÷ 3 = 60.9 (to 3 s.f.)).

2. Graphs and Charts

You'll usually be expected to make a graph of your results. Graphs make your data easier to understand — so long as you choose the right type.

Types of graphs and charts

Tip: Use simple scales when you draw graphs — this'll make it easier to plot points.

Tip: Whatever type of graph you make, you'll only get full marks if you:

1. Choose a sensible scale — don't do a tiny graph in the corner of the paper.
2. Label both axes — including units.
3. Plot your points accurately — using a sharp pencil.

Bar charts

You should use a bar chart when one of your data sets is categoric or ordered data, like in Figure 1.

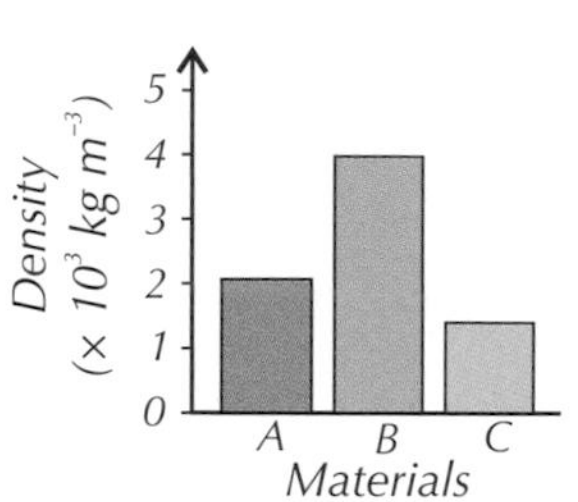

Figure 1: *Bar chart to show density of three materials.*

Pie charts

Pie charts are normally used to display categoric data, like in Figure 2.

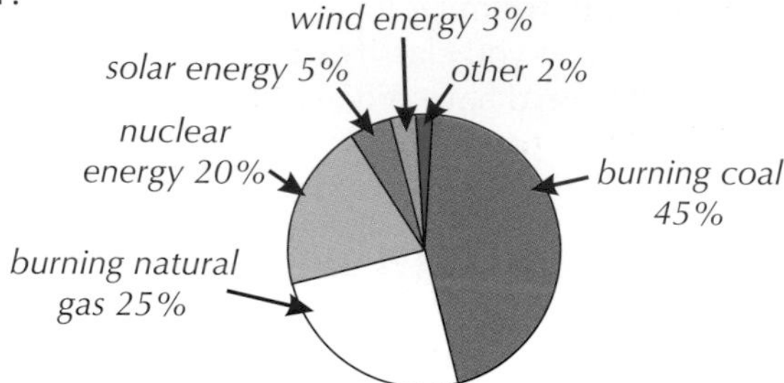

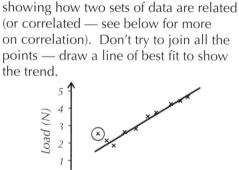

Figure 2: *Pie chart to show the different types of energy production in a particular country.*

Line Graphs

Line graphs are best when you have two sets of continuous data, like in Figure 3. Current and voltage are both continuous variables — you could get any value on the *x* or *y*-axis.

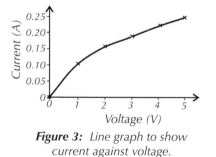

Current (A)
0.25
0.20
0.15
0.10
0.05
0
0
1
2
3
4
5
Voltage (V)

Figure 3: *Line graph to show current against voltage.*

Tip: A line of best fit should have about half of the points above it and half of the points below. You can ignore any anomalous points like the one circled in Figure 4.

Scatter graphs

Scatter graphs, like Figure 4, are great for showing how two sets of data are related (or correlated — see below for more on correlation). Don't try to join all the points — draw a line of best fit to show the trend.

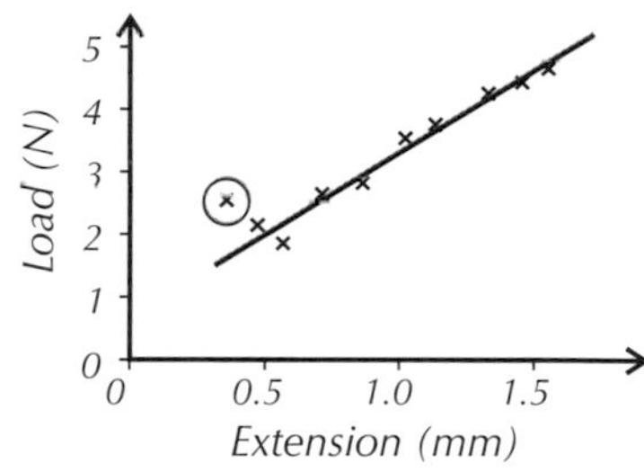

Figure 4: *Scatter graph showing the relationship between load and extension of a material.*

Scatter graphs and correlation

Tip: Computers can make it a lot quicker to collect, record and analyse big sets of data from experiments — but you've still got to understand what all the numbers and graphs they churn out mean.

Correlation describes the relationship between two variables — usually the independent one and the dependent one. Data can show positive correlation, negative correlation or no correlation (see Figure 5).

Positive correlation
As one variable increases the other also increases.

Negative correlation
As one variable increases the other decreases.

No correlation
There is no relationship between the variables.

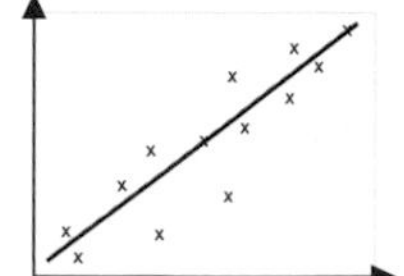

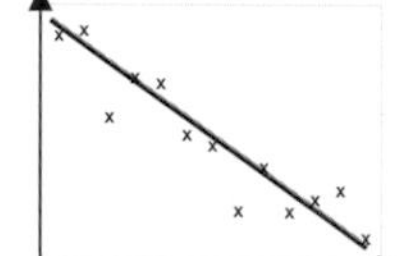

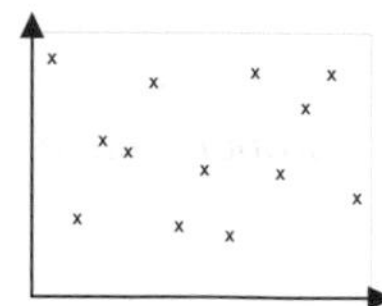

Figure 5: *Scatter graphs showing positive, negative and no correlation.*

Correlation and cause

Ideally, only two quantities would ever change in any experiment — everything else would remain constant. But in experiments or studies outside the lab, you can't usually control all the variables. So even if two variables are correlated, the change in one may not be causing the change in the other. Both changes might be caused by a third variable.

Tip: If an experiment really does confirm that changing one variable causes another to change, we say there's a causal link between them.

Example

Some studies have found a correlation between exposure to the electromagnetic fields created by power lines and certain ill health effects. So some people argue that this means we shouldn't live close to power lines, or build power lines close to homes. But it's hard to control all the variables between people who live near power lines and people who don't. Ill health in people living near power lines could be affected by many lifestyle factors or even genetics. Also, people living close to power lines may be more likely to believe that any ill health they suffer is due to the EM fields from the power lines if they are aware of the studies.

Tip: Watch out for bias too — for instance, a neighbourhood campaigning against unsightly power lines being built nearby may want to show that they are a danger to health.

Straight-line graphs

If you plot two variables that have a linear relationship, you'll get a straight-line graph. Using the fact that the equation of a straight line is $y = mx + c$ (where m = gradient and c = y-intercept), you can use your graph to work out certain values, and the relationship between your variables.

Tip: x and y have a linear relationship if $y = mx + c$, where m and c are constants.

Proportionality

If you plot two variables against each other and get a straight line that goes through the origin, the two variables are **directly proportional**. The y-intercept, c, is 0, so the equation of the straight line is $y = mx$, where m is a constant. The constant of proportionality, m, is the gradient of the graph.

Tip: Two variables are directly proportional if one variable = constant × other variable.

Tip: Remember the gradient is the slope of the line.

Example

The potential difference across a capacitor is directly proportional to the charge stored on it. You can see this by using the circuit in Figure 6. Use the variable resistor to keep the charging current constant for as long as possible. Take readings of potential difference across it until it's close to the battery p.d., and find the value of Q at each of these points in time using $Q = It$. Once you have all the data, plot a graph of Q against V (Figure 7). The graph you'll get is a straight line going through the origin — so charge and potential difference are directly proportional.

Tip: For more on capacitance see pages 57-70.

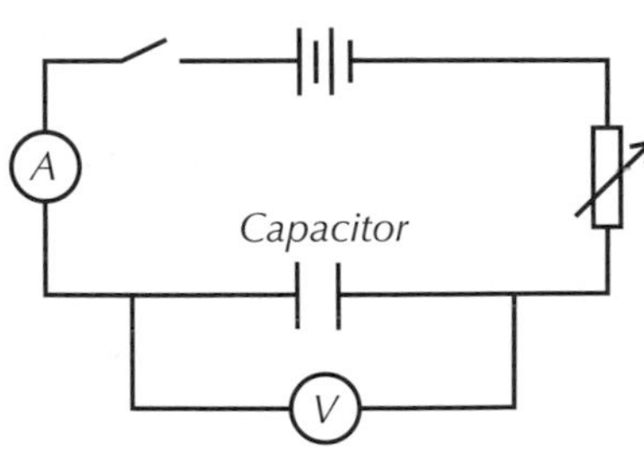

Figure 6: *Circuit for showing the proportional relationship between Q and V for a capacitor.*

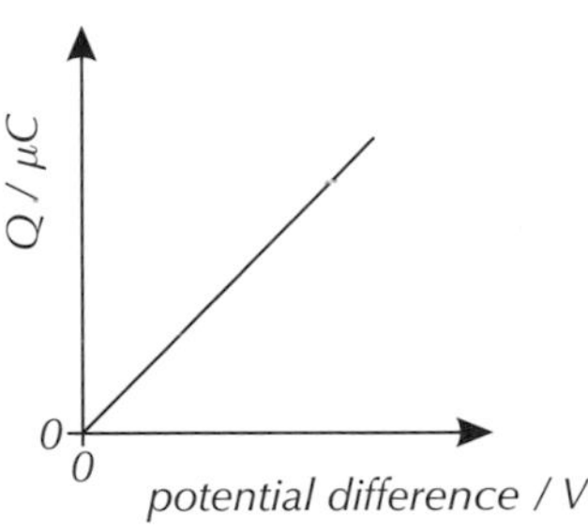

Figure 7: *A Q-V graph for a capacitor.*

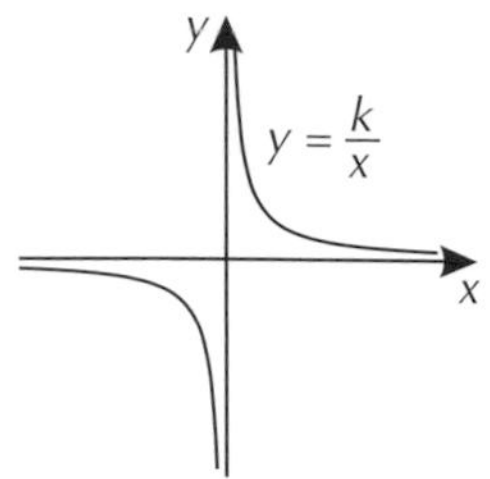

Figure 8: *An inverse proportionality relationship between x and y.*

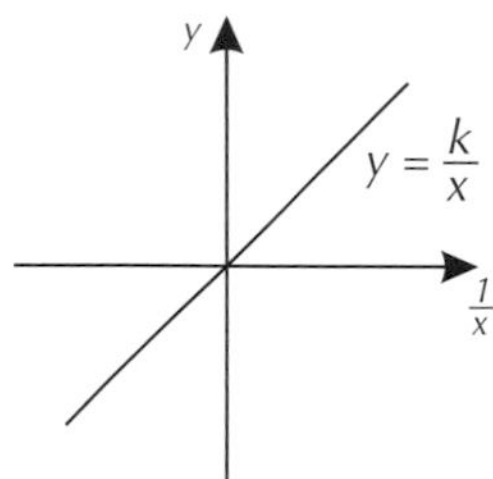

Figure 9: *If $y = \frac{k}{x}$, plotting y against $\frac{1}{x}$ gives a straight line through the origin.*

Non-linear relationships

Straight-line graphs are really easy to work with, but some variables won't produce a straight-line graph if you plot them against each other. You can sometimes change what you plot on the axes so that you get one though.

For example, say two variables are inversely proportional — then $y = \frac{k}{x}$, say, where k is a constant. If you plot y against x, you'll get a curved graph which shoots off to infinity (Figure 8). It's not very easy to work out the value of k from this graph, but if you plot y against $\frac{1}{x}$ you'll get a lovely straight-line graph (Figure 9) with a constant gradient of k that goes through the origin. This is because the graph plotted is $y = k\left(\frac{1}{x}\right)$, which is just the equation of a straight line in the form $y = mx + c$, where $m = k$ and $x = \frac{1}{x}$.

Finding the gradient and y-intercept

If you've plotted a straight-line graph, you can read the gradient and y-intercept straight off it. This means you can work out certain quantities from your graph.

Example

Returning to the example of the capacitor from page 281, you can use the Q-V graph to calculate the capacitance of the capacitor.

Q and V are directly proportional, so $Q = kV$. This is in the form $y = mx + c$, where $y = Q$, $m = k$ and $c = 0$. You know that $C = \frac{Q}{V}$, so $Q = CV$ and the gradient $(m) = C$. You can find the gradient of the straight-line graph by dividing the change in y (Δy) by the change in x (Δx).

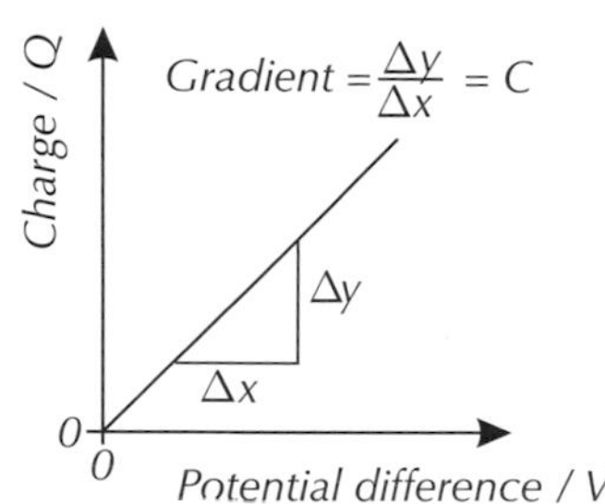

Figure 10: *Using a Q-V graph to work out the capacitance of a capacitor.*

Tip: For more on work functions, see page 258.

Example

The solid line in the graph in Figure 11 shows how the maximum kinetic energy of the electrons on a metal surface varies with the frequency of the light shining on it. You can use a graph like this to find the value of the work function of the metal (ϕ) by extending the graph back to the y-axis.

Rearranging the equation $hf = \phi + E_{K(max)}$ gives $E_{K(max)} = hf - \phi$. Since h and ϕ are constants, $E_{K(max)} = hf - \phi$ is just the equation of a straight line (in the form $y = mx + c$). You can just read ϕ from the graph — it's minus the intercept on the vertical axis. You'll just need to continue the line back to the y-axis to find the intercept, then the value of the y-intercept will be $-\phi$.

Tip: If you were to calculate the gradient, you should get h, Planck's constant.

Tip: Here, $y = E_{K\,(max)}$, $m = h$, x = frequency and $c = -\phi$.

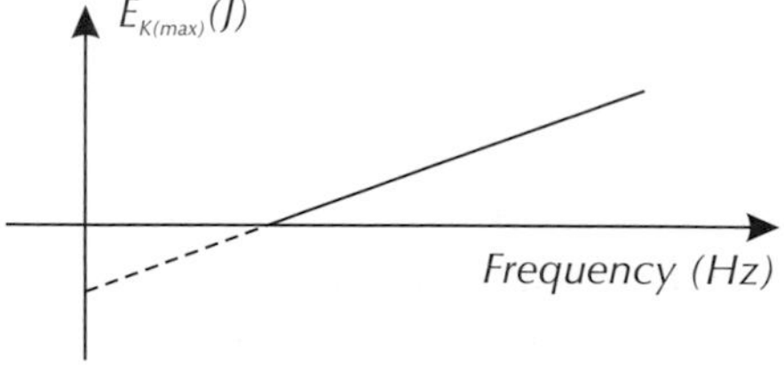

Figure 11: *You can extend the line on a graph to find the y-intercept.*

Working with exponentials and logarithms

A fair few of the relationships you need to know about in A2 physics are exponential — where the rate of change of a quantity is proportional to the amount of the quantity left. Here are just a few you should have met before (if they don't ring a bell, go and have a quick read about them):

- Charge on a capacitor — the decay of charge on a capacitor is proportional to the amount of charge left on the capacitor:

$$Q = Q_0 e^{-\frac{t}{RC}}$$

- Radioactive decay — the rate of decay is proportional to the number of nuclei left in a sample:

$$N = N_0 e^{(-\lambda t)}$$

- The activity of a radioactive sample behaves in the same way:

$$A = A_0 e^{(-\lambda t)}$$

Tip: See pages 57-70 for more on capacitors.

Tip: See pages 101-108 for more on radioactive decay and activity.

The natural logarithm

Working with exponentials becomes much easier when you know about the natural logarithm, ln. The natural logarithm is just the inverse of e, where:

$$\ln(e^x) = x$$

You can use this relationship when rearranging equations to find values inside exponentials. Taking the natural logarithm of both sides of an equation gets rid of the 'e'.

There are three other log rules you need to know about in A2 physics:

$$\ln(ab) = \ln a + \ln b \qquad \ln\frac{a}{b} = \ln a - \ln b \qquad \ln a^b = b\ln a$$

These rules allow you to manipulate equations involving exponentials so that you can find the value of any variable in the equation.

Exam Tip
These log laws won't be given to you in the exam, so make sure you learn them.

Example

If you know the activity of a radioactive source at two different points in time, you can find its decay constant, λ. Take the natural logarithm of both sides of the equation for activity (shown above), then use log laws to make λ the subject.

$$N = N_0 e^{(-\lambda t)} \Rightarrow \ln N = \ln[N_0 e^{(-\lambda t)}]$$ ← *Take the ln of both sides.*

$$\Rightarrow \ln N = \ln N_0 + \ln[e^{(-\lambda t)}]$$ ← *$\ln(ab) = \ln a + \ln b$*

$$\Rightarrow \ln N = \ln N_0 - \lambda t$$ ← *$\ln e^x = x$*

$$\Rightarrow \lambda = \frac{\ln N_0 - \ln N}{t}$$

Tip: The equation might still look complicated, but you can just use a calculator to find values of natural logarithms.

Natural logarithms and exponential graphs

Log laws can also come in useful when working with exponential graphs. The shape of an exponential graph can be tricky to work with, but taking the natural logarithm of both sides of an exponential equation can let you plot a straight-line graph from the data. These are much easier to work with.

Tip: After taking natural logs, the equation is in the form of $y = mx + c$, the equation of a straight line, where y is $\ln y$, m is $-a$ and c is $\ln k$.

Tip: A graph of y against x would give the value of k (the y-intercept), but not a.

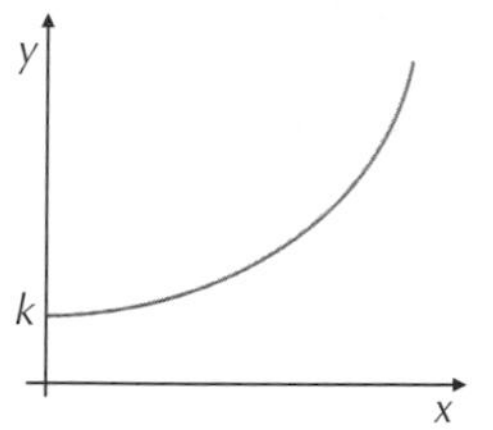

Tip: The zig-zagged line on the y-axis means some values have been missed out.

Tip: To find the value of an exponential, just type 'e□' (or 'eˣ') followed by the number on a calculator.

Tip: The log laws on the previous page can be used for any log.

Tip: If your calculator has a button that just says "log", it means log to the base 10. "ln" is actually log to the base e. $\log_{10} 10^x = x$ just like $\log_e e^x = x$.

Tip: The laws used here, in order, are:
$\log(ab) = \log a + \log b$
$\log a^b = b \log a$.

Example

Two variables, x and y, are related to each other by the formula $y = ke^{-ax}$, where k and a are constants. Taking the natural logarithm of both sides gives $\ln y = \ln k - ax$. A graph of $\ln y$ against x is a straight line, where $\ln k$ is the y-intercept and $-a$ is the gradient of the graph.

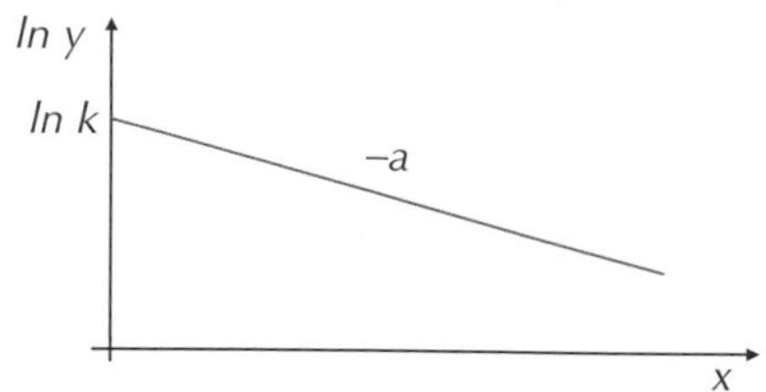

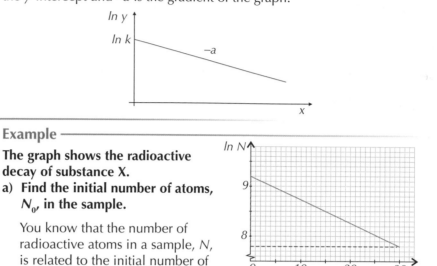

Example

The graph shows the radioactive decay of substance X.

a) Find the initial number of atoms, N_0, in the sample.

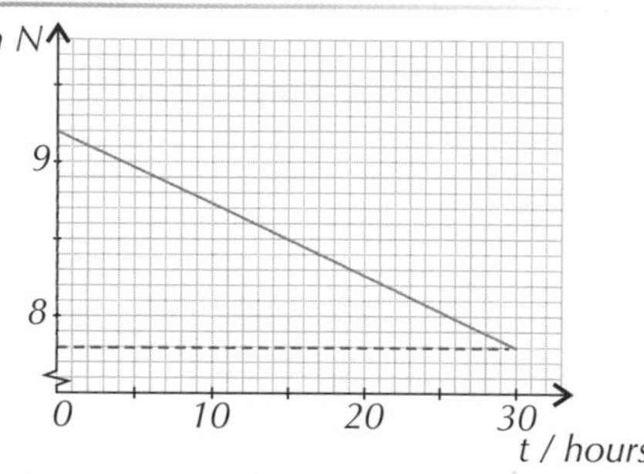

You know that the number of radioactive atoms in a sample, N, is related to the initial number of atoms by the equation $N = N_0 e^{-\lambda t}$.
So, $\ln N = \ln N_0 - \lambda t$ and $\ln N_0$ is the y-intercept of the graph = 9.2.

$$\ln N_0 = 9.2 \Rightarrow N_0 = e^{9.2} = 9900 \text{ atoms (to 2 s.f.)}$$

b) Find the decay constant λ of substance X.

$-\lambda$ is the gradient of the graph, so:

$$\lambda = \frac{\Delta \ln N}{\Delta t} = \frac{9.2 - 7.8}{30 \times 60 \times 60} = \frac{1.4}{108\,000} = 1.3 \times 10^{-5} \text{ (to 2 s.f.)}$$

Other logs

You can use logs to plot a straight-line graph of any power law — it doesn't have to be an exponential. Take the relationship between the energy stored in a spring, E, and the spring's extension, x: $E = kx^n$. Take the log (base 10) of both sides to get $\log E = \log k + n \log x$. So $\log k$ will be the y-intercept and n the gradient of the graph.

Example

The graph shows how the intensity of radiation from the Sun, I, varies with its distance, d. I is related to d by the equation $I = kd^n$. Find n.

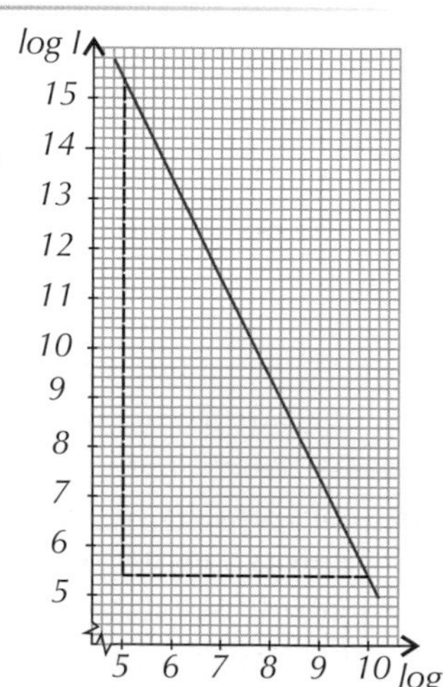

$$\log I = \log(kd^n)$$
$$= \log k + \log d^n$$
$$= \log k + n \log d$$

So n is the gradient of the graph.
Reading from the graph:

$$n = \frac{\Delta \log I}{\Delta \log d}$$
$$= \frac{15.4 - 5.4}{5 - 10}$$
$$= \frac{10}{-5} = -2$$

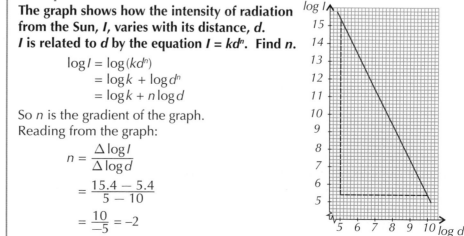

3. Error Analysis

Scientists always have to include the uncertainty of a result, so you can see the range the actual value probably lies within. Dealing with error and uncertainty is an important skill — you need to make sure that you know and try to minimise the uncertainty of your results and can evaluate how convincing they are.

Figure 1: *This ruler measures to the nearest millimetre. Any measurement you take using it will have an uncertainty of ± 0.5 mm.*

Types of error

Every measurement you take has an experimental uncertainty. Say you've done something outrageous like measure the length of a piece of wire with a centimetre ruler. You might think you've measured its length as 30 cm, but at best you've probably measured it to be 30 ± 0.5 cm. And that's without taking into account any other errors that might be in your measurement.

The ± bit gives you the range in which the true length (the one you'd really like to know) probably lies — 30 ± 0.5 cm tells you the true length is likely to lie in the range of 29.5 to 30.5 cm. The smaller the uncertainty, the nearer your value is likely to be to the true value, so the more accurate your result is likely to be. There are two types of error that cause experimental uncertainty:

Tip: To get the lowest possible value, subtract the value after the ± sign, and to get the highest possible value, add it.

Random errors

No matter how hard you try, you can't get rid of random errors. They can just be down to noise, or that you're measuring a random process such as nuclear radiation emission. You get random error in any measurement.

If you measured the length of a wire 20 times, the chances are you'd get a slightly different value each time, e.g. due to your head being in a slightly different position when reading the scale. It could be that you just can't keep controlled variables exactly the same throughout the experiment. Or it could just be the wind was blowing in the wrong direction at the time.

Systematic errors

You get systematic errors not because you've made a mistake in a measurement — but because of the apparatus you're using or your experimental method, e.g. using an inaccurate clock. The problem is often that you don't know they're there. You've got to spot them first to have any chance of correcting for them. Systematic errors usually shift all of your results to be too high or too low. They're annoying, but there are things you can do to reduce them if you manage to spot them (see next page).

Tip: A newton meter that always measures values 1 N greater than they should be will shift all your results up by 1 N — this would introduce a systematic error due to the apparatus used.

Example

You could investigate the local value of g (see page 37) using a pendulum, as shown in Figure 2.

- The pendulum's motion might be affected by vibrations in the room from people walking by, heavy vehicles driving past, etc. This introduces random errors.
- If there is any friction in the system, or if the length of the pendulum is measured inaccurately (it should be to the centre of gravity), all the readings will be shifted in the same direction. This would introduce a systematic error due to the experimental set-up.

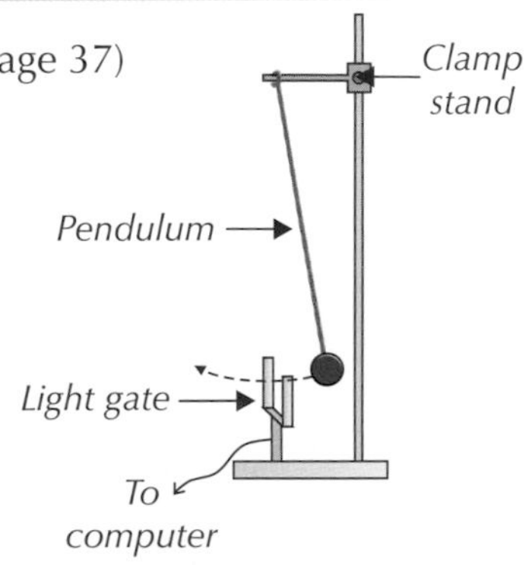

Figure 2: *An experiment to find the value of g.*

Tip: In experiments using pendulums, you usually ignore the mass of the string or rod — this can lead to systematic error.

Tip: It's almost impossible to remove any form of friction — even the surrounding air will contribute slightly.

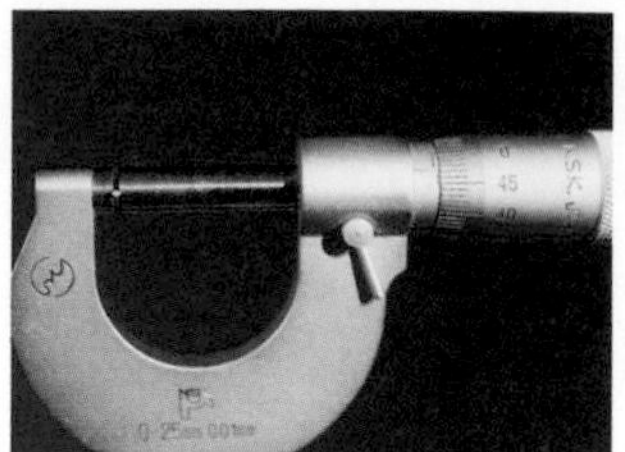

Figure 3: *This micrometer is very precise. It gives readings to within 0.01 mm.*

Tip: To calibrate a set of scales you could weigh a 10 g mass and check that it reads 10 g. If these scales are precise to the nearest 0.1 g, then you can only calibrate to within 0.05 g. Any measurements taken will have an uncertainty of ± 0.05 g.

Tip: Remember to remove anomalous results before averaging (see page 279).

Reducing uncertainty

There are a few different ways you can reduce the uncertainty in your results:

- Use higher precision apparatus:
  The more precisely you can measure something, the less random error (see page 285) there is likely to be in the measurement. So if you use more precise equipment you can instantly cut down the likely random error in your experiment. Using apparatus with a higher sensitivity will give you a higher precision (e.g. swapping a millimetre ruler for a micrometer to measure the diameter of a wire).
- Calibration:
  You can calibrate your apparatus by measuring a known value.
  If there's a difference between the measured and known value, you can use this to correct the inaccuracy of the apparatus, and so reduce your systematic error.
- Repeating measurements:
  By repeating a measurement several times and averaging, you reduce the random uncertainty in your result. The more measurements you average over, the less error you're likely to have.

Averaging

In the exam, you might be given a graph or table of information showing the results for many repetitions of the same experiment, and asked to estimate the true value and give an uncertainty in that value. Here's how to go about it:

1. Estimate the true value by averaging the results you've been given — just like in the experiment on page 279. (Make sure you state whatever average it is you take, e.g. mean, mode etc., otherwise you might not get the mark.)
2. To get the uncertainty, you just need to look how far away from your average value the maximum and minimum values in the graph or table you've been given are.

Example

A class measure the local value of *g* to 1 d.p. and record their results on the bar chart shown below. Estimate the true local value of *g*, giving a suitable range of uncertainty in your answer.

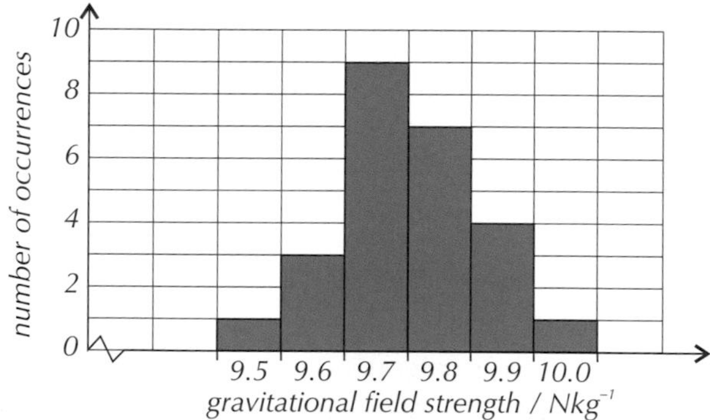

Figure 4: *A bar chart showing the values of* **g** *found in a class experiment.*

There were 25 measurements, so taking the mean:

$$\frac{(9.5 + (9.6 \times 3) + (9.7 \times 9) + (9.8 \times 7) + (9.9 \times 4) + 10.0)}{25} = 9.75\,\text{Nkg}^{-1}$$

(to 3 s.f.)

The maximum value found was 10.0 Nkg^{-1}, and the minimum value was 9.5 Nkg^{-1}. Both values are about 0.25 Nkg^{-1} from the average value, so the answer is 9.75 ± 0.25 Nkg^{-1}.

Tip: Just add up the heights of all the bars to find the total number of measurements.

Tip: If the maximum and minimum are different distances from the average, use the largest value after the ±.

Percentage uncertainty

You might get asked to work out the percentage uncertainty in a measurement. If you know the uncertainty of the measurement, just divide this by the measurement taken and multiply by 100, as shown below.

Examples

- The resistance of a filament lamp is given as 5.0 ± 0.4 Ω.

  The percentage uncertainty in the resistance measured is:

  Uncertainty → Measurement →
  $$\frac{0.4}{5.0} \times 100 = 8\%$$

- A balance is calibrated to within 0.1 g, and you measure a mass as 4.0 g.

  Saying that it's calibrated to 0.1 g means that the uncertainty in any measurement is ± 0.1 g.

  The percentage uncertainty is: (0.1 ÷ 4.0) × 100 = 2.5%.

  Here measuring a larger quantity reduces the percentage uncertainty in the measurement — a mass of 40.0 g has a percentage uncertainty of: (0.1 ÷ 40.0) × 100 = 0.25%.

Tip: See page 286 if you need a reminder of what calibrated means.

Most measuring equipment has the precision it's calibrated to written on it. Where it doesn't, you can usually use the scale as a guide (e.g. if a ruler has a 1 mm scale, it is probably calibrated to within 0.5 mm).

Tip: You should always choose appropriate measuring equipment for the precision you need to work with.

Error bars

Most of the time in science, you work out the uncertainty in your final result using the uncertainty in each measurement you make. When you're plotting a graph, you show the uncertainty in each measurement by using error bars to show the range the point is likely to lie in. You probably won't get asked to plot any error bars — but you might need to read off a graph that has them.

Example

The error in measuring the volume of a gas container can be found using the error bars in the graph below.

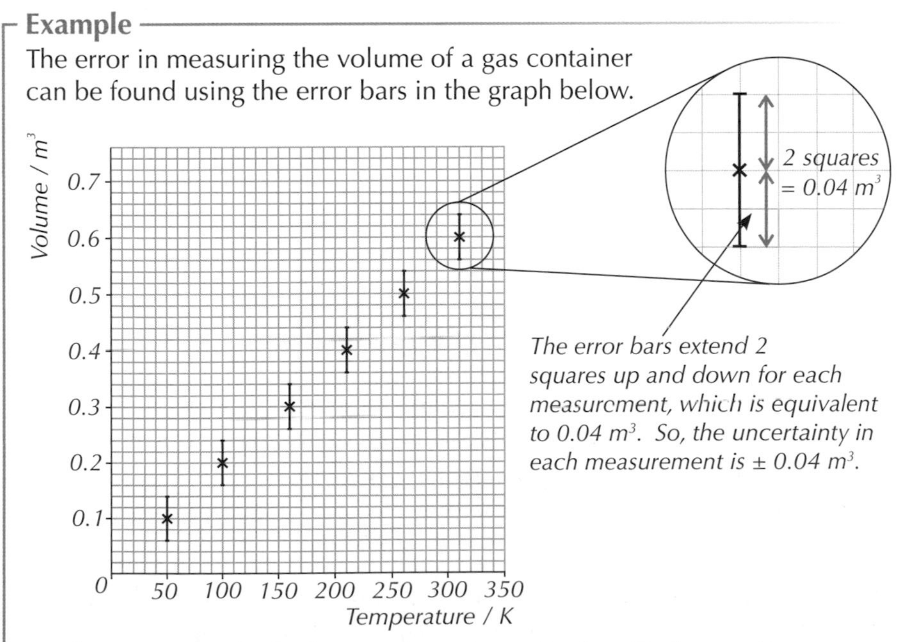

Volume / m³
0.7
0.6
0.5
0.4
0.3
0.2
0.1
0
50 100 150 200 250 300 350
Temperature / K
2 squares = 0.04 m³
The error bars extend 2 squares up and down for each measurement, which is equivalent to 0.04 m³. So, the uncertainty in each measurement is ± 0.04 m³.

Figure 5: *A graph of volume against temperature for a fixed mass of gas.*

Tip: Be careful — sometimes error bars are calculated using a set percentage of uncertainty for each measurement, and so will change depending on the measurement.

Measuring uncertainty of final results

Normally when you draw a graph you'll want to find the gradient or intercept. E.g. for a charge-p.d. graph, the gradient's C, the capacitance of the capacitor being tested. To find the value of C, you draw a nice line of best fit on the graph and calculate your answer from that.

You can then draw the maximum and minimum slopes possible for the data through all of the error bars. By calculating the value of the gradient (or intercept) for these slopes, you can find maximum and minimum values the true answer is likely to lie between. And that's the uncertainty in your answer.

Tip: When there is an error in the *y*-intercept, you can find it with the same method. Just draw the minimum and maximum lines of best fit and see where they cross the y-axis.

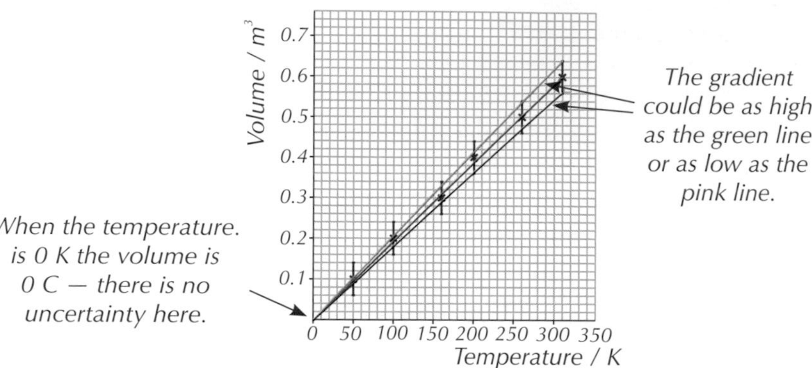

Volume / m^3
0.7
0.6
0.5
0.4
0.3
0.2
0.1
0
50
100
150
200
250
300
350
Temperature / K
The gradient could be as high as the green line or as low as the pink line.
When the temperature. is 0 K the volume is 0 C — there is no uncertainty here.

Figure 6: *The maximum and minimum slopes possible through the error bars.*

Evaluations

Now that you can measure uncertainty, you'll need to evaluate your results to see how convincing they are. You need to be careful about what words you use — valid, accurate, precise and reliable may all sound similar, but they all say different things about your results.

1. Valid results

A valid result answers the original question, using reliable data.
For example, if you haven't controlled all the variables your results won't be valid, because you won't be testing just the thing you wanted to.

Tip: It's possible for results to be precise but not accurate, e.g. a balance that weighs to 1/1000th of a gram will give precise results, but if it's not calibrated properly the results won't be accurate.

2. Accurate results

An accurate result is one that is really close to the true answer.
You can only say your results are accurate if you know the true value of what you're measuring.

3. Precise results

A precise result is one taken using sensitive instruments that measure in small increments.

Tip: Part of the scientific process (see page 2) involves other scientists repeating your experiment too — then if they get the same results you can be more certain they're reliable.

4. Reliable results

Reliable means the results can be consistently reproduced in independent experiments. And if the results are reproducible they're more likely to be true. If the data isn't reliable for whatever reason you can't draw a valid conclusion.

For experiments, the more repeats you do, the more reliable the data. If you get the same result twice, it could be the correct answer. But if you get the same result 20 times, it'd be much more reliable. And it'd be even more reliable if everyone in the class got about the same results using different apparatus.

If you have a large percentage uncertainty, your results won't be very reliable. A small percentage uncertainty means your results are more reliable.

Tip: A large percentage uncertainty means a large error in comparison to the size of the result.

4. Conclusions and Safety

Once you've got results, you can use them to form a conclusion. But be careful... your conclusion must be supported by your results, and you should keep in mind how much you can believe your results (see evaluations on the previous page). You'll also need to consider any risks that were involved and discuss the safety precautions used.

Drawing conclusions

The data should always support the conclusion. This may sound obvious but it's easy to jump to conclusions. Conclusions have to be specific — not make sweeping generalisations.

Example

A capacitor was discharged through a fixed resistor, and the charge on the plates was measured at times 0.0, 0.2, 0.4, 0.6, 0.8 and 1.0 s. Each time reading had an estimated error of 0.01 s and each charge reading had an estimated error of 10 μC. All other variables were kept constant. The results are shown in Figure 1.

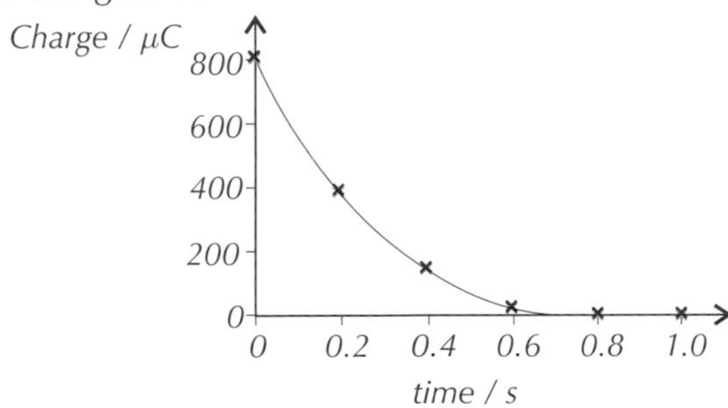

Figure 1: *Graph to show charge on the plates of a capacitor over time.*

A study concluded from this data that this type of capacitor discharges to 5% of its maximum charge in 0.5 s. This could be true — but the data doesn't support this. Because time increments of 0.2 s were used and the charge at in-between times wasn't measured, you can't tell when the charge becomes 5% of its maximum charge from this data. All you know is that the charge reaches this level at some point between 0.4 and 0.6 seconds.

Also, the graph only gives information about this particular experiment. You can't conclude that the discharge time would be this for all capacitors of this type and all circuits — only this one. In truth, the discharge time of a capacitor depends on the circuit it's connected to.

You must also consider the error in the charge readings. The error in each reading is 10 μC, which gives a percentage uncertainty of around 50% for the lowest charge reading. This means the results could be unreliable.

Tip: Taking more readings in an experiment can allow you to make stronger conclusions. If a measurement had been taken at a time of 0.5 s here, you'd have been able to say more about where the charge becomes 0 C. It's also good to do a practice experiment to get an idea of the time span in which you need to record data.

Tip: Whoever funded the research (e.g. a circuit components company) may have some influence on what conclusions are drawn from the results, but scientists have a responsibility to make sure that the conclusions they draw are supported by the data.

Risks, hazards and ethical considerations

In any experiment you'll be expected to show that you've thought about the risks and hazards. You'll need to take appropriate safety measures depending on the experiment. For example, anything involving lasers will usually need special laser goggles and to work with radioactive substances you'll probably need to wear gloves.

You need to make sure you're working ethically too. This is most important if there are other people or animals involved. You have to consider their welfare first.

Figure 2: *A scientist wearing laser goggles while working with lasers.*

Exam Help

1. Exam Structure and Technique

Passing exams isn't all about revision — it really helps if you know how the exam is structured and have got your exam technique nailed so that you pick up every mark you can.

Exam Tip
Make sure you have a good read through of this exam structure. It might not seem important now but you don't want to get any nasty surprises just before an exam.

Exam structure

For AQA A2-Level Physics you're going to have to sit through two exams (Unit 4 and Unit 5) and complete a practical assessment (Unit 6). These will make up 50% of your total A-level.

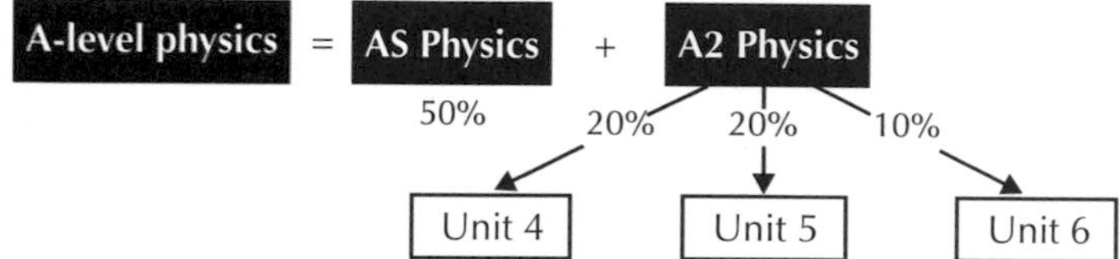

Unit 4 — Fields and further mechanics

This paper will be 1 hour 45 minutes long and have 75 marks up for grabs. It's worth 20% of your total A-Level and is made up of two sections. Section A has 25 multiple choice questions worth 1 mark each. Section B is made up of 4 or 5 structured questions worth 50 marks in total.

Exam Tip
Structured questions are just questions that are broken down into different parts that follow on from one another. You might work out a value in one part and need to use it in the next.

Unit 5 — Nuclear and thermal physics + a choice of 4 options

This paper will also be 1 hour 45 minutes long, contain 75 marks and be worth 20% of your total A-Level. It's also made up of two sections. Section A has 4 or 5 structured questions on nuclear and thermal physics, worth 40 marks. Section B has 4 or 5 structured questions on your option unit, worth 35 marks.

Unit 6 — Investigative and practical skills in A2 Physics

You'll do this unit in school with your teacher. It'll test your understanding of physics and your ability to collect and process data and use it to answer questions. It's worth 10% of your total A-Level.

There are two different ways in which you can complete Unit 6. You only need to do one of them — your school will decide which one you'll do:

- **Teacher assessed** — You'll do practical work throughout the year which your teacher will use to assess your practical skills. You'll also have to collect and process some data and use it to answer questions in a written test to assess your investigative skills. This will be marked by your teacher too.
- **Externally marked** — You'll complete five short practical exercises which aren't marked (but you still have to do), as well as a longer practical activity set by AQA. In the long practical you'll collect and process data and then use it to answer questions in a written test, marked externally.

***Figure 1:** Physics lesson — students investigating electric motors and electromagnetic fields.*

The assessments in Unit 6 test that you can use standard laboratory equipment, demonstrate safe and skilful practical techniques, take measurements with precision and accuracy, correctly record data and analyse and evaluate your experiment. This may sound a bit menacing but there's some stuff on pages 278-289 to help you out.

Quality of written communication (QWC)

Units 4 and 5 in A2-Level Physics will have a quality of written communication element — this just means that the examiner will assess your ability to write properly. In each of these units, there will be at least one part of a question where your written communication will be assessed. In these parts, you'll be awarded a mark between 0 and 7 which is based on the written quality and scientific accuracy of your answer. To get top marks, you need to make sure that:

- your scribble, sorry, writing is legible,
- your spelling, punctuation and grammar are accurate,
- your writing style is appropriate,
- you organise your answer clearly and coherently,
- you use specialist scientific vocabulary where it's appropriate.

The examiner will only give (or deduct) marks for QWC when the question tells you that it will be assessed, but you should make sure all your answers are clear and easy to read throughout the exam to avoid losing marks.

Exam Tip
You'll need to use a black biro, ballpoint pen or fountain pen to write your answers, so make sure that you've got a couple ready for the exam.

Exam Tip
You may be asked to draw and label a diagram for extra marks in QWC questions.

Time management

This is one of the most important exam skills to have. How long you spend on each question is really important in an exam — it could make all the difference to your grade. Check out the exam timings given by AQA that can be found on the previous page and on the front of your exam paper. These timings give you just under 1 and a half minutes per mark — try to stick to this to give yourself the best chance to pick up as many marks as possible.

Some questions will require lots of work for only a few marks but other questions will be much quicker. Don't spend ages struggling with questions that are only worth a couple of marks — move on. You can come back to them later when you've bagged loads of other marks elsewhere.

Examples

The questions below are both worth the same number of marks but require different amounts of work.

1 (a) What is gravitational potential?

(2 marks)

2 (a) Draw a labelled diagram of a circuit that could be used to investigate the rate of discharge of a capacitor through a fixed resistor.

(2 marks)

Question 1 (a) only requires you to write down a definition — if you can remember it this shouldn't take you too long.

Question 2 (a) requires you to draw a diagram including a number of components — this may take you a lot longer than writing down a definition, especially if you have to add quite a few components and work out whether they should be in parallel or series.

So, if you're running out of time it makes sense to do questions like 1 (a) first and come back to 2 (a) if you've got time at the end.

This is particularly important in Unit 4. The multiple choice questions are only worth 1 mark each, but some of them involve a lot of work. Don't get bogged down by these — if you're struggling, just move on and come back to them later.

Exam Tip
Everyone has their own method of getting through the exam. Some people find it easier to go through the paper question by question and some people like to do the questions they find easiest first. The most important thing is to find out the way that suits you best <u>before</u> the exam — that means doing all the practice exams you can before the big day.

Exam Tip
Don't forget to go back and do any questions that you left the first time round — you don't want to miss out on marks because you forgot to do the question.

Calculations

There's no getting away from those pesky calculation questions — they come up a lot in A2-Level Physics. The most important thing to remember is to show your working. You've probably heard it a million times before but it makes perfect sense. It only takes a few seconds more to write down what's in your head and it'll stop you from making silly errors and losing out on easy marks. You won't get a mark for a wrong answer but you could get marks for the method you used to work out the answer.

Exam Tip
It's so easy to mistype numbers into a calculator when you're under pressure in an exam. Always double-check your calculations and make sure the answer looks sensible.

Units

Make sure you always give the correct units for your answer.

Example

Here's an example of a question where you need to change the units so they match the answer the examiner wants.

1 Find the energy of a photon with wavelength 3.2×10^{-9} m. Give your answer in kJ.

(2 marks)

$E = \frac{hc}{\lambda}$ gives the energy of a photon in joules.
Make sure you convert the units to kilojoules by dividing by 1000.

Tip: A kJ is bigger than a J, so you'd expect the number to get smaller when you convert from J to kJ — each unit is worth more so you'll have fewer of them.

You might need to convert quantities into the right units before using a formula. Most formulas need quantities to be in something called SI units — the International System of Units. Here's a list of some of the common quantities you need to know and their SI units.

Exam Tip
Make sure you know what units quantities need to be in for different formulas — it could lose you easy marks if you don't.

Quantity name	*Unit name*	*Unit symbol*
Angle	*radians*	*rad*
Mass	*kilograms*	*kg*
Time	*seconds*	*s*
Energy, work, heat	*joules*	*J*
Absolute temperature	*kelvins*	*K*
Capacitance	*farads*	*F*
Potential difference, e.m.f.	*volts*	*V*
Charge	*coulombs*	*C*
Moment of force	*newton metres*	*Nm*
Power	*watts*	*W*
Magnetic flux	*webers*	*Wb*
Frequency	*hertz*	*Hz*

Figure 2: *Quantities and their SI units.*

Tip: You should already be familiar with all of these units and how to use them — but it's nice to see them all together.

Tip: There are alternative units for some of these quantities which you might be asked to use (e.g. MeV for energy), but these are the standard ones.

Significant figures

Use the number of significant figures given in the question as a guide for how many to give in the answer. You should try to give your answer to the lowest number of significant figures (s.f.) given in the question, and it's always good to write down the full unrounded answer, followed by your rounded answer. You should write down the number of significant figures you've rounded to after your answer too — it shows the examiner you really know what you're talking about.

Tip: The first significant figure of a number is the first digit that isn't a zero. The second, third and fourth significant figures follow on immediately after the first (even if they're zeros).

Examples

In this question the data given to you is a good indication of how many significant figures you should give your answer to.

1 (b) Calculate the electric field strength at this point.
(The charge on an alpha particle is $+3.20 \times 10^{-19}$ C.)

(2 marks)

The data in the question is given to 3 s.f. so it makes sense to give your answer to 3 s.f. too. But sometimes it isn't as clear as that.

3 (b) Calculate the work done in lifting an object with a mass of 14.1 kg from ground level to 11 m above ground.

(1 mark)

There are two types of data in this question — mass data and distance data. The mass data is given to 3 s.f. and the distance data is given to 2 s.f.. You should give your answer to the lowest number of significant figures given — in this case that's to 2 s.f.. The answer (using $g = 9.81$ Nkg^{-1}) is 1521.531 N, so the answer rounded correctly would be 1500 N (to 2 s.f.).

Figure 3: *When doing a long calculation with many stages, you shouldn't round any numbers until the very end. Use your calculator's memory function to store numbers along the way and make your life easier.*

Standard form

Sometimes it's easier to give your answer in standard form, or you might be given values in standard form. Standard form is used for writing very big or very small numbers in a more convenient way. Standard form must always look like this:

$$A \times 10^n$$

This number must always be between 1 and 10. (A)

'n' is the number of places the decimal point moves.

Examples

Here's how to write 3 500 000 in standard form.

- First remove zeros from the right or left until you get to a non-zero number on both sides. Write the rest down with a decimal point after the first digit and a '× 10' after the number:

$$3.5 \times 10$$

- Then count how many places the decimal point has moved to the left. This number sits to the top right of the 10.

6 5 4 3 2 1

$$3\,500\,000 = 3.5 \times 10^6$$

- Et voilà... that's 3 500 000 written in standard form.

Tip: So if the number had been 3 050 000, you'd start by writing 3.05 × 10.

Here are some more examples.

- You can write 450 000 as 4.5×10^5.
- The number 0.000056 is 5.6×10^{-5} in standard form — the n is negative because the decimal point has moved to the right instead of the left.
- You can write 0.003456 as 3.456×10^{-3}.

Tip: Your calculator might give you your answer in standard form already — result.

Answers

Unit 4

Section 1 — Further Mechanics

1. Conservation of Momentum

Page 7 — Application Questions

Q1 Momentum before = Momentum after
$0 = (125 \times v) + (1.0 \times 10) = 125v + 10$
$v = -10 \div 125 = -0.08$ ms^{-1}
So the boat moves at **0.08 ms^{-1}** in the opposite direction to the rock.

Q2 Momentum before = Momentum after
$(0.165 \times 2.25) + (0.165 \times -4.75) = (0.165 \times -4.25) + (0.165 \times v)$
$-0.4125 = -0.70125 + 0.165v$
So $v = 1.75$ ms^{-1}
Kinetic energy before:
$= (0.5 \times 0.165 \times 2.25^2) + (0.5 \times 0.165 \times (-4.75)^2)$
$= 2.2790...$ J
Kinetic energy after:
$= (0.5 \times 0.165 \times (-4.25)^2) + (0.5 \times 0.165 \times (1.75)^2)$
$= 1.7428...$ J
Kinetic energy is not conserved, so this is an inelastic collision.

Q3 Mass (per second) = density × volume (per second)
$= 1000 \times (8.4 \times 10^{-3})$
$= 8.4$ kg
To find the velocity of the water, consider the length of the cylinder of water shot out of the hose per second. This gives you the distance travelled per second.
$$\text{velocity} = \frac{\text{volume of water (per second)}}{\text{cross-sectional area of hose}} = \frac{8.4 \times 10^{-3}}{5.6 \times 10^{-4}} = 15 \text{ ms}^{-1}$$
Momentum = mass × velocity
$= 8.4 \times 15$
$= 126$ kgms^{-1}

Page 7 — Fact Recall Questions

Q1 Linear momentum = mass × velocity

Q2 Linear momentum is always conserved — i.e. the total linear momentum is the same before and after a collision.

Q3 An elastic collision is one where linear momentum and kinetic energy are conserved. An inelastic collision is one where linear momentum is conserved, but kinetic energy is not.
Some kinetic energy lost to the surroundings and/or converted to other forms (such as heat and sound).

2. Force, Momentum and Impulse

Page 10 — Application Questions

Q1 Velocity in ms^{-1} = $(125 \times 1000) \div 3600 = 34.7222...$ ms^{-1}
There are 1000 m in a km and 3600 seconds in an hour.
$$F = \frac{\Delta(mv)}{\Delta t} \Rightarrow \Delta t = \frac{mv - mu}{F} = \frac{(18\,000 \times 0) - (18\,000 \times 34.7222...)}{-62\,000}$$
$= $ **10 s (to 2 s.f.)**

Q2 a)

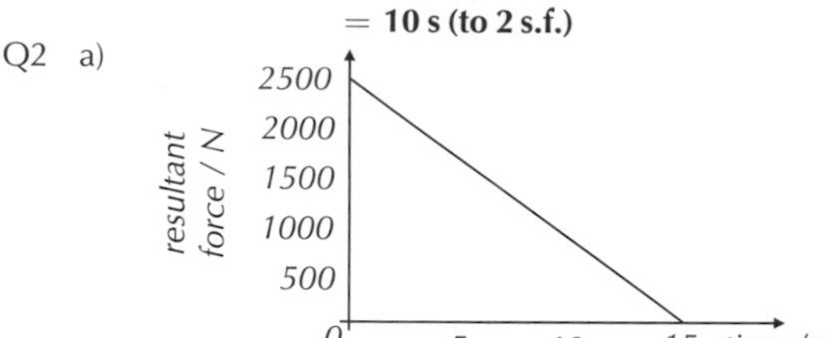

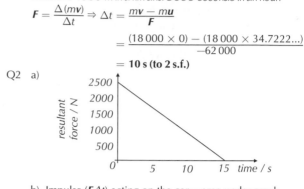

b) Impulse ($F\Delta t$) acting on the car = area under graph
$= \frac{1}{2} \times 15 \times 2500$
$= 18\,750$ Ns
So change in momentum = 18 750 kgms^{-1}
Now find the final velocity v:
$$\Delta(mv) = mv - mu \Rightarrow v = \frac{\Delta(mv) + mu}{m} = \frac{18\,750 + (1200 \times 25)}{1200}$$
$= $ **41 ms^{-1} (to 2 s.f.)**

Q3 a) 57 g = 57×10^{-3} kg.
$$F\Delta t = mv - mu \Rightarrow v = \frac{F\Delta t + mu}{m} = \frac{(-0.57) + [(57 \times 10^{-3}) \times 5.1]}{57 \times 10^{-3}} = -4.9 \text{ ms}^{-1}$$
So the speed = **4.9 ms^{-1}**.
The impulse and final velocity are negative because they're in the opposite direction to the ball's initial velocity.

b) The ball's final speed would be lower (or its velocity would be less negative). The impulse, or change in momentum, would be the same, but its initial momentum (and so velocity) would be higher. So its final speed in the opposite direction would be lower.

Page 10 — Fact Recall Questions

Q1 $F = \frac{\Delta(mv)}{\Delta t}$
Resultant force is equal to the rate of change of momentum.

Q2 Impulse is measured in Ns.

Q3 Impulse is equal to the change in momentum, so you would need to subtract the momentum of the ball before the collision from the momentum of the ball after the collision.

Q4 The area under a force-time graph for an object gives the impulse acting on the object.

3. Circular Motion

Page 13 — Application Questions

Q1 Period in seconds = 28 × 24 × 3600 = 2.419... × 10^6 s

Angular speed = $\omega = \frac{2\pi}{T}$

$= \frac{2\pi}{2.419... \times 10^6}$

$= 2.5972... \times 10^{-6}$ rad s^{-1}

$= \mathbf{2.6 \times 10^{-6}}$ **rad s^{-1} (to 2 s.f.)**

$\omega = \frac{v}{r} \Rightarrow v = r\omega = (384\,000 \times 1000) \times 2.5972... \times 10^{-6}$

$= \mathbf{1000}$ **ms^{-1} (to 2 s.f.)**

Q2 Frequency in s^{-1} = f = 4 ÷ 3600 = 1.1111... × 10^{-3} s^{-1}

$\omega = 2\pi f = 2 \times \pi \times 1.1111... \times 10^{-3}$

$= \frac{\pi}{450}$ rad s^{-1}

$\omega = \frac{\theta}{t} \Rightarrow \theta = \omega t = \frac{\pi}{450} \times 60 = \frac{2}{15}\pi$ **rad**

$\omega = \frac{v}{r} \Rightarrow v = r\omega = \frac{125}{2} \times \frac{\pi}{450}$

$= \mathbf{0.436}$ **ms^{-1} (to 3 s.f)**

Q3 Frequency in s^{-1} = f = 460 ÷ 60

2 cm from centre:

Angular speed = $\omega = 2\pi f = \frac{46}{3}\pi$ **s^{-1}**

Linear speed = $v = r\omega = 0.02 \times \frac{46}{3}\pi$ = **0.96 ms^{-1} (to 2 s.f.)**

4 cm from centre:

Angular speed = $\frac{46}{3}\pi$ **s^{-1}**

Linear speed = $0.04 \times \frac{46}{3}\pi$ = **1.9 ms^{-1} (to 2 s.f.)**

Angular speed is the same at any point on a solid rotating object.

Q4 Kinetic energy = $\frac{1}{2}mv^2$

$\omega = \frac{v}{r} \Rightarrow v = \omega r$

$\omega = 2\pi f \Rightarrow v = 2\pi f r$

$f = \frac{1}{T}$ and r is the length of the string l, so $v = \frac{2\pi l}{T}$

So kinetic energy $= \frac{1}{2}m\left(\frac{2\pi l}{T}\right)^2$

$= \frac{2m\pi^2 l^2}{T^2}$

Page 13 — Fact Recall Questions

Q1 Angle in radians = angle in degrees × $\frac{2\pi}{360}$

Q2 The angle that an object rotates through per second.

Q3 $\omega = \frac{v}{r}$

Q4 The period is the time taken for a complete revolution. The frequency is the number of complete revolutions per second.

Q5 $\omega = 2\pi f$

4. Centripetal Force and Acceleration

Page 16 — Application Questions

Q1 Frequency in s^{-1} = f = 15 ÷ 60 = 0.25 s^{-1}

Angular speed $\omega = 2\pi f = 2 \times \pi \times 0.25 = 0.5\pi$ rad s^{-1}

$\boldsymbol{F} = m\omega^2 r = 60 \times (0.5\pi)^2 \times \frac{8.5}{2}$ = **630 N (to 2 s.f.)**

This might seem like a lot, but it's about the same as the force experienced by the rider due to gravity.

Q2 The correct answer is **c**.

$\boldsymbol{a} = \omega^2 r$ so rearranging gives: $\omega = \sqrt{\frac{\boldsymbol{a}}{r}}$

$\omega = \frac{2\pi}{T}$ so rearranging gives: $T = \frac{2\pi}{\omega}$

So $T = \frac{2\pi}{\sqrt{\frac{\boldsymbol{a}}{r}}} \Rightarrow T = 2\pi\sqrt{\frac{r}{\boldsymbol{a}}}$

So time to complete 3 orbits = $3 \times T = 6\pi\sqrt{\frac{r}{\boldsymbol{a}}}$

Q3 If the biker's speed is the minimum possible speed for him to not fall, the centripetal acceleration towards the centre (i.e. down) at the top of the cylinder will be 9.81 ms^{-2}, due to gravity. The motorcycle will fall if its circular motion requires a centripetal force smaller than this.

So $\boldsymbol{a}$ = 9.81 ms^{-2} = $\frac{v^2}{r}$

Rearranging this: $v = \sqrt{\boldsymbol{a}r}$

$= \sqrt{9.81 \times 5}$ = 7.0 ms^{-1} (to 2 s.f.)

This is only about 16 mph — not very fast at all.

Page 16 — Fact Recall Questions

Q1 If an object is moving in a circle, centripetal acceleration is the acceleration of the object directed towards the centre of the circle. Centripetal force is the force towards the centre of the circle responsible for the centripetal force.

Q2 $\boldsymbol{a} = \omega^2 r$

$\boldsymbol{a}$ = centripetal acceleration in ms^{-2}

ω = angular speed (in rad s^{-1})

r = radius of circular motion in m

Q3 $\boldsymbol{F} = \frac{mv^2}{r}$

$\boldsymbol{F}$ = centripetal force in N

m = mass of object in kg

v = linear speed in ms^{-1}

r = radius of circular motion in m

5. Simple Harmonic Motion

Page 19 — Application Question

Q1 a) The girl's maximum kinetic energy is equal to her maximum gravitational potential energy, i.e.

$\frac{1}{2}mv^2 = mgh$

$= 35 \times 9.8 \times 0.4$

$= 137.2$ J

So $\frac{1}{2}mv^2 = 137.2 \Rightarrow v = \sqrt{\frac{2 \times 137.2}{m}}$

$= \sqrt{\frac{2 \times 137.2}{35}}$

= **2.8 ms^{-1}**

b)

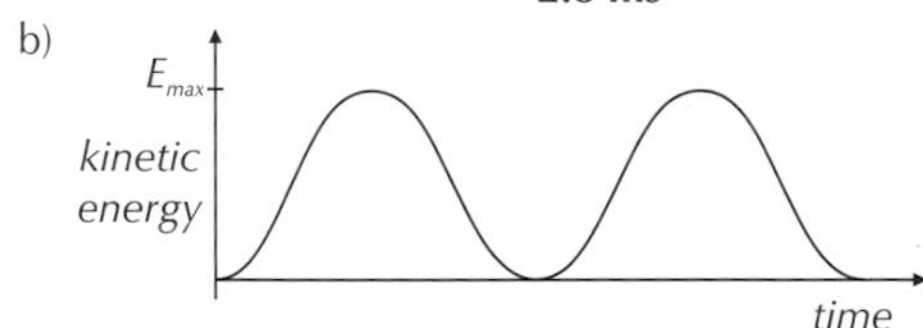

The kinetic energy starts at 0 as the girl starts from rest. It then varies sinusoidally (like a sine wave) between 0 and E_{max} as potential energy is converted to kinetic energy and back. The kinetic energy is at a maximum when the swing is at its lowest point.

Page 19 — Fact Recall Questions

Q1 The oscillation of an object in which the object's acceleration is directly proportional to its displacement from its equilibrium position, and the acceleration is always directed towards the equilibrium.

Q2 The frequency of oscillation is the number of complete cycles per second. The period of oscillation is the time taken for a complete cycle.

Q3 The velocity is $\frac{\pi}{2}$ radians ahead of the displacement.

Q4

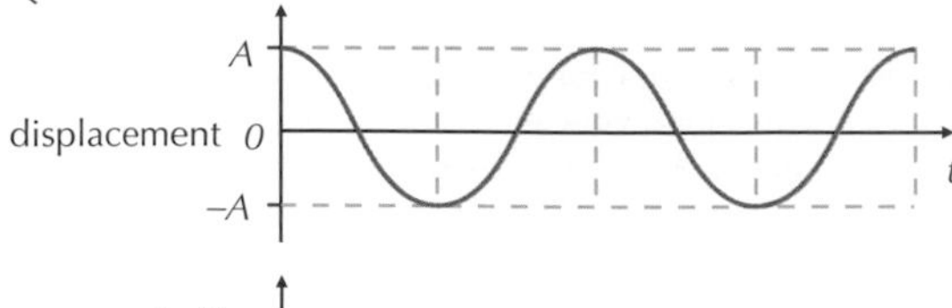

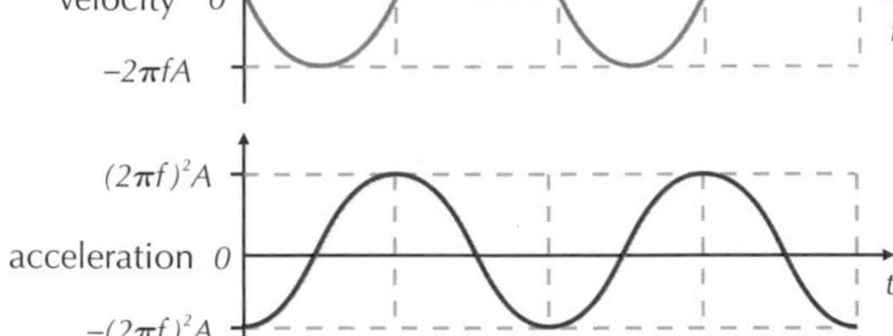

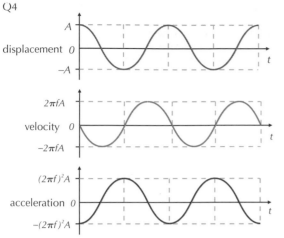

Q5 At its maximum displacement, the object's kinetic energy, E_K, is zero (so it has zero velocity). All of its energy is potential energy, E_P. As the object moves towards the equilibrium position, the restoring force does work on the object and transfers some E_P to E_K. At the equilibrium position, the object's E_P is zero and its E_K is maximum — so its velocity is maximum. As the object moves away from the equilibrium, all that E_K is transferred back to E_P again.

6. Calculations with SHM

Page 22 — Application Questions

Q1 a) Time to complete 1 oscillation = period = $T = \frac{1}{f} = \frac{1}{0.25} = 4$ s

Time to complete 15 oscillations = 15 × 4 = **60 s**

b) Acceleration at $\boldsymbol{x} = A$ given by $\boldsymbol{a} = (2\pi f)^2 A$
$= (2\pi \times 0.25)^2 \times 1.6$
$=$ **3.9 ms⁻² (to 2 s.f.)**

Q2 a) Frequency $= f = \frac{1}{T} = \frac{1}{0.75} = 1.333...\ \text{s}^{-1}$

Maximum velocity is given by: $v_{max} = 2\pi fA$

Rearranging this for amplitude:

$A = \frac{v_{max}}{2\pi f}$
$= \frac{0.85}{2 \times \pi \times 1.3333...}$
$= 0.101...$ m $=$ **0.10 m (to 2 s.f.)**

b) Velocity at $x = 0.1$ m:

$v = 2\pi f\sqrt{A^2 - x^2}$
$= 2 \times \pi \times 1.333... \times \sqrt{0.101...^2 - 0.1^2}$
$=$ **0.14 ms⁻¹ (to 2 s.f.)**

Q3 Period = T = time to complete 5 oscillations ÷ 5
$= \frac{4.5}{5} = 0.9$ s

Frequency $= f = \frac{1}{T} = \frac{1}{0.9} = 1.111...\ \text{s}^{-1}$

Amplitude $= A = 0.45$ m

Displacement at time t: $\boldsymbol{x} = A\cos(2\pi ft)$

At time $t = 10$, $\boldsymbol{x} = 0.45 \times \cos(2\pi \times 1.111... \times 10)$
$=$ **0.34 m (to 2 s.f.)**

Q4 Pendulum passes through equilibrium twice every period, so if it's set to 120 ticks per minute:

Period $= T = 120 \div 2 \div 60 = 1$ s

Frequency $= f = \frac{1}{T} = \frac{1}{1} = 1\ \text{s}^{-1}$

Amplitude $A = 6.2$ cm $= 0.062$ m

Max acceleration $= \boldsymbol{a}_{max} = (2\pi f)^2 A$
$= (2\pi \times 1)^2 \times 0.062$
$=$ **2.4 ms⁻² (to 2 s.f.)**

Page 22 — Fact Recall Questions

Q1 Acceleration $= \boldsymbol{a} = -(2\pi f)^2 x$

Velocity $= v = \pm 2\pi f\sqrt{A^2 - x^2}$

Q2 Displacement $= \boldsymbol{x} = A\cos(2\pi ft)$

Q3 Max velocity $= \boldsymbol{v}_{max} = 2\pi fA$

Q4 The correct answer is **b**.

Q5

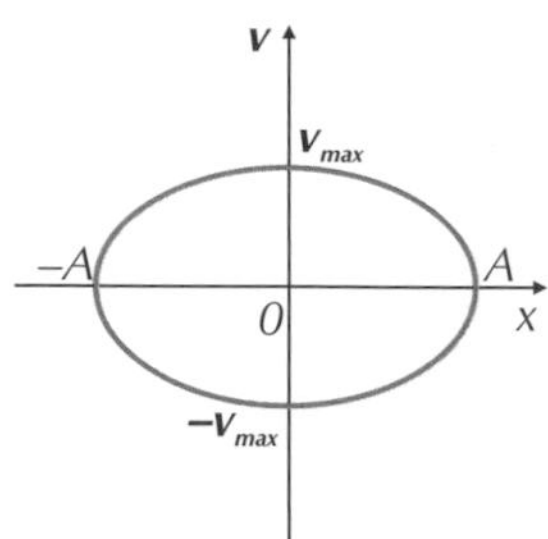

Q6

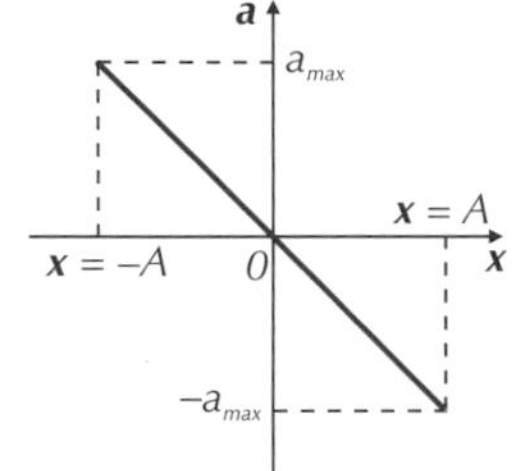

7. Simple Harmonic Oscillators

Page 26 — Application Questions

Q1 $T = 2\pi\sqrt{\frac{l}{g}}$
$= 2\pi\sqrt{\frac{2.50}{9.81}}$
$=$ **3.17 s (to 3 s.f.)**

Q2 Restoring force due to a spring $= \boldsymbol{F} = -k\boldsymbol{x}$

Extension in m $= 2.5 \div 100 = 0.025$ m

Treat each force independently, and add them together:

Force due to first spring $= \boldsymbol{F_1} = -(25 \times 0.025) = -0.625$ N

Force due to second spring $= \boldsymbol{F_2} = -(45 \times 0.025) = -1.125$ N

Total force $= \boldsymbol{F_1} + \boldsymbol{F_2} = -1.75$ N

So the size of the force $= 1.8$ N (to 2 s.f.)

Q3 Extension in m $= \boldsymbol{x} = 45 \div 1000 = 0.045$ m

Force given by: $\boldsymbol{F} = -k\boldsymbol{x}$, so rearranging this for spring constant: $k = -\frac{\boldsymbol{F}}{\boldsymbol{x}} = \frac{18}{0.045} = 400\ \text{Nm}^{-1}$

The force is in the opposite direction to the displacement, so the minus sign disappears.

Period $= T = 2\pi\sqrt{\frac{m}{k}} = 2\pi \times \sqrt{\frac{1}{400}} =$ **0.31 s (to 2 s.f.)**

Page 26 — Fact Recall Questions

Q1 a) Period of oscillation of a mass on a spring
$= T = 2\pi\sqrt{\frac{m}{k}}$

b) Set up a simple pendulum made of a bob at the end of a stiff rod. Attach it to an angle sensor and computer, so the angle of the pendulum can be recorded continuously as it oscillates. Vary each of length, mass and amplitude and observe how the period changes.

Q2 Period of oscillation of a simple pendulum is $T = 2\pi\sqrt{\frac{l}{g}}$

Q3 Graph of period squared against pendulum length:

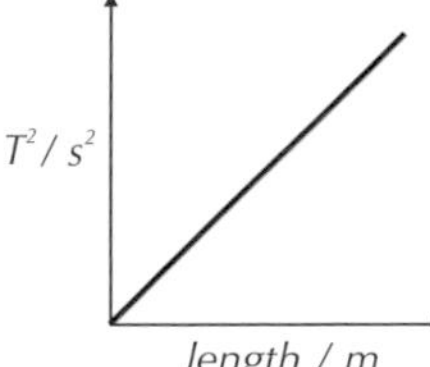

Graph of period squared against mass:

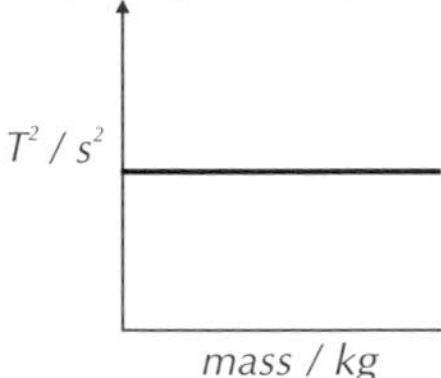

Graph of period squared against amplitude:

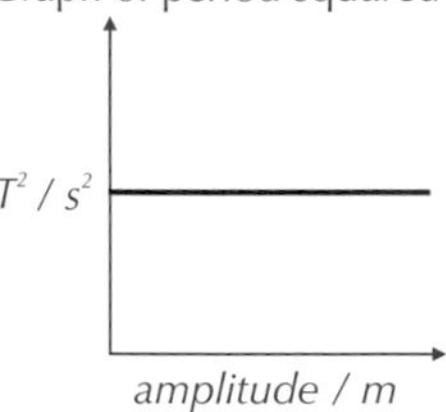

As T is independent of m and A, T^2 is too.

8. Free and Forced Vibrations

Page 30 — Fact Recall Questions

Q1 A free vibration involves no transfer of energy between the oscillating object and its surroundings. The object will continue to oscillate at its natural frequency and with the same amplitude forever. A forced vibration occurs if there's a periodic external driving force acting on the object.

Q2 Resonance occurs when the driving frequency approaches the natural frequency of an object and the object begins to oscillate with a rapidly increasing amplitude.

Q3 E.g. any three from: a radio's electric circuit resonating when it's tuned to the same frequency as a radio station / a glass resonating when driven by a sound wave at its natural frequency / a column of air in an organ pipe resonating when driven by the motion of air at its base / a swing in a playground resonating when it's pushed by someone at its natural frequency.

Q4 a) When the driving frequency is much less than the oscillator's natural frequency, the driver displacement and oscillator displacement are in phase (the oscillator can easily 'keep up' with the driver).

b) When the driving frequency is the same as the natural frequency (resonance), then the driver displacement and oscillator displacement are 90° out of phase.

c) When the driving frequency is much greater than the natural frequency, then the driver and oscillator displacement will be completely out of phase.

Q5 A damping force is a force that acts on an oscillator and causes it to lose energy to its surroundings, reducing the amplitude of its oscillations.

Q6 Light damping — damping such that an oscillating system takes a long time to stop, and the amplitude of the system reduces by only a small amount each period.
Heavy damping — damping such that the system takes less time to stop oscillating than a lightly damped system, and the amplitude gets much smaller each period.
Critical damping — damping such that the amplitude of an oscillating system is reduced (and so the system returns to equilibrium) in the shortest possible time.
Overdamping — extremely heavy damping such that an oscillating system takes longer to return to equilibrium than a critically damped system.

Q7

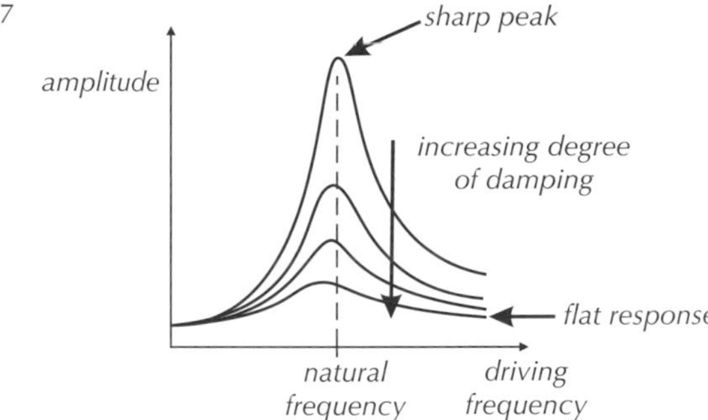

Exam-style Questions – Pages 32-33

1 The correct answer is **B**.
Momentum before = momentum after
$(0.25 \times 1.2) = (0.25 \times v) + (0.25 \times v)$
$v = 0.6$ ms^{-1}

2 The correct answer is **B**.
Maximum kinetic energy = $\frac{1}{2}mv_{max}^2$
Maximum velocity = $2\pi fA = \frac{2\pi A}{T}$ where A = 0.05 m
So maximum kinetic energy = $\frac{1}{2}m\left(\frac{2\pi A}{T}\right)^2$
$= (0.5 \times 1 \times 2^2 \times \pi^2 \times 0.05^2) \div T^2 = \frac{\pi^2}{200T^2}$

3 The correct answer is **C**.
The correct graph needs to show 1 complete cycle (i.e. 2 'peaks') in 3 seconds and zero potential energy at 0 and 1.5 s.

4 (a) This is an inelastic collision because kinetic energy is not conserved — some is converted to sound energy.
(2 marks — 1 mark for saying it is an inelastic collision, 1 mark for explaining that kinetic energy is not conserved.)

(b) (i) Impulse is equal to the change in momentum.
Momentum before = (125 × 2.40) = 300 kg ms^{-1}
Momentum after = 0
So impulse = **–300 kg ms^{-1}**
(2 marks — 1 mark for knowing that impulse is equal to the change in momentum, 1 mark for the correct answer.)

(ii) If the dodgem's initial speed was doubled, it's initial momentum would be doubled, and therefore the impulse would be doubled:
Impulse = 300 × 2 = **600 kg ms^{-1}**
(1 mark for correct answer, or if previous answer incorrect, 1 mark for correctly saying that impulse would double).

(iii) The resultant force acting on a body is equal to the change in momentum per unit time of that body ***(1 mark)***.

5 (a) (i) Period given by $T = 2\pi\sqrt{\frac{m}{k}}$
Rearrange this for k:
$k = \frac{4\pi^2 m}{T^2} = (4 \times \pi^2 \times 1.8) \div 3.2^2$
= 6.9 Nm^{-1} (to 2 s.f.)
(2 marks for correct answer, otherwise 1 mark for using the correct formula.)

(ii) Force given by Hooke's law: $F = -kx$
Maximum force will be at maximum displacement (i.e. the amplitude).
So $F = -6.9 \times 0.22 = -1.5$ N (to 2 s.f.)
So the magnitude of the force = 1.5 N **(to 2 s.f.)**
(2 marks for correct answer, otherwise 1 mark for using the correct formula.)

(iii) Velocity is given by: $v = \pm 2\pi f\sqrt{A^2 - x^2}$
Frequency is $f = 1 \div T = 1 \div 3.2 = 0.3125\ \text{s}^{-1}$
So $v = 2\pi \times 0.3125 \times (0.22^2 - 0.12^2)^{1/2}$
$= 0.3620...\ \text{ms}^{-1}$
Kinetic energy is: $E_K = \frac{1}{2}mv^2 = 0.5 \times 1.8 \times 0.3620...^2$
$=$ **0.12 J (to 2 s.f.)**
(4 marks for correct answer, otherwise 1 mark for calculating frequency, 1 mark for calculating velocity, and 1 mark for using the correct equation for kinetic energy.)

(iv) Max acceleration = $(2\pi f)^2 A$
$= (2 \times \pi \times 0.3125)^2 \times 0.22 = 0.85\ \text{ms}^{-2}$ (to 2 s.f.)

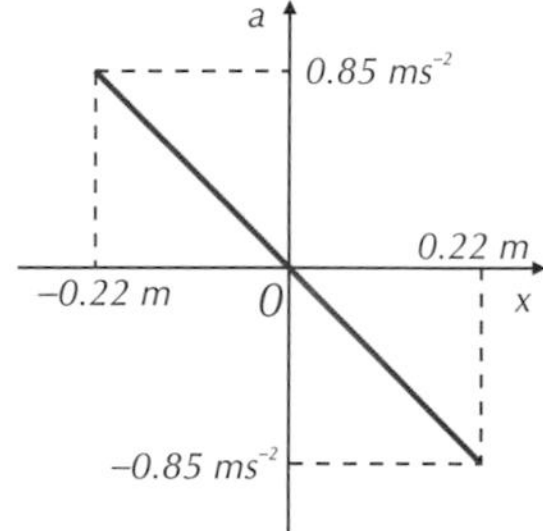

(3 marks — 1 mark for correct shape, 1 mark for calculating maximum acceleration, and 1 mark for indicating that they occur at the maximum displacement.)

(b) (i) The amplitude of the pendulum's oscillation will increase rapidly around its natural frequency ***(1 mark)***. This is called resonance ***(1 mark)***.

(ii) E.g. friction with the water acts to dampen the oscillation ***(1 mark)***. The resonance will occur at a frequency slightly less than the pendulum's natural frequency ***(1 mark)***. The pendulum's response will be flatter (i.e. the resonance peak will be less sharp) ***(1 mark)***.

Section 2 — Gravitation and Electric Fields

1. Gravitational Fields

Page 36 — Application Questions

Q1 $F = \frac{Gm_1m_2}{r^2}$
$= \frac{(6.67 \times 10^{-11}) \times (2.45 \times 10^{30}) \times (2.91 \times 10^{30})}{(1 \times 10^{11})^2}$
$=$ **4.76×10^{28} N (to 3 s.f.)**

Q2 $\frac{2.5}{0.5} = 5$, so the force will be $5^2 = 25$ times larger:
$25 \times 25 =$ **625 N**

Q3 a) 6 370 000 m + 10 000 m = 6 380 000 m = **6380 km**
b) The upwards force must balance the downwards force due to gravity:
$F = \frac{Gm_1m_2}{r^2}$
$= \frac{(6.67 \times 10^{-11}) \times (2500) \times (5.98 \times 10^{24})}{(6380 \times 10^3)^2}$
$=$ **24 500 N (to 3 s.f.)**

Page 36 — Fact Recall Questions

Q1 Any object with a mass will feel an attractive force due to gravity.

Q2 A gravitational field is a region in which an object will experience an attractive force (due to gravity).

Q3 a) $F = \frac{Gm_1m_2}{r^2}$
b) G is the gravitational constant, $6.67 \times 10^{-11}\ \text{Nm}^2\text{kg}^{-2}$.
c) The masses must be point masses, or act like uniform spheres (where all the mass acts as if it is at the centre).

Q4 a)

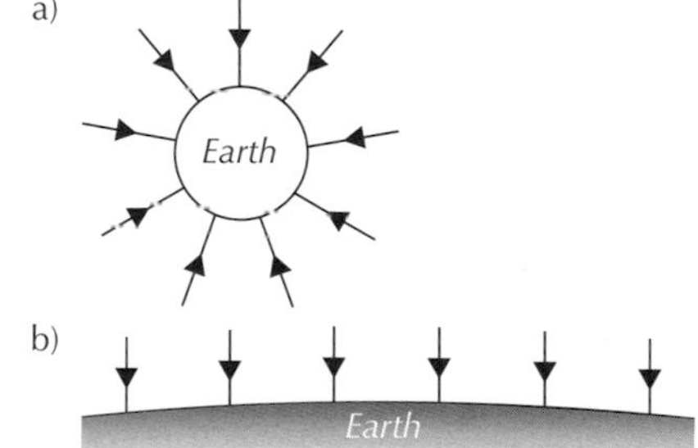

b)

2. Gravitational Field Strength

Page 39 — Application Questions

Q1 $g = \frac{F}{m} = \frac{581}{105} =$ **5.53 Nkg^{-1} (to 3 s.f.)**

Q2 $g = \frac{F}{m}$, so $F = gm$. The value of g is lower on the Moon, which means an object with the same mass will experience less force due to gravity (and so be easier to lift).

Q3 g due to the larger mass:
$g = \frac{GM}{r^2} = \frac{3Gm}{9x^2}$
g due to the smaller mass:
$g = \frac{GM}{r^2} = \frac{Gm}{(3x + x)^2} = \frac{Gm}{16x^2}$
Total g:
$g = \frac{3Gm}{9x^2} + \frac{Gm}{16x^2} =$ **$\frac{19Gm}{48x^2}$ (or $0.395...\frac{Gm}{x^2}$)**
The gravitational field for both objects is in the same direction, so it doesn't matter which way you add them up — in this case, left is positive.

Page 39 — Fact Recall Questions

Q1 $\boldsymbol{g}$ is the gravitational field strength (or the force per unit mass due to gravity), measured in Nkg^{-1}.

Q2 M is the mass of the object creating the gravitational field.

Q3 The correct graph is c).

3. Gravitational Potential

Page 42 — Application Questions

Q1 a) No change (G is a constant)

b) V will double (twice as negative) as it's related to $\frac{1}{r}$ ($V = -\frac{GM}{r}$).

c) $\boldsymbol{g}$ will be four times bigger as it's related to $\frac{1}{r^2}$ ($\boldsymbol{g} = -\frac{\Delta V}{\Delta r}$).

d) No change (mass is the same everywhere).

Q2 $\Delta W = m\Delta V = 1.72 \times 531$

$= \mathbf{913\ J}$ **(to 3 s.f.)**

Page 42 — Fact Recall Questions

Q1 Gravitational potential is the gravitational potential energy that a unit mass would have at a point. It's measured in Jkg^{-1}.

Q2

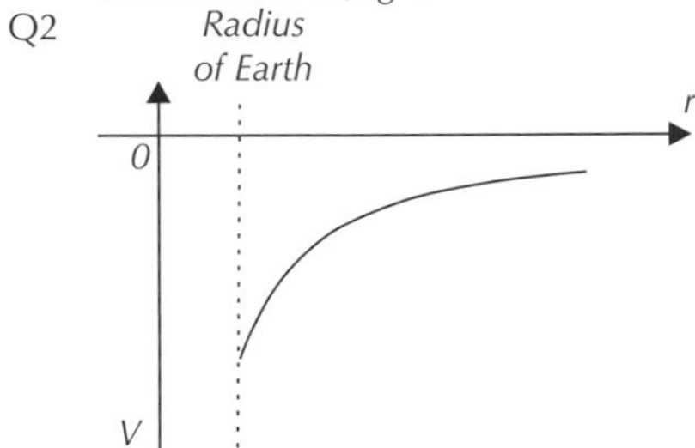

Q3 The gradient tells you the value of $-\boldsymbol{g}$ at that point.

Q4 ΔW is the work done.

4. Orbits

Page 44 — Fact Recall Questions

Q1 The speed of a satellite is inversely proportional to the square root of the radius of its orbit ($v \propto \frac{1}{\sqrt{r}}$), so as the radius increases the speed decreases.

Q2 The orbital period of a satellite is proportional to the square root of the radius cubed ($T \propto \sqrt{r^3}$), so as the radius increases the orbital period increases.

Q3 The total energy of a satellite is always the same. Because its gravitational potential energy is higher when its height is larger, its kinetic energy (and so speed) must be lower, and vice versa.

Q4 A geosynchronous satellite is a satellite that orbits directly over the equator and is always above the same point on Earth. It has an orbital period of 1 day.

Q5 Geosynchronous satellites are always above the same point of the Earth, so receivers don't need to be repositioned to keep up with them.

5. Electric Fields

Page 48 — Application Questions

Q1 $\boldsymbol{F} = \frac{1}{4\pi\varepsilon_0}\frac{Q_1Q_2}{r^2}$

$= \frac{1}{4\pi \times (8.85 \times 10^{-12})} \frac{(-1.60 \times 10^{-19})^2}{(5.22 \times 10^{-13})^2}$

$= \mathbf{8.45 \times 10^{-4}\ N}$ **(to 3 s.f.)**

Q2 Start by rearranging the formula for the magnitude of $\boldsymbol{E}$ to make r the subject:

$\boldsymbol{E} = \frac{1}{4\pi\varepsilon_0}\frac{Q}{r^2} \Rightarrow r^2 = \frac{1}{4\pi\varepsilon_0}\frac{Q}{\boldsymbol{E}}$

$\Rightarrow r = \sqrt{\frac{1}{4\pi\varepsilon_0}\frac{Q}{\boldsymbol{E}}}$

Then put the numbers in:

$r = \sqrt{\frac{1}{4\pi \times (8.85 \times 10^{-12})}\frac{4.15 \times 10^{-6}}{15\,000}}$

$= \mathbf{1.58\ m}$ **(to 3 s.f.)**

Q3 If the particle isn't moving, the upwards force from the electric field must balance the particle's weight, i.e.

$m\boldsymbol{g} = \boldsymbol{E}Q = \frac{VQ}{d}$

This comes from weight = $m\boldsymbol{g}$, $\boldsymbol{E} = \frac{\boldsymbol{F}}{Q}$ and $\boldsymbol{E} = \frac{V}{d}$.

Rearrange this to make d the subject, then put in the numbers:

$m\boldsymbol{g} = \frac{VQ}{d} \Rightarrow d = \frac{VQ}{m\boldsymbol{g}}$

$= \frac{(5.00 \times 10^{-9}) \times 2(1.60 \times 10^{-19})}{(6.64 \times 10^{-27}) \times 9.81}$

$= 0.02456...\text{ m} = \mathbf{2.46\ cm}$ **(to 3 s.f.)**

Page 48 — Fact Recall Questions

Q1 $\boldsymbol{F} = \frac{1}{4\pi\varepsilon_0}\frac{Q_1Q_2}{r^2}$

Q2 $\boldsymbol{E}$ is a measure of the force per unit charge (in an electric field).

Q3

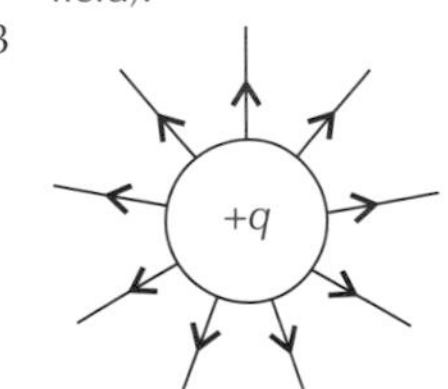

Q4 A uniform field is created.

6. Electric Potential

Page 51 — Application Questions

Q1 a) $V = \frac{1}{4\pi\varepsilon_0}\frac{Q}{r} = \frac{1}{4\pi\varepsilon_0}\frac{12.6 \times 10^{-6}}{5.19 \times 10^{-2}}$

$= \mathbf{2.18 \times 10^6\ V}$ **(to 3 s.f.)**

b) First find the new potential at the centre of the smaller sphere:

$V = \frac{1}{4\pi\varepsilon_0}\frac{Q}{r} = \frac{1}{4\pi\varepsilon_0}\frac{12.6 \times 10^{-6}}{((5.19 \times 10^{-2}) + (12.9 \times 10^{-2}))}$

$= 6.26... \times 10^5\text{ V}$

Then find the work done:

$\Delta W = Q\Delta V$

$= (0.152 \times 10^{-6}) \times [(2.18 \times 10^6) - (6.26... \times 10^5)]$

$= \mathbf{0.237\ J}$ **(to 3 s.f.)**

Q2 $\Delta W = Q\Delta V \Rightarrow \Delta V = \frac{\Delta W}{Q}$

$= \frac{5.14 \times 10^{-6}}{83.1 \times 10^{-9}}$

$= \mathbf{61.9\ V}$ **(to 3 s.f.)**

Page 51 — Fact Recall Questions

Q1 Electric potential is the electric potential energy that a unit positive charge (+1 C) would have at a particular point.

Q2 a) b)

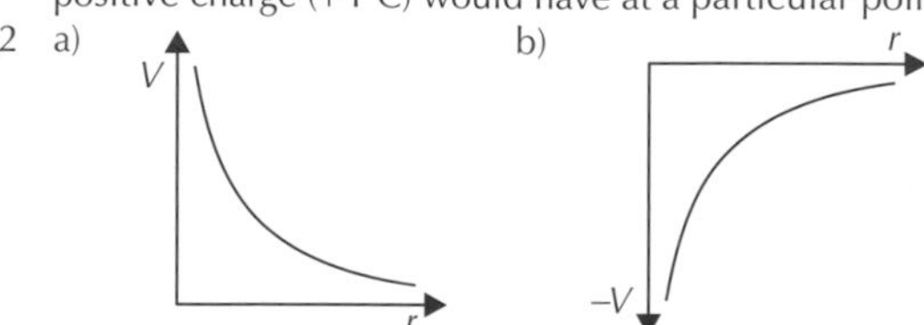

Q3 The electric potential difference between two points is the energy needed to move a unit charge between those points.

Q4 ΔW = work done in moving a charge.
Q = the charge being moved.
ΔV = electric potential difference through which the charge is moved.

7. Comparing Electric and Gravitational Fields

Page 52 — Fact Recall Questions

Q1 E.g.

1. Gravitational field strength $\boldsymbol{g}$ is the force a unit mass would experience in a gravitational field. Electric field strength $\boldsymbol{E}$ is the force a unit positive charge would experience in an electric field.
2. Newton's law and Coulomb's are the same but with G switched for $\frac{1}{4\pi\varepsilon_0}$ and m (or M) switched for Q.
3. Field lines for a radial gravitational field and a radial electric field have the same shape.
4. Gravitational potential V and electric potential V give the energy a unit mass or charge would have at a point.

Q2 E.g. Gravitational forces are always attractive but electric forces can be attractive or repulsive.

Exam-style Questions — Pages 54-56

1 The correct answer is **C** ***(1 mark)***.
Electric forces can be positive or negative.

2 The correct answer is **A** ***(1 mark)***.
There will be a uniform electric field pointing from the 100 V plate to the 0 V plate. The alpha particle is charged, so there will be an electrical force on it in this direction.

3 The correct answer is **B** ***(1 mark)***.
Gravitational field strength decreases as you move away from the mass by the inverse square law.

4 The correct answer is **A** ***(1 mark)***.
Take right to be the positive direction, then sum the gravitational field strength due to each mass:
$g = \frac{G(2m)}{r^2} - \frac{Gm}{r^2} = \frac{Gm}{r^2}$ (to the right).

5 (a) A force field is a region in which a body experiences a force. ***(1 mark)***

(b) (i) No — $\boldsymbol{g}$ depends on the distance from the centre of the Earth, so the height difference in a classroom will have a negligible effect. ***(2 marks — 1 mark for correct answer and 1 mark for correct reasoning.)***

(ii) $\boldsymbol{g} = \frac{GM}{r^2} \Rightarrow r = \sqrt{\frac{(6.67 \times 10^{-11}) \times (5.98 \times 10^{24})}{6.31}}$

$= 7.950... \times 10^6$ m

$= 7950.58...$ km

So altitude = 7950.58... – 6370 = **1580 km (to 3 s.f.)**
(3 marks for correct answer, otherwise 1 mark for correct rearrangement of formula to make r the subject and 1 mark for attempting to find the altitude by subtracting the radius of the Earth.)

(c) (i) First find the distance r:

$V = -\frac{GM}{r} \Rightarrow r = -\frac{GM}{V}$

$= -\frac{(6.67 \times 10^{-11}) \times (5.98 \times 10^{24})}{-20.6 \times 10^6}$

$= 1.936... \times 10^7$ m

Then find $\boldsymbol{g}$:

$\boldsymbol{g} = \frac{GM}{r^2}$

$= \frac{(6.67 \times 10^{-11}) \times (5.98 \times 10^{24})}{(1.936... \times 10^7)^2}$

$= 1.0639...$ Nkg^{-1}

$= \mathbf{1.06\ Nkg^{-1}}$ **(to 3 s.f.)**

(3 marks for correct answer, otherwise 1 mark for rearranging to make r the subject and 1 mark for correct r.)

(ii) $\boldsymbol{F} = mg = (2.53 \times 103) \times 1.063...$
= **2690 N (to 3 s.f.)** ***(1 mark)***

(d) A geosynchronous orbit ***(1 mark)***.

6 (a) (i) A uniform electric field is produced, pointing from the plate with the more positive potential to the plate with the less positive potential. ***(1 mark for uniform electric field, 1 mark for direction.)***

(ii) A radial electric field is produced, pointing away from the particle. ***(1 mark for radial electric field, 1 mark for direction.)***

(b) (i) $\Delta V = \frac{1}{4\pi\varepsilon_0}\frac{Q}{r}$

$= \frac{1}{4\pi\varepsilon_0}\frac{[79 \times (1.60 \times 10^{-19})]}{2.08 \times 10^{-12}}$

$= \mathbf{5.46 \times 10^4\ V}$ **(to 3 s.f.)**

(2 marks for correct answer, otherwise 1 mark for using correct value for Q (1.264×10^{-17}).)

(ii) $\Delta W = Q\Delta V$

$= 2 \times (1.6 \times 10^{-19}) \times (5.46... \times 10^4)$

$= \mathbf{1.74... \times 10^{-14}\ J}$

Work done in bringing the particle to a stop = loss in kinetic energy.

$\Delta W = E_k = \frac{1}{2}mv^2$

$\Rightarrow v = \sqrt{\frac{2E_k}{m}}$

$= \sqrt{\frac{2 \times 1.74... \times 10^{-14}}{6.64 \times 10^{-27}}}$

$= \mathbf{2.29 \times 10^6\ ms^{-1}}$ **(to 3 s.f.)**

(4 marks for correct answer, otherwise 1 mark for finding the work done, 1 mark for relating this to the kinetic energy lost and 1 mark for rearranging to find v.)

7 (a) $g = \frac{F}{m} \Rightarrow F = mg$

$= (203 \times 10^{-3}) \times 9.81$

$= 1.99\text{ N}$ (to 3 s.f.)

(1 mark)

(b) $F = \frac{1}{4\pi\varepsilon_0}\frac{Q_1Q_2}{r^2}$

$\Rightarrow r = \sqrt{\frac{1}{4\pi\varepsilon_0}\frac{Q_1Q_2}{F}}$

$= \sqrt{\frac{1}{4\pi\varepsilon_0}\frac{(-92.5 \times 10^{-6})(-34.7 \times 10^{-6})}{1.99...}}$

$=$ **3.81 m (to 3 s.f.)**

(4 marks for correct answer, otherwise 1 mark for use of correct formula, 1 mark for attempt to make r the subject and 1 mark for correct rearrangement.)

If you didn't get the correct answer for part a) but your calculations were all correct here, you get full marks as long as you used the same number as in part a) for F.

(c) (i) $\Delta W = Q\Delta V \Rightarrow \Delta V = \frac{\Delta W}{Q}$

$= \frac{18.5 \times 10^{-3}}{92.5 \times 10^{-6}}$

$=$ **200 V**

(2 marks for correct answer, otherwise 1 mark for correct rearrangement to make ΔV the subject.)

(ii) $E = \frac{V}{d} = \frac{200}{10.4 \times 10^{-2}}$

$=$ **1920 Vm^{-1} (to 3 s.f.)**

(1 mark)

Section 3 — Capacitance

1. Capacitors

Page 59 — Application Questions

Q1 $C = \frac{Q}{V}$ rearranged gives $Q = CV = 0.1 \times 230 =$ **23 C**

Q2 E.g. it would have to be very large to provide enough power and it could only power the device for a short time so it would need charging very often and it would be very dangerous.

Page 59 — Fact Recall Questions

Q1 The capacitance of an object is the amount of charge it is able to store per unit potential difference (p.d.) across it.

Q2 $C = \frac{Q}{V}$

Q3 ⊣⊢

Q4 E.g. use a variable resistor — constantly alter the resistance in the circuit to keep the current the same.

Q5 Any one of: e.g. camera flash / back-up power / smoothing out voltage supplies.

2. Energy Stored by Capacitors

Page 61 — Application Questions

Q1 $E = \frac{1}{2}CV^2 = \frac{1}{2} \times 40 \times 10^{-3} \times 230^2 =$ **1060 J (to 3 s.f.)**

Q2 $Q = It = 0.025 \times 10^{-3} \times 45 = 1.125 \times 10^{-3}\text{ C}$

$E = \frac{1}{2}\frac{Q^2}{C} = \frac{1}{2} \times \frac{(1.125 \times 10^{-3})^2}{5 \times 10^{-6}} =$ **0.13 J (to 2 s.f.)**

Page 61 — Fact Recall Questions

Q1 Like charges are forced together, against their electrostatic repulsion, onto the plates. Some of the energy taken to force them together is stored as electrical potential energy.

Q2 Electrical potential energy.

Q3 $E = \frac{1}{2}QV = \frac{1}{2}CV^2 = \frac{1}{2}\frac{Q^2}{C}$

3. Charging and Discharging

Page 66 — Application Questions

Q1 a) The capacitor losing 63% of its charge is the same as the capacitor discharging to 37% of its original charge, which takes a time equal to the time constant $\tau = RC$.
$\tau = RC = 400 \times 10^3 \times 15 \times 10^{-6} =$ **6 s**

b) $C = \frac{\tau}{R} = \frac{60}{400 \times 10^3} =$ **1.5 × 10^{-4} F**

c) The capacitor would have to be a lot bigger than the original one. The resistance of the resistor could be increased instead.

Q2 When the capacitor is fully charged, the charge is $Q = CV = 15 \times 10^{-9} \times 230 = 3.45 \times 10^{-6}\text{ C}$
Then after 0.01 seconds,
$Q = Q_0 e^{-\frac{t}{RC}} = 3.45 \times 10^{-6} \times e^{-\frac{0.01}{(50 \times 10^3)(15 \times 10^{-9})}}$
$=$ **5.59 × 10^{-12} C (to 3 s.f.)**

Q3 a) $\frac{Q}{Q_0} = 0.3$

b) $\frac{Q}{Q_0} = e^{-\frac{t}{RC}}$ so $0.3 = e^{-\frac{20}{RC}} \Rightarrow \ln 0.3 = \ln(e^{-\frac{20}{RC}})$

$\Rightarrow \ln 0.3 = -\frac{20}{RC} \Rightarrow RC = -\frac{20}{\ln 0.3} =$ **16.6 s (to 3 s.f.)**

Page 66 — Fact Recall Questions

Q1 Electrons flow from the negative terminal of the battery to the capacitor plate connected to it. This is due to them being repelled by the negative terminal, and attracted by the positive capacitor plate (which is positively charged due to electrons flowing from it to the positive battery terminal). The electrical insulator between the plates lets no charge pass across so it builds up on the plate.

Q2

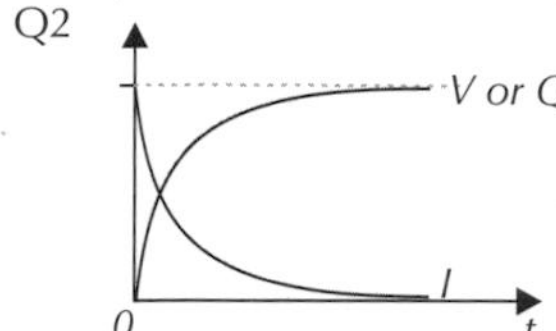

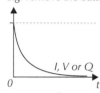

Q3 Resistance of the resistor and capacitance of the capacitor.

Q4 E.g. remove the battery and reconnect the circuit.

Q5

Q6 $Q = Q_0 e^{-\frac{t}{RC}}$

Q7 The time taken for the capacitor to discharge to $\frac{1}{e}$ (about 37%) of its original charge.

Exam-style Questions — page 68-70

1 The correct answer is **A** ***(1 mark)***.

The charge increases quickly and then levels off as it charges, and decreases quickly and then levels off as it discharges.

2 The correct answer is **C** ***(1 mark)***.

$Q = Q_0 e^{-\frac{t}{RC}}$ so $\frac{Q}{Q_0} = e^{-\frac{t}{RC}}$ where $\frac{Q}{Q_0}$ is 0.65.

So $\ln(0.65) = -\frac{1}{100 \times 10^3 \times C}$

so $C = -\frac{1}{100 \times 10^3 \times \ln(0.65)} = 2.3 \times 10^{-5}$ F (to 2 s.f.)

3 The correct answer is **C** ***(1 mark)***.

$Q = CV = 5 \times 10^{-3} \times 24 = 0.12$ C

and $Q = It$, so $I = \frac{Q}{t} = \frac{0.12}{30} = 4 \times 10^{-3}$ A $= 4$ mA

4 The correct answer is **B** ***(1 mark)***.

$E = \frac{1}{2}CV^2 = \frac{1}{2} \times 20 \times 10^{-6} \times 24^2 = 5.76 \times 10^{-3}$ J $= 5.76$ mJ

(Remember, the charge stored by capacitor is half the energy supplied by the power source.)

5 (a) (i)

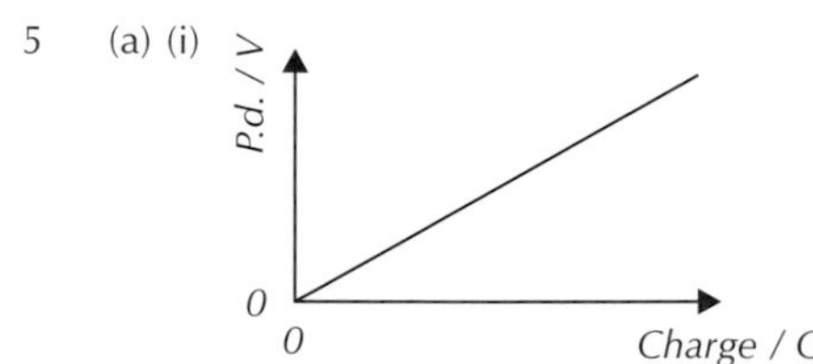

(1 mark for straight line through the origin.)

(ii) 1 / capacitance ***(1 mark)***.

(iii) Energy stored by the capacitor ***(1 mark)***.

Notice that the area enclosed by the line and each axis is exactly the same.

(b) (i) Power $= \frac{energy}{time}$, so $t = \frac{E}{P}$

$E = \frac{1}{2}CV^2 = \frac{1}{2} \times 0.1 \times 12^2 = 7.2$ J

So $t = \frac{7.2}{15} =$ **0.48 s.**

(3 marks for correct answer, otherwise 1 mark for finding the energy and 1 mark for substituting into the correct formula t = $\frac{E}{P}$.)

(ii)

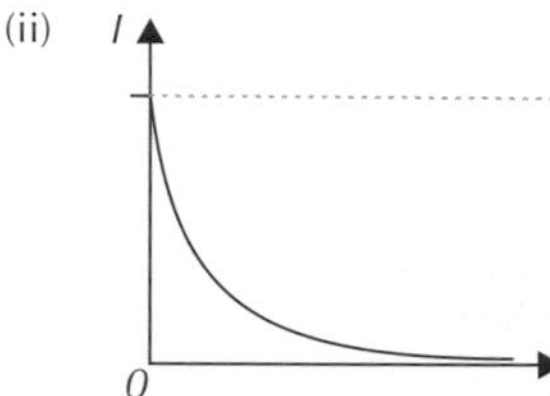

(1 mark for correct shape.)

(iii) Any one from: e.g. it would need to be very large / it would need to be recharged very often / it would not supply a constant current, meaning the intensity of light would drop over time.

(1 mark for any sensible answer.)

6 (a) The energy stored by the capacitor is half of the energy taken from the battery, so the capacitor stores 3.75 J of energy ***(1 mark)***.

Alternatively, you could use the formula for energy stored, $E = \frac{1}{2}CV^2$.

(b) (i) $\tau = RC = 2000 \times 3 \times 10^{-3} =$ **6 s** ***(1 mark)***

(ii) When the capacitor has lost 90% of its charge,

$\frac{Q}{Q_0} = 0.1$. Now $Q = Q_0 e^{-\frac{t}{RC}}$

so $t = -RC\ln\left(\frac{Q}{Q_0}\right) = -\tau\ln\left(\frac{Q}{Q_0}\right)$

$= -6 \times \ln(0.1) = 13.8... =$ **14 s (to 2 s.f.)**

(1 mark for correct rearrangement of the formula, 1 mark for Q/Q₀ = 0.1.)

(iii)

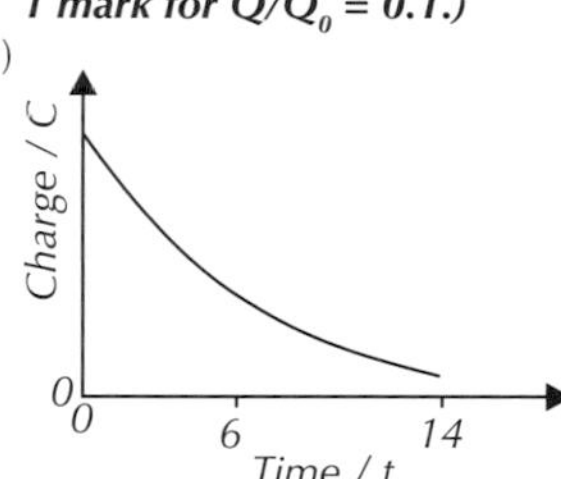

(1 mark for shape — charge should decrease to around 37% at 6 s and 10% at 14 s.)

Section 4 — Magnetic Fields

1. Magnetic Flux Density

Page 74 — Application Question

Q1 a) The force will act upwards.

b) $F = BIl = (9.21 \times 10^{-3}) \times 1.44 \times (2.51 \times 10^{-2})$
$= \mathbf{3.33 \times 10^{-4}\ N\ (to\ 3\ s.f.)}$

c) Change the d.c. supply for an a.c. supply.
When the direction of the current changes, the direction of the force will also change. So if the current changes direction rapidly (as in an a.c. supply) the wire will be pushed rapidly in opposite directions and vibrate.

Page 74 – Fact Recall Questions

Q1 a) You can use your left hand.

b) The first (index) finger represents the direction of the magnetic field, the second (middle) finger represents the direction of the current, and the thumb represents the direction of the force (or motion).

Q2 The current-carrying wire must be perpendicular to the magnetic field.

Q3 $\boldsymbol{B}$ is the magnetic flux density, measured in teslas (T).

2. Forces on Charged Particles

Page 78 — Application Questions

Q1 Only charged particles experience a force from magnetic fields (neutrons have no charge).

Q2 The force will act upwards (using the left-hand rule).
Because the particle is negatively charged, you need to point your second finger in the opposite direction to its actual motion. Or you could use your right hand instead.

Q3 $F = BQv$
$= (640 \times 10^{-3}) \times (3.2 \times 10^{-19}) \times (5.5 \times 10^{3})$
$= \mathbf{1.13 \times 10^{-15}\ N\ (to\ 3\ s.f.)}$

Q4 a) $F = \frac{mv^2}{r}$, $F = BQv$

$\Rightarrow \frac{mv^2}{r} = BQv$

$\Rightarrow B = \frac{mv^2}{Qvr}$

Cancelling the 'v's:

$B = \frac{mv}{Qr}$

b) $B = \frac{mv}{Qr}$

$= \frac{(1.67 \times 10^{-27}) \times (1.99 \times 10^{7})}{(1.60 \times 10^{-19}) \times 5.49}$

$= \mathbf{0.0378\ T\ \ (to\ 3\ s.f.)}$

Page 78 — Fact Recall Questions

Q1 It will follow a circular path.

Q2 Charged particles are produced and fired into a semicircular electrode, where a uniform magnetic field is applied perpendicular to the particle's motion. The particle follows a circular path and leaves the electrode, where it's accelerated by a potential difference before entering another semicircular electrode. Here it follows a slightly larger circular path due to its increased speed, before leaving the electrode. This process repeats, with the direction of the potential difference switching each time, until the particle finally exits the cyclotron at a very high speed.

3. Electromagnetic Induction

Page 81 — Application Question

Q1 a) Flux linkage is at its greatest when the area is normal to the magnetic field. If the angle with the normal is increased, the flux linkage decreases.
This is because the number of field lines passing through the area decreases.

b) $N\Phi = BAN \Rightarrow B = \frac{N\Phi}{AN}$

$= \frac{1.3 \times 10^{-6}}{(25 \times 10^{-4}) \times 10}$

$= 5.2 \times 10^{5}\ T = \mathbf{52\ \mu T}$

Don't forget to convert the area to m^2.

c) E.g. he could increase the area of the coil / increase the number of turns in the coil.
Increasing the area or the number of turns of the coil will increase the flux linkage of the coil, which will reduce the percentage error in the measurements.

Page 81 — Fact Recall Questions

Q1 An e.m.f. (and a current if the conductor is part of a circuit).

Q2 $\Phi = BA$

Q3 Flux linkage is measured in weber (Wb) turns.

Q4 $(N\Phi) = BAN\cos\theta$
$N\Phi$ is the flux linkage in Wb turns.
B is the magnetic flux density in T.
A is the area of the coil inside the magnetic field in m^2.
N is the number of turns on a coil.
θ is the angle between the normal to the plane of the coil and the magnetic field in °.

4. Faraday's Law and Lenz's Law

Page 85 — Application Questions

Q1 The plane's wings act as a conductor, and the Earth has a magnetic field that the plane cuts through, so electromagnetic induction occurs.

Q2 a) $\varepsilon_{max} = BAN\omega$
$= 1.5 \times 0.24 \times 50 \times 4\pi$
$= \mathbf{72\pi\ V\ (= 226\ V\ to\ 3\ s.f.)}$

Remember the maximum induced e.m.f. is when $\sin\omega t = 1$ (or −1).

b)

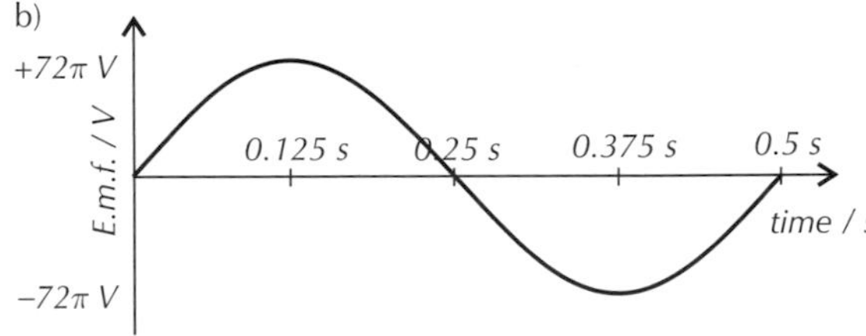

The coil does 1 full rotation in 0.5 s — 4π rad s^{-1} is equal to 720° per second.

c)

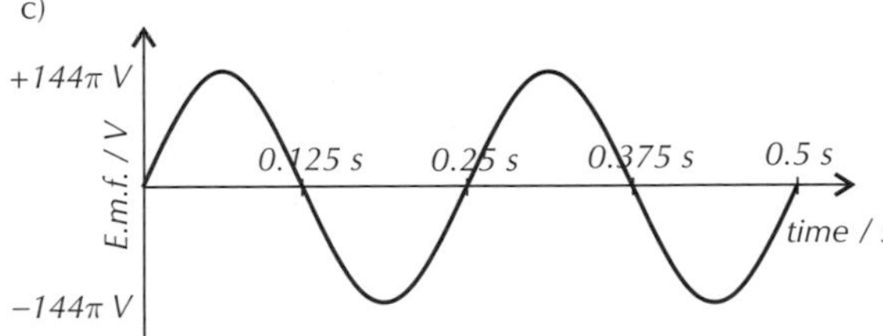

Doubling the speed will double both the frequency and the amplitude of the induced e.m.f.

Page 85 — Fact Recall Questions

Q1 Faraday's law states that the induced e.m.f. is directly proportional to the rate of change of flux linkage.

Q2 Rate of change of flux linkage = $N\frac{\Delta\Phi}{\Delta t}$.

Q3 Lenz's law states that the induced e.m.f. is always in such a direction as to oppose the change that caused it.

Q4 a)

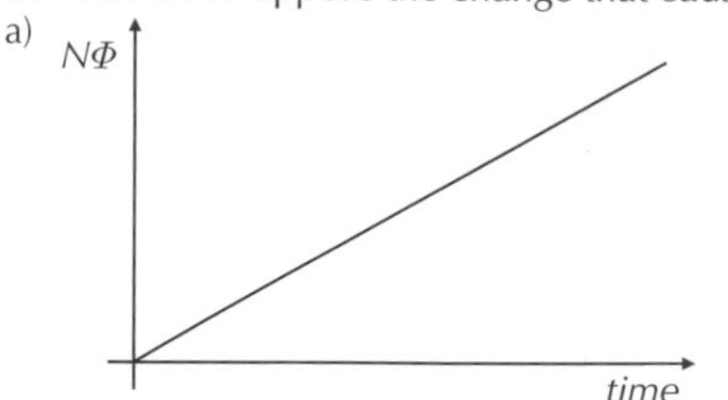

b) $N\Phi$ / Wb turns

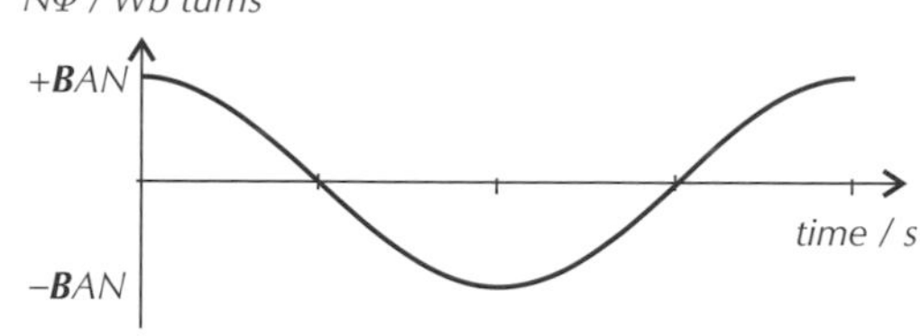

5. Transformers

Page 89 — Application Questions

Q1 The correct answer is a).

Q2 efficiency $= \frac{I_sV_s}{I_pV_p} = \frac{P_s}{P_p}$

$= \frac{62}{65}$

$=$ **0.95 (or 95%) (to 2 s.f.)**

Remember P = IV.

Q3 a) Any two from: e.g. resistance in the coils causes them to heat up; energy is lost when the core magnetises and demagnetises; induced eddy currents in the core cause it to heat up.

b) (i) A step-down transformer.

(ii) Efficiency $= \frac{I_sV_s}{I_pV_p} \Rightarrow I_p = \frac{[I_sV_s]}{\text{Efficiency} \times V_p}$

$= \frac{120}{0.85 \times 230}$

$=$ **0.61 A (to 2 s.f.)**

Page 89 — Fact Recall Questions

Q1 When an alternating current flows through the primary coil, the core magnetises and demagnetises quickly. This causes a rapid change in flux through the secondary coil, which induces an e.m.f.. The more turns in the secondary coil compared to the primary coil, the larger the induced e.m.f.

Remember, e.m.f. is just another way of saying voltage.

Q2 A step-down transformer.

Q3 E.g. using thick copper wires to reduce resistance; using a magnetically soft core that magnetises and demagnetises quickly; laminating the core to prevent eddy currents.

Q4 Power = current × voltage, so increasing the voltage reduces the current for a given amount of power. Energy loss due to heating is proportional to I^2R, so a lower current means less energy loss through heating of the wires.

Exam-Style Questions — Pages 91-93

1 The correct answer is **C** ***(1 mark)***

This is Faraday's law.

2 The correct answer is **B** ***(1 mark)***

Remember e.m.f. = ***Blv***, so it's proportional to the velocity.

3 The correct answer is **B** ***(1 mark)***

Increasing the frequency means the rate of change of flux linkage is larger (same flux change, shorter time), so it increases the maximum induced e.m.f.

4 The correct answer is **A** ***(1 mark)***

The resistance needs to be kept as low as possible to reduce heating in the wires. Thinner wires have a higher resistance.

5 (a) $F = BIl \Rightarrow l = \frac{F}{BI}$

$= \frac{4.5 \times 10^{-2}}{1.7 \times 190 \times 10^{-3}}$

$= 0.139... =$ **14 cm (to 2 s.f.)**

(2 marks for correct answer, 1 mark for correct working if answer incorrect.)

(b) E.g. by running an alternating current through the wire. By rotating the magnetic field (or using an alternating magnetic field). ***(1 mark for each method.)***

(c) (i) The current flows from Q to P ***(1 mark)***.

You could give anticlockwise as your answer.

(ii) $N\Phi = BAN\cos\theta$

$= 1.7 \times (10 \times 10^{-4}) \times 1 \times \cos 41°$

$= 0.00128... =$ **0.13×10^{-3} Wb turns (to 2 s.f.)**

(2 marks for correct answer, 1 mark for correct calculation and conversion of units from cm² to m² if answer incorrect.)

Remember 1 cm² = 1 × 10⁻⁴ m².

(d) (i) $\varepsilon_{max} = BAN\omega$

$= 1.7 \times (10 \times 10^{-4}) \times 1 \times 10\pi$

$=$ **0.017π V ($= 0.053$ V to 2 s.f.)** ***(1 mark)***

The e.m.f. is at a maximum when $\sin\omega t = 1$ (or −1).

(ii)

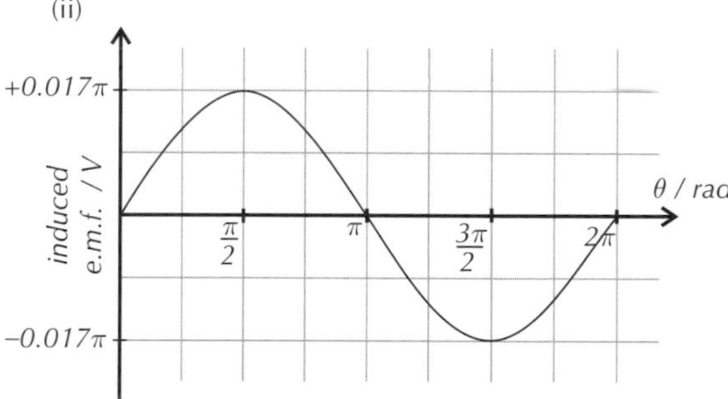

(2 marks available — 1 mark for correct sinusoidal shape and 1 mark for maximum and minimum induced e.m.f. marked correctly.)

6 (a) The particle will follow a circular path ***(1 mark)***.

(b) (i) $F = BQv$

$= 0.93 \times (1.60 \times 10^{-19}) \times (8.1 \times 10^{7})$

$=$ **1.2×10^{-11} N (to 2 s.f.)**

The force would act downwards.

(1 mark for correct force and 1 mark for direction.)

Find the direction of the force with Fleming's left-hand rule — because electrons have a negative charge, point your second finger in the opposite direction to its velocity. The magnitude of the charge on an electron is given in the exam data and formulae booklet.

(ii) The force will be 2.4×10^{-11} N (to 2 s.f.) upwards.
(1 mark for correct force and 1 mark for direction.)

If you didn't get the correct answer for b) (i), you'll get the marks for b (ii) as long as the force is double the force for the electron and in the opposite direction.

7 (a) (i) The e.m.f. will be greatest when $\theta = 90°$ or $270°$ ***(1 mark)***.

This is when the coil is parallel to the magnetic field.

(ii)

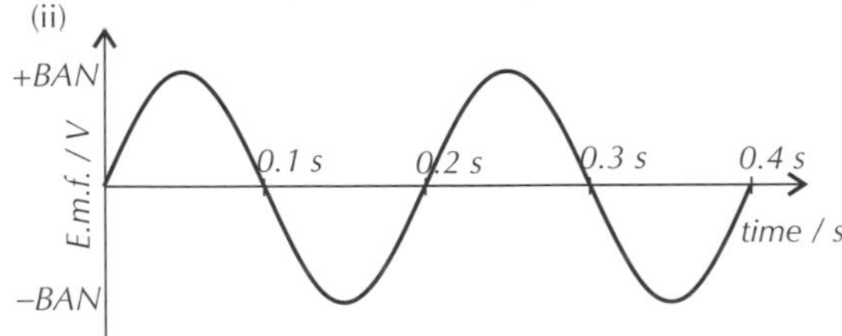

(1 mark for sinusoidal shape, 1 mark for correctly labelled axes and 1 mark for two complete wave cycles.)

Time period = 1/frequency, so one wave cycle takes 1/5 = 0.2 seconds to complete. You're not told the starting position of the coil, so it doesn't matter what part of the wave cycle the graph starts at.

(b) An alternating current is required ***(1 mark)***.

(c) The lower the resistance, the less the wires heat up, so the more efficient the transformer. ***(1 mark)***.

(d) (i) $\text{efficiency} = \frac{I_s V_s}{I_p V_p}$

$\Rightarrow \text{power out} = \text{efficiency} \times \text{power in}$

$= 0.91 \times (1.2 \times 10^3)$

$= 1092 = \mathbf{1.1\ kW}$ **(to 2 s.f.)**

(2 marks for correct answer, otherwise 1 mark for correct rearrangement to make power out the subject.)

(ii) $E = Pt = (1.2 \times 10^3 - 1.1 \times 10^3) \times (60^2 \times 3)$

$= 1080\,000\text{ J} = \mathbf{1.1\ MJ}$ **(to 2 s.f.)** ***(1 mark)***

Allow 1 mark here if the working is correct but the answer carried through from part (i) is incorrect.

Unit 5

Section 1 — Radioactivity and Nuclear Energy

1. The Atomic Nucleus

Page 97 — Application Questions

Q1 Initial $E_k = (4.0 \times 10^6) \times (1.60 \times 10^{-19}) = 6.4 \times 10^{-13}$ J

$$E_{elec} = \frac{Q_{lead}q_{alpha}}{4\pi\varepsilon_0 r} = 6.4 \times 10^{-13}\text{ J}$$

$$r = \frac{(+82e)(+2e)}{4\pi\varepsilon_0(6.4 \times 10^{-13})} = \frac{82 \times 2 \times (1.60 \times 10^{-19})^2}{4\pi \times (8.85 \times 10^{-12}) \times (6.4 \times 10^{-13})}$$

$= \mathbf{5.9 \times 10^{-14}\ m}$ **(to 2 s.f.)**

Q2 $$r = \frac{Q_{zinc}q_{alpha}}{4\pi\varepsilon_0 E_{elec}} = \frac{30 \times 2 \times (1.60 \times 10^{-19})^2}{4\pi \times (8.85 \times 10^{-12}) \times (1.0 \times 10^{-13})}$$

$= 1.381... \times 10^{-13}$m

Therefore nuclear radius $\approx$ $\mathbf{1.4 \times 10^{-13}\ m}$ **(to 2 s.f.)**

Q3 $E = 50\text{ MeV} = (5.0 \times 10^7) \times (1.60 \times 10^{-19}) = 8.0 \times 10^{-12}$ J

$$\lambda \simeq \frac{hc}{E} = \frac{(6.63 \times 10^{-34}) \times (3.00 \times 10^8)}{(8.0 \times 10^{-12})}$$

$= \mathbf{2.5 \times 10^{-14}\ m}$ **(to 2 s.f.)**

Q4 $E = 200\text{ MeV} = (2.0 \times 10^8) \times (1.60 \times 10^{-19}) = 3.2 \times 10^{-11}$ J

$$\lambda \simeq \frac{hc}{E} = \frac{(6.63 \times 10^{-34}) \times (3.00 \times 10^8)}{(3.2 \times 10^{-11})} = 6.215... \times 10^{-15}\text{m}$$

$$d \simeq \frac{1.22\lambda}{\sin\theta} = \frac{1.22 \times (6.215... \times 10^{-15})}{\sin 33°}$$

$= 1.392... \times 10^{-14}$m

Therefore nuclear radius $\simeq$ $\mathbf{7.0 \times 10^{-15}\ m}$ **(to 2 s.f.)**

Don't forget to divide by 2 if you're asked for the nuclear radius — the electron diffraction formula gives the diameter.

Page 97 — Fact Recall Questions

Q1 A stream of alpha particles from a radioactive source were fired at very thin gold foil.

Q2 The nuclei must be small since very few alpha particles were deflected by large angles — most just passed straight through the foil. The nuclei must be positive to repel the positively charged alpha particles.

Q3 Initial K.E. $= E_{elec} = \frac{Q_{nucleus}q_{alpha}}{4\pi\varepsilon_0 r}$ or $r = \frac{Q_{nucleus}q_{alpha}}{4\pi\varepsilon_0 E_{elec}}$

Q4 Electron diffraction

Q5 $\lambda \simeq \frac{hc}{E}$

Q6 $\sin\theta \simeq \frac{1.22\lambda}{d}$

2. Nuclear Radius and Density

Page 100 — Application Questions

Q1 Mass $= m = (21 + 24) \times (1.7 \times 10^{-27})$

$= \mathbf{7.7 \times 10^{-26}\ kg}$ **(to 2 s.f.)**

Q2 $r = r_0A^{1/3} = (1.4 \times 10^{-15}) \times (31)^{1/3} = \mathbf{4.4 \times 10^{-15}\ m}$ **(to 2 s.f.)**

Q3 Rearrange $r = r_0A^{1/3}$ for A:

$$A = \left(\frac{r}{r_0}\right)^3 = \left(\frac{4.2 \times 10^{-15}}{1.4 \times 10^{-15}}\right)^3 = \mathbf{27}$$

Don't forget to convert the radius from fm to m.

Q4 $r = r_0A^{1/3} = (1.4 \times 10^{-15}) \times (23)^{1/3} = 3.981... \times 10^{-15}$ m

$$V = \frac{4}{3}\pi r^3 = \frac{4}{3}\pi \times (3.981... \times 10^{-15})^3$$

$= \mathbf{2.6 \times 10^{-43}\ m^3}$ **(to 2 s.f.)**

Q5 $r = r_0A^{1/3} = (1.4 \times 10^{-15}) \times (207)^{1/3} = 8.281... \times 10^{-15}$ m

$V = \frac{4}{3}\pi r^3 = \frac{4}{3}\pi \times (8.281... \times 10^{-15})^3 = 2.379... \times 10^{-42}$ m^3

$m = (1.7 \times 10^{-27}) \times 207 = 3.519 \times 10^{-25}$ kg

$\rho = m/v = (3.519 \times 10^{-25}) \div (2.379... \times 10^{-42})$

$= \mathbf{1.5 \times 10^{17}}$ **kg m^{-3} (to 2 s.f.)**

Page 100 — Fact Recall Questions

Q1 a) 10^{-15} m

b) 10^{-10} m

Q2 The particles that make up the nucleus — protons and neutrons.

Q3 Nuclear radius is directly proportional to the cube root of the nucleon number.

Q4 Neutrons and protons have nearly the same mass as one another, and occupy about the same volume in a nucleus.

Q5 First calculate the nuclear radius from the nucleon number using the formula $r = r_0A^{1/3}$. From this, work out the nuclear volume (making the assumption that the nucleus is a sphere) using the formula $V = \frac{4}{3}\pi r^3$. Then calculate the nuclear mass by multiplying the nucleon number and the mass of a nucleon. Then use the formula $\rho = m/V$ to find the density.

3. Properties of Nuclear Radiation

Page 103 — Application Question

Q1 Since the radiation is blocked by aluminium, but not by paper, it must be beta-minus radiation.

Page 103 — Fact Recall Questions

Q1 When an unstable atom breaks down to become more stable, by releasing energy and/or particles.

Q2 Alpha (helium nuclei — two protons and two neutrons), beta-plus (positrons), beta-minus (electrons), gamma (high-frequency electromagnetic wave/photons).

Q3 Alpha — strong. Beta — weak. Gamma — very weak.

Q4 Look at how or if the radiation is deflected when it passes through a magnetic field perpendicular to its motion. If the radiation is positively charged it will curve one way, if it's negative it'll curve the other way, and if it's not charged it will continue in a straight line. The radius of curvature of its path can also tell you about its charge and mass. Alternatively, use a Geiger-Müller counter to measure the radiation passing through each of: paper, a few mm of aluminium and several cm of lead. If the radiation is blocked by the paper, it's alpha radiation. If it passes through the paper but is blocked by the aluminium, it's beta radiation. If it passes through the paper and the aluminium but is blocked by the lead, it's gamma radiation.

Q5 Alpha radiation is used in smoke detectors, because it is strongly ionising so it will allow a current to flow through the detector, but it is weakly penetrating, so it's blocked by the plastic of the detector, meaning that the detector is safe to use in the home (radiation cannot escape). Beta radiation is used to destroy cancer cells, because it can still ionise atoms, but it can penetrate the cancerous tissue further than alpha radiation. Gamma radiation is used in medical imaging, because it causes much less damage to body tissue, and also penetrates tissue easily.

4. Intensity and Background Radiation

Page 105 — Application Questions

Q1 20 cm = 0.20 m and count rate varies with inverse square law.

So count rate at 20 cm = $\frac{k}{0.20^2} = 54$ s^{-1}

Therefore $k = 54 \times 0.20^2 = 2.16$

So count rate at 45 cm (0.45 m) = $\frac{2.16}{0.45^2}$ = **11 s^{-1} (to 2 s.f.)**

Q2 If the intensity obeys the inverse square law, then $I = \frac{k}{x^2}$ will be true, with the same constant k for both pairs of measurements. Plug the 1st intensity and distance into the inverse square law:

$I = \frac{k}{x^2} \Rightarrow 4.0 \times 10^{-10} = \frac{k}{0.50^2}$

Therefore $k = 4.0 \times 10^{-10} \times 0.50^2 = 1.0 \times 10^{-10}$ (to 2 s.f.)

Do the same with the other values for intensity and distance:

$I = \frac{k}{x^2} \Rightarrow 1.8 \times 10^{-10} = \frac{k}{0.75^2}$

Therefore $k = 1.8 \times 10^{-10} \times 0.75^2 = 1.0 \times 10^{-10}$ (to 2 s.f.)

Both pairs of values give the same k (to 2 s.f.), so they obey the inverse square law.

Page 105 — Fact Recall Questions

Q1 The intensity is inversely proportional to the square of the distance from the source.

Q2 Take measurements of the intensity (or count rate) with a Geiger-Müller tube and counter at different distances from a radioactive source. Plot a graph of intensity against the inverse of the distance squared. If the data fits a straight line through the origin, then the inverse square law is verified.

Alternatively, you could plug each pair of values for distance and intensity into the inverse square law, and calculate a value of k for each — the values for k should all be the same.

Q3 The intensity of the radiation that reaches your body is much lower than when held closer.

Q4 E.g. Take three measurements of the background radiation (without the source present). Average these measurements and subtract this average from all measurements of the source's count.

Q5 Any three of:

- The air — rocks release radioactive radon gas, which emits alpha radiation.
- The ground and buildings — rocks contain radioactive materials.
- Cosmic radiation — high-energy particles from space collide with particles in the upper atmosphere and produce nuclear radiation.
- Living things — all living organisms contain radioactive carbon-14.
- Man-made medical or industrial sources.

5. Exponential Law of Decay

Page 110 — Application Questions

Q1 Activity = $A = \lambda N = (1.1 \times 10^{-13}) \times (4.5 \times 10^{18})$

= **$\mathbf{5.0 \times 10^5}$ Bq (to 2 s.f.)**

Q2 Find the number of times the activity halved in 24 hours — count the number of times, n, you have to divide 2400 by 2 to reach 75.

$n = 5$, therefore $T_{1/2} = 24 \div 5 =$ **4.8 hours**

Q3 Decay constant $\lambda = \frac{\ln 2}{T_{1/2}} = \frac{0.693...}{483}$

= **$\mathbf{1.44 \times 10^{-3}}$ s^{-1} (to 3 s.f.)**

Q4 Time in seconds = $t = 6.5 \times 3600 = 23\,400$ s

Activity at time $t = A = A_0e^{-\lambda t}$

$= (3.2 \times 10^3) \times e^{-(1.3 \times 10^{-4}) \times 23\,400}$ = **150 Bq (to 2 s.f.)**

Q5 Half-life in seconds = 1.17 × 60 = 70.2 s

Decay constant $\lambda = \frac{\ln 2}{T_{1/2}} = \frac{\ln 2}{70.2} = 9.8738... \times 10^{-3}$

Time in seconds = t = 35 × 60 = 2100 s

Number of atoms in sample at time $t = N = N_0 e^{-\lambda t}$

$= (2.5 \times 10^{15}) \times e^{-(9.8738... \times 10^{-3}) \times 2100}$ = **2.5 × 10⁶ (to 2 s.f.)**

Q6 Half-life of carbon-14 in seconds:

$T_{1/2} = 5730 \times (365 \times 24 \times 60 \times 60) = 1.8070... \times 10^{11}$ s

Decay constant $\lambda = \frac{\ln 2}{T_{1/2}} = \frac{\ln 2}{1.8070... \times 10^{11}}$

$= 3.8358... \times 10^{-12}\ s^{-1}$

Activity when animal died = A_0 = 1.2 Bq

Activity now = A = 0.45 Bq

Activity decreases exponentially according to: $A = A_0 e^{-\lambda t}$

Rearranging this for time $t = -\frac{1}{\lambda} \times \ln\left(\frac{A}{A_0}\right)$

$= 2.5569... \times 10^{11}$ s = **8100 years (to 2 s.f.)**

Page 110 — Fact Recall Questions

Q1 a) The probability of an atom decaying per unit time.

b) The number of atoms that decay per unit time.

c) The time it takes for the number of unstable nuclei in a sample of an isotope (or the sample's activity or count rate) to halve.

Q2 $N = N_0 e^{-\lambda t}$

Q3 Read off the activity at t = 0. Halve this value, draw a horizontal line to the curve, then a vertical line down to the x-axis. Read off the time — this the half-life. Repeat for a quarter of the original value and divide by two to check.

Q4 E.g. estimating the age of an object using radiocarbon dating; using radioactive isotopes as tracers in medical imaging.

6. Nuclear Decay

Page 113 — Application Questions

Q1 Beta-minus decay involves the conversion of a neutron to a proton and electron (along with the release of an anti-neutrino). So nucleon number A remains constant, and proton number increases by 1: $^{137}_{55}Cs \longrightarrow {}^{137}_{56}Ba + {}^{0}_{-1}\beta + {}^{0}_{0}\bar{\nu}_e$

You can check your answer by making sure that the total proton number on the left of the equation balances the total proton number on the right. Do the same for the nucleon number.

Q2 $^{211}_{85}At \longrightarrow {}^{207}_{83}Bi + {}^{4}_{2}\alpha$

Q3 $^{83}_{37}Rb + {}^{0}_{-1}\beta \longrightarrow {}^{83}_{36}Kr + {}^{0}_{0}\nu_e$

Page 113 — Fact Recall Questions

Q1 Too many neutrons, too few neutrons, too many nucleons or too much energy.

Too many neutrons and the nucleus will want to β⁻ decay. Too few neutrons and it will β⁺ decay. Too many nucleons all together and it will α decay. Too much energy and some energy will be released as γ radiation.

Q2

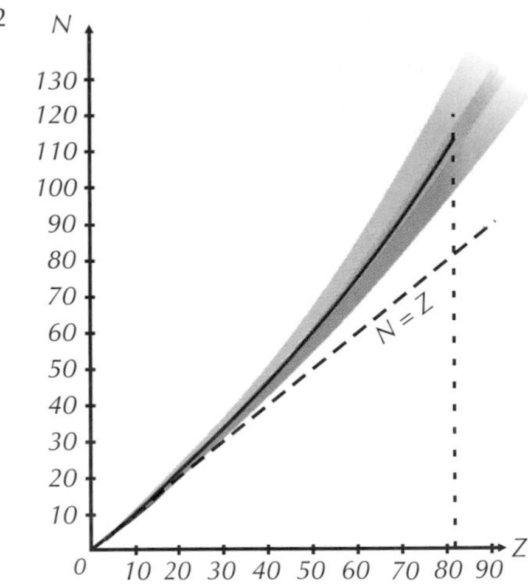

Q3 a) An alpha particle is released. The nucleon number decreases by 4, and the proton number decreases by 2.

b) An electron is released (as well as an antineutrino). The nucleon number remains the same, but the proton number increases by 1.

c) A positron is released (as well as a neutrino). The nucleon number remains the same, but the proton number decreases by 1.

Q4 If it's in an excited nuclear state, i.e. it has excess energy.

Q5 Any three of: energy, momentum, charge, nucleon number and lepton number.

7. Mass Defect and Binding Energy

Page 115 — Application Questions

Q1 Mass defect is equivalent to binding energy.

1u is roughly 931.5 MeV. Therefore the binding energy is 0.0989 × 931.5 = **92 MeV (to 2 s.f.)**

Q2 Mass of nucleus = 15.994915 u

Number of protons = 8, number of neutrons = 8

Total mass of nucleons = (8 × 1.00728 u) + (8 × 1.00867 u) = 16.1276 u

So mass defect = mass of nucleons – mass of nucleus = 16.1276 u – 15.994915 u = **0.133 u (to 3 s.f.)**

Q3 Binding energy = binding energy per nucleon × nucleon number = 8.79 MeV × 56 = 492.24 MeV

Convert from binding energy to mass defect:

Mass defect = binding energy ÷ 931.5 = **0.528 u (to 3 s.f.)**

Page 115 — Fact Recall Questions

Q1 The energy needed to separate all the nucleons in a nucleus. It is equivalent to the mass defect.

Q2 931.5 MeV

Q3

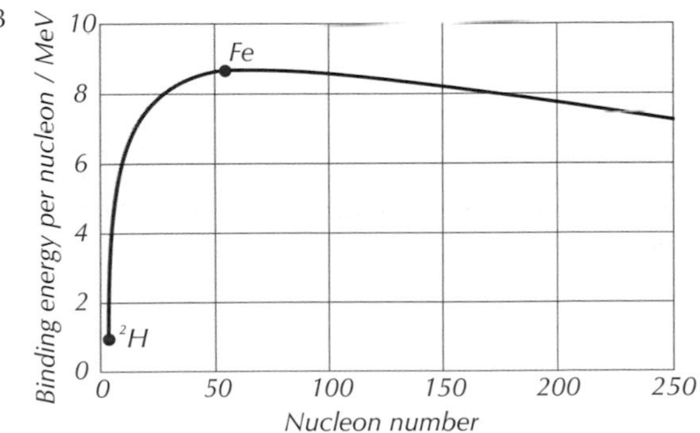

8. Nuclear Fission and Fusion

Page 118 — Application Questions

Q1 $\Delta m = m_p + m_p - m_{H\text{-}2} - m_e - m_\upsilon$
$= 1.00728 + 1.00728 - 2.01355 - 0.00055 - 0$
$= 0.00046$ u
In MeV: $\Delta m = 0.00046 \times 931.5 =$ **0.43 MeV (to 2 s.f.)**

Q2 First, calculate the number of neutrons produced by balancing the nucleon number A:
$A_{before} = 1 + 235$, $A_{after} = 94 + 139 + x$
Therefore number of neutrons produced $= x = 3$
So $\Delta m = m_n + m_{U\text{-}235} - m_{Zr\text{-}94} - m_{Te\text{-}139} - 3m_n$
$= 1.00867 + 234.99333 - 93.88431 - 138.90613 - (3 \times 1.00867)$
$= 0.18555$ u
In MeV: $\Delta m = 0.18555 \times 931.5 =$ **172.8 MeV (to 4 s.f.)**

Page 118 — Fact Recall Questions

Q1 The spontaneous or induced splitting of a larger nucleus into two smaller nuclei.

Q2 Spontaneous fission occurs randomly by itself, while induced fission occurs when a neutron hits a nucleus, making the nucleus unstable and causing it to fission.

Q3 The fusing of two smaller nuclei to form one larger nucleus.

Q4 For a reaction to be energetically favourable, energy must be released — this only happens if the binding energy per nucleon increases.
(The products have a greater total mass defect than the initial nuclei, and so more mass is converted to energy that is released.)

Q5 Nuclei are positively charged, so they are repelled by the electrostatic interaction. They must have a lot of energy to overcome this interaction (so that the strong nuclear interaction can take over and attract them together).

Q6

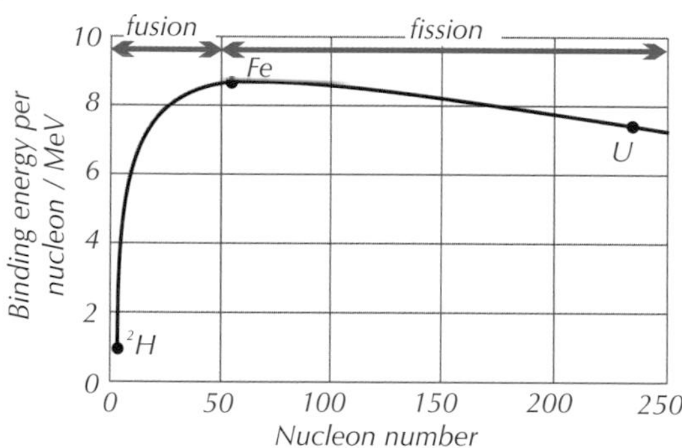

9. Nuclear Fission Reactors

Page 120 — Fact Recall Questions

Q1 When the neutrons released by nuclear fission cause other nuclei to fission and release more neutrons — and so on.

Q2 The material used for the moderator needs to be able to slow down neutrons so they can be absorbed by the uranium nuclei. The material used for the coolant needs to be a liquid or a gas at room temperature so it can be pumped around the reactor. It also needs to be efficient at transferring heat from the reactor to cool it. Graphite (or water) could be used as a moderator, and water could be used as a coolant.

Q3 The control rods are made of a material that absorbs neutrons (e.g. boron). By inserting them into the reactor, the number of neutrons in the reactor can be limited, and the rate of reaction can be controlled by controlling the amount that the control rods are inserted into the reactor.

Q4 E.g. reactor shielding — a thick concrete case that prevents radiation escaping and reach the nuclear workers; emergency shut-down by lowering the fuel rods fully into the reactor to slow down the reaction.

Q5 Unused fuel rods only emit weakly-penetrating alpha radiation, which can easily be blocked. Used fuel rods contain different radioactive isotopes which emit beta and gamma radiation too, both of which are more strongly penetrating.

Q6 When material is removed from the reactor, it is initially very hot, so it is placed in cooling ponds until the temperature falls to a safe level. The radioactive waste should then be stored underground in sealed containers until its activity has fallen sufficiently.

Exam-style Questions – pages 122-123

1 (a) (i) Energy in J $= (250 \times 10^6) \times (1.60 \times 10^{-19}$ eV)
$= 4.00 \times 10^{-11}$ J
Wavelength $\lambda \simeq \frac{hc}{E}$
$= (6.63 \times 10^{-34}) \times (3.00 \times 10^8) \div (4.00 \times 10^{-11})$
$= 4.97 \times 10^{-15}$ m (to 3 s.f.)
(3 marks for the correct answer, otherwise 1 mark for correctly calculating the electron energy in joules, and 1 mark for correct working.)

(ii) $\sin\theta = \frac{1.22\lambda}{d}$
Rearrange to get diameter: $d = \frac{1.22\lambda}{\sin\theta}$
$= 1.22 \times (4.969... \times 10^{-15}) \div \sin(57.4°)$
$= 7.1959... \times 10^{-15}$
So radius $= r = (7.1959... \times 10^{-15}) \div 2$
$= 3.60 \times 10^{-15}$ (to 3 s.f.)
(2 marks for the correct answer, otherwise 1 mark for correct working.)

(b) (i) Radius $= r = r_0A^{1/3} = (1.4 \times 10^{-15}) \times (23)^{1/3}$
$= 4.0 \times 10^{-15}$ m (to 2 s.f.)
(2 marks for the correct answer, otherwise 1 mark for attempting to use the correct formula.)

(ii) Density $= m \div V$
Assume nucleus is a sphere, so $V = (4/3) \times \pi r^3$
$V = (4/3) \times \pi \times (3.98... \times 10^{-15})^3$
$= 2.643... \times 10^{-43}$
Density $= (3.8 \times 10^{-26}) \div (2.643... \times 10^{-43})$
$= 1.4 \times 10^{17}$ kg m^{-3} (to 2 s.f.)
(3 marks for the correct answer, otherwise 1 mark for attempting to use the formula for the volume of a sphere, and 1 mark for attempting to use the formula for density.)

(c) Positive alpha particles were repelled, so the nucleus must also be positive. Only some alpha particles were deflected, while most just passed straight through, so the nucleus must be small compared to the size of the whole atom.
(1 mark for saying that the nucleus must be positive since it repelled positive alpha particles, 1 mark for saying it must be small since most alpha particles weren't repelled.)

2 (a) How to grade your answer (pick the description that best matches your answer):
0 marks: There is no relevant information.
1-2 marks: One or two of the components are

identified, but no explanation of their functions is given. Several errors with grammar, spelling, punctuation and legibility. Answer has lack of structure and information.
3-4 marks: All of the components are identified. The function of at least one component is explained. Only a few errors with grammar, spelling, punctuation and legibility. Answer has some structure, and information is presented logically.
5-7 marks: All of the components are identified. The functions of at least two components are explained. Grammar, spelling and punctuation are used accurately and there is no problem with legibility. Uses an appropriate form and style of writing, and information is well structured and logical.
Here are some points your answer may include:
A = control rods. They absorb neutrons, and by varying how far they are inserted into the reactor, the rate of reaction can be controlled.
B = shielding/concrete case. It stops radiation from escaping.
C = moderator. This slows down fast-moving neutrons so they can be absorbed by nuclei.

(b) A critical mass of fuel means there is just enough mass for the fission chain reaction to continue at a steady rate on its own (e.g. without any control rods).
(2 marks — 1 mark for stating there is a fission chain reaction, 1 mark for saying a critical mass is the amount needed for the chain reaction to continue at a steady rate on its own.)

(c) In an emergency shut-down, the control rods are lowered fully into the reactor ***(1 mark)*** to absorb neutrons causing the chain reaction to happen and slow down the reaction as quickly as possible ***(1 mark)***.

3 (a) (i) The energy needed to pull all the nucleons in a nucleus apart/the energy released when a nucleus forms ***(1 mark)***.

(ii)

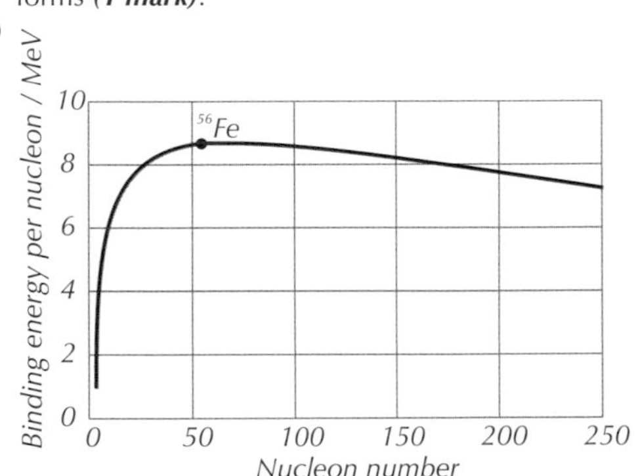

(3 marks — 1 mark for the overall shape, 1 mark for indicating Fe-56 is at the peak of the curve, 1 mark for indicating the peak is in the range 8-9.2 MeV)

(iii) Use the conversion 1 u = 931.5 MeV:
So binding energy per nucleon
= (0.62065 × 931.5) ÷ 66
= 8.760 MeV (to 4 s.f.)
(1 mark for correctly converting to MeV)

(b) (i) Use conservation of charge to find proton number of ^{94}Sr: a = 92 – 54 = 38
Use conservation of nucleon number to find number of neutrons:
b = (235 +1) – (140 + 94) = 2
(2 marks — 1 mark for correctly calculating each of a and b.)

(ii) The average binding energy of the final nuclei is greater than the binding energy of the initial nucleus ***(1 mark)***.

An increase in binding energy means an increase in the total mass defect, and so more mass is converted to energy.

(iii) Δm = (234.99333 + 1.00867) – (139.89194 + 93.89446 + (2 × 1.00867))
= 0.19826 u
so energy = 0.19826 × 931.5
= 184.7 MeV (to 4 s.f.)
(3 marks for the correct answer or incorrect answer due to using incorrect answer to part (b) (i), otherwise 1 mark for correctly calculating the mass defect and 1 mark for attempting to convert it to binding energy.)

4 (a) (i) $^{33}_{15}P \longrightarrow {}^{33}_{16}S + {}^{0}_{-1}\beta + {}^{0}_{0}\overline{\nu}_e$

Beta-minus radiation is made up of electrons. By balancing mass (nucleon number), charge (proton number) and lepton number, you can work out the other two products.

(3 marks — 1 for each correct product)

(ii) Half-life in s = 25.4 × 86400 = 2194560 s
Half-life $T_{1/2} = \ln 2 \div \lambda$
So rearrange: $\lambda = \ln 2 \div T_{1/2}$
$\lambda = \ln 2 \div 2194560$
= 3.16 × 10^{-7} s^{-1} (to 3 s.f.)
(2 marks for the correct answer, otherwise 1 mark for attempting to use the equation for decay constant.)

(iii) Number of atoms given by: $N = N_0 e^{-\lambda t}$
Rearrange for time: $t = -\ln\left(\frac{N}{N_0}\right) \times \frac{1}{\lambda}$
So $t = -\ln\left(\frac{7.0 \times 10^{13}}{1.6 \times 10^{15}}\right) \times \frac{1}{3.158... \times 10^{-7}}$
= 9.907... × 10^6 s = **110 days (to 2 s.f.)**
(2 marks for the correct answer, otherwise 1 mark for correct working.)

(b) (i) Intensity $I = \frac{k}{x^2}$
Rearrange for *k*: $k = I \times x^2$
At 0.2 m, $k = 3.6 \times 10^{-10} \times 0.2^2 = 1.44 \times 10^{-11}$ J
Intensity at 0.5 m = $1.44 \times 10^{-11} \div 0.5^2$
= 5.8 × 10^{-11} Jm^{-2} (to 2 s.f.)
(2 marks for the correct answer, otherwise 1 mark for correctly calculating k.)

(ii) Any two of:
Gamma radiation is strongly penetrating, so it can travel through the body and reach the detector.
Gamma radiation is weakly ionising, so it causes little damage to tissues in the body.
It decays to a stable/safe isotope.
It has a half-life long enough for radiation to be picked up by the detector, but short enough to limit the body's exposure to radiation.
(2 marks — 1 mark for each reason.)

Section 2 — Thermal Physics

1. The Three Gas Laws

Page 126 — Application Question

Q1 a) The volume has halved. As p and V are inversely proportional, the pressure will have doubled, i.e. p = **2.8 × 10⁵ Pa**.

b) Start temperature in K = 27 + 273 = 300 K.
End temperature in K = –173 + 273 = 100 K.
The temperature is divided by 3. As V and T are proportional, the volume will also be divided by 3, i.e. V = **10 cm³**.

Page 126 — Fact Recall Questions

Q1 Absolute zero

Q2 273 K

Q3 It must have a fixed mass.

Q4 a) Boyle's law states that at a constant temperature the pressure p and volume V of a(n ideal) gas are inversely proportional.

b)

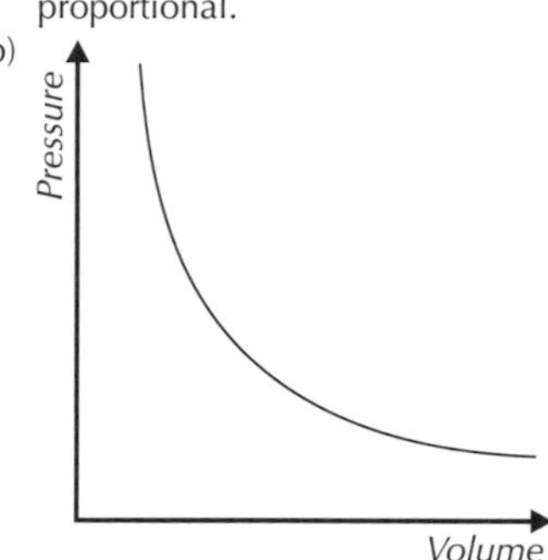

Q5 a) Charles' law states that at constant pressure, the volume V of a(n ideal) gas is directly proportional to its absolute temperature T.

b)

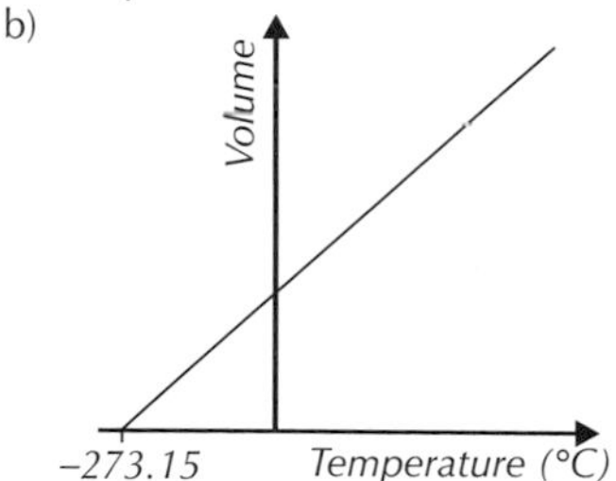

Q6 a) The pressure law states that at constant volume, the pressure p of a(n ideal) gas is directly proportional to its absolute temperature T.

b)

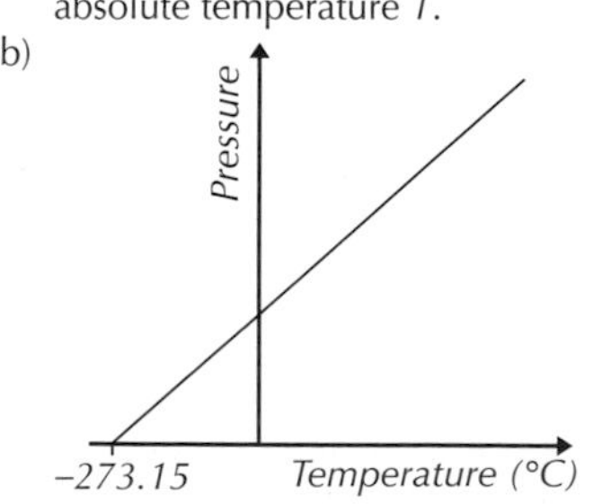

2. The Ideal Gas Equation

Page 129 — Application Questions

Q1 Molar mass = 12 + 16 + 16 = 44 g

Q2 $pV = nRT \Rightarrow V = \frac{nRT}{p}$

$= \frac{23 \times 8.31 \times (25 + 273)}{2.4 \times 10^5}$

$=$ **$0.24\ \text{m}^3$ (to 2 s.f.)**

Q3 $pV = NkT \Rightarrow p = \frac{NkT}{V}$

$= \frac{(8.21 \times 10^{24}) \times (1.38 \times 10^{-23}) \times 500}{4.05}$

$=$ **1.40×10^4 Pa (to 3 s.f.)**

Q4 $pV = NkT \Rightarrow T = \frac{pV}{Nk}$

$= \frac{(1.29 \times 10^5) \times 0.539}{(1.44 \times 10^{25}) \times (1.38 \times 10^{-23})}$

$=$ **350 K (to 3 s.f.)**

Q5 a) 1 mole of gas would have a mass of 44 g and 0.88 kg = 880 g. Moles of gas = $\frac{880}{44}$ = **20.**

b) $pV = nRT \Rightarrow T = \frac{pV}{nR}$

$= \frac{(2.3 \times 10^5) \times 0.39}{20 \times 8.31}$

$=$ **540 K (to 2 s.f.)**

Page 129 — Fact Recall Questions

Q1 The Avogadro constant, N_A, is the number of atoms in exactly 12 g of the carbon isotope $^{12}_{6}C$. Its value is 6.02×10^{23} mol⁻¹.

Q2 The molar mass of a substance is the mass (usually in grams) that one mole of that substance would have.

Q3 $pV = nRT$
p = pressure (in Pa)
V = volume (in m³)
n = number of moles of gas
R = molar gas constant (= 8.31 J mol⁻¹ K⁻¹)
T = temperature (in K)

Q4 Boltzmann's constant, k, is effectively the gas constant for one molecule of gas. It is equivalent to $\frac{R}{N_A}$, and its value is 1.38×10^{-23} JK⁻¹.

Q5 $pV = NkT$
p = pressure (in Pa)
V = volume (in m³)
N = number of molecules of gas
k = Boltzmann constant (= 1.38×10^{-23} JK⁻¹)
T = temperature (in K)

3. The Pressure of an Ideal Gas

Page 133 — Application Questions

Q1 a) The momentum of the molecule in the direction normal to the wall is equal to $m\boldsymbol{u}$. The collision is elastic, so it will rebound with velocity $-\boldsymbol{u}$ and momentum $-m\boldsymbol{u}$. So its change in momentum is $m\boldsymbol{u} - (-m\boldsymbol{u}) = 2m\boldsymbol{u}$.

b) Force is the rate of change of momentum, i.e. $2m\boldsymbol{u}$ × number of collisions per second. The time between collisions is $\frac{2l}{\boldsymbol{u}}$, and so the number of collisions per second is $\frac{\boldsymbol{u}}{2l}$. So force = $2m\boldsymbol{u} \times \frac{\boldsymbol{u}}{2l} = \frac{m\boldsymbol{u}^2}{l}$.

c) The force exerted by N molecules with velocity $\boldsymbol{u}_1$, $\boldsymbol{u}_2$... etc. will be equal to $\frac{m(\boldsymbol{u}_1^2 + \boldsymbol{u}_2^2 + etc.)}{l}$, or $\frac{mN\overline{\boldsymbol{u}^2}}{l}$.

The pressure is given by $\frac{\text{force}}{\text{area}}$, so $p = \frac{\left(\frac{mN\overline{\boldsymbol{u}^2}}{l}\right)}{l^2} = \frac{mN\overline{\boldsymbol{u}^2}}{V}$

The volume V is equal to l^3.

d) Molecules can move in three dimensions, so their mean square speed is given by $(c_{rms})^2 = \overline{\boldsymbol{u}^2} + \overline{\boldsymbol{v}^2} + \overline{\boldsymbol{w}^2}$ where $\boldsymbol{u}$, $\boldsymbol{v}$ and $\boldsymbol{w}$ are the components of their velocity in the three directions normal to the walls of the container. As the molecules move randomly, $\overline{\boldsymbol{u}^2} = \overline{\boldsymbol{v}^2} = \overline{\boldsymbol{w}^2}$ and so $(c_{rms})^2 = 3\overline{\boldsymbol{u}^2}$, or $\overline{\boldsymbol{u}^2} = \frac{1}{3}(c_{rms})^2$.

Substituting this into the equation from part c) gives $pV = \frac{1}{3}Nm(c_{rms})^2$.

Q2 $pV = \frac{1}{3}Nm(c_{rms})^2$

$\Rightarrow p = \frac{1}{3}\frac{Nm(c_{rms})^2}{V}$

$= \frac{1}{3}\frac{(5 \times 6.02 \times 10^{23}) \times (5.31 \times 10^{-26}) \times (8.11 \times 10^{6})}{1.44}$

$=$ **3.00×10^5 Pa (to 3 s.f.)**

Page 133 — Fact-Recall Questions

Q1 c_{rms} is the root mean square speed (of the molecules in a gas). I.e. the square root of the mean of the squared speeds of the molecules.

Q2 The average change of momentum in a collision is increased and the average time between collisions is reduced. These both mean that the rate of change of momentum is greater, so the force on the wall is increased.

Q3 The volume of the gas or the pressure of the gas.

Q4 E.g. All molecules are identical / the gas contains a large number of molecules / the molecules move rapidly and randomly / Newtonian mechanics apply.

4. Energy and Temperature

Page 137 — Application Questions

Q1 $\frac{1}{2}m(c_{rms})^2 = \frac{3}{2}kT$

$= \frac{3}{2} \times (1.38 \times 10^{-23}) \times 112$

$=$ **2.32×10^{-21} J (to 3 s.f.)**

Q2 Total initial energy $= nN_A \times \frac{3}{2}kT$

$= 2.44 \times (6.02 \times 10^{23}) \times \frac{3}{2} \times (1.38 \times 10^{-23}) \times 250$

$= 7.60... \times 10^6$ J

Total final energy $= nN_A \times \frac{3}{2}kT$

$= 2.44 \times (6.02 \times 10^{23}) \times \frac{3}{2} \times (1.38 \times 10^{-23}) \times 290$

$= 8.81... \times 10^6$ J

Energy supplied to system $= 8.81... \times 10^6 - 7.60... \times 10^6$

$=$ **1.22×10^6 J (to 3 s.f.)**

To answer this question, find the total kinetic energy of the gas molecules before and after the temperature change. The difference gives you the energy supplied to the gas.

Q3 a) Energy lost from 25 °C to 0 °C $= mc\Delta T$
$= 0.1 \times 4180 \times 25$
$= 10\,450$ J

Energy lost in freezing $= ml$
$= 0.1 \times 334\,000$
$= 33\,400$ J

Energy lost from 0 °C to –5 °C $= mc\Delta T$
$= 0.1 \times 2110 \times 5$
$= 1055$ J

Total energy lost $= 10\,450 + 33\,400 + 1055$
$=$ **44 900 J (to 3 s.f.)**

b) Energy transfer happens faster when the difference in temperature is larger. If the temperature of the freezer is brought closer to the temperature of the water, it will take longer to freeze.

Page 137 — Fact Recall Questions

Q1 a)

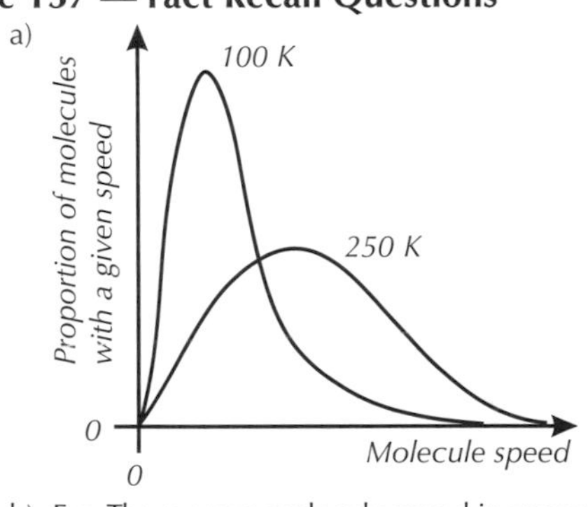

b) E.g. The average molecule speed increases / the distribution of molecule speeds becomes more spread out.

Q2 Energy is transferred between gas molecules when they collide — one molecule speeds up and the other slows down.

Exam-style Questions — Pages 139-140

1 (a)

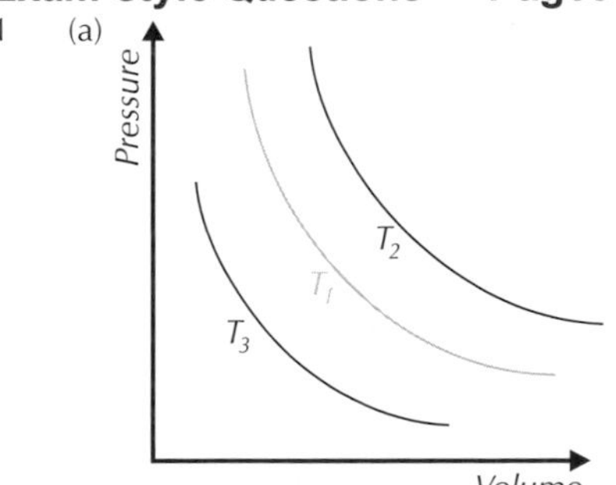

(2 marks available — 1 mark for each correct curve)

(b) (i) Increasing the temperature increases the average speed of the gas molecules ***(1 mark)***. This means they collide with the walls of the container more often and on average there's a larger change in momentum during a collision ***(1 mark)***. This means a greater force is exerted on the walls of the container in the same amount of time, and so the pressure is increased ***(1 mark)***.

(b) (ii)

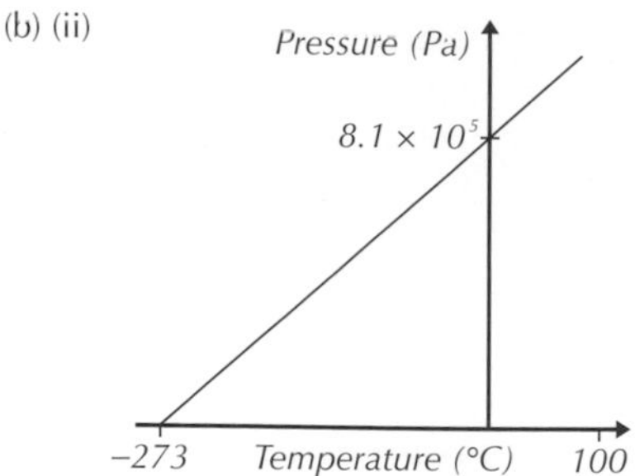

(2 marks available — 1 mark for straight-line graph and 1 mark for crossing through (–273, 0) and (0, 8.1 × 10⁵).)

(b) (iii) $pV = NkT \Rightarrow N = \frac{pV}{kT}$

$= \frac{(8.1 \times 10^5) \times 0.51}{(1.38 \times 10^{-23}) \times 273}$

$= 1.096... \times 10^{26}$

$= \mathbf{1.1 \times 10^{26}}$ **(to 2 s.f.)**

(2 marks for correct answer, 1 mark for correct working if answer incorrect.)

(b) (iv) Total mass of gas $= (1.096... \times 10^{26}) \times (2.7 \times 10^{-26})$
$= 2.96...$ kg

$\Delta Q = mc\Delta T$

$= 2.96... \times (2.2 \times 10^3) \times 150$

$= \mathbf{9.8 \times 10^5}$ **J (to 2 s.f.)**

(2 marks for correct answer, 1 mark for finding the mass of gas if answer incorrect.)

(c) E.g. any three from: all molecules of the gas are identical / the gas contains a large number of molecules / the molecules move rapidly and randomly / Newtonian mechanics apply / collisions between molecules and the walls of the container are elastic / no forces act between the molecules except during collisions / the forces that act during collisions are instantaneous / the molecules have negligible volume compared to the container.
(3 marks available — 1 for each correct answer.)

2 (a) (i) $\Delta Q = mc\Delta T$

$= (92 \times 10^{-3}) \times 2110 \times 25$

$= 4.853 \times 10^3$ J

$= \mathbf{4.9 \times 10^3}$ **J (to 2 s.f.)** ***(1 mark)***

(ii) $\Delta Q = ml$

$= (92 \times 10^{-3}) \times (3.3 \times 10^5)$

$= 3.036 \times 10^4$ J

$= \mathbf{3.0 \times 10^4}$ **J (to 2 s.f.)** ***(1 mark)***

(iii) Total energy needed $= (4.853 \times 10^3) + (3.036 \times 10^4)$
$= 3.5213 \times 10^4$ J

Time taken $= \frac{\text{total energy needed}}{\text{rate of energy supplied}}$

$= \frac{3.5213 \times 10^4}{50}$

$=$ **700 s (to 2 s.f.)**

(2 marks for correct answer, 1 mark for correct working if answer wrong.)

(b) It would slow down the melting of the ice ***(1 mark)***. Heat is transferred from hotter substances to colder substances — as the ice is colder than 25 °C, insulating the beaker will stop heat transfer into the ice from the surrounding air ***(1 mark)***.

3 (a) (i) Absolute zero is the lowest possible temperature any substance can have, and is equal to 0 K or –273 °C ***(1 mark)***.

(ii) The Avogadro constant is the number of atoms in exactly 12 g of the carbon isotope $^{12}_{6}C$ ***(1 mark)***.

Allow "the number of particles in exactly 1 mole of a substance".

(iii) Molar mass is the mass that 1 mole of a substance would have ***(1 mark)***.

(b) (i) $N = n \times N_A = 54.0 \times (6.02 \times 10^{23})$
$= \mathbf{3.25 \times 10^{25}}$ **(to 3 s.f.)** ***(1 mark)***

(b) (ii) $pV = nRT \Rightarrow T = \frac{pV}{nR}$

$= \frac{10^5 \times 4.18}{54.0 \times 8.31}$

$= 931.4... K =$ **931K (to 3 s.f.)**

(2 marks for correct answer, 1 mark for correct working if answer incorrect).

(b) (iii) Average kinetic energy $= \frac{1}{2}m(c_{rms})^2$

$= \frac{3}{2}kT$

$= \frac{3}{2} \times (1.38 \times 10^{-23}) \times 931.4...$

$= 1.928... \times 10^{-20}$ J

Total kinetic energy $= (1.928... \times 10^{-20})$
$\times (3.2508 \times 10^{25})$

$= \mathbf{6.27 \times 10^5}$ **J (to 3 s.f.)**

(3 marks for correct answer, otherwise 1 mark for using correct formula for the average kinetic energy and 1 mark for multiplying this answer by the number of molecules if answer incorrect.)

If you got the wrong answers for parts (i) or (ii) but your calculations here were correct, you get all the marks for part (iii).

Option A — Astrophysics

1. Lenses

Page 143 — Application Question

Q1 a)

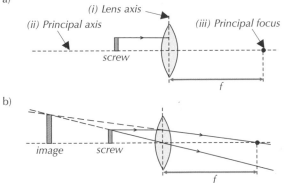

(i) Lens axis
(ii) Principal axis
(iii) Principal focus
screw
f

b)

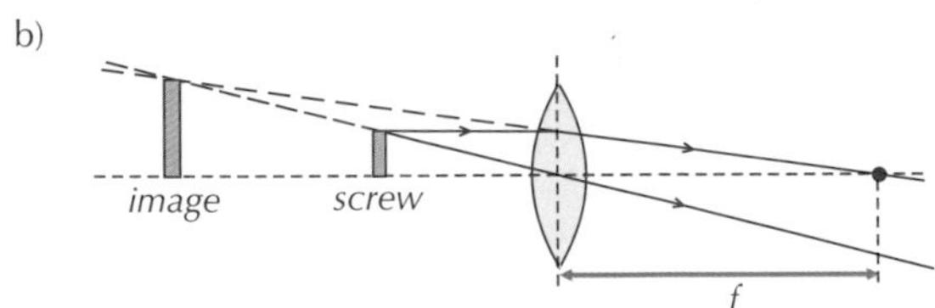

c) The image is virtual — the light rays from the object appear to have come from somewhere else (behind the object).
The image is upright — virtual images are the same way up as the object.
The image is magnified — it is bigger than the object.

Remember, if the image is formed on the same side of the lens as the object, it's virtual.

d) The image flips upside down because the object has become further away from the lens than the focal point of the lens. This means that a real inverted image is formed on the other side of the lens, so it will look upside down.

e) $u = 20$ cm and $v = 20$ cm,
so $\frac{1}{f} = \frac{1}{u} + \frac{1}{v} = \frac{1}{20} + \frac{1}{20} = \frac{1}{10}$ and $f =$ **10 cm**.

Page 143 — Fact Recall Questions

Q1 The principal focus.

Q2 The focal plane of a lens is the plane on to which all sets of incident parallel rays converge.

Q3 The focal length of a lens is the perpendicular distance between the lens axis and the focal plane.

Q4 A real image is an image formed when actual light rays from a point on an object pass through another point in space. The light rays actually meet and the image can be projected onto a screen. If the object is further away from a converging lens than the focal length, a real image will be formed.

Q5 A virtual image is an image formed when light rays from a point on an object appear to have come from somewhere else. The light rays never actually pass through the point they appear to come from, so the image can't be captured on a screen. If the object is closer to a converging lens than the focal length, a virtual image will be formed.

Q6 $\frac{1}{f} = \frac{1}{u} + \frac{1}{v}$

2. Optical Telescopes

Page 147 — Application Question

Q1 a) $M = \frac{f_o}{f_e} = \frac{0.52}{0.001} =$ **520**

b) $M = \frac{\text{angle subtended by image at eye}}{\text{angle subtended by object at unaided eye}}$

So angle subtended by object at the unaided eye is equal to $\frac{\text{angle subtended by image at eye}}{M} = \frac{2.08}{520} =$ **0.004 rad**

Page 147 — Fact Recall Questions

Q1 a) That the light rays are parallel to each other.

b)

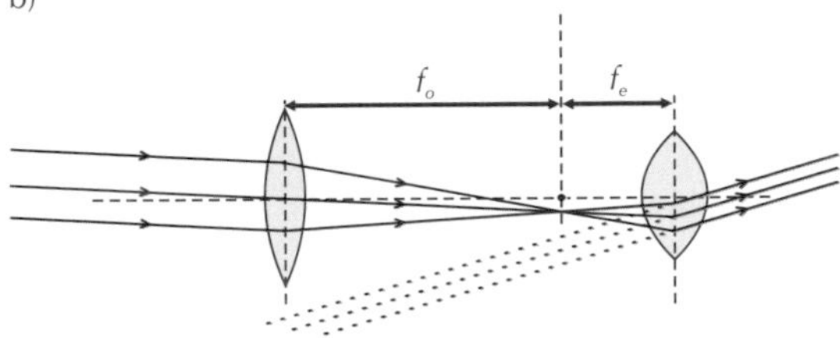

c) It is a virtual image (at infinity).

Q2 $M = \frac{f_o}{f_e}$, where f_o is the focal length of the objective lens and f_e is the focal length of the eye lens.

Q3 The length of an astronomical refracting telescope = $f_o + f_e$.
$M = \frac{f_o}{f_e}$, so an astronomical refracting telescope needs to be long in order to have a large f_o and therefore a large magnification.

Q4

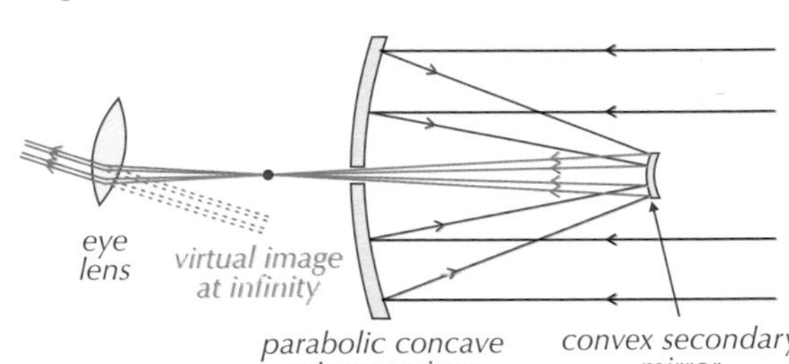

Q5 a) A CCD chip is a silicon chip divided into picture elements (pixels). Incident light causes electrons to be released, with the number of electrons released proportional to the intensity of the light. The electrons are trapped in 'potential wells' under each pixel of the CCD. An electron pattern is built up and when the desired exposure is complete, the charge is processed and converted into a digital signal.

b) The quantum efficiency of a CCD chip is the percentage of incident photons that cause an electron to be released. It is usually > 70%.

3. Comparing Telescopes

Page 150 — Application Questions

Q1 Telescope A

The resolving power is inversely proportional to the diameter of the dish — so the bigger the diameter, the higher the resolving power (for a given wavelength).

Q2 a) $\theta \approx \frac{\lambda}{D} = \frac{650 \times 10^{-9}}{3.2} =$ **2.0×10^{-7} radians (to 2 s.f.)**

b) $\lambda \approx \theta D = (1.99 \times 10^{-7}) \times 3.2$
$= 6.368 \times 10^{-7}$ m = **637 nm (to 3 s.f.)**

Page 150 — Fact Recall Questions

Q1 The smallest angular separation at which it can distinguish two points.

Q2 The light diffracts and produces a diffraction pattern when it passes through a circular aperture. The central circle of the pattern is called the Airy disc.

Q3 $\theta \approx \frac{\lambda}{D}$

Q4 a) Glass refracts different colours of light by different amounts and so the image for each colour is in a slightly different position. This blurs the image.

b) E.g. any two from: bubbles and impurities in the lenses absorb or scatter some light / building large lenses of good quality is expensive and difficult / large lenses are heavy and can only be supported at their edges, meaning they become distorted / for a large magnification the telescope has to be very long (due to a long focal length of the objective lens), so they need large buildings to house them.

Q5 E.g. any two from: it's easier to make good quality mirrors than lenses / mirrors don't suffer from chromatic aberration / it's cheaper to make large mirrors than lenses / mirrors can be supported from underneath, which means they are less likely to distort than lenses which cannot be supported in this way.

Q6 The effect is known as spherical aberration. If the shape of a mirror isn't quite parabolic (e.g. because the mirror has become distorted), parallel rays reflecting off different parts of the mirror do not all converge onto the same point. This causes the image produced by the mirror to be blurred.

4. Non-optical Telescopes

Page 154 — Application Question

Q1 a) $\frac{\text{collecting power of VISTA}}{\text{collecting power of optical telescope}}$

$= \frac{\text{diameter of VISTA}^2}{\text{diameter of optical telescope}^2}$

$= \frac{4.1^2}{1.02^2} = 16.15... =$ **16 (to 2 s.f.)**

b) E.g. The Rayleigh criterion says that $\theta \approx \frac{\lambda}{D}$, so a shorter wavelength gives a smaller minimum angle that can be resolved and so a better resolving power. Visible light has a shorter wavelength than infrared, so the resolving power of the telescope will be better in the visible region.

Remember — the smaller the angle between objects can be, the better the resolving power.

c) The telescope is used to detect infrared radiation. Water vapour in the atmosphere absorbs infrared radiation. The higher up you are, and the drier the atmosphere, the less infrared is absorbed, so infrared telescopes need to be in high-up, dry places.

d) E.g. increase the resolving power of the detector.

Page 154 — Fact Recall Questions

Q1 A radio dish consists of a parabolic fine-wire-mesh dish, an antenna and a preamplifier. The dish reflects radio waves and focuses them on to a detector, positioned on the end of the antenna at the focal point of the parabolic dish. The detector detects the radiation and the preamplifier amplifies the signal without adding too much noise.

Remember, radio waves have long wavelengths that don't notice the gaps in the wire mesh, but shorter wavelength radiation, e.g. visible light, will pass right through it.

Q2 Radio waves have a much longer wavelength than visible light, so for a similar diameter of telescope, the resolving power is much lower, because of the Rayleigh criterion.

Q3 Many radio telescopes can be linked together and their data can be combined to form a single image. This is equivalent to one huge dish the size of the separation of the telescopes. Due to the Rayleigh criterion, $\theta \approx \frac{\lambda}{D}$, a huge diameter means that very good resolving powers can be achieved despite the long wavelength of radio waves.

Q4 E.g. any two from: a mesh dish is easier to construct than a lens or a mirror / a mesh dish is cheaper than a lens or mirror / radio dishes don't need to be as precisely constructed.

Q5 U-V radiation has a shorter wavelength than visible light. The shorter the wavelength, the more precise the shape of the mirror must be, so U-V telescopes must be more precise than optical telescopes.

Q6 I-R telescopes produce their own infrared radiation, which will get mixed up with the I-R radiation being observed, so they need to be cooled to reduce their temperature and minimise the I-R produced by the telescope.

Q7 X-ray radiation is usually either absorbed by a material or passes straight through it. X-rays only reflect if they graze a mirror's surface. An X-ray telescope must use grazing mirrors to gradually alter the direction of the X-rays until they are focused.

Q8 a) E.g. strapped to a weather balloon / aeroplane / in space in orbit around the Earth.

b) E.g. on a mountain (at high altitude) somewhere dry / strapped to a weather balloon or aeroplane / in space in orbit around the Earth.

Q9 Collecting power is proportional to the mirror/dish diameter squared.

5. Parallax and Parsecs

Page 158 — Application Questions

Q1 20 pc = 20 × 3.26 ly = **65.2 ly**

Q2 a) The angle that Sirius moves in relation to distant background stars between either end of the Earth's orbit needs to be measured. The Earth orbits the Sun in 12 months, so it will take 6 months to move from one end of it's orbit to the other. The star will appear to move by its maximum amount between these two points.

b) First convert 0.37 arcseconds into degrees and then radians:

$0.37 \times \frac{1}{3600} = 1.0277... \times 10^{-4\,\circ}$

$1.0277... \times 10^{-4\,\circ} \times \frac{2\pi}{360} = 1.79... \times 10^{-6}$ rad

Then $d = \frac{r}{\theta} = \frac{1.50 \times 10^{11}}{1.79... \times 10^{-6}}$

$= 8.36... \times 10^{16}$ m = $\mathbf{8.36 \times 10^{16}}$ **m (to 3 s.f.)**

c) The distance to Sirius is $8.36... \times 10^{16}$ m. 1 light year = 9.46×10^{15} m, so Sirius is $(8.36... \times 10^{16}) \div (9.46 \times 10^{15})$ = 8.84 light years away (to 3 s.f.). So light from Sirius will take **8 years and 10 months** to reach Earth.

Q3 a) The radius of Mars.

b) $d = \frac{r}{\theta} = \frac{3389.5}{2.5 \times \frac{1}{3600} \times \frac{2\pi}{360}} =$ $\mathbf{2.80 \times 10^{8}}$ **km (to 3 s.f.)**

You need to use 2.5 arcseconds as you're given the radius of the planet, not the diameter.

Page 158 — Fact Recall Questions

Q1 Half the angle by which a nearby star appears to move in relation to the background stars in 6 months as the Earth moves from one end of its orbit to the other.

Q2 A parsec is a unit of distance equal to 3.08×10^{16} m. A star is exactly one parsec (pc) away from Earth if the angle of parallax, $\theta = 1$ arcsecond $= \left(\frac{1}{3600}\right)^\circ$.

Q3 The distance that light travels in a vacuum in one year.

Q4 Light travels at a constant (finite) velocity. It takes about 8 minutes to travel the distance between the Sun and Earth.

Q5 $\theta \approx \frac{r}{d}$ where r is the radius of the object, d is the distance to the object and θ is half the angle subtended by the object in radians. This assumes that θ is small.

Q6 It makes the distances measured more reliable and some methods only work for certain distances.

6. Magnitude

Page 162 — Application Questions

Q1 a) Difference in magnitude is 5.1 – 1.25 = 3.85
So the brightness ratio is:
$\frac{I_A}{I_B} = 2.5^{3.85} = 34.046... = 34.0$ (to 3 s.f.)
So Deneb is approximately **34 times** brighter than Alberio B.

Make sure you say that this is an approximate answer — if you used $100^{\frac{1}{5}}$ you'd actually get 34.7 to 3 significant figures.

b) Rearranging the formula, $M = m - 5\log\left(\frac{d}{10}\right)$.
So $M = 1.25 - 5\log\left(\frac{975}{10}\right) = -8.69... =$ **–8.70 (to 3 s.f.)**

Q2 a) $m = M + 5\log\left(\frac{d}{10}\right)$
$= -6.39 + 5\log\left(\frac{413}{10}\right) =$ **1.69 (to 3 s.f.)**

b) $M = m - 5\log\left(\frac{d}{10}\right)$
$= 1.64 - 5\log\left(\frac{75}{10}\right) =$ **–2.74 (to 3 s.f.)**

c) Bellatrix
d) Alnilam

Q3 Distance $= 3.4 \times 10^6$ pc
$m = M + 5\log\left(\frac{d}{10}\right) = -19.3 + 5\log\left(\frac{3.4 \times 10^6}{10}\right)$
= 8.35... = **8.4 (to 2 s.f.)**

Page 162 — Fact Recall Questions

Q1 Luminosity.

Q2 Distance from Earth and power output/luminosity.

Q3 The apparent magnitude of a star is how bright a star appears when viewed from Earth. The apparent magnitude scale is logarithmic, so a magnitude 1 star has an intensity 100 times greater than a magnitude 6 star.

Q4 2.5 times.

Q5 $\frac{I_2}{I_1} = (100^{\frac{1}{5}})^{m_1 - m_2} \approx 2.5^{m_1 - m_2}$

Q6 It is very bright (brighter than the star Vega, which has an apparent magnitude of 0).

Q7 What the star's apparent magnitude would be if it were 10 parsecs away from Earth.

Q8 $m - M = 5\log\left(\frac{d}{10}\right)$

Q9 A standard candle is an object for which the brightness can be calculated directly. Type 1a supernovae all have the same peak in absolute magnitude, so the distance to them can be calculated by comparing how bright they look to how bright they are known to be.

7. Stars as Black Bodies

Page 166 — Application Questions

Q1 To use the inverse square law, you must assume that the star's power output is the same in all directions, but it will be lower from sunspots because they are cooler ($P \propto T^4$).

Q2 a) $\lambda_{max}T = 0.0029$ so $\lambda_{max} = 0.0029 \div T$
$= 0.0029 \div 11\,000 =$ **2.64×10^{-7} m (to 3 s.f.)**

b)

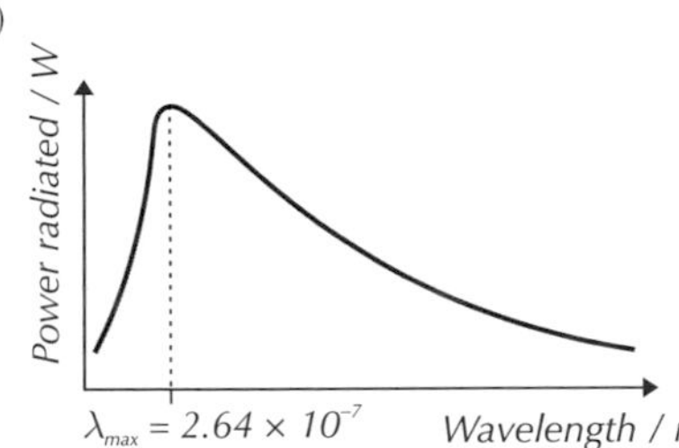

c) First convert the distance to metres:
$773 \text{ ly} = 773 \times (9.46 \times 10^{15}) = 7.31... \times 10^{18}$ m
Use the inverse square law $I = \frac{P}{4\pi d^2}$ to find the power output. Rearranging gives
$P = 4\pi I d^2 = 4\pi(3.7 \times 10^{-8})(7.31... \times 10^{18})^2$
$= 2.49... \times 10^{31}$ W
$P = \sigma A T^4$ so $A = \frac{P}{\sigma T^4} = \frac{2.49... \times 10^{31}}{(5.67 \times 10^{-8})(11\,000)^4}$
= **3.00×10^{22} m² (to 3 s.f.)**

Page 166 — Fact Recall Questions

Q1 A body that absorbs all electromagnetic radiation of all wavelengths and can emit all wavelengths of electromagnetic radiation.

Q2

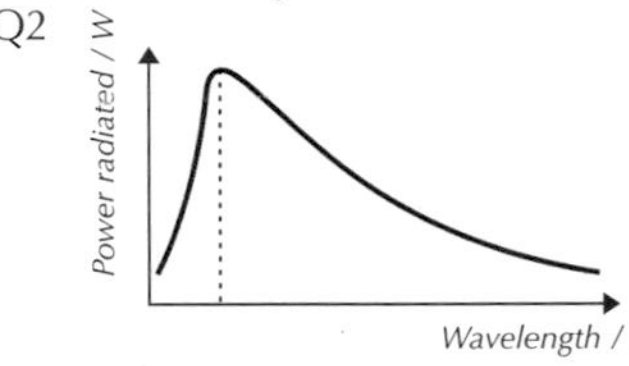

Q3 The temperature of the black body.

Q4 $\lambda_{max}T = 0.0029$ m K

Q5 $P = \sigma A T^4$

Q6 $I = \frac{P}{4\pi d^2}$

8. Stellar Spectral Classes

Page 170 — Application Question

Q1 a) Star 1.

b) Star 2, because it has molecular band absorptions from compounds like TiO. Compounds like this can only form in cooler stars.

c) Star 1, because it only has absorption lines from hydrogen and helium. Star 2 is not a class B star because it has absorption lines from molecules.

d) Spectral class M, because it has strong absorption lines for TiO.

e) 11 000 – 25 000 K.

Page 170 — Fact Recall Questions

Q1 Each atom, ion or molecule in the star absorbs particular wavelengths of radiation that correspond with the differences between its energy levels. So there will only be absorption lines in the spectra at the particular wavelengths corresponding to the ions, atoms or molecules found in the star.

Q2 Because the electron transitions in atomic hydrogen that absorb photons with a wavelength in the visible part of the electromagnetic spectrum are between the n = 2 and higher energy levels.

Q3

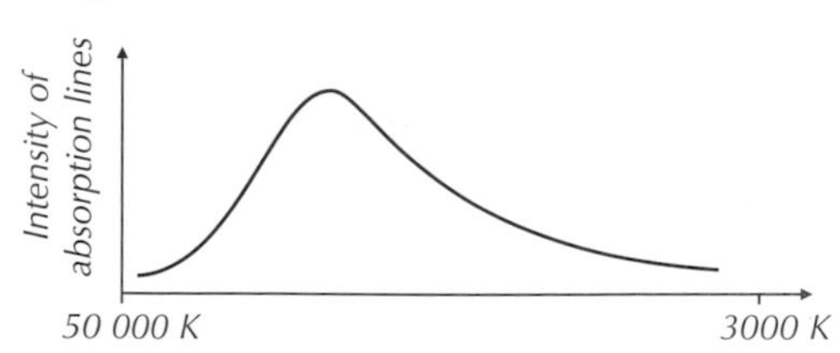

Q4 O, B, A, F, G, K, M

Q5 A blue star.

Q6 a) Metal ions and metal atoms.
b) Neutral atoms, and compounds such as TiO.
c) He^+, He and H.
d) Mostly neutral metal atoms.

Q7 F

Q8 A

9. The Hertzspung-Russell Diagram

Page 172 — Application Question

Q1 a) Star 2, because both stars are at about the same temperature, but Star 2 is much brighter, so it must be bigger due to Stefan's law.
b) White dwarf
c) Main sequence star
d) Star 1

Page 172 — Fact Recall Questions

Q1 Absolute magnitude from –10 to 15.

Q2 Spectral class or temperature (decreasing)

Q3

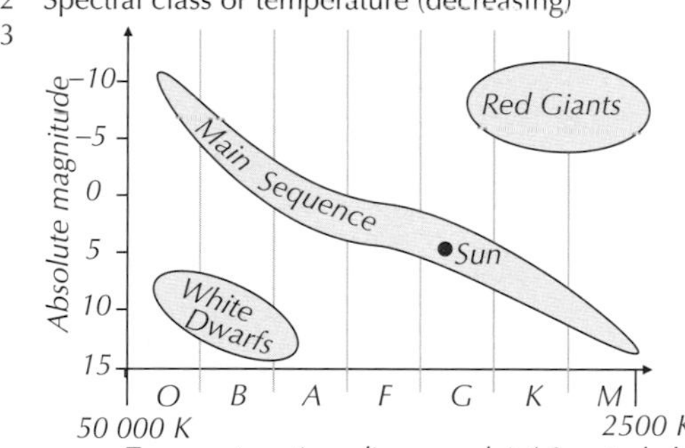

Q4 Hydrogen is fusing into helium.

10. Evolution of Sun-like Stars

Page 175 — Application Question

Q1 a) ***b*** is a red giant and ***a*** is the hottest main-sequence star.
b) ***c***
c) ***c - b - a - d*** (or ***c - b - d***)

Page 175 — Fact Recall Questions

Q1 Gravity

Q2 The main sequence

Q3 The pressure produced from the hydrogen fusion in the core of the star balances the gravitational force compressing the star, so it is stable.

Q4 When the core of a star runs out of hydrogen, hydrogen fusion, and the pressure caused by it, stops and the core starts to contract and heat up. The heat from the core of the star heats up the layer until it is hot enough for hydrogen to fuse into helium.

Q5 Core hydrogen burning stops in the star and the core of the star begins to contract, causing the outer layers to expand and cool, and the star becomes a red giant.

Q6 Once fusion stops in the core of a low-mass star, the pressure created by fusion is lost, so the core begins to contract under its own weight and heat up. Once the core gets to about the size of the Earth, electron degeneracy pressure stops it contracting any further. The hot dense core that is left over is a white dwarf. A planetary nebula is left behind by the outer layers of the star.

Q7 The remnants of the outer layers of a red giant, that are ejected as the star becomes a white dwarf.

11. Supernovae, Neutron Stars and Black Holes

Page 179 — Application Questions

Q1 No. The photon is within the Schwarzschild radius of the black hole. Inside the Schwarzschild radius, the escape velocity is greater than the speed of light, so the photon is doomed never to escape.

Q2 a) The mass of the Sun is 1.99×10^{30} kg, so the black hole has a mass of $(4.31 \times 10^6) \times (1.99 \times 10^{30})$
$= 8.57... \times 10^{36}$ kg = $\mathbf{8.58 \times 10^{36}}$ **kg (to 3 s.f.)**.

b) $R_S = \frac{2GM}{c^2} = \frac{2(6.67 \times 10^{-11})(8.57... \times 10^{36})}{(3 \times 10^8)^2}$
$= 1.271... \times 10^{10} = \mathbf{1.27 \times 10^{10}}$ **m (to 3 s.f.)**

c) The volume (V) of a sphere of radius r is $\frac{4}{3}\pi r^3$
The Sun has a radius of 6.96×10^8 m.

So $V_{Sun} = \frac{4}{3}\pi(6.96 \times 10^8)^3 = 1.412... \times 10^{27}$ m³

and $V_{black\ hole} = \frac{4}{3}\pi(1.27... \times 10^{10})^3 = 8.6... \times 10^{30}$ m³

$8.6... \times 10^{30} \div 1.412... \times 10^{27} = 6094.0...$
So the volume of the supermassive black hole at the centre of the galaxy is **6090 (to 3 s.f.) times** bigger than that of the Sun.

Page 179 — Fact Recall Questions

Q1 The electron degeneracy pressure cannot withstand the gravitational forces at this mass, so when the fusion reactions have stopped, the core will continue to contract further than a white dwarf.

Q2 The core contracts and the outer layers fall onto the core and rebound, causing a huge shockwave that propels the outer layers into space. The star experiences a brief and rapid increase in absolute magnitude when it explodes.

Q3 As the core of a massive star contracts, the electrons in the atoms get squashed into the atomic nuclei, where they combine with protons to form neutrons. The result is a neutron star made of neutrons.

Q4 The velocity that an object would need to travel at to have enough kinetic energy to overcome its gravitational potential energy.

Q5 A black hole is an object whose escape velocity is greater than the speed of light. They are formed when a star of core mass more than 3 solar masses contracts and collapses into an infinitely dense point.

Q6 The boundary of a region surrounding an object at which its escape velocity is equal to the speed of light.

Q7 The Schwarzschild radius of a black hole is the radius of the even horizon, or the radius at which the escape velocity is equal to the speed of light.

Q8 A supermassive black hole.

Q9 $R_s = \frac{2GM}{c^2}$

12. Doppler Effect and Red Shift

Page 183 — Application Questions

Q1 a) Star A, because the frequency of the absorption line is lower than it should be, so it is red-shifted.

b) $z = \frac{\Delta f}{f} = \frac{(4.57 \times 10^{14}) - (4.37 \times 10^{14})}{4.57 \times 10^{14}}$
$= 0.0437... = \mathbf{0.0438}$ **(to 3 s.f.)**

c) $z = \frac{v}{c}$ so $v = zc = 0.0437... \times (3.00 \times 10^8)$
$= 1.312... \times 10^7$
$= \mathbf{1.31 \times 10^7\ ms^{-1}}$ **(to 3 s.f.)**

Q2 a) Positive, because it is receding.

b) $z = \frac{v}{c} = \frac{463 \times 10^3}{3.00 \times 10^8} = 1.543... \times 10^{-3}$
$= \mathbf{1.54 \times 10^{-3}}$ **(to 3 s.f.)**

c) $z = -\frac{\Delta\lambda}{\lambda} = -\frac{\lambda - \lambda_{obs}}{\lambda}$, so making λ_{obs} the subject:
$\lambda_{obs} = \lambda(z + 1) = 0.21121(1.54... \times 10^{-3} + 1) = 0.21153...$
$= \mathbf{0.2125}$ **(to 4 s.f.)**

Remember, always give your answer to the lowest number of significant figures given in the question, or one more.

Page 183 — Fact Recall Questions

Q1 The sound waves travelling in the same direction as the police car are 'bunched up' in front of the police car, and those travelling in the opposite direction spread out behind it. The bunching up causes the frequency and therefore the pitch of the sound waves to be higher.

Q2 As a radiation source moves away from an observer, the wavelengths detected by the observer get longer and the frequencies get lower — this effect is called red shift. Blue shift is caused by a source moving towards the observer — the wavelengths of the radiation observed are shorter and the frequencies get higher than when the source is stationary.

Q3 $z = \frac{v}{c}$, assuming $v \ll c$.

Q4 Look for absorption lines with known wavelengths in the spectrum and see how their wavelengths have been shifted. If the absorption lines have a red shift, the source is moving away from us and if the absorption lines have been blue shifted, the source is moving towards us.

Q5 $z = \frac{\Delta f}{f}$ and $z = -\frac{\Delta\lambda}{\lambda}$.

Q6 The red shift of distant objects that is caused by space itself expanding and light waves stretching along with it (rather than the objects moving through space away from us).

13. The Big Bang Theory

Page 187 — Application Questions

Q1 1.4×10^7 pc $= 14 \times 10^6$ pc $= 14$ Mpc.
Use Hubble's law: $v = Hd$
The maximum value of Hubble's constant,
75 kms^{-1} Mpc^{-1}, gives the maximum recessional velocity:
$v = Hd = 75 \times 14 =$ **1050 kms^{-1}**.
The minimum value of Hubble's constant,
65 kms^{-1} Mpc^{-1}, gives the minimum recessional velocity:
$v = Hd = 65 \times 14 =$ **910 kms^{-1}**.

Q2 a) H has not been constant since the universe began.

b) If the universe is 13.7 billion years old, the observable universe is limited by the time taken for light to travel to us — some light won't have reached us yet so the actual size of the universe cannot be calculated.

Page 187 — Fact Recall Questions

Q1 On a large scale the universe is homogeneous and isotropic.

Q2 The red shift of distant objects is proportional to their distance.

Q3 $v = Hd$, where v is in kms^{-1}, H is in kms^{-1} Mpc^{-1} and d is in Mpc.

Q4 The theory that the universe started off very hot and very dense (perhaps as an infinitely hot, infinitely dense singularity) and has been expanding ever since.

Q5 If you assume the expansion of the universe has been constant, then the age of the universe is $1/H$, where H is Hubble's constant.

Q6 We can only measure the size of the observable universe, because only the light from within that distance has had enough time to reach us.

Q7 The expansion of the universe is thought to be accelerating, not decelerating as astronomers expected — dark energy might explain this.

Q8 Cosmic microwave background radiation is electromagnetic radiation in the microwave region that is found everywhere in the universe, and is largely homogeneous and isotropic. The Big Bang theory predicts that this radiation was produced in the very early universe, and that its wavelengths have been stretched by the expansion of the universe to match those observed today.

Q9 There is a large abundance of helium in the universe. This supports the Big Bang theory as it suggests that at some point the universe was hot enough for hydrogen to fuse into helium.

14. Applications of Red Shift

Page 190 — Application Questions

Q1 a) No, one of the stars is much brighter than the other.
From the graph you can see that one eclipse leads to a bigger drop in apparent magnitude than the other, so one of the stars must be dimmer.

b) At point A, both stars can be seen, as they are not in the same line of sight because they are near their maximum separation.
At point B, the stars are in the same line of sight, i.e. one behind the other. The dimmer star is behind the brighter star.
At point C, the stars are in the same line of sight. The brighter star is behind the dimmer star.

c) The time between the two big dips in apparent magnitude about 3 days.

Q2 $z = 0.12$, and $z = \frac{v}{c}$ so $v = zc = 0.12 \times 3.00 \times 10^8$
$= 3.6 \times 10^7$ m s^{-1} $= 3.6 \times 10^4$ km s^{-1}
Now use Hubble's law: $v = Hd$ and so
$d = \frac{v}{H} = \frac{3.6 \times 10^4}{65} = 553.8... = 550$ Mpc (to 2 s.f.)

Page 190 — Fact Recall Questions

Q1 If you take a spectral line from an element in the spectrum of a spectroscopic binary system, the line will periodically split into two lines (one red-shifted and one blue-shifted) then recombine. The lines which will reach their maximum separation in half the orbital period of the system.

Q2 Measure the time between zero and maximum separation between the red- and blue-shifted absorption lines of an element, and multiply by 2 to get the period.

Q3 As the stars eclipse each other, the apparent magnitude of the system drops because light from one star is blocked out by the other star.

Q4 Stars in our galaxy.

Q5 They have very large red shifts.

Q6 A quasar is a powerful galactic nucleus centred around a supermassive black hole. The strong radiation emitted is due to the mass of whirling gas falling into it.

Exam-style Questions — Pages 192-195

1 (a)

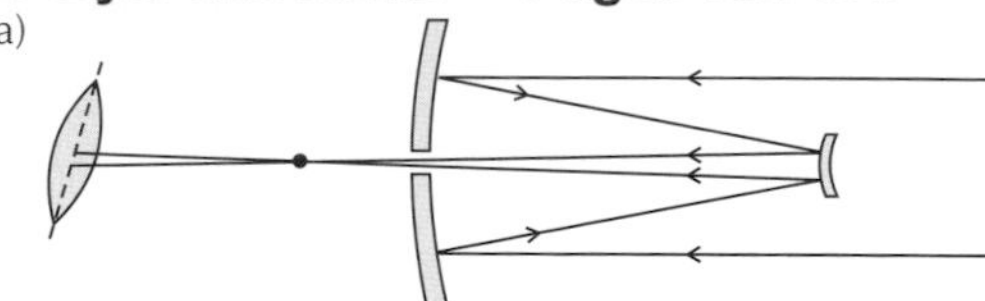

(2 marks — 1 for the primary concave and secondary convex mirrors drawn correctly, 1 mark for the path of both rays drawn correctly to the eyepiece.)

(b) (i) If a mirror in a Cassegrain arrangement isn't quite the right shape, the light rays refract by the wrong angles and there is no focal point. The image is blurry. ***(1 mark)***

(ii) By using a precisely made parabolic mirror ***(1 mark)***.

(c) The Earth's atmosphere absorbs most ultraviolet and some infrared wavelengths so the telescope would be unable to observe those wavelengths from Earth ***(1 mark)***.

(d) How to grade your answer (pick the description that best matches your answer):

0 marks: There is no relevant information.

1-2 marks: Some of the structure or operation of a CCD is described, but there is no complete description of its operation. Several errors with grammar, spelling, punctuation and legibility. Answer lacks structure and information.

3-4 marks: The structure of a CCD is described, and a description of its operation is given. Only a few errors with grammar, spelling, punctuation and legibility. Answer has some structure and information.

5-6 marks: The structure of a CCD is described and a full explanation of its operation is given. Grammar, spelling and punctuation are used accurately and there is no problem with legibility. Uses an appropriate form and style of writing and information.

Here are some points your answer may include:

- A CCD is a silicon chip divided into picture elements (pixels).
- Incident photons release electrons.
- The number of electrons liberated is proportional to the intensity of light.
- The electrons are trapped by potential wells under each pixel.
- The electron pattern is built up in the potential wells.
- When the exposure is complete, the charge is processed to give an image.
- The image produced is identical to the electron pattern.

2 (a) (i) A black body is a body that absorbs all electromagnetic radiation at all wavelengths and can emit all wavelengths of electromagnetic radiation ***(1 mark)***.

(ii) Assuming that Mu Cephei behaves as a black body, $\lambda_{max}T = 0.0029$ m K so

$T = \frac{0.0029}{\lambda_{max}} = \frac{0.0029}{828.6 \times 10^{-9}} = 3499.8...$ K

$=$ **3500 K (to 2 s.f.)**

(2 marks available for correct answer and 1 mark for correct assumption, otherwise 1 mark for using correct values in the equation, 1 mark for correct assumption.)

(b) (i) Find the surface area of Mu Cephei first:
Assume that Mu Cephei is a sphere and use that the radius of the Sun = 6.96×10^8 m

$A = 4\pi r^2 = 4\pi(1500 \times 6.96 \times 10^8)^2$

$= 1.369... \times 10^{25} = 1.37 \times 10^{25}$ m^2 (to 3 s.f.).

Using Stefan's law:

$P = \sigma AT^4 = (5.67 \times 10^{-8})(1.369... \times 10^{25})(3499.8...)^4$

$=$ **1.165... × 10³² W = 1.2 × 10³² W (to 2 s.f.).**

(3 marks for correct answer, otherwise 1 mark for substituting the correct values into the formula for a sphere's surface area, 1 mark for substituting the correct values into Stefan's law.)

(ii) Rearranging the inverse square law to make d the subject gives $d = \sqrt{\frac{P}{4\pi I}}$

So $d = \sqrt{\frac{1.165...... \times 10^{32}}{4\pi \times (5.1 \times 10^{-9})}} = 4.26... \times 10^{19}$ m

In light years,

$d = 4.26... \times 10^{19} \div (9.46 \times 10^{15})$

$=$ **4500 ly (2 s.f.)**

(2 marks for correct answer, otherwise 1 mark for substituting the correct values into the inverse square law to get distance.)

If you get an answer wrong, and then use the wrong value in the next part, you will get full marks for that part as long as you use the wrong value in the correct way.

(iii) E.g. Mu Cephei is not a perfect black body, so the value for surface temperature may be wrong ***(1 mark)***.

3 (a) Omicron[1] ***(1 mark)*** (as it has the highest value of apparent magnitude).

(b) (i) The absolute magnitude of an object is what the apparent magnitude would be if the object was 10 parsecs away ***(1 mark)***.

(ii) Sirius ***(1 mark)***, because its apparent magnitude is brighter than its absolute magnitude.

(c) (i) $m - M = 5\log\frac{d}{10}$

so $d = 10 \times 10^{\frac{m-M}{5}} = 10 \times 10^{\frac{1.83-(-6.87)}{5}}$

$= 549.5... =$ **550 parsecs (to 2 s.f.)**

(2 marks for correct answer, otherwise 1 mark for substituting into the correct formula.)

(ii) Wezen is in spectral class F, so it is a white star ***(1 mark)*** and contains metal ions ***(1 mark)***. The main absorption lines that you would expect to see in its line spectrum are lines due to metal ions ***(1 mark)***.

4 (a) (i) $\theta \approx \frac{\lambda}{D}$

$= \frac{8.5 \times 10^{-3}}{25} =$ **3.4 × 10⁻⁴ rad**

(2 marks for correct answer, otherwise 1 mark for substituting into the correct formula.)

(ii) For a 36 m dish, $\theta = \frac{\lambda}{D} = \frac{8.5 \times 10^{-3}}{36 \times 10^{3}}$
$= 2.36... \times 10^{-7}$ rad
$\frac{1.2 \times 10^{-4}}{2.36... \times 10^{-7}} = 508.235...$
= **510 times better (to 2 s.f.)**
(2 marks for correct answer, otherwise 1 mark for using the correct resolving power of the dish and the VLA.)

(b) (i) The formula $z = \frac{v}{c}$ only works for $v << c$ ***(1 mark)***, which means $z << 1$. The formula won't work for z = 5.95 ***(1 mark)***.

(ii) E.g. object A could be a quasar because it is a strong radio source ***(1 mark)*** with a very large red shift ***(1 mark)***.

5 (a) (i) Half the angle moved by an object in relation to the background stars over a period of 6 months, when the Earth is at opposite ends of its orbit ***(1 mark)***.

(ii) Only nearby stars appear to move, while distant stars appear to be stationary, so parallax only works for nearby stars ***(1 mark)***.

(b) (i) The stars have the same (of very similar) brightness as each other, because the drops in apparent magnitude are by the same amount for each eclipse. ***(1 mark)***.

(ii) 95 hours ***(1 mark)***.

(c) (i) As the stars orbit, the light from each star will be red-shifted and blue-shifted, relative to the average frequency of the light, as it travels away from and towards us respectively ***(1 mark)***.

(ii) When the observed wavelength is at its maximum, the star will be travelling away from us almost in our line of sight, at the orbital velocity, when it is at its minimum, it will be travelling towards us at the orbital velocity. When the two star is travelling perpendicular to our line of sight, the observed red shift will be between the maximum and minimum, so it will be 434.050 nm.

Use $\frac{\Delta\lambda}{\lambda} = -\frac{v}{c}$ to get $v = -\frac{c\Delta\lambda}{\lambda}$
$= -\frac{(3.00 \times 10^{8})(434.050 - 434.076)}{434.050}$
$= 17970.2...$ m s^{-1}
So the orbital velocity is 18 000 m s^{-1} (to 3 s.f.)
= 18 kms^{-1} (to 3 s.f.)
(3 marks for correct answer, otherwise 1 mark for correct rearranging of equation and 1 mark for substituting in the right values.)

(d) The stars will eventually become red giants ***(1 mark)***. The cores will contract further and heat up until helium fusion occurs in the core ***(1 mark)***.

6 (a)

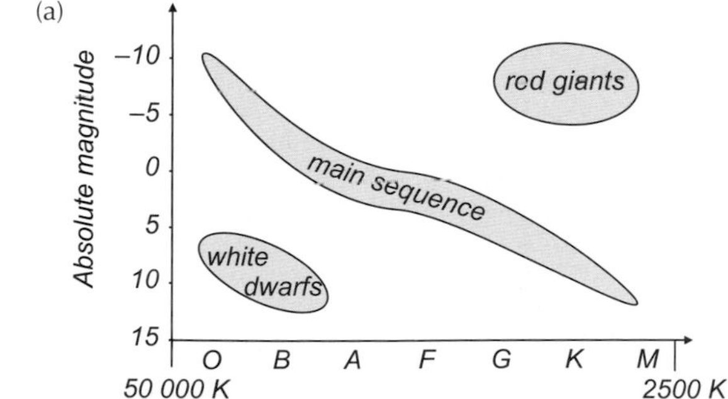

(3 marks available — 1 mark for correct shape of main sequence, 1 mark for red giants and white dwarfs correct, 1 mark for labelling temperature and spectral class scale correctly.)

(b)

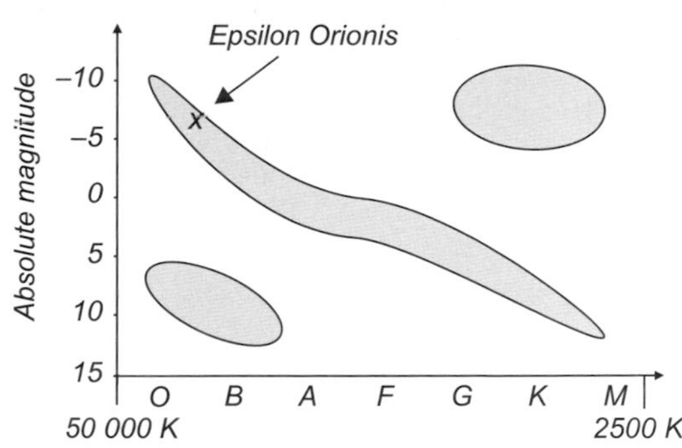

(1 mark for correctly plotting Epsilon Orionis on the H-R diagram at the correct absolute magnitude and between spectral classes O and B.)

(c) (i) When fusion in the core of the star stops, the core will begin to contract ***(1 mark)***. The gravitational forces will be so large that the core will not stop at a white dwarf or a neutron star, but will collapse to an infinitely dense point ***(1 mark)***. The gravitational forces of the infinitely dense point are so strong that it becomes a black hole ***(1 mark)***.

(ii) The Schwarzschild radius of a black hole is the radius at which the black hole's escape velocity is equal to the speed of light, c ***(1 mark)***.

7 (a) The universe started off very hot and very dense (perhaps as an infinitely hot, infinitely dense singularity) and has been expanding ever since ***(1 mark)***.

(b) (i) Hubble's law says that the further away a galaxy is, the faster it is moving away from us. It suggests that the universe is expanding so at one point it must have been denser and hotter ***(1 mark)***.

(ii) $H = 65$ kms^{-1}Mpc^{-1} $= \frac{65 \times 10^{3}}{3.08 \times 10^{22}}$
$= 2.11... \times 10^{-18}$ s^{-1}
$t = \frac{1}{H} = \frac{1}{2.11... \times 10^{-18}} = 4.738... \times 10^{17}$ s
= 15.0 × 10^{9} = 15 billion years (to 2 s.f.)
(3 marks for correct answer, otherwise 1 mark for correctly converting H to s^{-1} and 1 mark for substituting into correct formula.)

(c) E.g. Cosmic microwave background radiation: The Big Bang theory predicts that lots of EM radiation was given out in the early universe ***(1 mark)***. The cosmic microwave background radiation matched this prediction ***(1 mark)***. Relative abundances of H and He: The Big Bang theory predicts that the early universe was so hot that hydrogen fused to make helium ***(1 mark)***, which explains the relative abundances of H and He in the universe now ***(1 mark)***.

Option B — Medical Physics

1. Lenses

Page 200 — Application Questions

Q1 $u = 0.20$ m, $v = 0.36$ m

$m = \frac{v}{u} = \frac{0.36}{0.20} = \mathbf{1.8}$

Q2 Rearrange $P = \frac{1}{f}$ to get $f = \frac{1}{P}$.

$f = \frac{1}{P} = \frac{1}{2.4} =$ **0.42 m (to 2 s.f.)**

Q3 E.g.

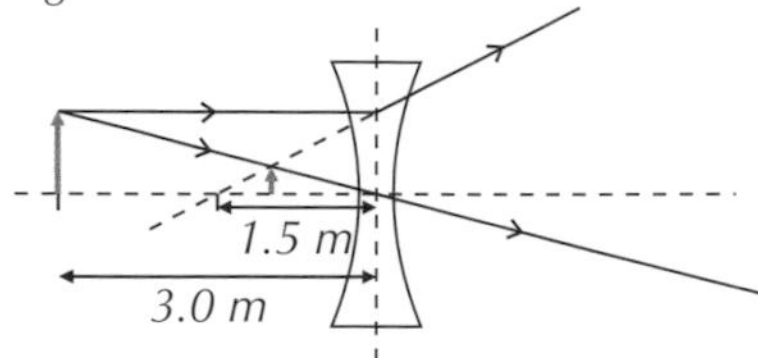

Q4 $u = 65$ cm, $v = 105$ cm and $\frac{1}{f} = \frac{1}{u} + \frac{1}{v}$.

Substituting in u and v gives:

$\frac{1}{f} = \frac{1}{65} + \frac{1}{105}$ so $f = 40.14... =$ **40.1 cm (to 3 s.f.)**

Remember you don't need to convert all the distances into metres before plugging them into the lens equation — they just need to all be in the same units.

Page 200 — Fact Recall Questions

Q1 A converging lens is convex in shape. It brings rays parallel to its principal axis together at its principal focus. A diverging lens is concave in shape. It causes parallel rays of light to diverge.

Q2 The principal focus of a converging lens is the point on which incident rays parallel to the principal axis converge. The principal focus of a diverging lens is the point that incident rays parallel to the principal axis appear to have come from.

Q3 Draw (at least) two rays coming from the same point on the image: one parallel to the principal axis which refracts through the principal focus and one that travels straight through the lens' centre and does not refract. Where the rays meet is where the image is formed.

Q4 A real image is formed when light rays from an object are made to pass through another point in space. A real image can be captured on a screen. A virtual image is formed when light rays from an object diverge therefore appear to have come from another point in space. Virtual images are formed on the same side of the lens as the object. The rays of light don't actually pass through the point where the image appears to be, and so this type of image cannot be captured on a screen.

Q5 The lens equation. $\frac{1}{f} = \frac{1}{u} + \frac{1}{v}$ where u = object distance from the lens, v = image distance from the lens and f = focal point of the lens.

Q6 $P = \frac{1}{f}$

2. Physics of the Eye

Page 204 — Fact Recall Questions

Q1 a) The cornea does most the focusing for the eye.

b) The iris controls the size of the pupil to regulate the intensity of light entering the eye.

c) The ciliary muscles are used to change the shape of the lens by contracting or relaxing.

Q2 retina

Q3 The cornea, aqueous humour and the lens refract and focus light on to the retina. The eye's lens changes shape depending on the object distance, which changes the focal length, so that an image is always formed on the retina.

Q4 a) The furthest distance the eye can focus on comfortably.

b) The closest distance the eye can focus on.

Q5 a) At the back of the retina.

b) There is one type of rod and three types of cones.

Each type of cone is sensitive to different colours of light — red, green or blue.

Q6 a) The minimum distance between objects that can be distinguished.

b) There must be at least one rod or cone between the rods or cones detecting the light from each object.

Q7 Persistence of vision is where an afterimage remains for a short amount of time on the retina after a bright image is removed.

Q8 Any two of: e.g. cinema / television / fluorescent lights.

3. Defects of Vision

Page 207 — Application Questions

Q1 a)

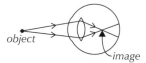

object

image

b) Myopia.

c) A person with myopia can't focus on distant objects as their far point is closer than infinity. A diverging lens with its principal focus at the eye's faulty far point can be used to correct this. This means distant objects at infinity, which were blurry, now appear to come from the eye's far point and will be in focus.

Q2 The focal point of the lens used should be –4.2 m, because it should be a diverging lens that makes distant rays appear to come from the uncorrected far point of 4.2 m.

So $f = -4.2$ m and $P = \frac{1}{-4.2} =$ **–0.24 D (to 2 s.f.)**.

Q3 A lens correcting hypermetropia takes an object at 0.25 m and creates a virtual image at the patient's uncorrected near point. So $u = 0.25$ and $f = 0.27$.

$\frac{1}{f} = \frac{1}{u} + \frac{1}{v}$ so $\frac{1}{v} = \frac{1}{f} - \frac{1}{u} = \frac{1}{0.27} - \frac{1}{0.25} = -0.29...$

so $v = -3.375$.

So the uncorrected near point is **3.4 m (to 2 s.f.)**.

Remember, a negative value just means on the same side of the lens as the object, but the near point is always on the same side of the lens as the object, so you can ignore it here.

Page 207 — Fact Recall Questions

Q1 Myopia is short-sightedness, where people can't focus on distant objects. Their far point is closer than infinity.

Q2 a) Hypermetropia is long-sightedness, where people can't focus clearly on near objects.

Their near point is further away than normal (25 cm or more).

b) Converging lens.

Q3 a) Someone who suffers from astigmatism will have different focal lengths for different planes. This may be cause by an irregularly shaped cornea or lens.

b) The prescription will give the power and axis angle of the cylindrical lens.

4. Physics of the Ear

Page 209 — Fact Recall Questions

Q1 The amount of sound energy passing per second per unit area (power per unit area).

Q2 Outer ear — pinna and auditory canal.
Middle ear — ossicles (malleus, incus and stapes) and Eustachian tube.
Inner ear — semicircular canals, cochlea and auditory nerve.

Q3 E.g. the ossicles act as a lever system. They pass on the vibrations of the eardrum to the oval window. They also amplify the force of the vibrations and reduce the energy reflected back from the inner ear.

Q4 The pressure variations at the oval window are about 20 times greater than those at the eardrum.

Q5 Sound waves are funnelled by the pinna into the auditory canal in the outer ear. The variations in air pressure due to the sound waves cause the tympanic membrane (eardrum) to vibrate. The tympanic membrane is connected to the malleus, which passes vibrations via the incus to the stapes (small bones in the middle ear). The force of the vibrations is increased by about 50% by the ossicles. The vibration of the stapes causes the oval window to vibrate, which causes pressure waves in the fluid of the cochlea. The pressure waves cause the basilar membrane to vibrate (which part vibrates the most depends on the frequency of the sound), which causes certain hair cells to vibrate enough to trigger an electrical impulse in the auditory nerve which is sent to the brain and interpreted as sound.

5. Intensity and Loudness

Page 212 — Application Questions

Q1 Humans experience hearing loss at high frequencies as a result of aging, so only younger people can hear the very highest frequencies in the range of human hearing. The annoying high frequency noise deters young people but cannot be heard by older people.

Q2 Intensity level $= 10\log\left(\frac{I}{I_0}\right)$ and $I_0 = 1 \times 10^{-12}$ Wm^{-2}.

$40 = 10\log\left(\frac{I}{1 \times 10^{-12}}\right)$ so $4 = \log\left(\frac{I}{1 \times 10^{-12}}\right)$.

Raise each side to the power 10, to get rid of the log:

$10^4 = 10^{\log\left(\frac{I}{1 \times 10^{-12}}\right)}$ and so $10^4 = \left(\frac{I}{1 \times 10^{-12}}\right)$

so $I = 10^4 \times (1 \times 10^{-12}) = \mathbf{1 \times 10^{-8}\ Wm^{-2}}$

Page 212 — Fact Recall Questions

Q1 The intensity of the sound and its frequency.

Q2 The ear's response to sound is logarithmic and so it needs a logarithmic scale to reflect this.
The perceived loudness of a sound doesn't increase linearly with intensity, but logarithmically.

Q3 The decibel, dB

Q4 It is an adjusted decibel scale which takes into account the ear's response to different frequencies.

Q5 The threshold of hearing is the minimum intensity of sound that can be heard by a normal ear at 1000 Hz. Its value is 1×10^{-12} Wm^{-2}.

Q6 E.g. Old age and excessive exposure to noise.

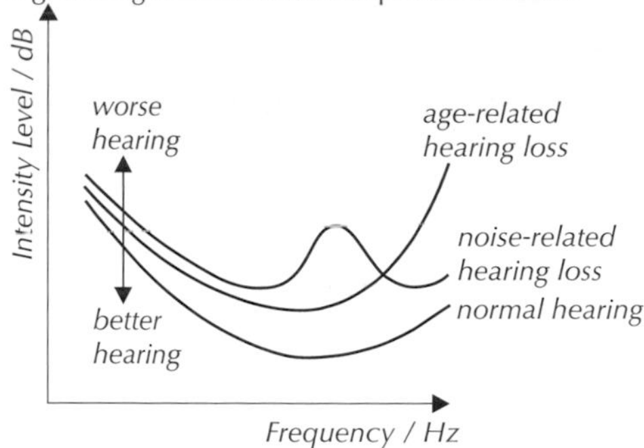

6. Physics of the Heart

Page 217 — Application Question

Q1 Point P shows the depolarisation and contraction of the atria. The QRS wave then shows the depolarisation and contraction of the ventricles (and the repolarisation and relaxation of the atria). Point T then shows the repolarisation and relaxation of the ventricles.

Page 217 — Fact Recall Questions

Q1 The heart is a double pump because the left-hand side pumps blood from the lungs to the body, and the right-hand side pumps blood from the body back to the lungs.

Q2 They only allow blood to flow in one direction.

Q3 The nerve cell has a cell body containing the nucleus. Dendrites extend from the cell body. The nerve fibre (axon) is a long, thin core surrounded by a myelin sheath.
The dendrites carry signals from other cells to the cell body.

Q4 Sodium ions (Na^+ ions) and potassium ions (K^+ ions).

Q5 Typical nerve cell: about –70 mV,
heart nerve cell: about –80 mV

Q6

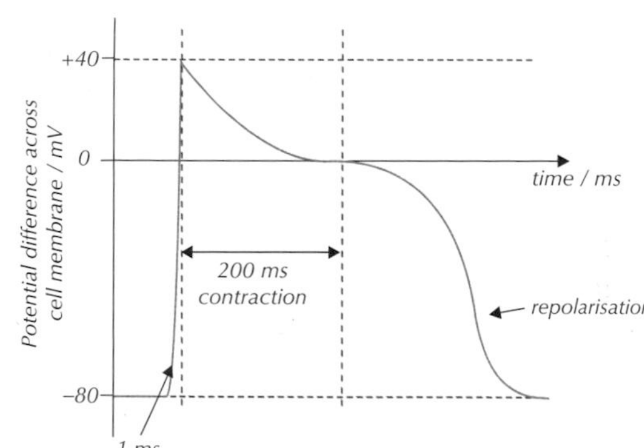

Q7 Any two from: e.g. amplify the signal using a high impedance amplifier / remove hairs and dead skin cells (e.g. using sandpaper) / use a conductive gel / make sure the patient remains relaxed and still during the procedure.

7. X-ray Production

Page 220 — Application Question

Q1 $E_{max} = Q \times V = 1.60 \times 10^{-19} \times 85.0 \times 10^3 = \mathbf{1.36 \times 10^{-14}\ J}$
Assume here that the maximum photon energy is the same as the maximum kinetic energy of the electrons.

Page 220 — Fact Recall Questions

Q1 a)

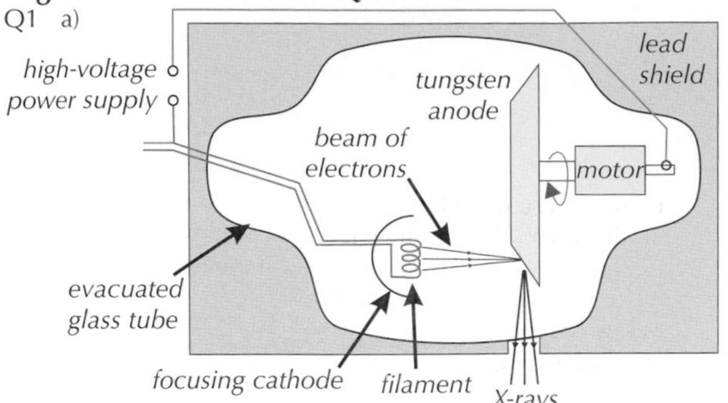

b) A lot of the electrons' energy is converted to heat, so rotating the anode prevents it from overheating.

c) E.g. reducing the size of the anode focal point (e.g. by decreasing the slope of the anode) / increasing the distance between the anode and the object.

Q2 When electrons smash into the (tungsten) anode, they decelerate and some of their kinetic energy is converted into electromagnetic energy, as X-ray photons. This results in a continuous spectrum of X-ray radiation.
X-rays are also produced when electrons are knocked out of tungsten atoms and outer shell electrons fall inwards to take their place. As they do this, they release energy in the form of X-ray photons with set energies that correspond to energy level transitions, producing the spikes seen in the graph.

Q3 a) Intensity increases with tube voltage, approximately in proportion to the square of the voltage. The maximum photon energy also increases proportionally to the tube voltage.

b) Intensity increases with tube current, approximately in proportion to the current. The maximum photon energy isn't affected by the current.

8. X-ray Imaging

Page 223 — Application Question

Q1 a) $\mu_m = \frac{\mu}{\rho} \Rightarrow \mu = \mu_m \rho$

$= 0.133 \times 1900$

$= \mathbf{252.7\ m^{-1}}$

$= \mathbf{253\ m^{-1}}$ **(to 3 s.f.)**

b) $I = I_0 e^{-\mu x}$

$= 30.0 \times e^{-(252.7 \times (0.690 \times 10^{-2}))}$

$= \mathbf{5.25\ Wm^{-2}}$ **(to 3 s.f.)**

Page 223 — Fact Recall Questions

Q1 E.g. make sure the patient keeps still to reduce blurring of the image / put a lead collimator grid between the patient and the film to stop scattered radiation fogging the film / use an intensifying screen next to the film surface.

Q2 The half-value thickness is the thickness of material required to reduce the intensity of the X-rays travelling through the material to half its original value.

Q3 X-rays are attenuated (or absorbed) more by materials with a higher atomic number. Bone has a higher average atomic number than soft tissues and so it absorbs more X-rays, and clear images can be formed around bones. Most of the X-rays just pass straight through soft tissue, so it's difficult to produce a clear image.

Q4 Barium has a high atomic number and so it shows up clearly in X-ray images compared to the soft tissue around it, which has a low atomic number. This helps improve the contrast between tissues on an X-ray image.
A patient can be given a barium meal to swallow so that the barium can be tracked as it passes through their body by X-rays.

Q5 A computed tomography (CT) scan is a scan in which a narrow, monochromatic X-ray beam is rotated around the body and picked up by thousands of detectors. These feed a signal to a computer, which works out how much attenuation has been caused by each part of the body and produces a very high quality image.

Q6 a) Intensifying screens contain crystals that fluoresce, so when they absorb X-rays they re-emit visible light. They're placed close to photographic film, so that the visible light emitted exposes the film in the correct areas and a clear image is produced.

b) E.g. intensifying screens reduce the exposure to X-rays needed to produce a clear image.

9. Magnetic Resonance Imaging

Page 225 — Application Question

Q1 a) Yes — kidney is a soft tissue, and so an MR scan would produce a high quality image.

b) Yes — the brain is a soft tissue and an MR scan can be used to create good contrast and resolution between different tissue types.

c) No — people with pacemakers can't have MR scans because of the strong magnetic fields involved.

d) No — MR scans give poor images of bones compared to using X-rays, so it would be better to use some form of X-ray scan.

e) Yes — imaging a blood clot requires contrast between soft tissues (the clot itself and surrounding veins, muscles etc.).

Page 225 — Fact Recall Questions

Q1 A large superconducting magnet produces a uniform magnetic field which causes hydrogen nuclei in the patient's body to align themselves with the field. Radio waves are used to excite the hydrogen nuclei, which emit radio frequency signals when they de-excite. These are detected and sent to a computer to produce an image.

Q2 Contrast can be controlled by varying the time between pulses.

Q3 The correct answer is d).

Q4 Any two from, e.g. there are no known side effects; MR scans give better resolution for soft tissue types; radiation used in MR imaging is non-ionising; multi-plane images can be made from the same scan; MR scans can be weighted to give better contrast between tissue types; MR gives real-time images.

Q5 Any two from, e.g. the patient might be fitted with a pacemaker; the problem might be bone-related, and MR scans don't image bones very effectively; it might not be affordable or cost-effective.

10. Ultrasound

Page 229 — Application Questions

Q1 a) $Z = \rho c \Rightarrow c = \frac{Z}{\rho}$

$= \frac{1.5 \times 10^6}{1000}$

$= \mathbf{1500\ ms^{-1}}$

b) $\frac{I_r}{I_0} = \left(\frac{Z_2 - Z_1}{Z_2 + Z_1}\right)^2$

$= \left(\frac{(1.5 \times 10^6) - (8.0 \times 10^6)}{(1.5 \times 10^6) + (8.0 \times 10^6)}\right)^2$

$= 0.4681...$

So the percentage = 0.4681... × 100

= **47% (to 2 s.f.)**

Q2 a) E.g. ultrasound imaging has no known side effects; ultrasound can produce real-time moving images; ultrasound is non-ionising.

b) E.g. ultrasound is much quicker; ultrasound is much cheaper.

Page 229 — Fact Recall Questions

Q1 Ultrasound is sound with a frequency higher than humans can hear (>20 000 Hz).

Q2 The acoustic impedance, Z, is defined as the density (ρ) multiplied by the speed of sound in the material (c). It affects how much of a wave will be reflected when it passes between materials.

Q3 The piezoelectric effect is when a material produces a potential difference when it's deformed, or vice versa.

Q4 Ultrasound waves are generated and detected by an ultrasound transducer. Inside the transducer, an alternating potential difference is applied to piezoelectric crystals, which vibrate to create a sound wave. When the wave is reflected and returns, it causes the crystals to vibrate, which in turn creates an alternating potential difference that is detected in an adjoining circuit.

Q5 Ultrasound imaging doesn't work if there are any air gaps involved because the difference in acoustic impedance between the air and the soft tissue would cause the majority of an ultrasound signal to be reflected back. Because of this, a coupling medium with similar acoustic impedance to the skin is needed between the transducer and the body.

Q6 a) Short pulses of ultrasound are sent into the body while an electron beam sweeps across a cathode ray oscilloscope. Reflected pulses are detected and show up as vertical deflections on the oscilloscope screen. The time difference between reflected pulses allows a computer to calculate the depth of an object.

b) B-scans are like A-scans, but the electron beam sweeps down the screen rather than across, and the amplitude of reflected pulses is shown as the brightness of spots on the screen. A linear array of transducers allows a 2D image to be formed of inside the body.

c) E.g. A-scans can be used to measure the depth of an eyeball. B-scans can be used to form a 2D image of a fetus.

Q7 a) E.g. it's relatively cheap / it uses non-ionising radiation.

b) Any two from: e.g. it can't image areas with air gaps (e.g. lungs) / it has a lower resolution that other methods / it can't be used to image bone.

11. Endoscopy

Page 233 — Application Questions

Q1 a) $\sin\theta_c = \frac{n_2}{n_1} \Rightarrow \theta_c = \sin^{-1}\left(\frac{n_2}{n_1}\right)$

$= \sin^{-1}\left(\frac{1.54}{1.61}\right)$

$= \mathbf{73.0° \text{ (to 3 s.f.)}}$

b) (i) It would not be totally internally reflected.

(ii) It would be totally internally reflected.

(iii) It would be totally internally reflected.

If the angle of incidence is greater than the critical angle, the light will be totally internally reflected.

Q2 $\sin\theta_c = \frac{n_2}{n_1} \Rightarrow n_2 = n_1 \times \sin\theta_c$

$= 1.70 \times \sin 65°$

$= \mathbf{1.54 \text{ (to 3 s.f.)}}$

Q3 a) E.g. non-coherent bundles could send down light into the digestive tract, like a flexible torch.

b) E.g. coherent bundles could transmit real-time images back from the digestive tract, like a video camera.

Page 233 — Fact Recall Questions

Q1

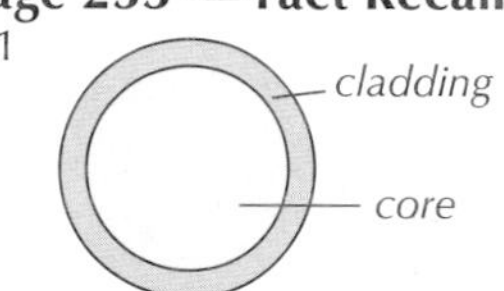

Q2 Total internal reflection

Q3 a) Coherent optical fibre bundles have fibres in the same relative position at both ends, whereas non-coherent optical fibres don't.

b) Coherent

Q4 An endoscope is a long, flexible tube that contains two bundles of optical fibres — a non-coherent bundle to carry light and a coherent bundle to carry images back.

Q5 E.g. to examine inside the body; for seeing what's happening during keyhole surgery.

Q6 E.g. the hole(s) required are much smaller, so there's less exposure to infection; recovery times are much quicker.

Exam-style Questions — Pages 235-237

1 (a) A — The cornea
B — The lens
C — The retina
D — The optic nerve
(2 marks available — 1 mark for every 2 correct answers.)

(b) (i) Persistence of vision is where an afterimage remains for a short amount of time on the retina after a bright image has been removed ***(1 mark)***.

(b) (ii) E.g. watching television, viewing things under fluorescent lights.
(2 marks available — 1 mark for each situation.)

(c) The eye can distinguish between two objects if there is at least one rod or cone between the images of the objects formed on the retina ***(1 mark)***. So a higher density of rods and/or cones will allow for better spatial resolution ***(1 mark)***. The yellow spot has a higher density of cones than the rest of the retina, and so spatial resolution is best at the yellow spot ***(1 mark)***.

(d) In an A-scan, a short pulse of ultrasound is sent into the eyeball ***(1 mark)***. Part of the pulse is reflected at the boundary at the back of the eye and picked up on a CRO screen ***(1 mark)***. The time it takes for this echo to come back can be used to calculate the depth of the eyeball ***(1 mark)***.

2 (a) The pinna ***(1 mark)***.

(b) The ossicles amplify the force of the vibrations arriving at the oval window from the eardrum ***(1 mark)***. The area of the oval window is also smaller than the eardrum, which results in increased pressure differences at the oval window ***(1 mark)***.

(c) The threshold of hearing I_0 is the minimum intensity of sound that can be heard by normal ears ***(1 mark)*** at a frequency of 1000 Hz (1 kHz) ***(1 mark)***.

(d) (i) Intensity level $= 10\log\left(\frac{I}{I_0}\right)$

$\Rightarrow I = I_0 \times 10^{\frac{IL}{10}}$

$= (1 \times 10^{-12}) \times 10^{\frac{81}{10}}$

$= \mathbf{1.3 \times 10^{-4}\ Wm^{-2}}$ **(to 2 s.f.)**

(2 marks for correct answer, otherwise 1 mark for correct rearrangement to make I the subject.)

(ii) The ear responds differently to sound of different frequencies ***(1 mark)***, and so the intensity level of a sound in dB might not reflect the perceived loudness. A dBA scale would show how loud (and therefore how much of a nuisance) the machine seems to the workers ***(1 mark)***.

3 (a)

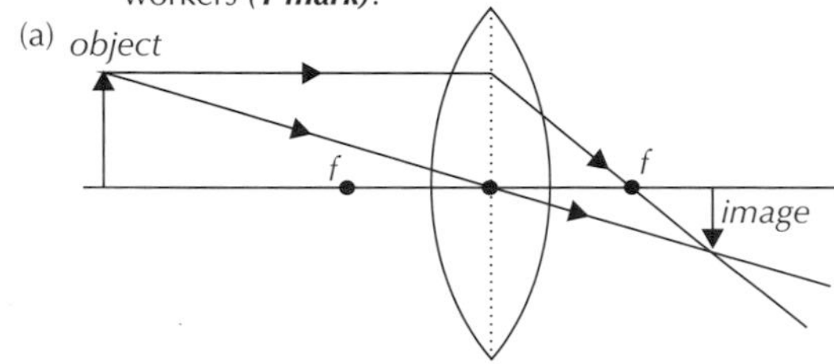

(2 marks in total — 1 mark for ray parallel to the axis passing through the principal focus and 1 mark for a second correct ray and labelled image.)

(b) $m = \frac{v}{u} \Rightarrow u = \frac{v}{m}$

$= \frac{(29.3 \times 10^{-2})}{1.61}$

$= \mathbf{0.182\ m\ or\ 18.2\ cm}$ **(to 3 s.f.)**

(2 marks for correct answer, otherwise 1 mark for correct rearrangement to make u the subject.)

(c) (i) A corrective lens will produce a virtual image ***(1 mark)*** at the person's uncorrected near point, 4.9 m ***(1 mark)***.

A converging lens will be used.

(ii) power $= \frac{1}{f}$, so power $= \frac{1}{u} + \frac{1}{v}$

$= \frac{1}{0.25} + \frac{1}{-4.9}$

$= \mathbf{+3.8\ D}$ **(to 2 s.f.)**

(2 marks for correct answer, otherwise 1 mark for correct working.)

Remember, v is negative for virtual images.

(d) Astigmatism ***(1 mark)***.

4 (a) (i) When the X-rays are produced a lot of heat is also produced at the focal spot — a small part of the anode ***(1 mark)***. Rotating the anode means the same part of it is never producing X-rays for more than a few milliseconds, and so it doesn't overheat ***(1 mark)***.

(ii) When electrons collide with the anode, they decelerate and some of their kinetic energy is lost. This is converted into X-ray photons with a range of energies that depends on the amount of energy lost by the electrons ***(1 mark)***.

(iii) As well as losing kinetic energy, beam electrons can knock other electrons out of inner shells in the anode atoms ***(1 mark)***. When this happens, outer shell electrons fill the gaps left by the inner electrons and release X-ray photons with fixed energies that coincide with differences between energy levels of the atom ***(1 mark)***.

(b) (i) The half-value thickness of a material is the thickness of material needed to reduce the intensity (of a beam of X-rays) to half its original value ***(1 mark)***.

(ii) $I = I_0 e^{-\mu x} \Rightarrow \frac{I}{I_0} = e^{-\mu x}$

$\Rightarrow x = -\frac{1}{\mu}\ln\left(\frac{I}{I_0}\right)$

$= -\frac{1}{9.64}\ln\left(\frac{1}{5}\right)$

$= 0.1669...\text{ m} = \mathbf{16.7\ cm}$ **(to 3 s.f.)**

(3 marks for correct answer, otherwise 1 mark for correct substitution of $I/I_0 = 1/5$ and 1 mark for correct rearrangement to make x the subject.)

(c) Any two from: e.g. CT scans produce better resolution images of bones than MR and ultrasound / CT scans are cheaper than MR scans / CT scans take less time than MR scans / CT scans aren't in an enclosed space, unlike MR scans ***(2 marks available — 1 for each correct point.)***

5 (a) The valves in the heart are found between the atria and the ventricles, as well as in the arteries leaving the ventricles of the heart ***(1 mark)***. The valves prevent blood going backwards into the ventricles or atria when the heart contracts ***(1 mark)***.

(b) (i)

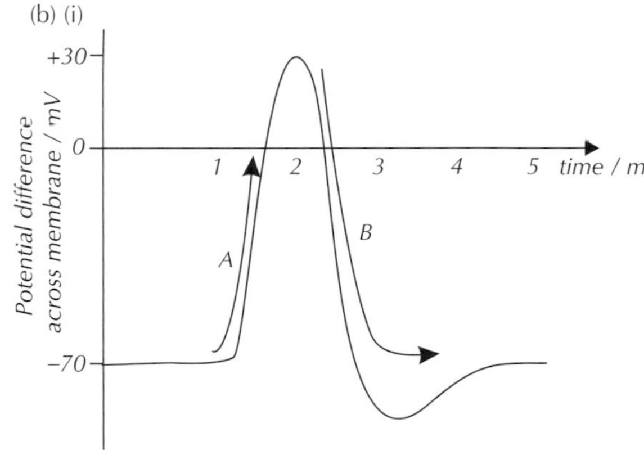

(2 marks available — 1 for both axes labelled correctly and 1 for correct scale on the y-axis.)

(ii) A — rapid polarisation.
B — depolarisation.
(2 marks available — 1 for each part.)

(c) The sino-atrial nodes produce electrical signals ***(1 mark)*** which cause the heart muscle to contract around 70 times per minute ***(1 mark)***.

(d) (i) An ECG trace shows the electrical signal produced by the heart at the surface of the body ***(1 mark)***.

(ii) Any two from: e.g. placing electrodes on the body in pairs near arteries / removing hairs and dead skin cells (e.g. using sandpaper) to get a good contact / using conductive gel to get a good contact / getting the patient to remain still / using a high impedance amplifier.
(2 marks available — 1 for each point.)

6 (a) (i) The critical angle of total internal reflection is the smallest angle of incidence above which a wave travelling from a medium with a higher optical density to one with a lower optical density will be totally internally reflected (none of the wave will leave the first medium). ***(1 mark.)***

(ii) $\sin\theta_c = \frac{n_2}{n_1} \Rightarrow \theta_c = \sin^{-1}\frac{n_2}{n_1}$

$= \sin^{-1}\frac{1.15}{1.25}$

$= \mathbf{66.9°}$ **(to 3 s.f.)**

(3 marks for correct answer, otherwise 1 mark for correct rearrangement to make θ_c the subject.)

(b) (i) A coherent optical fibre bundle is a bundle of optical fibres where the relative positions of fibres are the same at each end ***(1 mark)***.

(ii) E.g. coherent optical fibre bundles can be used to transmit images from inside a patient during surgery ***(1 mark)***.

(c) Here are some points your answer may include:

- Keyhole surgery requires a much smaller cut than traditional surgery ***(1 mark),*** and so exposure to potential infection is reduced ***(1 mark)***.
- Damage done to the body is reduced ***(1 mark),*** and so recovery times are shorter ***(1 mark)***.
- Because recovery time is shorter, the patient takes up hospital resources for less time ***(1 mark)***, which reduces the overall cost of the procedure ***(1 mark)***.

Option D — Turning Points in Physics

1. Discovering Electrons

Page 241 — Application Question

Q1 a) The equation $\frac{1}{2}mv^2 = eV$ shows that if you increase the anode potential, V, the velocity of the electrons will also increase.

b) kinetic energy $= \frac{1}{2}mv^2 = eV$
$= (1.60 \times 10^{-19}) \times 12\,000 = \mathbf{1.92 \times 10^{-15}\ J}$

c) $Fd = \frac{1}{2}mv^2$
so $F = (1.92 \times 10^{-15}) \div (1.25 \times 10^{-9})$
$= \mathbf{1.54 \times 10^{-6}\ N}$ **(to 3 s.f.)**

Page 241 — Fact Recall Questions

Q1 The invisible rays that were thought to cause the glow that appears on the wall of a discharge tube when a potential difference is applied across the terminals.

Q2 When heat gives the free electrons in a metal enough energy to break free from the metal's surface.

Q3

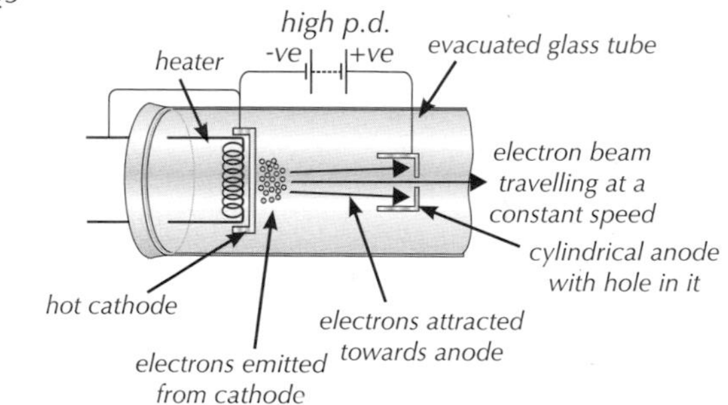

Q4 $F = \frac{eV}{d}$

Q5 The formula for the work done in moving a charge through a potential difference is $\Delta W = Q\Delta V$. When the charge, Q, is the charge on an electron, e, and the ΔV is the potential difference between an anode and cathode, V, then $\Delta W = eV$. The kinetic energy, $\frac{1}{2}mv^2$, that an electron will have when it has been accelerated (from rest) is equal to the work done in accelerating it through the potential difference. So $\frac{1}{2}mv^2 = \Delta W = eV$.

2. Specific Charge of an Electron

Page 244 — Application Question

Q1 a) The beam will deflect towards the positive plate.

b) The electric force on the electron is $F = \frac{eV}{d}$ and the magnetic force on the electron is $F = Bev$. When the beam is not deflecting, the forces are equal, so $\frac{eV}{d} = Bev$. So $B = \frac{V}{vd}$.

c) The kinetic energy of an electron entering the field is 4.2 keV, which is 4200e in J. So $4200e = \frac{1}{2}mv^2$ and

$e/m = \frac{\frac{1}{2}v^2}{4200}$.

Rearranging the equation given in part b) to find v,

$v = \frac{V}{Bd} = \frac{5000}{2.6 \times 10^{-3} \times 50 \times 10^{-3}} = 3.84... \times 10^7\ \text{m s}^{-1}$

$e/m = \frac{\frac{1}{2}v^2}{4200} = \frac{\frac{1}{2}(3.84... \times 10^7)^2}{4200}$

$= \mathbf{1.76 \times 10^{11}\ C\ kg^{-1}}$ **(to 3 s.f.)**

Page 244 — Fact Recall Questions

Q1 E.g. Use a fine-beam tube (a glass bulb with magnetic field coils either side of it, filled with low-pressure hydrogen and containing an electron gun). Direct the electron beam at right angles to the magnetic field so that the beam travels in a circle. The electron beam will pass through the low-pressure gas, exciting hydrogen atoms. The excited hydrogen atoms will de-excite and emit light, so that the path of the electron beam can be seen. Measure the radius of the circle formed by the beam, the voltage of the electron gun and the magnetic field strength of the magnetic field.

Q2 The magnetic force on the electron is acting as a centripetal force so $\frac{mv^2}{r} = Bev$ and so $r = \frac{mv}{Be}$.

Q3 The specific charge of the electron is roughly 1800 times greater than the specific charge of a hydrogen ion, so it either has a much bigger charge, or is very light. This led physicists to believe there may be particles smaller than the atom.

3. Millikan's Oil-Drop Experiment

Page 248 — Application Question

Q1 a) The drop is moving at a steady speed, so it is at its terminal velocity and the two forces acting on it, weight and viscous drag, are equal.

So $mg = 6\pi\eta rv \Rightarrow \frac{4}{3}\pi r^3 \rho g = 6\pi\eta rv \Rightarrow r = \sqrt{\frac{9\eta v}{2\rho g}}$

$r = \sqrt{\frac{9 \times (1.8 \times 10^{-5}) \times (2.5 \times 10^{-5})}{2 \times 980 \times 9.81}}$

$= 4.589... \times 10^{-7}$ m

= 4.6 × 10⁻⁷ m (2 s.f.)

b) The electric force is equal to the weight of the drop, so

$\frac{QV}{d} = \frac{4}{3}\pi r^3 \rho g \Rightarrow Q = \frac{\frac{4}{3}\pi r^3 \rho g d}{V}$

$= \frac{\frac{4}{3} \times \pi \times (4.589... \times 10^{-7})^3 \times 980 \times 9.81 \times 4.0 \times 10^{-3}}{98}$

= 1.6 × 10⁻¹⁹ C (to 2 s.f.)

c) In part b), $\frac{\frac{4}{3}\pi r^3 \rho g d}{V} = 1.6 \times 10^{-19}$ C

The distance has been doubled and the p.d. halved, so in this experiment:

$Q = \frac{\frac{4}{3}\pi r^3 \rho g(2d)}{\frac{V}{2}} = 4 \times \frac{\frac{4}{3}\pi r^3 \rho g d}{V}$

$= 4 \times (1.6 \times 10^{-19}$ C)

= 6.4 × 10⁻¹⁹ C (to 2 s.f.)

Page 248 — Fact Recall Questions

Q1 $F = 6\pi\eta rv$, where F is the viscous drag force on a sphere moving through a fluid, η is the viscosity of the fluid, r is the radius of the sphere and v is the speed of the sphere.

Q2

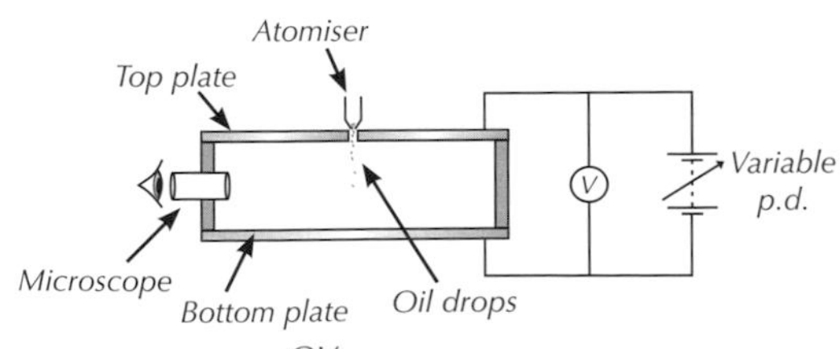

Q3 Electric force, $F = \frac{QV}{d}$.

Q4 a) The weight of the drop and the viscous drag force.

b) The weight of the drop, the viscous drag force and the electric force.

c) The weight of the drop and the electric force.

Q5 The weight of the drop is equal to the electric force on the drop, so $\frac{QV}{d} = mg = \frac{4}{3}\pi r^3 \rho g$. So $\frac{QV}{d} = \frac{4}{3}\pi r^3 \rho g$.

Q6 He found that the charge on oil droplets was always a multiple of 1.6×10^{-19} C. He concluded that charge cannot exist in smaller 'packets' and that this must be the charge on an electron.

Q7 Millikan's discovery meant that the mass of an electron could be calculated.

4. Light — Newton vs Huygens

Page 252 — Application Question

Q1 a) According to the corpuscular theory, the corpuscles of light travel in straight lines. So if the pinhole is made narrower, the beam of light corpuscles will be narrowed too.

b) Light is a wave and can diffract. Making the pinhole smaller will make the size of the gap closer to the wavelength of the light and cause it to diffract more, so the beam will get wider.

Page 252 — Fact Recall Questions

Q1 Newton believed that light was made up of a stream of tiny particles called corpuscles. Reflection was due to a force that pushed the particles away from a surface. Refraction worked if the corpuscles travelled faster in a denser medium.

Q2 Light was known to travel in straight lines and waves were known to bend around obstacles, so Newton said that light must be made of particles and not waves.

Q3 Huygens principle says that every point along a wavefront can be considered as a point source of secondary wavelets (spherical wavelets that come from each point) that spread out in the forward direction at the speed of the wave. The new wavefront is the surface that is tangential to all of these secondary wavelets.

Q4 E.g. Newton was very successful and respected / Huygens' theory couldn't explain light polarisation / Huygens' theory couldn't explain why sharp shadows were formed by light.

Q5 They struggled to get two coherent light sources, because light is usually emitted in random bursts.

Q6 Young used one light source shining through a slit to create a point light source, and put a slide with two thin slits in front of this light source to create two coherent light sources, one from each slit, avoiding the problem described in Q5. He projected the two coherent light sources onto a screen and observed bright and dark fringes being formed.

Q7 It gave evidence of light diffracting and showing interference, both properties of waves and not particles.

Q8 The discovery that light travelled slower in water than in air.

5. Electromagnetic Waves

Page 255 — Application Question

Q1 a) The wavelength is double the distance between two adjacent nodes, so $\lambda = 0.01 \times 2 = 0.02$ m.

b) $c = f\lambda = 1.5 \times 10^{10} \times 0.02 = 3.0 \times 10^8$ ms^{-1}

Page 255 — Fact Recall Questions

Q1 Light could be polarised, which is a property of transverse waves only.

Q2 $c = \frac{1}{\sqrt{\mu_0 \varepsilon_0}}$, where
ε_0 = the permittivity of free space = 8.85×10^{-12} Fm^{-1}
and μ_0 = the permeability of free space = $4\pi \times 10^{-7}$ Hm^{-1}.

Q3 The discovery that light travelled at the speed that Maxwell had calculated for electromagnetic waves.

Q4 Hertz showed that radio waves had all the properties of electromagnetic waves, including reflection, refraction, diffraction, interference, polarisation and the same velocity.

6. The Photoelectric Effect

Page 261 — Application Question

Q1 a) $E = \frac{hc}{\lambda} = \frac{(6.63 \times 10^{-34})(3.00 \times 10^{8})}{(550 \times 10^{-9})} = 3.616... \times 10^{-19}$ J
$= \mathbf{3.62 \times 10^{-19}}$ **J (to 3 s.f.)**

b) $\frac{1}{2}mv_{max}^2 = hf - \phi = E - \phi$
$= 3.616... \times 10^{-19} - (2.1 \times 1.6 \times 10^{-19})$
$= 2.56... \times 10^{-20}$ J $= \mathbf{2.56 \times 10^{-20}}$ **J (to 3 s.f.)**

c) $\frac{1}{2}mv_{max}^2 = eV_s$ so $V_s = \frac{1}{2}mv_{max}^2 \div e$
$= 2.56... \times 10^{-20} \div (1.60 \times 10^{-19})$
$= 0.160...$ V $=$ **0.160 V (to 3 s.f.)**

d) The new maximum kinetic energy is the maximum kinetic energy gained from a photon minus the work done by the electron against the potential difference eV.
So $E = \frac{1}{2}mv_{max}^2 - eV$
$= 2.56... \times 10^{-20} - (1.60 \times 10^{-19} \times 0.14)$
$= 3.236... \times 10^{-21}$ J $= \mathbf{3.24 \times 10^{-21}}$ **J (to 3 s.f.)**

Page 261 — Fact Recall Questions

Q1 For a given metal, no photoelectrons are emitted if the radiation has a frequency below the threshold frequency.
The photoelectrons are emitted with a variety of kinetic energies ranging from zero to some maximum value, which increases with the frequency of the radiation.
The maximum kinetic energy of the photoelectrons is unaffected by varying the intensity of the radiation.
The number of photoelectrons emitted per second is proportional to the intensity of the radiation.
The emission of photoelectrons is instantaneous as soon as the frequency is above the threshold frequency.

Q2 Einstein believed that EM waves (and the energy that they carry) can only exist in discrete packets called photons and that photons have a one-on-one, particle-like interaction with an electron in a metal surface. Photons transfer all their energy to that one electron.

Q3 Wave theory predicts that the electrons should gradually gain energy from the incident waves until they have enough energy to escape — there is no explanation for why this never happens. The photon theory of light says that photons have a one-on-one, particle-like interaction with an electron — each photon transfers all its energy to one specific electron. Electrons cannot build up energy — they either get enough from one photon of the correct frequency to escape, or don't get any. This is why there is a threshold frequency.

Q4 The work function of a metal is the amount of energy that an electron needs to break the bonds holding it in the metal.

Q5 The threshold frequency is f_0 such that $hf_0 = \phi$, so $f_0 = \frac{\phi}{h}$.

Q6 Wave theory predicts that the kinetic energy of a photoelectron should increase with light intensity. In reality, the kinetic energy of a photoelectron is only affected by the frequency of the light, and the intensity has no effect at all. Photoelectrons have a kinetic energy equal to the energy of the photon that collided with them, hf, minus the energy used to break the bonds of the metal, the work function, ϕ, and any energy they lose whilst leaving the metal. The maximum kinetic energy a photoelectron can have is just the energy supplied by the photon, minus the work function.

Q7 Maximum kinetic energy = $hf - \phi$

Q8 The stopping potential of a metal for a certain frequency of incident light is the minimum voltage that will stop photoelectrons being emitted. It is related to the maximum kinetic energy of a photoelectron by the equation $\frac{1}{2}mv_{max}^2 = eV_s$.

Q9 At first, the stopping potential of the metal at that frequency is less than or equal to the applied p.d., so no photoelectrons are emitted. Once the frequency has been increased, the stopping potential is higher than the applied p.d., so some photoelectrons are emitted, creating a current through the circuit.

7. Wave-Particle Duality

Page 264 — Application Questions

Q1 $\lambda = \frac{h}{p} = \frac{h}{mv}$, so the de Broglie wavelength is inversely proportional to the velocity of the electron. Therefore increasing the velocity will decrease the de Broglie wavelength of the electrons.

Q2 $\lambda = \frac{h}{\sqrt{2meV}}$
$= \frac{6.63 \times 10^{-34}}{\sqrt{2(9.11 \times 10^{-31})(1.6 \times 10^{-19})(4200)}}$
$= 1.894... \times 10^{-11}$ m

$= \mathbf{1.9 \times 10^{-11}}$ **m (to 2 s.f.)**

Q3 a) $p = \frac{h}{\lambda} = (6.63 \times 10^{-34}) \div (1.71 \times 10^{-10})$
$= 3.87719... \times 10^{-24}$ kgms^{-1}
$= \mathbf{3.88 \times 10^{-24}}$ **kgms^{-1} (to 3 s.f.)**

Make sure you always include units with your answer — it could get you some precious extra marks in the exam.

b) $m_e = 9.11 \times 10^{-31}$ kg,
$v = p \div m_e$
$= 3.87719... \times 10^{-24} \div 9.11 \times 10^{-31}$
$= 4.2559... \times 10^{6}$ ms^{-1}
$E_k = \frac{1}{2}mv^2 = \frac{1}{2} \times 9.11 \times 10^{-31} \times (4.2559... \times 10^{6})^2$
$= 8.250... \times 10^{-18}$ J
$= \mathbf{8.25 \times 10^{-18}}$ **J (to 3 s.f.)**

Q4 For the alpha particle, $\lambda = \frac{h}{p} = \frac{h}{mv} = \frac{6.63 \times 10^{-34}}{6.64 \times 10^{-27} \times 75}$
$= 1.331... \times 10^{-9}$ m

For the electron, $\lambda = 1.331... \times 10^{-9}$ m
$\lambda = \frac{h}{p} = \frac{h}{mv}$ so $1.331... \times 10^{-9} = \frac{6.63 \times 10^{-34}}{9.11 \times 10^{-31} \times v}$
$v = \frac{6.63 \times 10^{-34}}{9.11 \times 10^{-31} \times 1.331... \times 10^{-9}} = \mathbf{5.47 \times 10^{5}}$ **ms^{-1} (to 3.s.f.)**

Page 264 — Fact Recall Questions

Q1 All particles can be shown to have both particle and wave properties. Waves can also show particle properties.

Q2 Diffraction shows light has wave properties, and the photoelectric effect shows light has particle properties.

Q3 Electron diffraction

8. Electron Microscopes

Page 266 — Fact Recall Questions

Q1 Around 150 V.

Q2 An electron gun produces a beam of electrons with a certain de Broglie wavelength (dependent on the anode potential). A set of electromagnetic coils known as a condenser lens focuses the electrons into a thin, straight beam onto the sample, the structure of which may cause some of the electrons to diffract. Two more sets of electromagnetic coils use magnetic fields to deflect the electrons so that they form a magnified image, which is projected onto a fluorescent screen.

Q3 A very fine probe is positioned very close (around 1 nm) to a sample's surface. A potential is applied so that the probe is negatively charged in relation to the sample. Electrons 'tunnel' from the probe to the surface which produces a small electrical current. A bigger distance results in a smaller current. The probe scans the surface of the sample and produces a 3D image of it, by measuring either the current at a set distance from the sample, or the distance of the probe from the sample at a set current.

Q4 Piezoelectric transducers are used. When a p.d. is applied to them, they experience a tiny change in length, which moves the probe.

9. Michelson-Morley Experiment

Page 268 — Fact Recall Questions

Q1 Everything, including light, moves relative to a fixed background known as the ether.

Q2 Michelson and Morley hoped to measure the variance in the speed of light parallel and perpendicular to the motion of the Earth, and find a difference between them. With this difference, they would be able to measure the absolute speed of the Earth.

Q3 a) To split the light source into two beams, by reflecting some light and transmitting the rest.

b) To reflect the light back to the semi-silvered glass block, where the two beams will once again converge, forming an interference pattern.

c) To make sure that both beams of light travel through the same amount of glass and air.

Q4 They expected that rotating the interferometer would result in a shift in the interference pattern seen, due to the change in whether each beam was moving parallel or perpendicular to the absolute motion of the Earth.

Q5 The failure of the Michelson-Morley experiment to detect absolute motion is significant because it showed that the speed of light has the same value for all observers (it is invariant), and that it's impossible to detect absolute motion — the ether doesn't exist.

10. Special Relativity

Page 273 — Application Questions

Q1 $l = l_0\sqrt{1 - \frac{v^2}{c^2}}$

$= (6.7 \times 10^{-2})\sqrt{1 - \frac{(0.98c)^2}{c^2}} = (6.7 \times 10^{-2})\sqrt{1 - 0.98^2}$

$= 0.0133...\text{ m} = \mathbf{1.3 \times 10^{-2}\ m}$ **(to 2 s.f.)**

Q2 a) (i) $d = v \times t = (2.8 \times 10^8) \times (77 \times 10^{-9})$

$= 21.56\text{ m} = \mathbf{22\ m}$ **(to 2 s.f.)**

(ii) $l = l_0\left(1 - \frac{v^2}{c^2}\right)^{\frac{1}{2}}$

so $d = d_0 \times \left(1 - \frac{v^2}{c^2}\right)^{\frac{1}{2}}$

$= 21.56 \times \left(1 - \frac{(2.8 \times 10^8)^2}{(3.00 \times 10^8)^2}\right)^{\frac{1}{2}}$

$= 7.74...\text{ m} = \mathbf{7.7\ m}$ **(to 2 s.f.)**

b) $m = m_0\left(1 - \frac{v^2}{c^2}\right)^{-\frac{1}{2}} = (9.11 \times 10^{-31})\left(1 - \frac{(2.8 \times 10^8)^2}{(3 \times 10^8)^2}\right)^{-\frac{1}{2}}$

$= 2.537... \times 10^{-30}\text{ kg} = \mathbf{2.5 \times 10^{-30}\ kg}$ **(to 2 s.f.)**

c) $E = mc^2 = (2.537 \times 10^{-30})(3.00 \times 10^8)^2$

$= 2.283.. \times 10^{-13} = \mathbf{2.3 \times 10^{-13}\ J}$ **(to 2 s.f.)**

Q3 You know the half-life, so you need to calculate the time taken in the reference frame of the particles.

First, the distance in the reference frame of the particles is $d = d_0 \times \left(1 - \frac{v^2}{c^2}\right)^{\frac{1}{2}}$ (from length contraction).

In the reference frame of the particles,

$t = \frac{d}{v} = d_0 \times \left(1 - \frac{v^2}{c^2}\right)^{\frac{1}{2}} \div v$

$= 20 \times \left(1 - \frac{(0.95c)^2}{c^2}\right)^{\frac{1}{2}} \div 0.95c$

$= 20 \times (1 - 0.95^2)^{\frac{1}{2}} \div (0.95 \times 3.00 \times 10^8)$

$= 2.19... \times 10^{-8}\text{ s}$

Half-life $= 11.0 \times 10^{-9}$ s, so

$2.19... \times 10^{-8}$ is equal to $\frac{2.19... \times 10^{-8}}{11.0 \times 10^{-9}} = 1.992...$ half-lives

So the time taken in the reference frame of the particles to get between the two detectors is around 2 half-lives. So the ratio is around $1 \div (2^2) = 0.25$.

Page 273 — Fact Recall Questions

Q1 A space or system of coordinates that we use to describe the position of an object.

Q2 A frame of reference in which Newton's first law is obeyed.

Q3 Physical laws have the same form in all inertial frames. The speed of light in free space is invariant.

Q4 An observer of two events that is moving at a constant velocity, v, in relation to the events will measure a longer time interval, t, between the two events than the time measured by an observer who is stationary relative to the events, t_0. The equation for this time is $t = t_0\left(1 - \frac{v^2}{c^2}\right)^{-\frac{1}{2}}$.

Q5 Muons travel from the upper atmosphere towards ground at speeds close to c. They have a short half-life, and we expect the intensity of muons to decrease a certain amount as they travel between two points in the atmosphere. But the time taken in their reference frame is shorter than the time taken in our reference frame, so the intensity of the muons drops less than we would expect. This is evidence for time dilation.

Q6 $l = l_0\sqrt{1 - \frac{v^2}{c^2}}$

Q7 The faster an object moves, the more massive it gets. The relativistic mass of an object is the mass of the object when it is moving at a certain velocity.

Q8 $E = mc^2$ and $E = \frac{m_0c^2}{\left(1 - \frac{v^2}{c^2}\right)^{\frac{1}{2}}}$.

Exam-style Questions — Pages 275-277

1 (a) (i) Themionic emission is the release of electrons from a metal's surface ***(1 mark)*** when the metal is heated ***(1 mark)***.

(ii) E.g. So the electrons only interact with the sample / only get diffracted by the sample and can form a clear image of it. ***(1 mark)***.

(b) The electrons diffract around the atoms and molecules of a sample's structure to produce an image of it — this will only happen with waves ***(1 mark)***. The electrons would not be able to do this as particles, as they would either pass straight through the sample or be absorbed/blocked by it ***(1 mark)***.

(c) (i) Use the equation for the de Broglie wavelength of an electron:. $\lambda = \frac{h}{\sqrt{2meV}}$ and rearrange for V:

$$\sqrt{V} = \frac{h}{\lambda\sqrt{2me}}$$

$$\text{so } V = \frac{h^2}{2me\lambda^2}$$

$$= \frac{(6.63 \times 10^{-34})^2}{2(9.11 \times 10^{-31})(1.60 \times 10^{-19})\lambda^2}$$

$$= \frac{1.51 \times 10^{-18}}{\lambda^2} \text{ (to 3 s.f.)}$$

(3 marks available — 1 mark for rearranging for V, 1 mark for substituting in the constants and 1 mark for the final answer.)

(ii) The de Broglie wavelength should be similar in size to the diameter of the atom, 2.20×10^{-10} m.

So $V = \frac{1.51 \times 10^{-18}}{(2.20 \times 10^{-10})^2}$ = **31 V (to 2 s.f.)**

(2 marks for correct answer, otherwise 1 mark for putting the correct wavelength into the equation for the anode potential.)

(d) $p = mv = h \div \lambda$, so increasing the speed decreases the de Broglie wavelength of the electrons ***(1 mark)***. This means they will diffract around smaller objects, and so will be able to form a more detailed image ***(1 mark)***.

2 (a) (i) Physical laws have the same form in all inertial frames ***(1 mark)***.

The speed of light in free space is invariant ***(1 mark)***.

(ii) An inertial frame of reference is a space or system of coordinates in which Newton's first law is obeyed ***(1 mark)***.

(b) $m = (m_0)\left(1 - \frac{v^2}{c^2}\right)^{-\frac{1}{2}}$

$$= m_0\left(1 - \frac{(2.9 \times 10^8)^2}{(3.00 \times 10^8)^2}\right)^{-\frac{1}{2}}$$

$= 3.905... m_0$

$\approx$ **$4m_0$**

(2 marks for correct answer, otherwise 1 mark for substituting in the correct values.)

(c) The time measured by the observer would be longer ***(1 mark)*** — this is known as time dilation ***(1 mark)***.

3 (a) (i) Two bright fringes formed on the screen behind the two slits ***(1 mark)***. Newton's corpuscular theory said that light behaved as a particle and naturally travelled in straight lines, so only two fringes would be formed ***(1 mark)***.

(ii) A pattern of many fringes ***(1 mark)*** will be seen, with a bright central fringe and decreasingly bright fringes further out. In this experiment light shows the wave properties, interference and diffraction ***(1 mark)*** which supports Huygens' wave theory of light ***(1 mark)***.

(iii) E.g. any of: Newton had had many correct theories in the past / Newton was very well respected so his theory was accepted / Huygen's theory was based on longitudinal waves which did not explain the polarisation of light / diffraction of light had not been observed yet.

(1 mark for any correct answer)

(b) E.g. the photoelectric effect ***(1 mark)*** — wave theory can't explain it.

4 (a) How to grade your answer (pick the description that best matches your answer):

0 marks: There is no relevant information.

1-2 marks: Some of the details of the cathode ray discharge tube and the properties discovered are covered, but there is no overall description covered. Several errors with grammar, spelling, punctuation and legibility. Answer lacks structure and information.

3-4 marks: The cathode ray discharge tube is covered, and at least one relevant discovery is described. Only a few errors with grammar, spelling, punctuation and legibility. Answer has some structure and information.

5-6 marks: The cathode ray discharge tube is fully described, and a full explanation of the key properties that led scientists to predict subatomic particles is given. Grammar, spelling and punctuation are used accurately and there is no problem with legibility. Uses an appropriate form and style of writing and information.

Here are some points your answer may include:

- A discharge tube is an evacuated glass tube with a cathode and an anode and a potential difference applied between them.
- When the potential difference is applied, a glow appears on the wall of the discharge tube.
- Cathode rays were shown to have energy, momentum and mass, showing that they were made up of particles.
- Cathode rays were shown to have a negative charge, also showing that they were made up of particles.
- They were shown to have the same properties no matter what gas was in the tube and what the cathode was made of.
- They were shown to have a huge charge-to-mass ratio, showing they were either highly charged or subatomic.

5 (a) The circular motion of the electron beam means that the magnetic force on the electron is acting as a centripetal force. Magnetic force is given by $F = Bev$ and centripetal force is given by $F = \frac{mv^2}{r}$.

So $Bev = \frac{mv^2}{r}$ and rearranging, $\frac{e}{m} = \frac{v}{Br}$.

(2 marks for correct answer, otherwise 1 mark for correctly identifying $F = Bev$ and $F = \frac{mv^2}{r}$.)

(b) $\frac{e}{m} = \frac{v}{Br} = \frac{(8.44 \times 10^6)}{(1.20 \times 10^{-3})(4.00 \times 10^{-2})}$

= 1.76 x 10^{11} C kg^{-1} (to 3 s.f.)

(3 marks available for correct answer, otherwise 1 mark for substituting the correct numbers into the correct equation and 1 mark for giving the answer to 2 or 3 significant figures.)

(c) The specific charge of an electron is much greater than the highest specific charge known at the time, that of the H^+ ion, meaning that it either has much more charge, or is much lighter ***(1 mark)***. He assumed that electrons had the same charge and that they were much lighter, suggesting that they were subatomic particles ***(1 mark)***.

6 (a) The distance between two antinodes is half the wavelength of the wave ***(1 mark)***. Use this wavelength and the frequency in the equation $c = f\lambda$ to calculate the wave speed ***(1 mark)***.

(b) $c = f\lambda = (400 \times 10^3) \times (375 \times 2) =$ **3.00 x 10^8 m s^{-1}**

(1 mark for correct answer)

(c) $c = \frac{1}{\sqrt{\mu_0 \varepsilon_0}} = \frac{1}{\sqrt{(4\pi \times 10^{-7}) \times (8.85 \times 10^{-12})}}$

= 2.998... × 10^8 m s^{-1} = **3.00 x 10^8 ms^{-1} (to 3 s.f.)**

(2 marks for correct answer, otherwise 1 mark for substituting correct values into correct equation.)

(d) The results of Hertz's experiment showed that radio waves travel at the same speed as electromagnetic waves. This provided evidence that radio waves were electromagnetic waves and was evidence for Maxwell's electromagnetic theory of light ***(1 mark)***.

Glossary

Absolute magnitude (*M*)
What an object's apparent magnitude would be if it were 10 parsecs away from Earth.

Absolute motion
The idea that everything, including light, moves relative to a fixed background — something called the ether.

Absolute zero
The lowest possible temperature a substance can have, equal to 0 K or –273 °C.

Absorption line
A dark line in the continuous spectrum of a source that corresponds to a wavelength of light that has been absorbed by electrons as they are excited into higher energy levels.

Accurate result
A result that's really close to the true answer.

Acoustic impedance
The density of a material multiplied by the speed of sound in the material.

Action potential
A series of changes in the potential difference across the cell membrane of a nerve when it is stimulated.

Active galactic nucleus
A supermassive black hole at the centre of a galaxy that emits intense radiation as matter falls into it.

Activity
The number of unstable nuclei in a radioactive sample that decay each second.

Alpha particle
A particle formed of two protons and two neutrons (the same as a helium nucleus).

Alpha radiation
Nuclear radiation made up of alpha particles.

Angular magnification
The measure of a telescope's power, equal to the angle subtended by the image at the eye divided by the angle subtended by the object at the unaided eye.

Angular speed
The angle a rotating object moves through per second.

Anode
An electrode which becomes positively charged.

Anomalous result
A result that doesn't fit in with the pattern of the other results in a set of data.

Apparent magnitude
A measure of brightness of an object as observed from Earth.

Aqueous humour
Watery substance in the eye which lets light pass through the pupil to the lens.

Astigmatism
A visual defect caused by an irregularly shaped cornea or lens which has different focal lengths for different planes.

Astronomical refracting telescope
A telescope made up of two converging lenses.

Atrioventricular (AV) node
A node in the heart between the atria and the ventricles that passes electrical signals from the atria to the ventricles.

Auditory nerve
A nerve that carries electrical signals triggered by vibrating hair cells in the inner ear to the brain.

Avogadro constant, N_A
The number of particles in a mole, defined as the number of atoms in exactly 12 g of the carbon isotope $^{12}_{6}C$. It is equal to 6.02×10^{23} mol^{-1}.

Axial ray
A ray that is parallel to the principal axis of a lens.

Axon
Long thin branch of a nerve cell that carries signals away from the cell body. Also known as the nerve fibre.

B

Background radiation
The weak level of nuclear radiation found everywhere.

Balmer series
The absorption lines in an absorption line spectrum caused by the electrons in atomic hydrogen moving between the first excitation level (n = 2) and higher energy levels.

Basilar membrane
A membrane in the cochlea made to vibrate by pressure waves. Different parts have different natural frequencies and vibrate for different sounds, causing hairs to trigger electrical impulses in the auditory nerve.

Beta-minus radiation
Nuclear radiation made up of electrons.

Beta-plus radiation
Nuclear radiation made up of positrons.

Big Bang theory
A theory to explain the formation of the universe. It says that the universe started off very hot and very dense (perhaps as an infinitely hot, infinitely dense singularity) and that space has been expanding ever since.

Binding energy
The energy released when a nucleus forms, as well as the energy required to separate all the nucleons in that nucleus. Equivalent to the mass defect of the nucleus.

Black body
A body that absorbs all electromagnetic radiation of all wavelengths and can emit all wavelengths of electromagnetic radiation.

Black hole
An object whose escape velocity is greater than the speed of light.

Blue shift
The shift in wavelength and frequency of a source moving away from us towards (or beyond) the blue end of the electromagnetic spectrum.

Boltzmann's constant, *k*
A constant used in the equation of state of an ideal gas, equal to 1.38×10^{-23} JK^{-1}.

Boyle's law
For an ideal gas at a constant temperature, the pressure *p* and volume *V* are inversely proportional.

Brightness
The power received from an object per unit area at Earth.
Also known as intensity.

C

Capacitance
The amount of charge an object is able to store per unit potential difference (p.d.) across it.

Capacitor
An electrical component that can store charge, made up of two conducting plates separated by a dielectric.

Categoric data
Data that can be sorted into categories.

Cathode
An electrode which becomes negatively charged.

Cathode ray
A beam of electrons emitted from a cathode.

CCD (Charge-coupled device)
A sensitive light detector, made up of a silicon chip about the size of a postage stamp, divided up into a grid of millions of identical picture elements (pixels), used to capture images digitally.

Centripetal acceleration
The acceleration of an object moving with circular motion. It's directed towards the centre of the circle.

Centripetal force
The force on an object moving with circular motion. It's directed towards the centre of the circle, and is responsible for the object's curved path.

Chain reaction (nuclear)
When the neutrons released by a nuclear fission cause other nuclei to fission and release more neutrons — and so on.

Charles' law
For an ideal gas at constant pressure, the volume *V* is directly proportional to its absolute temperature *T*.

Chromatic aberration
A problem with using lenses caused by the lens refracting different colours of light by different amounts, resulting in the image for each colour being in a slightly different position.

Ciliary muscles
Muscles in the eye which control the shape of the lens by contracting and relaxing.

Cochlea
A spiral-shaped, fluid-filled cavity in the inner ear, which allows pressure waves caused by sounds to reach the basilar membrane.

Collecting power
A measure of how much radiation a telescope can collect, proportional to its collecting area.

Constructive interference
When two waves interfere to make a wave with a larger displacement.

Continuous data
Data that can have any value on a scale.

Control rods
Rods inserted into a nuclear reactor to control the rate of fission by absorbing neutrons.

Converging lens
A lens which brings parallel light rays together. They are convex in shape.

Cornea
A transparent, convex shaped 'window' at the front of the eye. It has a high refractive index and does most of the eye's focusing.

Corpuscles
Tiny hypothetical particles that Isaac Newton believed light to be made of.

Correlation
The relationship between two variables. Variables can show positive correlation, negative correlation or no correlation.

Cosmic microwave background radiation (CMBR)
Microwave radiation that is distributed homogeneously and isotropically throughout the universe.

Cosmological principle
On a large scale, the universe is homogeneous and isotropic.

Coupling medium
A liquid or gel used in ultrasound scans that displaces air and has an impedance close to that of body tissue.

Critical damping
Damping such that the amplitude of an oscillation is reduced in the shortest possible time.

Critical mass
The amount of fuel needed for a fission chain reaction to continue at a steady rate on its own.

D

Damping
A force which causes an oscillating object to lose energy and so causes the amplitude of the object's oscillation to decrease.

Dark energy
A type of energy that fills the whole of space, and might explain the accelerating expansion of the universe.

dBA scale
An adjustment of the decibel scale which takes into account the ear's response to different frequencies.

de Broglie wavelength
The wavelength associated with a particle, as part of the theory of wave-particle duality.

Decay constant
The probability of an atom decaying in unit time. A measure of how quickly an isotope will decay.

Decibel (dB) scale
A logarithmic scale used to measure the intensity level of sound.

Dendrites
Branches of a nerve cell that carry signals from other nerve cells to the cell body.

Dependent variable
The variable that you measure in an experiment.

Depolarisation
A decrease in the potential difference across a cell's membrane, making it less negative (i.e. more positive) than the resting potential.

Destructive interference
When two waves interfere to make a wave with a reduced displacement.

Diffraction
When waves spread out as they pass through a narrow gap or go round obstacles.

Directly proportional
Two variables are directly proportional if one variable = constant × the other variable. This means that a change in one results in a change in the other and that the changes are always related by the same constant.

Discrete data
Data that can only take certain values.

Diverging lens
A lens which causes parallel rays of light to diverge (spread out). They are concave in shape.

Doppler effect
The change in the frequency and wavelength of a wave for a source moving towards or away from an observer.

Driving frequency
The frequency of a periodic external driving force which causes an object to oscillate.

E

Elastic collision
A collision that conserves both linear momentum and kinetic energy.

Electric field strength
The force per unit positive charge experienced by a body in an electric field.

Electric potential
The electric potential energy that a unit positive charge (+1 C) would have at a specific point.

Electric potential difference
The energy needed to move a unit charge between two points in an electric field.

Electrocardiogram (ECG)
A graph against time of the electrical signal measured at the surface of the body caused by the potential difference between the polarised and depolarised parts of the heart.

Electron capture
When an atomic nucleus captures one of its own electrons, causing a proton to change into a neutron, and a neutrino to be released.

Electron degeneracy pressure
The pressure that stops electrons being forced into the atomic nucleus, e.g. in the dense core of a star.

Electron diffraction
When a beam of electrons is directed through a thin metal foil, interference between the electrons produces a diffraction pattern similar to that produced by light.

Electron gun
A device that uses thermionic emission and a high potential difference to accelerate electrons.

Electronvolt
The kinetic energy carried by an electron after it has been accelerated through a potential difference of 1 volt.

e.m.f.
Short for electromotive force. The voltage across a conductor that produces a current if the conductor is connected in a circuit.

Endoscope
A long (flexible) tube containing a non-coherent bundle of optical fibres to carry light and a coherent bundle of optical fibres to transmit images.

Equal loudness curve
A curve showing the intensities needed for different frequencies of sound to have the same perceived loudness.

Equation of state of an ideal gas
The ideal gas equation applied to gas molecules (rather than moles), given by $pV = NkT$.

Escape velocity
The velocity that an object would need to travel at to have enough kinetic energy to escape a gravitational field.

Eustachian tube
A tube in the middle ear connected to the throat. It opens up the middle ear to the throat, to help maintain the correct pressure in the ear.

Event horizon
The boundary of the region around an object in which its escape velocity is greater than c.

Exponential change
A change in the amount of something that is proportional to the amount of that something left.

Exponential function, e^x
Two variables are related exponentially (e.g. $y = e^x$) if any constant change in one results in the same proportional change in the other (e.g. by a given percentage). The value of e is around 2.72.

Far point
The furthest distance that the eye can focus comfortably.

Farad
The standard unit of capacitance. 1 farad (F) = 1 coulomb per volt (CV^{-1}).

Faraday's law
The induced e.m.f. is directly proportional to the rate of change of flux linkage.

Fleming's left-hand rule
A rule for showing which direction the force on a current-carrying wire perpendicular to a magnetic field acts. The thumb represents the direction of force, the first finger represents the direction of the magnetic field and the second finger represents the direction of the current from positive to negative.

Flux linkage
The magnetic flux in a coil multiplied by the number of turns on the coil.

Focal length
The focal length of a lens is the distance between the lens axis and its focal plane.

Focal plane
The plane perpendicular to the principal axis of a lens, on which the principal focus lies.

Force field
A region in which a body experiences a force.

Fovea
The part of the retina with the highest concentration of cones. It is found in the centre of the yellow spot.

Frame of reference
A space or coordinate system that we decide to use to describe the position of an object.

Frequency
The number of complete revolutions or cycles that a rotating or oscillating object makes per second.

Fundamental unit of charge
The fundamental unit of charge is defined to be 1.60×10^{-19} C (the magnitude of the charge on an electron).

Gamma radiation
Nuclear radiation made up of high-frequency electromagnetic waves/photons.

Geiger-Müller tube
An instrument used to detect nuclear radiation. It is attached to a counter that measures the amount of radiation.

Geosynchronous satellite
An Earth satellite that orbits directly over the equator at the same point on Earth, and whose orbital period is exactly 24 hours.

Gravitational field strength
The force per unit mass, $\boldsymbol{g}$, experienced by a body in a gravitational field.

Gravitational potential
The gravitational potential energy that a unit mass would have at a specific point.

Gravitational potential difference
The energy needed to move a unit mass between two points in a gravitational field.

Half-life
The average time it takes for the number of unstable nuclei (or the activity or count rate) in a sample of a radioactive isotope to halve.

Half-value thickness
The thickness of material required to reduce the intensity (of X-rays) to half its original value.

Hertzsprung-Russell (H-R) diagram
A graph of absolute magnitude against temperature or spectral class for stars.

Homogeneous
Meaning every part of something is the same as every other part.

Hubble's Law
The recessional velocity of a distant object is proportional to its distance, $v = Hd$.

Huygens' principle
Every point on a wavefront may be considered to be a point source of secondary wavelets that spread out in the forward direction at the speed of the wave. The new wavefront is the surface that is tangential to all of these secondary wavelets.

Hypermetropia
Someone who has hypermetropia is long-sighted — they are unable to focus clearly on near objects.

Ideal gas
A theoretical gas that obeys the three gas laws.

Ideal gas equation
A combination of the three gas laws, given by $pV = nRT$.

Impulse
The impulse acting on an object is equal to the change in momentum of the object.

Independent variable
The variable that you change in an experiment.

Inelastic collision
A collision that conserves linear momentum, but not kinetic energy.

Inertial frame
A frame of reference in which Newton's first law is obeyed. (Newton's first law says that objects won't accelerate unless they're acted on by an external force.)

Intensity
The power received from an object per unit area at Earth.
Also known as brightness.

Intensity of sound
The amount of sound energy passing per second per unit area (power per unit area).

Inverse square law
A law that relates two variables by a factor of $1/r^2$.

Iris
The coloured part of the eye. It consists of radial and circular muscles that control the size of the pupil, which regulates the intensity of light entering the eye.

Isotope
Isotopes of an element have the same number of protons, but different numbers of neutrons in their nuclei.

Isotropic
Meaning everything looks the same in every direction.

Kinetic energy
The energy of an object due to its motion.

Length contraction
A consequence of Einstein's theory of special relativity which says that an object moving in the same direction as its length looks shorter to an external observer.

Lens
A shaped piece of glass (or other material) that changes the direction of rays of light by refraction.

Lens axis
The axis passing through the centre of a lens vertically and perpendicular to the principal axis.

Lenz's law
The induced e.m.f. is always in such a direction as to oppose the change that caused it.

Light year
The distance that electromagnetic waves travel through a vacuum in one year.

Linear attenuation coefficient
A value for a material that shows how strongly X-rays are attenuated within that material.

Luminosity
The total amount of energy emitted by an object in the form of electromagnetic radiation each second. Also known as power output.

Magnetic field
A region in which a force acts on magnetic materials or magnetically susceptible materials.

Magnetic flux
The magnetic flux (in Wb) passing through an area is given by the magnetic flux density multiplied by the area. It can also be thought of as the number of magnetic field lines passing through the area.

Magnetic flux density
The value of magnetic flux density, in T, is given by the force on one metre of wire carrying a current of one amp at right angles to the magnetic field. Also called magnetic field strength.

Magnetic resonance (MR) imaging
A method of imaging soft tissue in which the patient is placed inside a huge superconducting magnet.

Main sequence
A phase of a star's evolution in which the star is fusing hydrogen in its core.

Mass attenuation coefficient
A measure of how much radiation is absorbed by a material per unit mass.

Mass defect
The difference between the mass of a nucleus, and the sum of the individual masses of the nucleons. Equivalent to the binding energy of the nucleus.

Mean square speed, $(c_{rms})^2$
The average of the squared speeds of the particles in a gas.

Mechanical energy
The sum of the potential and kinetic energy of an object.

Model
A simplified picture or representation of a real physical situation.

Moderator
A material (often water) in a nuclear reactor that slows down neutrons so they can be captured by uranium nuclei (or other fissionable nuclei, e.g. ^{239}Pu), as well as absorbing them to reduce the chance of meltdown.

Molar gas constant *R*
A constant used in the ideal gas equation, equal to 8.31 $\text{J mol}^{-1}\,\text{K}^{-1}$.

Molar mass
The mass that 1 mole of a substance would have.

Mole
An amount of substance containing N_A particles, all of which are identical. N_A is the Avogadro constant.

Momentum
The momentum of an object is the product of its mass and velocity.

Myopia
Someone who has myopia is short-sighted — they are unable to focus on distant objects.

Natural frequency
The frequency of an object oscillating freely.

Natural logarithm, ln
The logarithm to the base e. The natural logarithm is defined as $\ln e^x = x$.

Near point
The closest distance that the eye can focus on.

Neutron star
A star made up of neutrons, formed by the collapse of a red giant with a high core mass.

Neutron rich
Isotopes that contain many more neutrons than protons are neutron rich, making them unstable. They typically undergo beta-minus decay to increase their stability.

Newton's second law
The resultant force acting on an object is equal to the object's mass times the acceleration (or the rate of change of momentum) of the object.

Non-axial ray
A ray that is not parallel to the principal axis of a lens.

Nuclear fission
The spontaneous or induced splitting of a larger nucleus into two smaller nuclei.

Nuclear fusion
The fusing of two smaller nuclei to form one larger nucleus.

Nuclear radiation
Particles or energy released by an unstable atom as it decays. Made up of alpha, beta-minus or beta-plus particles, or gamma rays.

Nucleon
A particle that makes up an atomic nucleus (a proton or neutron).

Nucleon number
The total number of nucleons in an atomic nucleus. Also known as the mass number.

Nucleus
The small, positive core of an atom where most of the atom's mass is concentrated.

Optic nerve
A nerve that carries signals from the rods and cones at the back of the retina to the brain.

Orbital period
The time taken for a satellite to complete a full orbit.

Orbital speed
The speed at which a satellite travels.

Ordered / ordinal data
Categoric data where the categories can be put in order.

Ossicles
A collection of three bones (malleus, incus and stapes) in the middle ear that allow vibrations to travel between the outer ear and the inner ear, whilst amplifying the force of the vibrations.

Overdamping
Heavy damping such that the system takes longer to return to equilibrium than a critically damped system.

Parallax
A measure of how much a nearby object (e.g. a star) appears to move in relation to be fixed background due to the observers motion (e.g. as the Earth orbits the Sun). Measured as an angle of parallax.

Parsec
The distance of an object from Earth if its angle of parallax is equal to 1 arcsecond = $\left(\frac{1}{3600}\right)^\circ$

Period
The time taken for a rotating or oscillating object to complete one revolution or cycle.

Persistence of vision
Where an afterimage remains on the retina for a short amount of time after a bright image is removed.

Phase difference
A measure of how much one wave lags behind another wave. It can be measured in degrees, radians or fractions of a cycle.

Photodetectors
Cells in the retina of the eye that detect light and convert it to an electrical signal. There are two types, rods and cones.

Photoelectric effect
The emission of electrons (photoelectrons) from a metal when light of a high enough frequency is shone on it.

Photon
A discrete wave packet of electromagnetic radiation.

Piezoelectric crystals
Crystals that produce a potential difference when they are deformed, or vice versa.

Planetary nebula
The remnants of the outer layers of a red giant, that are ejected as the star becomes a white dwarf.

Point charge
A charge with negligible volume, or a uniform sphere whose charge acts as if it is concentrated at the centre.

Point mass
A mass with negligible volume, or a uniform sphere whose mass acts as if it is concentrated at the centre.

Potential energy
Energy that is stored (e.g. elastic potential energy is energy stored in something that has been stretched or compressed, like a spring).

Power (of a lens)
The power is the reciprocal of its focal length.

Power output
The total amount of energy emitted by an object in the form of electromagnetic radiation each second. Also known as luminosity.

Pressure law
For an ideal gas at constant volume, the pressure p is directly proportional to its absolute temperature T.

Principal axis
An axis of a lens that passes through its centre, perpendicular to its surface on both sides.

Principal focus
The principal focus of a converging lens is the point where incident rays parallel to the principal axis of the lens converge. For a diverging lens, it is the point that rays from a distant object on the principal axis appear to have come from.

Proper time
The time interval between two events as measured by an observer that is stationary in relation to the events.

Proton number
The number of protons in an atomic nucleus, Z.

Proton rich
Isotopes that have a high proton to neutron ratio are proton rich, making them unstable. They typically undergo beta-plus decay to increase their stability.

Radial field
A field symmetric about a central point.

Radian
A unit of measurement for angles. There are 2π radians in a complete circle.

Radioactive decay
When an unstable atom breaks down to become more stable, by releasing energy and/or particles.

Radioactive source
A material that emits alpha, beta or gamma radiation as it decays.

Radiocarbon dating
A technique used to date objects. Radioactive carbon-14 is present in living organisms, but the amount of carbon-14 decreases after the organism dies. By measuring the current activity due to radioactive carbon-14 it's possible to estimate the number of years since the organism died.

Random error
An error introduced by variables which you cannot control.

Ray diagram
A diagram showing rays of light passing through an optical system, sometimes showing image formation.

Rayleigh criterion
The resolving power of a telescope is roughly equal to the wavelength of the radiation it is detecting divided by the aperture diameter: $\theta \approx \frac{\lambda}{D}$.

Real image
An image formed when light rays from a point on an object are made to pass through another point in space. The light rays are actually there, and the image can be captured on a screen.

Recessional velocity
The speed at which an object is receding from Earth.

Red giant
Stars with a high luminosity and a low temperature. A red giant is a phase of a star's evolution in which the star is fusing larger elements than hydrogen in its core or there is fusion in it's shells. The fusion energy causes its outer layers to expand and cool, making it appear red.

Red shift
The shift in wavelength and frequency of a source moving away from us towards (or beyond) the red end of the electromagnetic spectrum.

Reflecting telescope
A telescope that uses mirrors to focus the rays of light.

Refraction
When a wave changes direction and speed as it enters a medium with a different optical density.

Relativistic mass
The mass of a body in motion, which is predicted by Einstein's theory of special relativity to increase with velocity and approach infinity as the velocity approaches the speed of light.

Reliable result
A result that can be consistently reproduced in independent experiments.

Repolarisation
The return of a cell membrane to its resting potential.

Resolving power
A measure of how much detail a telescope can see.

Resonance
When an object, driven by a periodic external force at a frequency close to its natural frequency, begins to oscillate with a rapidly increasing amplitude.

Resonant frequency
A frequency at which a stationary wave is formed because an exact number of waves are produced in the time it takes for a wave to get to the end of the vibrating medium and back again.

Resting potential
The potential difference across a cell membrane when it is at rest (e.g. when a nerve is not conducting an electrical impulse).

Retina
The layer at the back of the eye where images are formed. It contains light-sensitive cells called rods and cones.

Right-hand rule
Shows the direction of the magnetic field around a current-carrying wire. If you curl your right hand into a fist and stick your thumb out, the thumb represents the direction of the current and the fingers represent the direction of the magnetic field.

Root mean square speed
The square root of the average of the squared speeds of the particles in a gas.

Rutherford scattering experiment
The scattering of alpha particles by a thin metal foil, demonstrating the existence of a small and positively charged atomic nucleus.

S

Satellite
A smaller mass that orbits a larger mass.

Scanning tunnelling microscope (S.T.M.)
An electron microscope in which electrons tunnel from a fine probe to the sample, resulting in a weak electrical current which depends on the distance of the probe from the sample. It creates a 3D image of the sample's surface.

Schwarzschild radius (R_s)
The event horizon of a black hole.

Simple harmonic motion
The oscillation of an object where the object's acceleration is directly proportional to its displacement from its equilibrium position, and is always directed towards the equilibrium.

Simple harmonic oscillator
A system that oscillates with simple harmonic motion (like a simple pendulum).

Sino-atrial (S-A) node
A node in the wall of the right atrium of the heart that produces electrical signals that control the heartbeat.

Solenoid
An electromagnet consisting of multiple coils of wire.

Spatial resolution
A measure of the ability to form separate images of objects that are close together.

Specific charge
The ratio of mass to charge for a particle.

Specific heat capacity
The amount of energy needed to raise the temperature of 1 kg of a substance by 1 K (or 1 °C).

Specific latent heat
The quantity of thermal energy required to change the state of 1 kg of a substance (e.g. to melt or vaporise it without changing its temperature).

Spectral class
Groups which stars are classified into according to their temperature and the relative strength of certain absorption lines.

Spherical aberration
A problem with using mirrors to focus light, caused by the mirror being not quite the right shape so that there is no clear focal point and the image is blurry.

Standard candle
Objects in space that you can calculate the brightness of directly, without knowing their distance.

Stationary wave
A wave with fixed positions of minimum and maximum oscillation (nodes and antinodes) created by the superposition of two progressive waves with the same frequency (or wavelength) and amplitude, moving in opposite directions.

Stefan's law
The power output of a black body is proportional to the fourth power of the body's temperature and is directly proportional to its surface area:
$P = \sigma A T^4$

Step-down transformer
A transformer that decreases the voltage of an alternating current.

Step-up transformer
A transformer that increases the voltage of an alternating current.

Stopping potential
The stopping potential of a metal for a certain frequency of incident light is the minimum voltage that will stop photoelectrons being emitted.

Strong nuclear force
The interaction that binds nucleons together in nuclei.

Supermassive black hole
A black hole with a mass larger than 10^6 solar masses.

Supernova
The explosion of a high-mass star after its red-giant phase, caused by the core collapsing and the outer layers of the star falling in and rebounding, creating huge shockwaves.

Systematic error
An error that can be introduced by the experimental apparatus or method.

T

Terminal velocity
The maximum velocity of an object through a fluid reached when the driving force is matched by the frictional force.

Teslas
The tesla is the unit of magnetic flux density. One tesla is equal to one weber (the unit of magnetic flux) per square metre.

Theory
A possible explanation for something. (Usually something that has been observed.)

Thermal neutrons
Neutrons in a nuclear reactor that have been slowed down enough by a moderator that they can be captured by uranium nuclei (or other fissionable nuclei, e.g. ^{239}Pu).

Thermionic emission
The release of free electrons from a metal's surface when the metal is heated.

Threshold frequency
The lowest frequency of light that when shone on a metal will cause the emission of photoelectrons.

Threshold of hearing
The minimum intensity of sound that can be heard by a normal ear at a frequency of 1000 Hz.

Time constant
The time taken for the charge on a discharging capacitor to fall to $\frac{1}{e}$ (about 37%) of its initial charge, or for the charge of a charging capacitor to rise to about 63% of the full charge.

Time dilation
A consequence of Einstein's theory of special relativity which says that an observer of two events that is moving at a constant velocity in relation to the events will measure a longer time interval between the two events than the proper time.

Total internal reflection
When all light is completely reflected back into a medium at a boundary with another medium, instead of some of it being refracted. It only happens at angles of incidence greater than the critical angle.

Transformer
A device that makes use of electromagnetic induction to change the size of the voltage of an alternating current.

Transmission electron microscope (T.E.M.)
An electron microscope that directs a beam of electrons through a thin sample using 'electromagnetic lenses' and observes the diffraction of the electrons to produce an image of the sample's structure.

Tympanic membrane
Also known as the eardrum. It separates the outer and middle ears. Sound waves which enter the ear make it vibrate and these vibrations are passed to the ossicles.

Type 1a supernova
A type of supernova that always has the same peak in absolute magnitude. Often used as standard candles.

Ultrasound
Sound with a frequency higher than humans can hear (> 20 000 Hz).

Valid result
A result which answers the question it was intended to answer.

Validation
The process of repeating an experiment done by someone else, using the theory to make new predictions, and then testing them with new experiments, in order to support or refute the theory.

Variable
A quantity in an experiment or investigation that can change or be changed.

Vector
A quantity with both a size and a direction (e.g. velocity).

Virtual image
An image formed when light rays from a point on an object appear to have come from another point in space. The light rays aren't really where the image appears to be, so the image can't be captured on a screen.

Viscosity
A measure of how thick a fluid is.

Viscous drag force
A force that acts in the opposite direction to the velocity of an object moving in a fluid, due to the viscosity of the fluid.

Vitreous humour
Jelly-like substance that keeps the eye's shape.

Wave-particle duality
The idea that particles and waves can each display both particle and wave-like behaviour.

Wavelets
Wave-like oscillations that were thought to originate from every point along a wavefront and spread out in the forward direction, according to Huygens' principle.

Weber
The weber is the unit of magnetic flux.

White dwarf
Stars with a low luminosity and a high temperature, left behind when a low-mass star stops fusing elements and contracts.

Wien's displacement law
The higher the surface temperature of a black body, the shorter the peak wavelength of its radiation:
$\lambda_{max}T = 0.0029$ m K

Work function
The minimum amount of energy required for an electron to escape a metal's surface.

X-ray tube
A device in which X-rays are produced by firing electrons at a rotating (tungsten) anode.

Yellow spot
A sensitive region of the retina, which has the fovea at its centre.

Acknowledgements

Photograph acknowledgements

Cover Photo **Richard Kail**/Science Photo Library, p 1 **Edward Kinsman**/Science Photo Library, p 2 Science Photo Library, p 3 Science Photo Library, p 4 (top) **Steve Allen**/Science Photo Library, p 4 (bottom) **David Parker**/Science Photo Library, p 7 **Andrew Lambert Photography**/Science Photo Library, p 10 **Tim McCaig**/iStockphoto, p 12 **Lawrence Berkeley Laboratory**/ Science Photo Library, p 16 **Steve Allen**/Science Photo Library, p 18 **Adam Hart-Davis**/Science Photo Library, p 19 **GIPhotoStock**/Science Photo Library, p 29 **Mark Williamson**/Science Photo Library, p 30 **GoranQ**/iStockphoto, p 35 **Victor de Schwanberg**/Science Photo Library, p 38 **Henn Photography**/Science Photo Library, p 41 **Adam Hart-Davis**/Science Photo Library, p 42 **Carlos Dominguez**/Science Photo Library, p 43 **Detlev van Ravenswaay**/Science Photo Library, p 44 **Hughes Aircraft Company**/Science Photo Library, p 45 **Emilio Segre Visual Archives/American Institute of Physics**/Science Photo Library, p 47 **Ted Kinsman**/Science Photo Library, p 50 **Charles D. Winters**/Science Photo Library, p 57 **GIPhotoStock**/ Science Photo Library, p 59 **Andrew Lambert Photography**/Science Photo Library, p 60 **Charles Doswell, Visuals Unlimited**/Science Photo Library, p 61 **Sheila Terry**/Science Photo Library, p 64 **Chris Knapton**/Science Photo Library, p 71 **GIPhotoStock**/Science Photo Library, p 72 **GIPhotoStock**/Science Photo Library, p 73 **Emilio Segre Visual Archives/American Institute of Physics**/Science Photo Library, p 75 **Lawrence Berkeley Laboratory**/Science Photo Library, p 77 **CC Studio**/ Science Photo Library, p 81 **G.Glatzmaier, Los Alamos National Laboratory/ P.Roberts, UCLA**/Science Photo Library, p 82 **Chemical Heritage Foundation**/Science Photo Library, p 85 **Gabrielle Voinot/Look at Sciences**/Science Photo Library, p 87 (top) **National Physical Laboratory (c) crown copyright**/Science Photo Library, p 87 (bottom) **GIPhotoStock**/Science Photo Library, p 89 **Chris B Stock**/Science Photo Library, p 94 **Royal Astronomical Society**/Science Photo Library, p 97 Science Photo Library, p 102 **Tim Beddow**/Science Photo Library, p 105 **James King-Holmes**/Science Photo Library, p 109 **Patrick Landmann**/Science Photo Library, p 113 **ISM**/Science Photo Library, p 116 **European Space Agency**/Science Photo Library, p 119 **Patrick Landmann**/Science Photo Library, p 125 (top) Science Photo Library, p 125 (bottom) **Sheila Terry**/Science Photo Library, p 128 Science Photo Library, p 134 **Martyn F. Chillmaid**/Science Photo Library, p 137 **Martin Dohrn**/Science Photo Library, p 141 **GIPhotoStock**/Science Photo Library, p 142 (top) **B.G. Thomson**/Science Photo Library, p 142 (bottom) **Zennie**/iStockphoto, p 145 **Emilio Segre Visual Archives/American Institute of Physics**/Science Photo Library, p 146 (top) **Babak Tafreshi, TWAN**/Science Photo Library, p 146 (bottom) **GIPhotoStock**/Science Photo Library, p 149 **Andrew Lambert Photography**/Science Photo Library, p 151 (top) **Dr P P Kronberg**/Science Photo Library, p 151 (bottom) **Joseph Sohm**/ Science Photo Library, p 152 **David Ducros**/Science Photo Library, p 153 (top) **Simon Fraser**/Science Photo Library, p 153 (bottom) **NASA/Carla Thomas**/Science Photo Library, p 156 **NASA**/Science Photo Library, p 161 **NASA/ESA/STSCI/High-Z Supernova Search Team**/Science Photo Library, p 162 **John Sanford**/Science Photo Library, p 163 **Detlev van Ravenswaay**/ Science Photo Library, p 164 **National Library of Congress**/Science Photo Library, p 168 **National Optical Astronomy Observatories**/Science Photo Library, p 171 **Mark Garlick**/Science Photo Library, p 173 **NASA/ESA/STSCI/J.Hester & P.Scowen, ASU**/Science Photo Library, p 174 (top) **Royal Observatory, Edinburgh**/Science Photo Library, p 174 (bottom) **Kim Gordon**/Science Photo Library, p 176 **CXC/SAO/F. Seward et al/NASA**/Science Photo Library, p 177 **NASA/ESA/ STSCI/J. Bahcall, Princeton IAS**/Science Photo Library, p 178 **Emilio Segre Visual Archives/American Institute of Physics**/ Science Photo Library, p 180 **David R. Frazier**/Science Photo Library, p 182 **Matthew Russell, Visuals Unlimited**/Science Photo Library, p 184 **NASA/2MASS/J. Carpenter, T. H. Jarrett, R. Hurt**/Science Photo Library, p 186 **NASA/WMAP Science Team**/Science Photo Library, p 189 Science Photo Library, p 190 **NASA/ESA/STSCI/Hubble Heritage Team**/Science Photo Library, p 196 **David Parker**/Science Photo Library, p 198 **Berenice Abbott**/Science Photo Library, p 202 **Eye of Science**/ Science Photo Library, p 204 **Photostock-Israel**/Science Photo Library, p 206 (top) **Patrick Dumas/Look at Sciences**/Science Photo Library, p 206 (bottom) **JOTI**/Science Photo Library, p 208 **Steve Gschmeissner**/Science Photo Library, p 212 **Kate Jacobs**/Science Photo Library, p 217 **AJ Photo**/Science Photo Library, p 218 **General Electric Research and Development/ Emilio Segre Visual Archives/American Institute of Physics**/Science Photo Library, p 221 **Pasieka**/Science Photo Library, p 222 **Miriam Maslo**/Science Photo Library, p 223 **Maximilian Stock Ltd**/Science Photo Library, p 224 **Pasieka**/Science Photo Library, p 225 (top) **Zephyr**/Science Photo Library, p 225 (bottom) **Mehau Kulyk**/Science Photo Library, p 227 **Doncaster and Bassetlaw Hospitals**/Science Photo Library, p 228 **Zephyr**/Science Photo Library, p 230 **Sam Ogden**/Science Photo Library, p 231 **Kevin Curtis**/Science Photo Library, p 232 **Dr P. Marazzi**/Science Photo Library, p 233 **Mark Thomas**/Science Photo Library, p 239 (top) **Falk Kienas**/iStockphoto, p 239 (bottom) **Gavran333**/iStockphoto, p 243 **Library of Congress**/Science Photo Library, p 248 Science Photo Library, p 249 (top) **Sheila Terry**/Science Photo Library, p 249 (bottom) Science Photo Library, p 251 **GIPhotoStock**/Science Photo Library, p 253 **Emilio Segre Visual Archives/American Institute of Physics**/ Science Photo Library, p 254 Science Photo Library, p 257 **US Library of Congress**/Science Photo Library, p 258 **Pierre Marchal/Look at Sciences**/Science Photo Library, p 259 **Charles D. Winters**/Science Photo Library, p 263 **Andrew Lambert Photography**/Science Photo Library, p 265 **Northwestern University**/Science Photo Library, p 266 **Philippe Plailly**/Science Photo Library, p 278 Science Photo Library, p 279 **Andrew Lambert Photography**/Science Photo Library, p 285 **Adam Hart-Davis**/Science Photo Library, p 286 **Andrew Lambert Photography**/Science Photo Library, p 289 **Geoff Tompkinson**/ Science Photo Library, p 290 **Ria Novosti**/Science Photo Library, p 293 **Jon Stokes**/Science Photo Library.

Index

Data Tables

This page summarises some of the constants and values that you might need to refer to when answering questions in this book. It's helpfully split up into stuff that's in all the compulsory A2 sections, and stuff that's only in the optional sections. Everything here will be provided in your exam Data and Formulae Booklet somewhere... so you need to get used to looking them up and using them correctly. If a number isn't given on this sheet — unlucky... you'll need to remember it as it won't be given to you in the exam.

Unit 4 and Unit 5 Sections 1 and 2

Fundamental constants and values

Quantity	Value
acceleration due to gravity, g	$9.81\ ms^{-2}$
atomic mass unit, u	1.661×10^{-27} kg
the Avogadro constant, N_A	$6.02 \times 10^{23}\ mol^{-1}$
the Boltzmann constant, k	$1.38 \times 10^{-23}\ JK^{-1}$
electron charge/mass ratio, e/m_e	$1.76 \times 10^{11}\ Ckg^{-1}$
electron rest mass, m_e	9.11×10^{-31} kg
gravitational constant, G	$6.67 \times 10^{-11}\ Nm^2kg^{-2}$
gravitational field strength, g	$9.81\ Nkg^{-1}$
magnitude of the charge of electron, e	1.60×10^{-19} C
molar gas constant, R	$8.31\ JK^{-1}mol^{-1}$
neutron rest mass, m_n	$1.67(5) \times 10^{-27}$ kg
permittivity of free space, ε_0	$8.85 \times 10^{-12}\ Fm^{-1}$
the Planck constant, h	6.63×10^{-34} Js
proton charge/mass ratio, e/m_p	$9.58 \times 10^{7}\ Ckg^{-1}$
proton rest mass, m_p	$1.67(3) \times 10^{-27}$ kg
speed of light in a vacuo, c	$3.00 \times 10^{8}\ ms^{-1}$

Unit 5 Option A: Astrophysics

Fundamental constants and values

Quantity	Value
the Hubble constant, H	$65\ kms^{-1}Mpc^{-1}$
the Stefan constant, σ	$5.67 \times 10^{-8}\ Wm^{-2}K^{-4}$
the Wien constant, α	2.90×10^{-3} mK

Astronomical units of distance

Unit of distance	Value
astronomical unit, AU	1.50×10^{11} m
light year, ly	9.46×10^{15} m
parsec, pc	206265 AU
	3.08×10^{16} m
	3.26 ly

Unit 5 Option D: Turning Points in Physics

Fundamental constants and values

Quantity	Value
permeability of free space, μ_0	$4\pi \times 10^{-7}\ Hm^{-1}$

PATB61